Penguin Mod

Brain and

Perceptic

Penguin Modern Psychology Readings

General Editor
B. M. Foss

Advisory Board
P. C. Dodwell
Marie Jahoda
S. G. Lee
W. M. O'Neil
R. L. Reid
Roger Russell
P. E. Vernon
George Westby

Brain and Behaviour 2

Perception and Action

Selected Readings

Edited by K. H. Pribram

Penguin Books

Penguin Books Ltd, Harmondsworth,
Middlesex, England
Penguin Books Inc., 7110 Ambassador Road,
Baltimore, Maryland 21207, U.S.A.
Penguin Books Australia Ltd, Ringwood,
Victoria, Australia

First published 1969

Printed by Universal Litho. in the
United States of America

Set in Monotype Times Roman

Contents

Part Three Cognition and the Agnosias

Part Four Motor Function and Action

Part Five Conation: The Neural Programming of Behaviour

Part One Sensory Processes and Perception: The Units

One of the basic questions in psychology is: 'How do inputs become stimuli?' Part of the answer comes from everyday experience and much experimental analysis. For example, we know that only selected parts of an organism's environment make an impact sufficient to elicit reactions or to be stored for future use. But what laws govern this selection? The initial articles in this volume detail how the use of microelectrodes has allowed the classification of neurons in the visual and somatic systems according to the input dimension which excites them. That the problem is not a simple one is clear from the evidence: what appears to be the situation is that the nervous system is so constructed that it analyses from the complexities of the receptive mechanism some sort of alphabet which is then reconstituted into perceptions.

1 D. N. Spinelli

Visual Receptive Fields In the Cat's Retina: Complications

D. N. Spinelli, 'Visual receptive fields in the cat's retina: complications', *Science*, vol. 152 (1966), pp. 1768–9.

Abstract. Visual receptive fields have been mapped with moving patterns in the cat's retinal ganglion cells. A small, general-purpose computer was used to collect a matrix of 2,500 data points covering a 25°-by-25° region of space. The analysis of 40 units reveals the existence of many nonconcentric receptive fields and also the presence of line and edge detectors.

Various attempts have been made to classify unit responses recorded from retinal ganglion cells. Perhaps the most generally accepted classification deals with the 'on-center' and 'off-center' aspects of the recordings, the surround showing a response 'opposite' to that of the center of the field.

The suggestion has been that the fields are more or less concentric and that the more complex responses obtained from higher stations in the visual system are composed or integrated from these elementary concentric units. There have been, however, a few indications that such a view of the structure of the receptive field recorded from ganglion cells may be oversimplified. For example, Rodieck and Stone (1) point out that all of the receptive fields they mapped were to some extent radially asymmetric, and that in some cases the surround region could be detected over only part of the receptive field or not at all. Kuffler (2) had also noted the 'asymmetry' of some fields.

The present investigation was undertaken as part of a larger program delineating efferent control of input in the visual system. In these studies the control mechanisms of an XY plotter were used to move a white disc on a black background on any X or Y dimension. A Computer for Average Transients (CAT 400A) was used to compute averaged response histograms in a fashion similar to that described by Rodieck and Stone (1). While this method affords a great deal of precision it is not very flexible, so that the shape of the receptive field, which is two-dimensional, has either to be inferred or reconstructed laboriously from a number of such scans, or to be attained by mapping point-by-point by hand.

To gain a better understanding of receptive-field organization we decided to take full advantage of the flexibility of the $X-Y$ stimulus control system used and to use a small, general-purpose computer (PDP-8), to collect and display the data. A program was designed that could achieve the following:

1. Generate appropriate electrical functions for the X and Y servo amplifiers so that the visual stimulus, consisting of a white disc (200 cd-m^2) 0·2° in diameter on a black background (0·02 cd-m^2) would be moved along a matrix of 50 by 50 points, starting with the bottom row and then returning the disc and moving it up row by row. The region of space scanned was 25° by 25°.

2. Control traveling time from one horizontal point to the next; in this experiment traveling time was held to 70 msec., so that one horizontal scan required 3·5 seconds; a 1·3-second interval was allowed after the return of the disc between one scan and the next.

3. Count and store the number of spikes produced by the unit while the stimulus moved along the matrix, so as to generate subsequently a matrix of 50 by 50 data points. Each data point thus contained the number of spikes produced by the unit while the stimulus moved with uniform speed from one point to the next, with the exception of the first point in each horizontal row, which contained the number of spikes generated during the 70 msec. before movement started.

4. Print out all of the 2,500 data points or any of the horizontal or vertical rows.

5. Display on an oscilloscope face any of the horizontal (H) or vertical (V) rows.

6. Show the whole matrix as an isometric display.

7. Display, two-dimensionally, only those points where activity exceeded a given value.

This last feature of the program is most useful because it allows direct appreciation of the receptive-field shape; this is obtained by displaying only those points where activity was more than three standard deviations away from the mean of the spontaneous activity of the unit.

Forty units were studied with this method in five cats. Unit activity was recorded from optic-nerve fibers with tungsten microelectrodes aimed stereotaxically at the intracranial and the optic-foramen. Surgery was performed under thiopental sodium anesthesia, after which the animal was immobilized with Flaxedil (gallamine triethiodide) and artificially ventilated. All wounds and pressure points were infiltrated with a long-acting local anesthetic (Zyljectin),

Plate 1 (see central inset), a_e1 through b_e5, shows, in order of increasing complexity, ten of the receptive fields studied with this method. In the $-e$ columns are shown points where activity was more than three standard deviations from the mean background, thus displaying clear-cut excitatory regions; in the $-i$ columns all points of the same fields with one count or more are shown: this displays inhibitory regions as dark areas. Plate 2 shows the effect of dark adaptation on an on-center receptive field; this figure also shows the remarkable repeatability of these mappings.

It is immediately apparent from the data that while there is no doubt about the circular organization of some receptive fileds (a_e1 is one example), much greater complexity can also be found, and that more often than not, the analysis of a single axis taken at the appropriate level would have left one with the impression of dealing with a classically concentric receptive field (Plate 3).

Rodieck and Stone (1) have demonstrated that the receptive field of a unit mapped with a moving light is directly correlated with the receptive field of the unit mapped with stationary spots, and, moreover, that the response of a unit to two stimuli presented simultaneously is the sum of the responses of the unit to two stimuli presented sequentially.

If this is the case it follows that the receptive field is a direct indication of the visual stimulus to which the unit is most responsive, namely, a black line for unit b_i3, an edge for b_i5, and so on (Plate 1). Fields like b_i3 and b_i5 in Plate 1 have been described in the cat's visual cortex and attributed to different ways of combining concentric receptive fields (3). However, it appears that the cat's retinal receptive fields are rather more complicated than had been supposed. Therefore, the hypothesis that more complex receptive fields have been combined from the activity of units with concentric ones in some simple fashion may need revision, at least for line and edge detectors.

References
1. R. W. RODIECK and J. STONE, *J. Neurophysiol.*, vol. 28 (1965), p. 833.
2. S. W. KUFFLER, *J. Neurophysiol.*, vol. 16 (1953), p. 37.
3. D. H. HUBEL and T. N. WIESEL, *J. Physiol.*, *London*, vol. 160 (1962), p. 106.
4. H. B. BARLOW, R. FITZHUGH, and S. KUFFLER, *J. Physiol.*, *London*, vol. 137 (1957), p. 338.

2 R. Jung

Neuronal Integration in the Visual Cortex and its Significance for Visual Information

Excerpts from R. Jung, 'Neuronal integration in the visual cortex and its significance for visual information', in W. A. Rosenblith, ed., *Sensory Communication*, M. I. T. Press, 1961, chapter 32, pp. 627–74.

In the following pages I shall treat two topics, one neurophysiological and the other psychophysiological: (1) the integration of information from various afferents by neurons in the visual cortex, resulting in convergence of specific retinal and vestibular receptors and of nonspecific reticulothalamic afferents; (2) the correlation of these neuronal mechanisms in the cat with subjective visual perception in man.

I shall survey first some of the work on extracellular recording of neuronal discharges in the primary visual area of the cat, done in our laboratory during the past eight years. Second I shall discuss more in detail the recent experiments on neuronal mechanisms of vision by Baumgartner, Grüsser, Grüsser-Cornehls, and their collaborators, some of which are not yet published.

It is the purpose of this paper to summarize the results of our experiments on the coordination of retinal and nonretinal afferents and on neuronal integration in the visual cortex. I hope to show in the discussion that the neuronal organization of visual mechanisms and some apparently contradictory neuronal responses to stimulation by diffuse light and patterned light can be explained by two mechanisms of inhibition in antagonistic and synergistic neurons, and that nearly all neuronal findings can be understood when a definite information value is assigned to the specific antagonistic neuronal response types: brightness information to the B neurons and darkness information to the reciprocally functioning D neurons of the visual cortex. Thus I wish to show the remarkable agreement between the results of neuronal recordings and psychophysiology. Subjective sensory information may be used as a guide for our neurophysiological experiments. The microphysiology of cortical neurons only corroborates with modern techniques the detailed visual observations of the classical sensory physiologists of the nineteenth century.

Methods

Glass capillaries of the Ling–Gerard type with tips 0·5 to 3 microns in diameter, filled by the method of Tasaki *et al.* (1954), were used to record extracellularly single-neuron activity from the cortex of cats in Bremer's *encéphale isolé* preparation with artificial respiration.

For physiological stimulation of the visual cortex two methods were employed: (1) a diffuse white light, shed on a ground glass disc placed in front of the eyes with dilated pupils; continuous illumination at 30 to 500 lux, intermittent stimulation with light and dark phases of equal duration at 30 to 500 lux, and light flashes, 0·3 millisecond in duration at 3,000 to 12,000 lux; and (2) pattern stimulation of the eye for simultaneous white–black contrast, provided by a grid of bright and dark stripes, illuminated from behind, that was exposed at different positions of the contrasting fields to the receptive area of the recorded cortical neuron (Baumgartner and Hakas, 1959).

Electrical stimulation of the optic nerve, the reticulothalamic system, or the cortex was provided by a thyratron stimulator or by square-wave pulses 0·5 msec. in duration.

Since, during vestibular stimulation, it was necessary to avoid activation of other receptors and movements of the animal, labyrinthine polarization was provided at the round window of the ear by weak galvanic currents of 0·1 to 0·3 milliampere, as described by Grüsser, Grüsser-Cornehls, and Saur (1959). These currents are known to excite vestibular receptors only, without acoustic manifestations. In all experiments with diffuse light the *encéphale isolé* cat showed spontaneous eye movements. For pattern stimulation and labyrinthine stimulation, eye movements were abolished by application of curare or by cutting the external eye muscles.

A six-beam cathode-ray oscillograph, built by J. F. Tönnies, was used to record simultaneously several neuronal spikes, electrocorticograms, and a photocell record of light stimulation.

In the following discussion we use the terms 'neuronal responses' or 'neurons' in interpreting the spike records from units in the visual cortex. No distinction is made here between axons and cell bodies, both of which are parts of the neuron.[1]

1. This distinction is made in some special studies on the lateral geniculate body in order to exclude presynaptic optic nerve fibers (Grüsser and Saur, 1960), and in some studies of receptive fields in the visual cortex, in order to exclude optic radiation fibers.

Results

Types of responses of cortical neurons

In the course of our experiments it became necessary to classify the various neuronal responses to visual and other stimuli. Since the response to light stimulation is obviously the most important for the visual system, we have adopted such a classification since our first papers (von Baumgarten and Jung, 1952; Jung, von Baumgarten, and Baumgartner, 1952). The letters A, B, C, D, and E are used for different response patterns of cortical neurons to 'light-on' and 'light-off', thus expanding the classical distinctions of retinal 'on', 'off', and 'on–off' elements (Figure 1). Further work has confirmed the reality of these neuronal groups, and it has been possible to relate them to certain visual information values and to demonstrate that these groups represent fixed patterns and inherent properties of these neuronal systems with their afferent connections from retinal receptors. The variations of the responses to light-on and off with patterned stimulation of the retina (Figure 6) becomes understandable only when one assigns a distinct information value to the main neuronal types. It can be shown that these neuronal groups have a specific significance for visual messages coming from the retina. No significant correlations exist between these neuronal response types and those to thalamic stimulation (Akimoto and Creutzfeldt, 1957–8; Creutzfeldt and Akimoto, 1957–8) or vestibular stimulation (Grüsser and Grüsser-Cornehls, 1960; Grüsser, Grüsser-Cornehls, and Saur, 1959).

In the following pages the responses of cortical neurons are classified after binocular light stimulation, as illustrated in Figure 1. Most cortical neurons show the same response to monocular stimulation of either the ipsilateral or contralateral eye but no response to stimulation to the other eye. Thus the combinations of the monocular types – B–A, C–A, D–A or A–B, A–C, and so forth – are by far the most frequent in Grüsser and Grüsser-Cornehls's results (1960; see also Grüsser, Grüsser-Cornehls, and Saur, 1959). Most neurons in the visual cortex respond only to *monocular* retinal afferents. Thus stimulation of a single eye with light would show many nonresponsive neurons, which would respond, however, to illumination of the other eye or to binocular light or dark stimuli.

A neurons are not responsive to diffuse light or dark stimuli but may respond to thalamic or vestibular stimulation. They seem to be a heterogeneous group. Although the number of A neurons

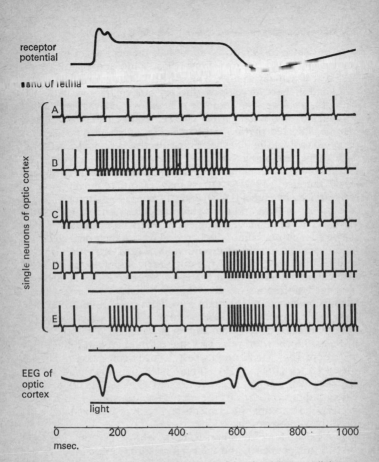

Figure 1. Five types of neuronal responses of the visual cortex to light and dark stimulation and their relation to receptor excitation and to the EEG (from Jung, Creutzfeldt, and Grüsser, 1957). Topmost graph shows receptor potential recorded with microelectrode, intracellularly from outer plexiform layer of the retina. Bottom graph shows cortical potentials with on and off effect from gross electrode recording on cortical surface (macrorhythms). Graphs A–E, schematic representation of discharges of different neuronal types: A neuron, no reaction to light or dark; B neuron, activated by light, inhibited by dark with delayed after-activation (similar to on element of retina). C neuron, inhibitory break for both light and dark; D neuron, inhibited by light and activated by dark (reciprocal of B neuron, similar to off element of retina). E neuron, pre-excitatory inhibition precedes delayed activation by light, early activation by dark (similar to on–off elements of retina)

was estimated in 1955 to be about half the neurons of the visual cortex (Baumgartner and Jung, 1955; Jung and Baumgartner, 1955), it is actually smaller. The more fully our methods of visual stimulation have developed (flicker, binocular, and patterned stimuli), the fewer unresponsive A neurons we have found. Jung, Creutzfeldt, and Baumgartner (1957) found that some A neurons can be activated rhythmically by flicker, although they may not respond to single light flashes. Some inactive B, D, and E neurons, not to be confounded with A neurons, can be activated by thalamoreticular stimulation to respond to light stimuli (Akimoto and Creutzfeldt, 1957–8). Others may respond to moving stimuli, as described by Hubel (1958), and still others to patterned light at the border of light and dark contrast (Baumgartner and Hakas, 1962) or to optic-nerve stimulation. Even supramaximal optic-nerve stimulation cannot discharge all cortical neurons, however, and 28 per cent remain unresponsive (type 1a of Grützner, Grüsser, and Baumgartner, 1958). After optic-nerve stimulation combined with illumination to the other eye, 16 per cent of 211 neurons remained unresponsive. It is believed that A neurons are a stabilizing system to maintain a medium background of excitation in the cortex (Jung, 1958a) and may be a reserve system for special visual functions that cannot yet be defined exactly.

B neurons show on responses and off inhibition at diffuse illumination. They constitute the best-defined neuronal group in the visual cortex (Jung, 1953a; Jung, von Baumgarten, and Baumgartner, 1952; Jung, Creutzfeldt, and Grüsser, 1957) and represent about a fourth of the cortical neurons in area 17. They correspond to retinal on elements and seem to be correlated with brightness information.

C neurons show inhibition to both light-on and off. They are rare (3 to 5 per cent), and their information value cannot yet be determined. After stimulation of one eye an inhibitory C response may be obtained from some neurons that show on responses of the B type from the other eye (Grüsser and Grüsser-Cornehls, 1960).

D neurons show off responses and on inhibition at diffuse illumination (Jung, 1953a; Jung, Creutzfeldt, and Grüsser, 1957), corresponding to off elements in the retina. They show strong primary inhibition to brief light flashes, followed by late activation (Baumgartner, 1955). D neurons mediate darkness information.

E neurons respond with strong off responses and constant on inhibition followed by late activation to light-on, corresponding to on–off elements in the retina. They show a shorter pre-excitatory inhibition after brief light flashes than do D neurons (Baumgartner, 1955).

Responses of the E type were found frequently in about 18 per cent of cortical neurons during the first years of our experiments in which faint patterns during illumination were not rigorously excluded. The proportion of E neurons has decreased and of D neurons increased as the diffuseness of light stimuli has been brought under increasing control. E neurons may show transitions to D neurons (Jung, 1953a). Responses of the E type can also be obtained from D neurons near the border contrast of patterned stimuli. An abnormal on–off response similar to E neurons may occur in an asphyxiated cortex when respiration is insufficient. These 'pseudo-E neurons' can be restored to their original responses (B or D) if anoxic damage is avoided. From results on contrast stimulation (Baumgartner, 1961; Baumgartner and Hakas, 1962) it seems probable, though not yet certain, that the information value of E neurons corresponds to the darkness information of D neurons, and that E neurons may be only a subgroup of the D system.

After *nonspecific thalamic stimulation*, five different response types (I–V) were found in the neurons of area 17 (Akimoto and Creutzfeldt, 1957–8; Creutzfeldt and Akimoto, 1957–8). Type I shows no response, whereas the other types respond by a different pattern of activation or inhibition after relatively long latencies. Except in types I and III, all neurons show inhibitory silent periods before or after activation. The latencies are more variable and longer after thalamic stimulation than after light stimulation. For responses after *vestibular stimulation*, see Figure 4.

After *optic-nerve stimulation*, four different response types have been described (Grüsser and Grützner, 1958; Grützner, Grüsser, and Baumgartner, 1958).

These different responses to nonretinal stimuli show no statistical relation to the neuronal responses that follow light stimulation. Neither thalamoreticular nor optic-nerve stimulation alters the A, B, C, D, and E responses to light stimuli. These neuronal responses seem to be fixed patterns of the retinocortical chain, which can only be modified by contrasting light stimuli.

Neuronal responses to patterned light

Our earlier experiments from 1951 on were all done with diffuse light stimulation until in 1958 Baumgartner (1961; Baumgartner and Hakas, 1959, 1962) began to use patterned light with

19

white–black contrast. Although the neuronal responses obtained in contrasting fields seem to differ from those in diffuse light, the results may be explained by the same laws of reciprocal inhibition of antagonistic neurons in the same field, by lateral inhibition of synergistic neurons in surrounding fields, and by the information value of antagonistic neuronal systems. The mechanism of lateral inhibition was elucidated by Hartline's work on *Limulus* (1949; Hartline and Ratliff, 1957) and Kuffler's experiments on spot stimulation of the cat's retina (1953; Barlow, FitzHugh, and Kuffler, 1957). Similar neuronal organizations to Kuffler's retinal receptive fields (on and off centers and surrounding zones of reciprocal responses) were also found in cortical neurons by Baumgartner and Hakas (1959, 1960) and Hubel and Wiesel (1959).

In pattern vision, information is usually conveyed by contours and not single spots of light. For this reason Baumgartner has used contrast patterns instead of spots of light as stimuli to explore the neuronal responses to patterned light and to determine the receptive fields of cortical neurons. He has done the following experiments in my laboratory. A grid of vertical or horizontal stripes was illuminated from behind and exposed to the receptive fields. The grid was shifted in steps that differed about 41 degrees from left to right and from right to left. Baumgartner and Hakas (1959, 1960) compared the neuronal responses to light-on and light-off in these various positions. They recorded from three different levels of the visual system and found essentially the same contrast responses in axons of retinal ganglion cells in the optic nerve, in geniculate neurons and in cells of the visual cortex of the cat. An example from a geniculate neuron showing reversed responses at the border contrast was presented at this symposium, in the discussion following Ratliff's presentation.

In the bright stripe of the grid, the various neuronal types respond qualitatively to light-on and off in the same way as they do in diffuse light. In the dark field, however, the neurons show mainly a reversed response to light-on and off as if they were in the dark at light-on and faintly illuminated at light-off. The intensity of the responses varies with different positions of the grid and the relation to the zone of bright–dark contrast. The spike frequency seems dependent upon the projection of this border zone to the receptive-field center of the neuron.

Figure 6 (page 33) illustrates these neuronal reactions in various positions of the contrasting grid of bright and dark stripes: strict reciprocity is maintained in the responses of the antagonistic B and D neurons to patterned contrast stimuli. In light-activated B neurons the on response is greatly enhanced at the bright border zone to the dark stripe. In the middle zone of a bright stripe of about 5 degrees aperture, the neuronal responses have about the same frequency as in diffuse light stimulation (see Figure 6, left and center). The B neurons discharge increasingly as the dark stripe is approached from the middle of the bright stripe (with a relative weak on response) and show a maximum on response, when the receptive-field center projects to the bright zone immediately at the border of the dark stripe (Figure 6, lateral peaks above white stripe). When the projection of the field center of a B neuron crosses the dark contour, the on discharge is suddenly diminished or inhibited, and eventually a reversal of the responses to light-on and off occurs: a B neuron projecting upon the dark stripe is largely inhibited by light-on and activated by light-off.

These alterations and paradoxical on inhibitions and off discharges of B neurons correlate exactly with our subjective experience in simultaneous contrast: at light-on, the dark zone in the contrasting field appears blacker and the white zone whiter than the indifferent *Eigengrau*, the subjective gray visual background without illumination. The B neurons also conserve their type of discharge with a high-frequency peak and brief silent period when they are activated by light-off in the black zone, and they do not show the more gradual decline of the off responses of D neurons.

D neurons, which respond by inhibition to light-on and by activation to light-off, reverse their response when they cross the border from the bright to the dark stripe. Projecting to the dark stripe, they respond to light-on by activation with a continuously diminishing discharge. A short pre-excitatory inhibition may precede this unusual on activation. Since the off activation is not always completely suppressed in the dark stripe, on–off responses of D neurons are frequently seen in the border zone.

E neurons, which respond to both light-on and off, show reactions to contrast patterns similar to those of D neurons when their field projection approaches the contrasting border in the bright stripe. They reverse to strong on activation when the border of the dark stripe is crossed. In the median region of the bright or dark stripe, an on–off response reappears, but off activation is less pronounced in the dark than in the bright stripe.

Receptive-field centers. The diameter of the receptive-field center can be measured by comparing neuronal responses in the different grid positions of the white–dark contrast stimulus. Baumgartner and Hakas (1960) have compared these central cores of the receptive fields in retinal, geniculate, and cortical neurons. The receptive-field center, determined by the responses of the neurons at the border of the bright and dark stripes, was computed from the distance of the contrast borders during the activation period of the neuron. From the distance of the eye to the contrast object, together with the optical constants of the eye, the diameter of the receptive-field center on the retina was measured in millimeters. This receptive-field center is only the central part of the whole receptive field that Hartline (1940a) and Kuffler (1953) and collaborators (Barlow, Fitzhugh, and Kuffler, 1957) determined in retinal ganglion cells. The surrounding area of inhibition cannot be measured precisely by Baumgartner's method. Baumgartner's receptive-field centers correspond approximately to Kuffler's on and off centers.

The horizontal diameter of the receptive-field centers of cortical neurons was significantly smaller than the field centers of retinal and geniculate neurons. Those cortical neurons that could be distinguished from radiation fibers had an average diameter about half that of the receptive-field centers of retinal and geniculate neurons (Baumgartner and Hakas, 1960).

The considerable overlap that Hartline has found in his first studies on the receptive field of retinal ganglion cells (1940a, b) should become smaller in cortical neurons when their receptive-field center is measured without the surrounding zone of lateral inhibition.

Convergence of retinal, reticulothalamic and vestibular afferent impulses at single neurons of the visual cortex

Specific and nonspecific coordination. Most neurons of the visual cortex were found to receive convergent impulses from specific retinogeniculate, nonspecific reticulothalamic (Akimoto and Creutzfeldt, 1957–8; Creutzfeldt and Akimoto, 1957–8) and vestibular afferents (Grüsser, Grüsser-Cornehls, and Saur, 1959; Grüsser and Grüsser-Cornehls, 1960). Although some indications of convergence of specific and nonspecific afferents in the visual cortex were obtained with macroelectrodes (Bremer and Stoupel, 1958, 1959; Dumont and Dell, 1958; and Jasper and Ajmone-Marsan, 1952), it was not clear whether these impulses converged at the same cortical neurons. Li, Cullen, and Jasper (1956) were unable to activate the same neuron in the somatosensory cortex by stimulation of both specific and nonspecific thalamic nuclei, although Li (1956) described some facilitation by the latter. However, Akimoto and Creutzfeldt (1957–8) in our laboratory demon strated the convergence of specific retinal and nonspecific thalamic afferents on single neurons of the visual cortex. About two-thirds of the neurons of area 17 examined showed this convergence and

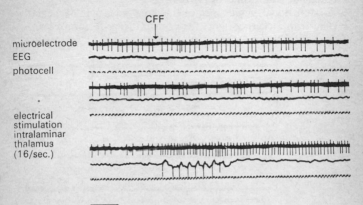

Figure 2. Increase in flicker frequency and CFF of a B neuron in the visual cortex by thalamic stimulation (from Jung, Creutzfeldt, and Grüsser, 1957). Flicker at rising frequency gives regular neuronal discharges up to 18 per second. This is followed by breaks in firing as a sign of critical fusion frequency (CFF at 18 per second). At frequencies of 19 to 41 per second, the neuron can no longer respond to each flash and shows interruptions in firing. After a brief series of thyratron pulses (16 per second) in the intralaminar thalamus, the neuron follows the high flicker frequency of 41 per second and responds to each flash with a discharge. After 1 or 2 seconds, interruptions in the response appear once again

dependence of retinal and thalamic impulses. No consistent correlations were found between the various types of neuronal response after retinal stimulation (A, B, C, D, and E) and after single nonspecific thalamic stimuli (I, II, III, IV, and V). Some A neurons ordinarily unresponsive to light showed different responses to thalamic stimulation during illumination and darkness (Jung, Creutzfeldt, and Baumgartner, 1957). This observation makes it probable that A neurons receive subliminal impulses from the retina at cortical or subcortical levels that cannot be discovered in the usual spike records after stimulation by light alone. It has also been possible to drive weakly responding B, D, and E

23

neurons to respond strongly to the same light stimulus during and after repeated thalamic stimulation. However, thalamic stimulation is not able to change the response type to diffuse retinal stimulation: type A remained A, B, B, and so forth, even when these neurons were stimulated by thalamoreticular shocks (Creutzfeldt and Akimoto, 1957–8).

The functional significance of this convergence is particularly evident with flickering light: the critical flicker-fusion frequency (CFF) of cortical neurons is, on the whole, raised by nonspecific

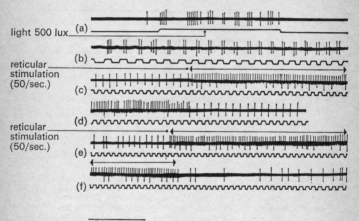

light 500 lux (a)

reticular stimulation (50/sec.) (b)

(c)

(d)

reticular stimulation (50/sec.) (e)

(f)

.500 msec.

Figure 3. Inhibitory effect of reticular stimulation on flicker responses of a B neuron in the visual cortex. (a) The B neuron shows little spontaneous discharge but typical activation during illumination with high-frequency initial discharge and periodic maintained discharge. (b) Responses to flickering light of 6 to 10 per second with gradual diminution of initial discharge until a stimulus–response rate of 1 : 1 is reached at the end. (c, d) Flicker at 16 per second gives a regular rate of 1 : 1 discharges. However, during reticular stimulation at 50 per second, the flicker responses are inhibited and become irregular with pauses and doublets. The inhibiting pauses disappear at cessation of stimulation, but a few doublets continue. (e, f) At flicker frequencies of 20 per second the limit of the critical-fusion frequency (neuronal CFF) is attained, and the neuronal response fails once. After reticular stimulation, multiple pauses appear again, and inhibitory pauses continue after cessation of stimulus.

The effects of stimulation by the same implanted electrode in the mesencephalic reticular formation in the same freely moving cat were observed behaviorally and filmed by Grüsser before these neuronal recordings were made: 50 stimuli per second of identical strength resulted in the arrest of spontaneous activity and searching movements of the head and eyes to the upper visual field and both sides

thalamic stimuli (Figure 2; Creutzfeldt and Grüsser, 1959; Jung, Creutzfeldt, and Grüsser, 1957). Only in rare instances does in hibition occur, and CFF is diminished. This lowering of the CFF is seen better after reticular stimulation (Figure 3). The facilitation and inhibition of cortical neurons and the alteration of neuronal CFF may correspond to the influence of attention and fatigue on visual perception and on the flicker-fusion frequency.

The long and variable latencies following stimulation of the nonspecific thalamus are in striking contrast to the short and practically constant latencies of neurons following optic-nerve stimulation or high-intensity illumination. Creutzfeldt and Akimoto have offered the following hypothesis to explain this difference: specific optic-nerve afferents discharge cortical neurons directly, probably via axosomatic synapses over a disynaptic pathway from the geniculate body; but nonspecific afferents act on these neurons only as modulators, possibly by axodendritic synapses and over multisynaptic pathways, thus facilitating or inhibiting cortical neurons that receive convergence from various sources.

Vestibulovisual coordination. Experiments have shown (Grüsser and Grüsser-Cornehls, 1960; Grüsser, Grüsser-Cornehls, and Saur, 1959) that nearly all the neurons of the visual cortex that the authors recorded were activated by labyrinthine polarization. They found further that this activation altered the responses of cortical neurons to light stimulation. Their results can be summarized as follows. Four types of response to labyrinthine polarization were observed in cortical neurons (Figure 4): α, no activation by labyrinthine polarization; β, activation by onset, not by cessation, of labyrinthine polarization; γ, no response to onset, but activation by cessation; δ, activation by onset and cessation. Type δ was most frequent, type α was rarely seen. When the same neuron was stimulated by both positive and negative labyrinthine polarization, nearly all combinations of responses ($\alpha- \alpha+$, $\delta- \alpha+$, and so forth) could be elicited; δ responses to both stimuli ($\delta - \delta+$) provided the most frequent combinations.

During labyrinthine polarization, the activated neurons showed slow adaptation within 3 to 10 sec. Similarly, following cessation of polarization, the frequency of the neurons decreased within 3 to 10 sec. to the level of spontaneous activity when they were activated by termination of the stimulation. Definite inhibition of neuronal discharge could not be observed during and after labyrinthine stimulation. The latencies of neuronal activation following labyrinthine polarization were variable and measured 25 to 200 msec. The bursts of neuronal discharges following brief light flashes were increased in all light-responsive neurons (B, D, and E) by labyrinthine polarization; the duration of the silent

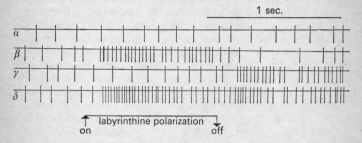

Figure 4. Four types of responses of neurons in the visual cortex during and after labyrinthine polarization (schematic drawing from the results of Grüsser and co-workers). α, no response (rare); β, activated by onset, no response from cessation of polarization; γ, no response from onset, activated by cessation of polarization; δ, activated by onset and by cessation of labyrinthine polarization (most frequent)

periods sometimes decreased, sometimes increased. The critical flicker frequency was raised significantly in most of the cortical neurons during neuronal activation by polarization of the labyrinth (Grüsser and Grüsser-Cornehls, 1960). The activation of cortical neurons during or after labyrinthine polarization decreased slowly within several seconds. Constant rhythmic interruptions were not apparent, but some fluctuations of discharge rate resulted in bursts at higher frequencies. This was particularly evident when the labyrinth was polarized while neuronal discharges were induced by flickering light. In this case, some pauses in discharge, occurring at intervals of 200 to 800 msec., were recorded. However no clear relation between these pauses and nystagmic eye movements induced by labyrinthine polarization was found in those experiments in which the eye movements were not abolished by curare or other means.

The relation of neuronal activity in the visual cortex to vestibular nystagmus and to optokinetic nystagmus elicited by moving patterns needs further investigation.

Binocular coordination. The visual cortex is usually considered as an area in which binocular integration occurs between the two halves of the visual fields. However single-neuron recordings of Grüsser-Cornehls and Grüsser (unpublished), which compare monocular and binocular diffuse light stimuli, have not been able to demonstrate binocular convergence for most neurons of area 17. These investigators collected data on neuronal responses following monocular and binocular stimulation in various combinations, and the results of their experiments with a special binocular stimulator have now been worked out and will be published in detail.

In the geniculate relay, optic-nerve fibers of the two eyes end separately in different layers, and accordingly Grüsser and Saur (1960) have found that geniculate neurons are activated by monocular stimuli only. A minority of the neurons showed less evoked activity to binocular stimulation than to monocular stimulation. Genuine binocular convergence in geniculate neurons, as described by Erulkar and Fillenz (1958), was not confirmed when stray light from the other side was rigorously avoided.

In the cat's visual cortex most neurons respond only to stimulation from one eye. Some modulation of monocular activation by stimulation of the other eye or binocular convergence may occur in about one-third of the neurons of area 17. Genuine binocular convergence at neurons that respond to monocular stimulation of either eye separately is rare: only about one-tenth of the cortical neurons in area 17 show clear binocular convergence. Binocular interaction manifests itself mainly by inhibition from one eye depressing the excitation from the other dominant eye, when identical stimuli are presented to both eyes. The type of response of these neurons to light stimulation usually differs from one eye to the other. (An example is shown in figure 2 of Grüsser, Grüsser-Cornehls, and Saur, 1959; this neuron was activated by ipsilateral light, like a B neuron, and inhibited by contralateral light-on and off, like a C neuron.) Most neurons classified as binocular B neurons also show on responses of the B type to stimulation from one eye but are, like A neurons, unresponsive to stimulation from the other eye. Summation of similar responses from the two eyes at single neurons was exceedingly rare, although recently Hubel and Wiesel (1959) described such binocular summation for corresponding parts of the visual field to stimulation with a spot of light. Grüsser and Grüsser-Cornehls obtained their results by diffuse light stimulation with pattern vision excluded. Contrasting stimuli may give some different results.

The predominance of monocularly influenced neurons in the visual cortex, found by Grüsser-Cornehls and Grüsser, indicates that binocular integration cannot be a simple convergence of both monocular afferents on the same neurons of area 17. If such neuronal convergence occurs at all, it needs higher visual centers above the primary receiving area, as the coordination for stereoscopic vision probably does also. The relation of neuronal discharges to binocular flicker is discussed below.

Thus binocular coordination is possible only on the basis of independent monocular projection in geniculate and cortical neurons. This monocular neuronal activation in the final paths of the cortex agrees well with psychophysiological experience, which has shown that each eye independently develops a complete visual image that is only secondarily modified by the mechanisms of binocular rivalry and stereoscopic vision.

Correlations of cortical neuronal activity in cats with subjective visual sensation in men

The psychophysiological correlations with our findings in the neuronal system of the visual cortex have been described in other papers (Jung, 1959). In summary, the following twelve parallels have been found between neuronal discharges in the primary visual cortex of the cat (area 17) and the psychophysiological results of sensory experiments with human subjects.

Diffuse illumination of light-adapted eyes
1. Brightness of light sensation and Weber–Fechner law. In the human eye, equal increments of subjective brightness correspond to a logarithmic function of the intensity of the stimulating light, according to the Weber–Fechner law. Correspondingly, the discharges of the B neurons of the visual cortex that are activated by light increase approximately with the logarithm of the stimulus intensity, if light adaptation is held constant. Simultaneous with the activation of B neurons, there is inhibition of the D neurons, which are activated by darkness. The brighter the light stimulus, the more rapidly the B neurons fire, and the stronger is the inhibition of the D neurons (Jung and Baumgartner, 1955).

2. Flicker fusion. The fusion of flickering light (subjective CFF) occurs at frequencies of about 50 per second (at a light intensity of 500 lux) in both man and cat (Kappauf, 1936). The critical flicker frequency of single neurons (neuronal CFF) is defined as the flicker rate at which individual neurons fail to respond to each flash. This neuronal CFF, up to which single neurons can

follow flickering light, varies under similar conditions in different cortical neurons between 5 and 50 per second. The highest neuronal CFF of single cortical neurons, 50 per second (at 500 lux), corresponds to the maximal flicker frequency of the EEG and the subjective CFF in humans (Grüsser and Creutzfeldt, 1957). The CFF of retinal receptors (cones) is much higher (Grüsser, 1957, 1960).

3. Porter's law. Subjective CFF occurs at higher flicker frequencies as the light intensity is increased. Correspondingly, the neuronal CFF of cortical neurons is also higher at higher light intensities of the flicker.

4. Brightness enhancement (Brücke–Bartley effect). In subjective experiences described in 1864, Brücke found that maximal brightness at different flicker frequencies always occurs below the flicker fusion (subjective CFF). Correspondingly, the maximal impulse frequency of all cortical neurons responding to flickering light (1.1 light–dark ratio) is below the flicker frequency of their neuronal CFF. In an average cell population of cortical B neurons the mean maximal impulse frequency occurs around flicker rates of 10 per second, which corresponds to Bartley's brightness enhancement (Bartley, 1959), although in individual neurons it may vary between 3 and 25 per second (Grüsser and Creutzfeldt, 1957). This maximum is also found in retinal neurons (Grüsser and Creutzfeldt, 1957) but can be explained only partly by properties of retinal receptors (Svaetichin, 1956b; Grüsser, 1957, 1960; Grüsser and Rabelo, 1958; Hartline, 1938).

5. Alterations of CFF by attention and thalamic stimulation. Just as subjective CFF can be raised by attention and arousal, the neuronal CFF, that is, the maximal frequency up to which single cortical neurons can follow flickering light, may also be raised by stimulation of nonspecific thalamic nuclei and the reticular formation (Jung, Creutzfeldt, and Grüsser, 1957; Creutzfeldt and Grüsser, 1959; Jung, 1958b).

6. Local adaptation. In subjective experience, a bright image fades out within seconds when the projection on the retina is held constant by a mirror system. Correspondingly, the discharge frequency of cortical neurons in response to continuous illumination – after the initial peak of discharge has waned – gradually decreases until an average rate of discharge is reached at around 10 per second, which is also present in the absence of a light stimulus. This neuronal behavior is probably due to a gradual decline in the receptor potential in the outer plexiform layer of the retina (Grüsser, 1960).

7. After-images following brief light stimuli (successive contrast). After-images show a rhythmic alternation of light and dark phases. Correspondingly, cortical neurons also show rhythmic activation and inhibition phases with similar time course (Jung, von Baumgarten, and Baumgartner, 1952; Jung and Baumgartner, 1955; Jung, Creutzfeldt, and Grüsser, 1957). After brief light flashes, the primary image corresponds to the primary activation of B neurons and the Purkinje second after-image to the secondary activation; the third after-image of Hess corresponds to the tertiary activation of B neurons following a single flash. The dark intervals between images and after-images correspond to the activation of D neurons and the inhibition of B neurons. This is shown in Figure 5 (Grüsser and Grützner, 1958).

8. Subjective coordination of visual perception with vestibular stimuli. The vestibular component in the regulation of the spatial stability of the visual world (*Raumkonstanz der Sehdinge*) corresponds to different types of modulation and activation of the majority of the cortical neurons of area 17 by polarization of the labyrinth, shown in Figure 4 (Grüsser and Grüsser-Cornehls, 1960). This vestibular activation was not found at geniculate neurons (Grüsser, Grüsser-Cornehls, and Saur, 1959).

9. Subjective brightness with monocular or binocular illumination and binocular rivalry. In the human eye, there is very little subjective binocular brightness summation, and strong rivalry occurs between the corresponding areas of the two eyes when different stimuli are conveyed from their receptive fields (Hering's binocular rivalry). Correspondingly, 90 per cent of the cortical neurons of area 17 are activated or inhibited only by monocular stimulation and are not influenced by the other eye alone, although some modulation may occur in about 30 per cent of cortical neurons with binocular stimulation.

Only a small number of neurons can be influenced by each of the two eyes separately. Binocular convergent impulses manifest themselves chiefly as inhibition from one eye to light activation of the other eye, as one might expect from binocular rivalry (Grüsser and Grüsser-Cornehls, 1960, and unpublished work).

10. Binocular flicker sensations. Since Sherrington's experiments (1897, 1906) it is well known that binocular synchronous and alternate flicker of the two eyes has little mutual influence on visual experience, and that each monocular mechanism develops independently a complete visual image. Only at the limit of CFF does binocular flicker show a little higher frequency than monocular flicker. Correspondingly, there is little if any rein-

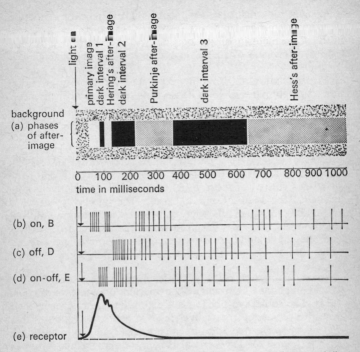

Figure 5. Correlations of subjective after-image of man and neuronal discharges in retina and visual cortex of the cat, following a brief light flash (300 lux) (modified from Grüsser and Grützner, 1958). (a) Scheme of successive phases of after-images (according to Fröhlich, 1929). Time in milliseconds. (b to e) Schematic responses of neurons and receptors: (b) retinal on neurons and cortical B neurons; (c) retinal off neurons and cortical D neurons; (d) retinal on-off neurons and cortical E neurons; (e) receptor response of the outer plexiform layer of the retina with intracellular recording.

The light flash is marked by a descending arrow. In (b–e) the arrows are shifted to the right because Fröhlich's subjective *Empfindungszeit* is 20 to 40 msec. longer than the latency of B neurons in the visual cortex. The shaded area surrounding the after-images signifies the background of observation and the *Eigengrau* of the eye.

The scheme combines retinal and cortical responses, although cortical neurons show lower frequency and stronger periodicity. A pause in the primary activation of cortical B neurons is concurrent with the initial E discharge. During longer illumination both correspond to the *bande noire* of Charpentier (Jung, 1961) and after short flashes probably to dark interval 1. The scheme of Grüsser and Grützner (1958) has been corrected appropriately, as they also described a pause in on–off neurons between 200 and 450 msec.

forcement by synchronous binocular flicker and little reduction by alternate binocular flicker in cortical neurons. The neuronal CFF of the majority of neurons in area 17 is determined by only one eye (Grüsser-Cornehls and Grüsser, unpublished experiments).

11. Regulation of visual attention. The variation in attention for visual stimuli may have its neuronal correlate in the convergence of specific retinal and nonspecific thalamic impulses upon cortical neurons. A subjective visual sensation in the central area of the visual field, evoked solely by an arousing stimulus without illumination (the *Schreckblitz* of Ebbecke, 1943; the *Weckblitz* of Ahlenstiel, 1949), may correspond to the arousal of cortical neurons of area 17. Nonspecific thalamic impulses modify the discharge pattern of most visual neurons after a relatively long latency of between 20 and 150 msec. The number of neurons responding to retinal afferents can be increased by stimulation of the nonspecific system, which increases the readiness of cortical neurones to respond to visual impulses (Akimoto and Creutzfeldt, 1957–8; Creutzfeldt and Akimoto, 1957–8; Jung, 1958b).

Patterned light stimulation (white–black contrast)

12. Simultaneous contrast at the margin of white and black fields. The subjective phenomena of border contrast have their objective correlates in certain changes in neuronal responses that depend upon their relation to the border of the white and dark stripes (Figure 6). The cortical B neurons show a maximum of discharges at light-on when their receptive field is stimulated by white light at the margin of a dark field. They show a minimum of discharges at light-on and a reversal of their responses to light-on and off when their receptive field is situated in the dark stripe. A receptive field corresponding to the dark stripe reverses the discharge of B neurons to the D type of response: at light-on the B neuron is inhibited, and at light-off it is activated, although the total light shed on the retina is certainly increased at light-on and diminished at light-off. A reversal of the response may occur in D neurons; that is to say, they change to activation at light-on and inhibition at light-off when their receptive fields correspond to the dark stripe (Baumgartner and Hakas, 1959, 1960, 1962; Baumgartner, 1961; Figure 6). Although D neurons then seem to respond like B neurons at light-on, they conserve their peculiar type of discharge at light-off and do not show the high-frequency peak of initial on response of the B neurons. In other words, D neurons exposed to the dark stripe respond to light-on as they

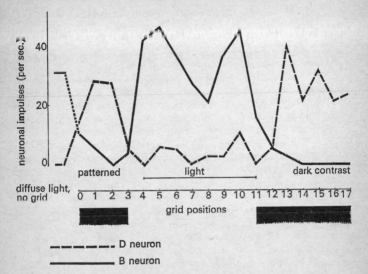

Figure 6. Diagram of responses to contrast pattern and diffuse light in a cortical B and D neuron from the same experiment (from unpublished experiments of Baumgartner). The responses to light-on are plotted for spike frequencies per second on the ordinate (spikes counted in the first 500 msec. following light-on) in relation to the projections of the receptive field to contrast pattern and diffuse light, on the abscissa.

The bright stripe has a visual angle of 5 degrees 41 minutes and is exposed in grid positions 3 to 11 by steps moving across the receptive fields of the neurons from left to right. Reciprocal activation and inhibition of the two antagonistic neurons and contrast enhancement of the discharge at the border of bright and dark stripes are clearly shown in the peaks and troughs of the upper graphs. This neuronal behavior may be explained satisfactorily by two factors: (1) *reciprocal inhibition* of antagonistic neurons in the same receptive field, and (2) *lateral inhibition* of synergic neurons in the surrounding field

usually do to light-off, after they have been exposed to diffuse light or to the bright stripe.

This neuronal behavior can be understood in physiological and psychological terms, if one accepts the following *four assumptions*, which are discussed later in detail:

1. Retinal on and off neurons as well as cortical B and D neurons discharge reciprocally. When the on or B neurons are activated, the corresponding off or D neurons are inhibited in the same retinal or cortical region.

33

2. Retinal on and off neurons as well as cortical B and D neurons show lateral inhibition of the same type of neurons in the surrounding retinal or cortical area during light adaptation. Lateral facilitation of neurons of the reciprocal type may be secondary to the lateral and reciprocal inhibition.

3. Activation of the on-center neurons in the retina and the B neurons in the cortex corresponds to the perception of brightness.

4. Activation of the off-center neurons in the retina and D and E neurons in the cortex corresponds to the perception of darkness.

Assumptions 1, 3, and 4 are supported by experiments with both diffuse and contrast light stimulation. Assumption 2 is derived from experiments with contrast light in cats (p. 19) and spots of light in *Limulus* (Hartline, 1949; Hartline and Ratliff, 1957) and in cats (Kuffler, 1953; Barlow, FitzHugh, and Kuffler, 1957). Although Kuffler's 1953 paper stresses the variability of response in the same retinal neuron, the later paper, with Barlow and FitzHugh (1957), discusses also the relation of his 'on center' to a sensation of whiteness and of his 'off center' to a sensation of blackness; in addition, it offers an explanation of simultaneous contrast by lateral inhibition in the retina. [. . .]

Functional significance of convergence in the visual cortex

Our results demonstrate the convergence and coordination of various afferent impulses from the eye, the labyrinth, and the nonspecific thalamus at neurons of the visual cortex. This cortical area is generally considered only as a specialized receiving area for messages coming from the retina and as a binocular projection of both homonymous retinal fields. However, the function of its neuronal apparatus is apparently an integration of visual information from the retina with the results of vestibulo-optokinetic coordination and with the activity of the nonspecific system of the brain stem.

Many questions still remain about the functional significance and the mechanism of this integration and of its relation to other sense organs. The correlations of neuronal coordination in the visual cortex with psychophysiological experiences that have been described indicate that objective foundations for various subjective visual phenomena are not beyond the reach of our present experimental methods. Neurophysiology, psychology, and technical science may each contribute to such a synthesis.

The relation of retinal and thalamoreticular convergence to sensory facilitation by attention and possible differences in the synaptic transmission of specific and nonspecific afferents have been discussed by Akimoto and Creutzfeldt (1957–8; Creutzfeldt and Akimoto, 1957–8). The significance of this convergence for special attentional mechanisms of the vestibulovisual coordination of ocular movements and for the stability of the visual world has been mentioned briefly in another paper (Jung, 1958b). The functional significance of specific and nonspecific coordination is evident from the alteration of the frequency up to which visual neurons are able to follow flickering light (neuronal CFF) by thalamic and reticular stimuli, described above and illustrated in Figures 2 and 3.

The significance of nonspecific reticular afferents to the visual cortex is also demonstrated by the following experiments. Neuronal recordings from area 17 during retinal anoxia (described in Baumgartner, Creutzfeldt, and Jung, 1961) have shown a consistent difference after mesencephalic transection: intraocular ischemia knocks out spontaneous discharges in the *cerveau isolé* preparation but not in the *encéphale isolé*. These experiments permit the following conclusions: acute exclusion of specific afferent impulses depresses 'spontaneous' neuronal activity in area 17 only when the connections with the lower brain stem are interrupted; thus activity of cortical neurons can be maintained by the ascending brain-stem connections (cf. Magoun, 1952) – including the reticular formation and the lower cranial nerve afferents – in the absence of specific afferents. One may conclude that both specific and nonspecific afferents are important to the maintenance of the neuronal activity of the visual cortex. The neurons of a primary receiving area of the cerebral cortex, although driven by specific afferent impulses, are also dependent upon nonspecific influx from the lower brain stem for the maintenance of normal 'spontaneous' activity. Specific visual afferents and the nonspecific thalamic nuclei seem insufficient to maintain an active waking state without the lower brain stem, as suggested by Bremer's old experiments (1938) on the electroencephalogram in *encéphale* and *cerveau isolé* preparations. It appears that the corticothalamic visual system needs some afferent input from the periphery (either from the adequate specific receptors or from other afferents, for example, vestibular or trigeminal) over the reticular formation to drive the cortex and to maintain average neuronal activity during the waking state. The cortical neurons may maintain some activity if either the specific retinal or the nonspecific brain-stem influx is cut off. But neuronal activity in the visual cortex drops nearly to zero when both brain-stem reticular and eye afferents are blocked, although connections with

35

the thalamus remain intact. However, we have induced only acute short depression of specific afferents by local retinal anoxia, which causes pain in *encéphale isolé*, and have not excluded them for a longer time by cutting both optic nerves. Such chronic specific deafferentation should be investigated by further experiments in *cerveau isolé* and *encéphale isolé* preparations after cutting of the trigeminal and optic nerves. [. . .]

Reciprocal inhibition and lateral inhibition as basic mechanisms of neuronal organization

Two relatively simple inhibitory mechanisms are basic to neuronal responses to stimulation with diffuse and patterned light and may be used to explain the coordination of neuronal organization in the visual system: (a) *reciprocal inhibition* of antagonistic neurons in the same region; and (b) *lateral inhibition* of synergistic neurons in neighboring regions.

We prefer also to explain some secondary activation phenomena in these neuronal systems by inhibition and consequent disinhibition: examples of such phenomena are after-activation of the same neurons in successive contrast following postexcitatory inhibition (Figure 5) and simultaneous activation of antagonistic neurons in neighboring fields. The reciprocal organization of this neuronal system, with its tendency to balance both activation and inhibition in antagonism, will necessarily result in a preponderance of excitation of antagonistic neurons when the agonistic group is inhibited, as in Hartline's disinhibition in the *Limulus* eye. During light stimulation, excitation is probably prevalent in the on system, first in the retina, because it is directly activated by the receptors, and second in the relay-stations – retina, geniculate body, and cortex – because only excitatory spikes can be transmitted by nerve fibers and not inhibition as such. Inhibition may result only from synaptic action by a special transmitter (Eccles, 1957). However, the silence of inhibitory pauses may also cause a relative excitation in a reciprocally organized system.

Several other visual phenomena, which have been found by psychophysiological experiments and which were discussed earlier, may be explained by these two principles of neuronal inhibition: for example, the Weber–Fechner logarithmic relation of stimulus and response (by interaction of receptive fields and increasing lateral inhibition with increasing light intensity), successive contrast (by antagonistic periodicity of reciprocal inhibition), and the pattern effects of simultaneous contrast (by lateral inhibition). The mechanisms of lateral inhibition in the organization of receptive fields have been discussed for the retina by Barlow (1953), Barlow, FitzHugh, and Kuffler (1957), Kuffler (1953), and Kuffler, FitzHugh, and Barlow (1957), and for the cortex by Baumgartner (in press).

A simple device to demonstrate the reciprocal function of the two systems (the on and off neurons in the retina and the B and D neurons in the cortex) and to prove the prevalence of the on system over the off system is stimulation with brief flashes of light, consisting of nearly simultaneous on and off stimuli. These responses of neurons to flash were first investigated by Baumgartner (1955) in the visual cortex and later by Grüsser and Rabelo (1958) in the retina. The results showed that the neurons of the on and off systems are not discharged simultaneously following a light flash. The on system with terminal activation of cortical B neurons predominates first, showing primary discharge simultaneously with a brief inhibition of the on–off neurons (E neurons in the cortex) and a longer inhibition of the off neurons (D neurons in the cortex). The following periodic and reciprocally alternating after-discharges of both systems can be explained by successive interaction of excitatory and inhibitory processes and reciprocal action of the on and off systems (Grüsser and Rabelo, 1958). These mechanisms seem to be similar to reciprocal innervation and postinhibitory rebound in the spinal cord. The alternating phases of reciprocal activation and inhibition of the 'brightness system' (B neurons) and the 'darkness system' (D and E neurons) offer a neurophysiological explanation of the after-images following light flashes as summarized in Figure 5. In psychophysiological investigations, Ebbecke (1920) and Fröhlich (1929) have compared these subjective phases of the after-image with Sherrington's principles of reciprocal innervation and successive induction in the spinal cord. Sherrington himself had applied these principles to flicker vision in 1897, although objective data on neuronal discharges in the visual and spinal system were not yet available at that time. This is another example of mutual stimulation between neurophysiology and psychophysiology.

Significance of simultaneous contrast, receptive field centers, and lateral inhibition in the cortex

The physiological significance of simultaneous-contrast mechanisms in the retina and cortex is evidently the functional compensation of physical and physiological irradiation of light effects, as Hering demonstrated (1878, 1920, 1931). The normal imperfections of our dioptric apparatus, denounced by Helmholtz (1896b), can be compensated effectively by these physiological mechanisms of lateral inhibition and reciprocal field organization of neurons. Contrast mechanisms are present even in entirely differently organized eyes of lower forms, as has been shown by Hartline and collaborators in *Limulus* (1949; Hartline and Ratliff, 1957). But in cat and man simultaneous-contrast mechanisms are not confined to the retina; they are at work as well in the cortex. Contrast phenomena at higher levels were first demonstrated psychophysiologically by Hering's binocular contrast (1920, 1931). Monocular cortical contrast mechanisms are apparently responsible for the narrowing of the receptive fields of cortical neurons, found by Baumgartner and Hakas (1960) and described above.

These contrast mechanisms showing lateral inhibition of excited neurons are not specific to the visual system. It seems to be a general principle of neuronal organization that local excitation causes a surrounding field of neuronal inhibition. Jung and Tönnies (1950), using coarse cortical recordings of cortical potentials, and Creutzfeldt, Baumgartner, and Schoen (1956), using microelectrode data on single neurons in the sensorimotor cortex, have described constant inhibitory responses at the fringe of single electrical stimuli of the normal cortex. Excitatory irradiation prevails only in abnormal conditions of a preconvulsive state following repetitive stimulation (Jung and Tönnies, 1950). Kuffler's findings (1953) of the organization of on and off responses in the center and margin of retinal receptive fields show the same principles of lateral inhibition. The experiments of Barlow, FitzHugh, and Kuffler (1957) demonstrate further that lateral inhibition is not constant and can be diminished and reversed to lateral excitation and irradiation during dark adaptation. A similar sheet of inhibition surrounding a core of excitation was found in the somatosensory system and its cortex by Mountcastle (1957; Mountcastle, Davies, and Berman, 1957). These authors also describe reciprocal inhibition and different types of response in cortical neurons. Simultaneous inhibitory and excitatory reactions have also been seen in neuronal populations of other regions of the cortex even under such complex conditions as the conditioned reflexes (Ricci, Doane, and Jasper, 1957). Continuously discharging neurons similar to A neurons of the visual cortex were found in the motor cortex by Ricci, Doane, and Jasper (1957), in the sensory cortex by Cohen *et al.* (1957), and in the auditory cortex by Erulkar, Rose, and Davies (1956).

The apparent discrepancies between Baumgartner's results and those of Hubel and Wiesel (1959) on the diameter of receptive fields in cortical neurons may be due to their methods and to the particular field shapes and the surrounding zone of lateral inhibition at the cortical level. Hubel and Wiesel with their spotlight method found relatively large receptive fields, whereas Baumgartner with his simultaneous-contrast method found smaller field centers in the cortex than in the retina and the geniculate body. Baumgartner and Hakas's method measured only the core of activation (called the receptive-field centers) mostly in horizontal directions. Hubel and Wiesel (1959) determined the whole receptive field with the surrounding area of lateral inhibition and found differently shaped field centers, elongated and ellipsoid, mainly with the long axis vertical. These differences in the shape of receptive fields explain some effects specific to the direction of movement, first described by Hubel (1958) in cortical neurons. Baumgartner's investigations and other experiments on moving contrast stimuli, which are now in progress in our laboratories and which were briefly mentioned by Grüsser, Grüsser-Cornehls, and Saur (1959), have shown that the irregularities that sensitize the neurons to moving stimuli are predominantly found in D neurons, activated by light-off and dark contrast, or in E neurons, which may belong to an enlarged darkness system. Baumgartner and Hakas's findings (1960) of smaller receptive-field centers in cortical neurons may be explained by a pronounced effect of lateral inhibition in the cortex. From psychophysiological experience, it seems probable that the mechanisms of lateral inhibition are not confined to the retina but are active also in supra-retinal relay stations of the visual system. Thus central contrast mechanisms may also be able to improve the dim picture of scotopic vision, even when lateral inhibition is suppressed in the retina during dark adaptation, as was shown by Barlow, Fitz-Hugh, and Kuffler (1957): the receptive-field center is narrowed down in the cortex by progressive action of lateral inhibition and simultaneous contrast. We believe that only the central core of the whole receptive field yields positive information. The surrounding halo, which responds reciprocally, varies in different conditions and may represent only a regulatory phenomenon of contrast and lateral inhibition. The area about which the neuron provides information, therefore, seems to be the receptive-field center, as determined by Baumgartner's contrast method, and not the whole receptive area from which illumination influences the firing of units, as defined by Hartline (1940a), Kuffler (1953), and Hubel and Wiesel (1959).

Consideration of the receptive-field center as the essential area of neuronal visual information suggests the apparent paradox: cortical neurons see more sharply than retinal neurons, owing to central mechanisms of lateral inhibition and simultaneous contrast.

Lateral inhibition is certainly not confined to visual mechanisms, as is shown by Mountcastle's findings (1957) in somatosensory neuronal systems. A narrowing of the response area of single neurons to tone frequencies was found by Katsuki *et al.* (1958) between the cochlear nerve and the colliculus, but not further up in the cortex, apparently caused by similar neuronal contrast mechanisms in lower acoustic relay stations. It seems probable that lateral inhibition is a general principle of afferent communication in various modalities, designed to increase sensory discrimination through contrast.

The synaptic mechanism of reciprocal and lateral inhibition is not yet clear and should be investigated by intracellular recordings similar to Eccles's work on the spinal cord (1957; Brock, Coombs, and Eccles, 1952; Phillips, 1956). Some indications for an electrotonic mechanism probably located on dendrites may be derived from Granit's work on the alteration of on and off responses by retinal polarization (1946; Gernandt and Granit, 1947).[. . .]

Appreciation of nineteenth-century sensory physiology

Nearly all the correlations that we have found between neuronal discharges in cats and visual sensations in man originate in the basic findings of the great pioneers in subjective visual physiology of the last century, mainly by Purkinje, Helmholtz, Hering, and von Kries. Consequently, a discussion of these correlations seems to me appropriate. Subsequent to Purkinje's findings (1819), Aubert's observations (1865) on vestibular influence on visual verticality, Fechner's psychophysics (1860), and Brücke's findings on flicker fusion and brightness enhancement (1864), Helmholtz's work (1896b), and Hering's observations and theories (1878, 1920, 1931) – all important discoveries in the physiology of vision were made and tested on man by precise measurement of subjective sensations. These pioneers discovered the laws of successive contrast in the train of after-images and the various phenomena of simultaneous contrast, visual–vestibular coordination, binocular rivalry, and so forth. The general principles of regulated stability of the visual world were developed clearly by Hering (1920, 1931), although the special neuronal mechanisms assuring this stability remained unknown. Our observations made with microelectrodes are no more than objective demonstrations at the neuronal level of these laws and principles, formulated by the classical psychophysiologists.

We are made humble when we compare our elaborate micro-electrode techniques and our rather sophisticated interpretations with the insights that the great sensory physiologists of the nine-teenth century had through precise observations of purely subjective experience. The now fashionable concepts of informa-tion and communication theories were not unknown to these scientists. In 1868 Helmholtz (1896a) foresaw the essentials of our modern communication theories when he contrasted the limited number of 26 letters of the alphabet through which the rich variety of written communication is achieved with the enormous number of visual receptors and neurons that produce the innumerable visual sensations. He also pointed out some differences between mechanical models having only single units for special functions and brain mechanisms working with millions of parallel units.

Psychophysiology and neurophysiology have too long dwelt apart, ignoring the many correlations between their two ways of exploring the same object of sensory communication. Coordina-tion of these two lines of research will be possible when scientists remain aware of the differences in method and approach between subjective perceptual psychophysiology and objective neuronal electrophysiology. Then we may avoid muddling through the problems of sensory physiology by equivocations and succeed in achieving true convergence and mutual stimulation of the two scientific approaches.

Conclusions

I hope that our results will refute the reproach of atomistic re-search that we sometimes hear from psychologists who denounce investigations at the neuronal level. Although single-neuron recording picks out only a very few from the millions of cortical nerve cells, it does not result in a meaningless sample of brain functions if the sample is carefully selected and analysed. An investigation of the neuronal activity in a regulated complex system like the cortex may reveal basic mechanisms if the system is examined with reasonable experiments under well-planned conditions. The theoretical bases for physiological experiments on sensory communication are supplied by subjective experience.

Psychophysiology of the sense organs has preceded neurophysiological analysis of sensory mechanisms by more than 100 years, and it still provides the searchlights on this route of research.

The coordination of psychophysiological and neurophysiological experiments will lead us further than either of these approaches alone. The combination of the two may indicate a *via regia* to the exploration of human sensory information. The unilateral pursuit of only one method without regard to the other risks either blind neurophysiological recording or fanciful psychological hypotheses, and either of them may lead to minor sidetracks and end in a jungle of barren facts or luxuriantly growing speculations. With the help of the highly developed engineering techniques that facilitate our neurophysiological and psychophysiological research, a further advance on this path should not be too difficult and may elucidate some of the many unknown mechanisms of sensory communication.

References

AHLENSTIEL, H. (1949), 'Der Weckblitz als hypnagoge Vision', *Nervenarzt*, vol. 20, pp. 124–7.

AKIMOTO, H., and O. CREUTZFELDT (1957–8), 'Reaktionen von Neuronen des Optischen Cortex nach Elektrischer Reizung unspezifischer Thalamuskerne', *Arch. Psychiat. Nervenkr.*, vol. 196, pp. 494–519.

AUBERT, H. (1865), *Physiologie der Netzhaut*, E. Morgenstern, Breslau.

BARLOW, H. B. (1953), 'Summation and inhibition in the frog's retina', *J. Physiol.*, vol. 119, pp. 69–88.

BARLOW, H. B., R. FITZHUGH, and S. W. KUFFLER (1957), 'Change of organization in the receptive fields of the cat's retina during dark adaption', *J. Physiol.*, vol. 137, pp. 338–54.

BARTLEY, S. H. (1959), 'Central mechanisms of vision', *Handbook of Physiology. Neurophysiology I*, American Physiological Society, Washington, D.C., pp. 713–40.

BAUMGARTEN, R. VON, and R. JUNG (1952), 'Microelectrode studies on the visual cortex', *Rev. Neurol.*, vol. 87, pp. 151–5.

BAUMGARTNER, G. (1955), 'Reaktionen einzelner neurone im optischen cortex der katze nach lichtblitzen', *Pflügers Arch. Ges. Physiol.*, vol. 261, pp. 457–69.

BAUMGARTNER, G. (1961), 'Die Reaktionen der Neurone des Zentralen Visuellen Systems der Katze in Simultanen Helligkeitskontrast', in R. Jung and H. Kornhuber, eds., *Neurophysiologie und Psychophysik des Visuellen Systems*, Springer, Berlin, Göttingen, Heidelberg, pp. 296–311.

BAUMGARTNER, G., O. CREUTZFELDT, and R. JUNG (1961), 'Microphysiology of cortical neurons in acute anoxia and in retinal ischemia', in T. S. Meyer and H. Gastaut, eds., *Cerebral Anoxia and the Electroencephalogram*, C. C. Thomas, Springfield, Ill., pp. 5–33.

BAUMGARTNER, G. and P. HAKAS (1959), 'Reaktionen einzelner opticusneurone und corticaler nervenzellen der katze im Hell-Dunkel-Grenzfeld (Simultankontrast)', *Pflügers Arch. Ges. Physiol.*, vol. 270, p. 29.

BAUMGARTNER, G., and P. HAKAS (1960). 'Vergleich der receptiven Felder einzelner on-Neurone des N. opticus, des Corpus geniculatum laterale und des optischen Cortex der Katze', *Zbl. Ges. Neurol. Psychiat.*, vol. 155, pp. 243–4.

BAUMGARTNER, G., and P. HAKAS (1962), 'Die Neurophysiologie des simultanen Helligkeitskontrastes: Reziproke Reaktionen antagonistischer Neuronengruppen des visuellen Systems', *Pflügers Arch. Ges. Physiol.*, vol. 274, pp. 489–510.

BAUMGARTNER, G., and R. JUNG (1955), 'Hemmungsphänomene an einzelnen corticalen Neuronen und ihre Bedeutung für die Bremsung convulsiver Entladungen', *Arch. Sci. Biol.*, vol. 39. pp. 474–86.

BREMER, F. (1938), *L'Activité Électrique de l'Écorce Cérébrale*, Paris, Hermann.

BREMER, F., and N. STOUPEL (1958), 'De la modification des réponses sensorielles corticales dans l'éveil réticulaire', *Acta Neurol. Psychiat. Belg.*, vol. 58, pp. 401–3.

BREMER, F., and N. STOUPEL (1959), 'Facilitation et inhibition des potentiels évoqués corticaux dans l'éveil cérébral', *Arch. Int. Physiol.*, vol. 67, pp. 240–75.

BROCK, C. G., J. S. COOMBS, and J. C. ECCLES (1952), 'The recording of potentials from motoneurones with an intracellular electrode', *J. Physiol.*, vol. 117, pp. 431–60.

BRÜCKE, E. (1864), 'Über den Nutzeffekt intermittierender Netzhautreizungen', *Sitzber. Akad., Wiss. Wien (Math.-Nat. Kl.)*, vol. 49 (11), pp. 128–53.

COHEN, M. J., S. LANDGREN, L. STRÖM, and Y. ZOTTERMAN (1957), 'Cortical reception of touch and taste in the cat: A study of single cortical cells', *Acta Physiol. Scand.*, vol. 40, suppl. 135.

CREUTZFELDT, O., and H. AKIMOTO (1957–8), 'Konvergenz und gegenseitige Beeinflussung von Impulsen aus der Retina und den unspezifischen Thalamuskernen an einzelnen Neuronen des optischen Cortex', *Arch. Psychiat. Nervenkr.*, vol. 196, pp. 520–48.

CREUTZFELDT, O., G. BAUMGARTNER, and L. SCHOEN (1956), 'Reaktionen einzelner Neurone des sensomotorischen Cortex nach elektrischen Reizen', *Arch. Psychiat. Nervenkr.*, vol. 194, pp. 597–619.

CREUTZFELDT, O., and O.-J. GRÜSSER (1959), 'Beeinflussung der Flimmerreaktion einzelner corticaler Neurone durch elektrische Reize unspezifischer Thalamuskerne', *Proc. 1st Int. Congr. Neurol. Sci., Brussels, Vol. III. EEG Clinical Neurophysiology and Epilepsy*, Pergamon, London, pp. 349–55.

DUMONT, S., and P. DELL (1958), 'Facilitations spécifiques et non spécifiques des réponses visuelles corticales', *J. Physiol.*, vol. 50, pp. 261–4.

EBBECKE, U. (1920), 'Über zentrale Hemmung und die Wechselwirkung der Sehfeldstellen', *Pflügers Arch. Ges. Physiol.*, vol. 186, pp. 200–19.

EBBECKE, U. (1943), 'Über ein entoptisches Phänomen bei Schreck', *Klin. Mbl. Augenhlk.*, vol. 109, pp. 190–3.

ECCLES, J. C. (1957), *The Physiology of Nerve Cells*, Johns Hopkins Press, Baltimore.

ERULKAR, S. D., and M. FILLENZ (1958), 'Pattern of discharge of single units of the lateral geniculate body of the cat in response to binocular stimulation', *J. Physiol.*, vol. 140, 6p–7p.

43

ERULKAR, S. D., J. E. ROSE, and P. W. DAVIES (1956), 'Single unit activity in the auditory cortex of the cat'. *Bull. Johns Hopkins Hosp.*, vol. 99, pp. 55–86.

FECHNER, G. T. (1860), *Elemente der Psychophysik*, parts 1 and 2, Breitkopf and Härtel, Leipzig.

FRÖHLICH, F. W. (1929), *Die Empfindungszeit*. Gustav Fischer, Jena.

GERNANDT, B., and R. GRANIT (1947), 'Single fibre analysis of inhibition and the polarity of the retinal elements', *J. Neurophysiol.*, vol. 10, pp. 295–302.

GRANIT, R. (1946), 'The distribution of excitation and inhibition in single fibre responses from a polarized retina,' *J. Physiol.*, vol. 105, pp. 45–53.

GRÜSSER, O.-J. (1957), 'Receptorpotentiale einzelner Zapfen der Katze', *Naturwissenschaften*, vol. 44, p. 522.

GRÜSSER, O.-J. (1960), 'Rezeptorabhängige Potentiale der Katzenretina und ihre Reaktionen auf Flimmerlicht', *Pflügers Arch. Ges. Physiol.*, vol. 271, pp. 511–25.

GRÜSSER, O.-J., and O. CREUTZFELDT (1957), 'Eine neurophysiologische Grundlage des Brücke-Bartley-Effektes: Maxima der Impulsfrequenz retinaler und corticaler Neurone bei Flimmerlicht mittlerer Frequenzen', *Pflügers Arch. Ges. Physiol.*, vol. 263, pp. 668–81.

GRÜSSER, O.-J., and U. GRÜSSER-CORNEHLS (1960), 'Mikroelektrodenuntersuchungen zur Konvergenz vestibulärer und retinaler Afferenzen an einzelnen Neuronen des optischen Cortex der Katze', *Pflügers Arch. Ges. Physiol.*, vol. 270, pp. 227–38.

GRÜSSER, O.-J., GRÜSSER-CORNEHLS, and G. SAUR (1959), 'Reaktionen einzelner Neurone im optischen Cortex der Katze nach elektrischer Polarisation des Labyrinths', *Pflügers Arch. Ges. Physiol.*, vol. 269, pp. 593–612.

GRÜSSER, O.-J., and A. GRÜTZNER (1958), 'Reaktionen einzelner Neurone des optischen cortex der katze nach elektrischen Reizserien des Nervus opticus', *Arch. Psychiat. Nervenkr.*, vol. 197, pp. 405–32.

GRÜSSER, O.-J., and C. RABELO (1958), 'Reaktionen einzelner retinaler Neurone auf Lichtblitze. I: Einzelblitze und Blitzreize wechselnder Frequenz', *Pflügers Arch. Ges. Physiol.*, vol. 265, pp. 501–25.

GRÜSSER, O.-J., and G. SAUR (1960), 'Monoculare und binoculare Lichtreizung einzelner Neurone im Geniculatum laterale der Katze', *Pflügers Arch. Ges. Physiol.*, vol. 271, pp. 595–612.

GRÜTZNER, A., O.-J. GRÜSSER, and G. BAUMGARTNER (1958), 'Reaktionen einzelner Neurone im optischen Cortex der Katze nach elektrischer Reizung des Nervus opticus', *Arch. Psychiat. Nervenkr.*, vol. 197, pp. 377–404.

HARTLINE, H. K. (1938), 'The discharge of impulses in the optic nerve of pecten in response to illumination of the eye', *J. Cell. Comp. Physiol.*, vol. 11, pp. 465–77.

HARTLINE, H. K. (1940a), 'The receptive fields of optic nerve fibers', *Amer. J. Physiol.*, vol. 130, pp. 690–99.

HARTLINE, H. K. (1940b), 'The effects of spatial summation in the retina on the excitation of the fibers of the optic nerve', *Amer. J. Physiol.*, vol. 130, pp. 700–711.

HARTLINE, H. K. (1949), 'Inhibition of activity of visual receptors by illuminating nearby retinal areas in the Limulus eye', *Fed. Proc.*, vol. 8, p. 69.

HARTLINE, H. K., and F. RATLIFF (1957), 'Inhibitory interaction of receptor units in the eye of Limulus', *J. Gen. Physiol.*, vol. 40, pp. 357-76.

HELMHOLTZ, H. VON (1896a), 'Die neueren Fortschritte in der Theorie des Sehens (1868)', in *Vorträge und Reden*, vol. *I*, 4th edn, Vieweg, Braunschweig, pp. 265-365.

HELMHOLTZ, H. VON (1896b), *Handbuch der physiologischen Optik*, 2nd edn, C. Voss, Hamburg and Leipzig.

HERING, E. (1878), *Zur Lehre vom Lichtsinne*, Gerold, Vienna.

HERING, E. (1920), *Grundzüge der Lehre vom Lichtsinn*, Springer, Berlin.

HERING, E. (1931), *Wissenschaftliche Abhandlungen*, Thieme, Leipzig.

HUBEL, D. H. (1958), 'Cortical unit responses to visual stimuli in nonanesthetized cats', *Amer. J. Ophthalmol.*, vol. 46, pp. 110-22.

HUBEL, D. H. (1959), 'Single unit activity in striate cortex of unrestrained cats', *J. Physiol.*, vol. 147, pp. 226-38.

HUBEL, D. H., and T. N. WIESEL (1959), 'Receptive fields of single neurones in the cat's striate cortex', *J. Physiol.*, vol. 148, p. 574.

JASPER, H. H., and C. AJMONE MARSAN (1952), 'Thalamocortical integrating mechanisms', *Res. Publ. Ass. nerv. ment. Dis.*, vol. 30, pp. 493-512.

JUNG, R. (1953a), 'Neuronal discharge', *EEG clin. Neurophysiol.*, suppl. vol. 4, pp. 57-71.

JUNG, R. (1953b), 'Nystagmographie: Zur Physiologie und Pathologie des optischvestibulären Systems beim Menschen', *Handb. Inner. Med.*, vol. V. Springer, Berlin, pp. 1325-79.

JUNG, R. (1958a), 'Excitation, inhibition and coordination of cortical neurons', *Exp. Cell. Res.*, suppl. vol. 5, pp. 262-71.

JUNG, R. (1958b), 'Coordination of specific and nonspecific afferent impulses at single neurons of the visual cortex', H. H. Jasper, *et al.* (eds.), *Reticular Formation of the Brain*, Little, Brown, Boston, pp. 423-34.

JUNG, R. (1959), 'Microphysiology of cortical neurons and its significance for psychophysiology', *Festschrift Prof. C. Estable. An. Facult. Med. Montevideo*, vol. 44, pp. 323-32.

JUNG, R. (1961), 'Korrelationen von Neuronentätigkeit und Sehen', in R. Jung and H. Kornhuber (eds.), *Neurophysiologie und Psychophysik des visuellen Systems*, Symposium Freiburg, Springer, Berlin, Göttingen, Heidelberg, pp. 410-34.

JUNG, R., R. VON BAUMGARTEN, and G. BAUMGARTNER (1952), 'Mikroableitungen von einzelnen Nervenzellen im optischen Cortex: Die lichtaktivierten B-Neurone'. *Arch. Psychiat. Nervenkr.*, vol. 189, pp. 521-39.

JUNG, R., and G. BAUMGARTNER (1955), 'Hemmungsmechanismen und bremsende Stabilisierung an einzelnen Neuronen des optischen Cortex: Ein Beitrag zur Koordination corticaler Erregungsvorgänge', *Pflügers Arch. Ges. Physiol.*, vol. 261, pp. 434-56.

JUNG, R., O. CREUTZFELDT, and G. BAUMGARTNER (1957), 'Microphysiologie des neurones corticaux: processus de coordination et d'inhibition du cortex optique et moteur', *Colloq. int. Microphysiol.*, *Centre nat. Rech. sci.*, no. 67, pp. 411-34.

JUNG, R., O. CREUTZFELDT, and O.-J. GRÜSSER (1957), 'Die Mikrophysiologie kortikaler Neurone und ihre Bedeutung für die Sinnes- und Hirnfunktionen', *Dtsch. med. Wschr.*, vol. 82, pp. 1050–59.

JUNG, R., and R. HASSLER (1960), 'The extrapyramidal motor system' in *Handbook of Physiology. Neurophysiology* II. American Physiological Society, Washington, D.C., pp. 863–927.

JUNG, R., and J. F. TÖNNIES (1950), 'Hirnelektrische Untersuchungen über Entstehung und Erhaltung von Krampfentladungen: Die Vorgänge am Reizort und die Bremsfähigkeit des Gehirns', *Arch. Psychiat, Nervenkr.*, vol. 185, pp. 701–35.

KAPPAUF, W. E. (1936), 'Flicker discrimination in the cat', *Psychol. Bull.*, vol. 33, pp. 597–8.

KATSUKI, Y., J. SUMI, H. UCHIYAMA, and T. WATANABE (1958), 'Electric responses of auditory neurons in cat to sound stimulation', *J. Neurophysiol.*, vol. 21, pp. 569–88.

KUFFLER, S. W. (1953), 'Discharge patterns and functional organization of mammalian retina', *J. Neurophysiol.*, vol. 16, pp. 37–68.

KUFFLER, S. W., R. FITZHUGH, and H. B. BARLOW (1957), 'Maintained activity in the cat's retina in light and darkness', *J. gen. Physiol.*, vol. 40, pp. 638–702.

LI, C.-L. (1956), 'The facilitation of cortical sensorineuronal responses following stimulation of an unspecific thalamic nucleus', *J. Physiol.*, vol. 131, pp. 115–24.

LI, C.-L., C. CULLEN, and H. JASPER (1956), 'Laminar microelectrode studies of specific somatosensory cortical potentials', *J. Neurophysiol.*, vol. 19, pp. 111–43.

MAGOUN, H. W. (1952), 'An ascending reticular activating system in the brain stem', *Arch. Neurol. Psychiat.*, vol. 67, pp. 145–54.

MOUNTCASTLE, V. B. (1957), 'Modality and topographic properties of single neurons of cat's somatic sensory cortex', *J. Neurophysiol.*, vol. 20, pp. 408–34.

MOUNTCASTLE, V. B., P. W. DAVIES, and A. L. BERMAN (1957), 'Response properties of neurons of cat's somatic sensory cortex to peripheral stimuli', *J. Neurophysiol.*, vol. 20, pp. 374–407.

PHILLIPS, C. G. (1956), 'Intracellular records from Betz cells in the cat', *Quart. J. exp. Physiol.*, vol. 41, pp. 58–69.

PURKINJE, J. (1819), *Beiträge zur Kenntnis des Sehens in subjektiver Hinsicht*, J. G. Calve, Prague.

RICCI, G., B. DOANE, and H. JASPER (1957), 'Microelectrode studies of conditioning: technique and preliminary results', IV. Congr. Int. EEG Clin. Neurophysiol. *Acta med. Belg.*, pp. 401–15.

SHERRINGTON, C. (1897), 'On reciprocal action in the retina as studied by means of some rotating discs', *J. Physiol.*, vol. 21, pp. 33–54.

SHERRINGTON, C. (1906), *The Integrative Action of the Nervous System*, Constable, London.

SVAETICHIN, G. (1956a), 'Spectral response curves from single cones', *Acta physiol. scand.*, vol. 39, suppl. 134, pp. 17–46.

SVAETICHIN, G. (1956b), 'Receptor mechanisms for flicker and fusion', *Acta physiol., scand.*, vol. 39, suppl. 134, pp. 47–54.

TASAKI, I., E. H. POLLEY, and F. ORREGO (1954), 'Action potentials from individual elements in cat geniculate and striate cortex', *J. Neurophysiol.*, vol. 17, pp. 454–74.

3 F. Morrell

Electrical Signs of Sensory Coding

F. Morrell, 'Electrical signs of sensory coding', *The Neurosciences: A Study Program*, Rockefeller University Press, 1967, pp. 452–69.

If one places conductive electrodes on the surface of the scalp of the human or of other animals and amplifies the signal about a million times, a potential difference can be recorded between any two of the electrodes. This potential has the form of a more or less sinusoidal and regular oscillation with a dominant frequency of about 8 to 13 cycles per second in the adult of the species.

Intrinsic Rhythms

In human electroencephalography, the frequency range just given has been designated the *alpha* rhythm; the range would have to be extended somewhat to include all those rhythms exhibiting similar physiologic behavior in other species or in the immature organism. Yet extending the frequency range only a few cycles in both directions would, with few exceptions, encompass all the dominant brain rhythms from all species and all ages thus far examined. For example, in Figure 1, the brain wave patterns of frog, guinea pig, rabbit, cat, monkey, and man are compared. The gross similarities across all species are plainly seen. It is equally evident that there are differences among these records. Yet the range of variation, at least with respect to dominant frequency, is extremely limited. These particular tracings were randomly selected from the various 'preparations' used in our laboratory. Considering the gross differences in genetic makeup of the several species and the vast variations in life experience to which each had been exposed, it is difficult to believe that the frequency of brain rhythms might be directly related to the coding of sensory experience or to the information the brain contains. Indeed, the shifts in brain wave frequency in the same individual during the transition from a waking to a sleeping state (see M. Jouvet, this volume [not included here]), or from waking to aroused state (see below), are far greater than are the differences among species, as shown in Figure 1.

The 8 to 13 cycles per second alpha rhythm under discussion may be described as the dominant pattern in the electroencephalogram. There are also subdominant rhythms characteristic of particular regions such as the *beta* activity of 18 to 24 cycles per second, which constitutes the spontaneous resting rhythm of

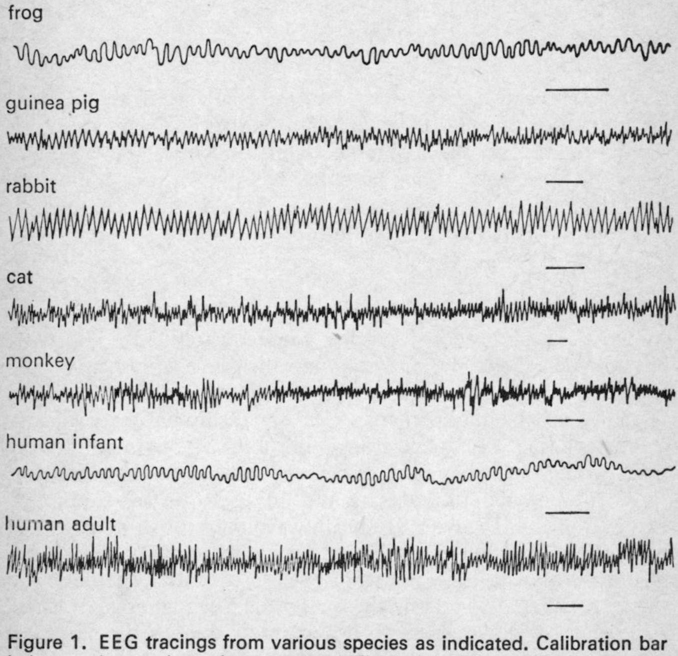

frog

guinea pig

rabbit

cat

monkey

human infant

human adult

Figure 1. EEG tracings from various species as indicated. Calibration bar below each record equals one second. The human infant and adult records were obtained with scalp electrodes; all others were derived from electrodes on the surface of cortex

rolandic motor cortex in man, and the 4 to 7 cycles per second *theta* rhythm of the hippocampus, which is best seen in the rabbit and cat although traces of it remain in man and monkey. Slower rhythms of 1 to 3 cycles per second called *delta* are normally present during sleep, but when present in the waking state are important diagnostic signs of intracranial pathology. Space limitations prevent any further consideration of these subdominant rhythms in this chapter.

Activation Pattern

One of the defining characteristics of alpha rhythms is that they are most prominent when the human or animal is awake and is not engaged in transaction of visual business. Figure 2 illustrates the classical 'activation pattern' (1) or suppression of alpha rhythm and its replacement by low-voltage fast activity when a subject opens the eyes and looks at an object on a viewing screen. It is generally accepted (2) that the slower, higher-voltage, more regular, oscillatory rhythms are associated with decreasing levels of vigilance (3). Exceptions to this general rule may be induced pharmacologically (4, 5), and are sometimes seen during transi-

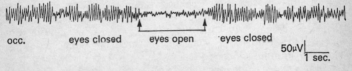

occ.   eyes closed   eyes open   eyes closed

50μV |___
1 sec.

Figure 2. Activation pattern. Blocking of the human alpha rhythm produced by eye opening in a normal human subject. Derivation is from right occipital electrode referred to linked ears

tional stages between wakefulness and sleep and during the rapid-eye-movement (REM) stage of sleep (6). Nevertheless, electro-encephalographers have repeatedly commented (7) upon the apparent paradox that higher-voltage electrical rhythms are characteristic of 'idling' neurons, i.e. neurons which, at that moment, are not under specific stimulation. It has been presumed (for a thorough discussion of the history of ideas about brain waves see references 7–11) that nerve cells having nothing specific to do were somehow available to get into step with one another to produce a *synchronized* rhythm. On the other hand, under the influence of specific excitation, cellular firing patterns become highly differentiated, versatile, organized, and asynchronous with one another. The electrical pattern of the population (the EEG) then exhibits the low-voltage, high-frequency, and less regular features shown in Figure 2 (eyes open). Accordingly, the alpha 'blocking' (12, 13) or arousal reaction (14) or activation pattern (1) has also been called *desynchronization* to indicate the basic physiological mechanism that was thought to underlie it. (7).

Several forms of activation pattern or desynchronization have been identified. There is (i) a diffuse or *generalized* form affecting all regions of both cerebral hemispheres, and (ii) a *localized* form limited to specific cortical regions. Furthermore, in the time domain one may distinguish between a form that is (iii) *tonic* in the sense of maintaining wakefulness over long periods of time, and one that is (iv) *phasic* and mediates sudden, brief shifts in attention in response to shades of sensory stimulation.

Anatomy and literature

The anatomical substrate for all of the electrocortical reactions described above is not in the primary afferent pathways, but in the more medially coursing, multisynaptic reticular formations of the mesencephalon (14) and thalamus (15, 16). Although it has been argued (8) that the *generalized* and *tonic* reactions were attributable to the mesencephalic reticular system, while the *localized* and *phasic* forms depended on the thalamic system, there are circumstances in which such clear-cut distinctions are difficult to document. For instance, a sudden, unexpected, and startling stimulus delivered to any sensory modality results in a generalized desynchronization of all cortical regions. This has been shown by Moruzzi and Magoun (14) to be mediated by the ascending mesencephalic reticular formation. If the stimulus is of no biological importance and is repeated many times, the generalized desynchronization rapidly wanes (habituation [17]), and eventually gives way to a localized desynchronization usually limited to the cortical region appropriate to the stimulus modality used. In this example, a diffuse activation known to be mediated by the mesencephalic system exhibits temporal characteristics that are phasic rather than tonic. In fact, this is the neural basis of the orienting reflex.

On the other hand, localized desynchronization habituates much less readily than the generalized form. Voronin and Soko-lov (18) report that visual stimuli continue to induce localized blocking of the occipital alpha rhythm even after hundreds of presentations. Moreover, the topography of localized activation, although usually maximal in the cortical receiving area for the stimulus modality, is strongly influence by the animal's prior associations with that stimulus, i.e. by conditioning. Thus, an acoustic signal of conditioned stimulus (CS), which had been repeatedly paired with a visual or unconditioned stimulus (UCS) may ultimately induce desynchronization mainly in the visual area (19, 20). This latter form of activation pattern has been shown to depend upon the integrity of the intralaminar reticular nuclei of the thalamus (21, 22). The response is certainly phasic, in that it does not outlast the duration of the stimulus. It is curiously persistent to repeated stimulation and, under proper recording conditions, lasts at least as long as a behavioral conditioned response, finally altering its electrical morphology (see following text) at about the stage when behavioral conditioned responses disappear because the animal had become satiated.

There have been numerous studies (23–30) dealing in great detail with the time course of habitation and of conditioning of alpha blocking, the various circumstances which influence it, and both the topographic and morphologic alterations in brain wave patterns that occur as a result of repeated stimulus presentation. Several reviews (26, 31–3) will provide adequate coverage of the field for those particularly interested. Investigations have been carried out in human subjects (23, 25, 27, 28, 30) by recording electrical activity from scalp electrodes, and in animals having implanted electrodes in local brain regions (29).

Clinical observations

Recently, we have had the opportunity to examine some of the characteristics of stimulus-induced localized desynchronization by recording directly from the surgically exposed visual cortex in a conscious human subject. Our findings have caused us to question the accuracy of the localizations previously obtained by use of scale electrodes.

The observations were carried out in the course of a therapeutic procedure to relieve this patient of medically intractable epilepsy caused by the scar surrounding a previously drained abscess in the left posterior temporal region. As the cortical zone involved was adjacent to the area of cortical representation for speech, the operation was carried out under local anesthesia only. (Having the patient awake and able to converse during the operation makes it possible to map the speech area physiologically, and thus affords an extra margin of safety for the patient against inadvertent surgical injury to speech function. This is now standard neurosurgical practice, see chapter XVIII in reference 7.) The local anesthesia entirely eliminates pain from the skin incision; the brain itself is not pain sensitive. The location of the lesion was such as to require a posterior bone flap, which was carried to the midline, thus exposing the entire occipital lobe of the left hemisphere. Cotton wick electrodes were placed upon the surface of the brain in many places and with many arrangements in order to define and map the area of electrical abnormality responsible for the convulsive seizures. Microelectrodes were also employed to search for single cells having the abnormal electrical characteristics we have come to associate with epileptic discharge in experimental animals. Eventually, it was determined that the abnormal zone lay anterior to the occipital pole, sharply confined to the posterior temporal region. Thus, the observations reported here were derived from cortex, which appeared to be normal in every way measured, even though it was adjacent to (about 5 centimeters away) an epileptogenic lesion.

After distributing the electrodes above and below the calcarine fissure, as shown in the diagram of Figure 3, the patient was instructed to fixate upon a small red dot in the center of a viewing screen. Maintenance of fixation was monitored by previously applied periorbital electrodes and was, in fact, satisfactory for the duration of this test. Immediately upon fixation there was a generalized alpha blocking or desynchronization lasting several seconds, after which fairly prominent alpha activity recurred (despite continued maintenance of fixation) at all recording sites (Figure 3). Thereupon, various sectors of the visual field were illuminated (Figure 3a', b', c') for 1 to 3 seconds. Figure 3a, b, and c illustrates the pattern of brain wave tracings that correspond, respectively, to each of the sector stimuli. Illumination of the upper 30° of the right visual field (Figure 3a') resulted in a sharply localized desynchronization seen only in electrodes 4 and 5 – i.e. below the calcarine fissure (Figure 3a). A stimulus subtending an arc from 90° to 135° (Figure 3b') elicited desynchronization limited to electrodes 2 and 3 (Figure 3b) just above the fissure. Stimulation of the lowermost 30° of the field (Figure 3c') gave rise to desynchronization only at electrode 1 (Figure 3c). Finally, full-screen illumination (Figure 3d') yielded alpha blocking at all electrode sites (Figure 3d). These differential distributions remained consistent for some 10 to 12 replications for each sector. The particular localizations shown correspond exactly to the known anatomical distribution of fibers in the primary afferent pathway according to the specific retinal elements stimulated for each sector of the visual field. Moreover, lesions of those portions of striate cortex exhibiting the localized desynchronization illustrated in Figure 3 lead to visual-field deficits in sectors closely approximating those that were stimulated in the present study (34). Thus, these data are in good agreement with both anatomical and behavioral evidence previously obtained by others for the primary visual pathway.

The degree of spatial discreteness exhibited by the localized activation patterns in this patient is comparable only to that

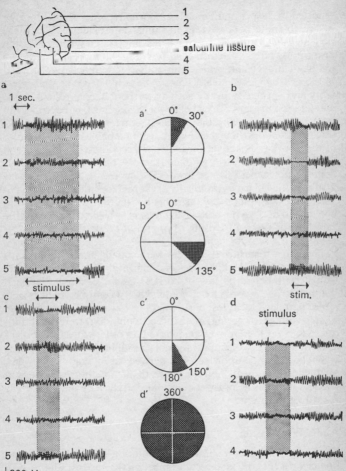

Figure 3. Electrocorticogram from left occipital cortex in an unanesthetized subject. Channel designations refer to electrode numbers positioned around the calcarine fissure as indicated in the diagram. Patient was required to fixate upon a small red dot in the center of the viewing screen. Stimulation for 1 to 3 seconds was carried out in particular sectors of the contralateral visual field as indicated in a', b' and c', or with full field illumination (d'). The resulting desynchronization was limited to correspondingly small segments of occipital cortex (a, b, c).

reported by Jasper and Penfield (35) who recorded focal blocking of the rolandic beta rhythm in human motor cortex when the patient was instructed to move his fingers. Desynchronization or blocking of beta rhythm occurred in the area of representation for hand movement, while beta activity continued undisturbed in the nearby 'face' area. These findings indicate a spatial selectivity and specificity in the activity of the thalamic reticular system (at least in man) not only between modalities, but even within the same modality. The anatomical system responsible for generating localized desynchronization must be capable of activation or of distributing its activation in a manner almost as specific and discrete as that of the primary sensory and motor pathways themselves. Jasper's suggestion (16) that the thalamic reticular system is indeed topographically organized (see also reference 36) is emphatically supported, as is his notion that this same neural network in normal physiological usage may be responsible for the capacity for precise focusing of attention on small, selected segments of the sensory field.

The cortical surface electrodes were equally spaced at 1-centimeter intervals. A localized desynchronization might occupy only 1 to 2 centimeters or less of cortical tissue. Because the usual scalp electrode records from not less than 3 centimeters, it is easy to see that such local responses might be 'swamped' by the much higher-voltage, on-going, undisturbed alpha rhythm in surrounding tissue and therefore be undetected. In other words, reports of 'habituation', i.e. disappearance of the alpha blocking response when based only upon records derived from scalp electrodes, might actually mean nothing more than that the response had become sufficiently localized to escape detection by that particular recording technique.

Alpha Provocation

Figure 4b illustrates a stimulus presentation in which one could not clearly identify a desynchronization (compare Figure 4a). Figure 4b clearly demonstrates several morphological features that have been regarded as transitional stages between alpha blocking and alpha provocation (27). The stimulus onset was not associated with any definite decrease in voltage, but after a latency of 250 to 300 milli-seconds, the alpha frequency suddenly increased. This was followed by a spindle-like alpha 'burst' (in electrodes 2 and 4), which was abruptly truncated upon cessation of the stimulus. Comparison of the response to stimulation in

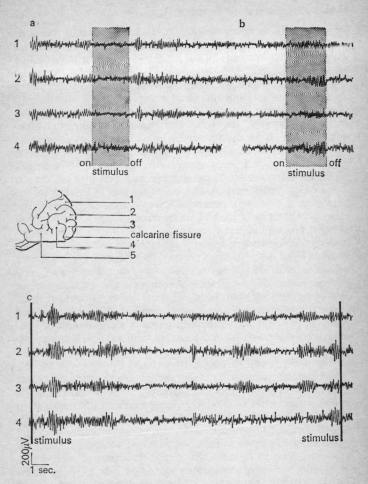

Figure 4. Electrocorticograms from the same patient as in Figure 3. Same electrode placement. Stimuli were full field illumination for the durations indicated in a and b. In c the stimuli were 50 μ sec. flashes. Various stages of activation are shown. 4a exhibits classical desynchronization. 4b reveals partial activation denoted by increase in alpha frequency and, then, alpha provocation exemplified by spindle-shaped burst of high voltage alpha terminated abruptly when the stimulus ceases. 4c illustrates spontaneous alpha burst pattern which alternates with much lower voltage, mixed frequency, asynchronous activity. On this latter background it was difficult to discern any effect of brief visual stimuli

Figure 4a with that occurring on presentation of exactly the same stimulus (full-field illumination) in Figure 4b serves to emphasize that the activation pattern is a graded response; it is not all-or none in character.

The details of any particular electrical response are related to some extent to stimulus intensity; a pistol shot, for instance, invariably produces maximal desynchronization. Except for such extremes, however, the form and duration of the activation pattern depends much more crucially on such things as novelty, prior associations with the stimulus, the biological significance of the stimulus, and, most importantly, on the state of vigilance of the subject at the time the stimulus impinges on the nervous system (3). This latter, as was noted, is closely related to the background or 'spontaneous' EEG patterns, drowsiness and sleep being characterized by an absence of alpha rhythm and either a predominance of low-voltage, 4 to 7 cycles per second activity (drowsiness) or higher-voltage waves at 2 to 3 cycles per second mixed with 14 cycles per second 'spindles' (slow-wave or spindle stage of sleep). Presentation of a moderate stimulus in any of these states of lowered level of awareness may produce not an activation pattern, but rather a burst of high-voltage alpha rhythm. Interpretation of this phenomenon is still unclear. Some authors (7, 37) prefer to think in terms of a continuum of consciousness extending from the excited, aroused (low-voltage fast pattern), through the waking but relaxed state (alpha rhythm) into drowsiness and then sleep (slower and slower rhythms). We ignore for this exposition the stage of REM or paradoxical sleep (Jouvet, this volume [not included here]). Stimulus-induced alpha provocation would then be interpreted as a sign of arousal from a lower level of consciousness. Other workers (3, 30) have suggested that alpha provocation is a sign of active 'inhibition', and believe that the same stimulus may on one occasion induce 'excitation', denoted by low-voltage, high-frequency activation patterns and, on other occasions, 'inhibition', denoted by alpha bursts or alpha augmentation. Signal significance is regarded as at least as important as the subject's state of consciousness and/ or the character of on-going electrical rhythms at the instant of stimulus application.

Finally, if not already obvious from the figures, it must be mentioned that alpha rhythms normally have a periodic waxing and waning appearance (Figure 1, last tracing; Figure 2). Usually, the modulation is even and gradual. However, sometimes it is more extreme, and results in the appearance of spontaneous high-voltage, alpha bursts interspersed with epochs of very much lower amplitude, as illustrated in Figure 4c. If we now returned to our earlier statements concerning synchrony and desynchrony, we would be obliged to predict that the alpha bursts represent synchronous discharge of whatever elements give rise to the EEG, whereas the low-voltage periods in between should represent asynchronous firing of those elements. As mentioned above, microelectrodes were also used in the study of this same patient. The tracings shown in the next section are intracellular records of human nerve cells sampled simultaneously with the EEG of the cortical surface. They allow a direct test of the prediction stated above, and at least the beginnings of a cellular and neuronal inter-pretation of the brain wave patterns in man.

Sources of the EEG

Gas-sterilized glass capillary micropipettes were filled with 2M-K citrate and had a tip resistance of 20 to 40 megohms in saline. A pressor-foot consisting of a clear plastic disk drilled with many tiny holes was placed on the cortical surface of the occipital pole and held in place by special clamps to the bony margins of the craniotomy. The pressure was not great enough to cause visible blanching of the cortical surface, although there was undoubtedly slowing of the surface circulation. A sterile micromanipulator (also attached to the bony margin) was used to lower the micro-electrodes through the predrilled holes in the plastic pressor-foot. Many active cells were encountered, leading us to doubt that there was significant cortical ischemia. (Throughout this pro-cedure the patient was awake, and continued to report correctly objects placed in his right visual field.) Five extremely stable cells were impaled and held for 5 to 8 minutes. Figure 4c is an excerpt of the electrocorticogram obtained during impalement. The electrocorticogram from the surface electrode nearest the penetration (electrode 2) and the amplified microelectrode record-ing were fed to an Ampex FR-1300 tape recorder for later play-back and analysis, and were also monitored on an oscilloscope. These cells exhibited stable resting potentials of 55 to 78 milli-volts and normal spontaneous action potentials, excitatory postsynaptic potentials (EPSPs) and inhibitory postsynaptic potentials (IPSPs). Among the many observations made, the ones pertinent to this report are the following:

1. There was very little correlation between the activity (either spikes or synaptic potentials) of single cells and surface EEG

waves during periods of desynchronization or during the low-voltage activity between alpha bursts. Cross-correlation computations yielded values of 0·2 to 0·1.

2. During alpha-burst activity in the EEG, cross correlations were above 0·5 in all five cells (two were 0·5, one at 0·61, one at 0·69, and one at 0·78). However, there were tantalizing and inconstant phase shifts, with the cellular potential leading in some cases and the EEG in others. It was suspected, of course, that the reasons for the observed jitter was the attempt to compare a unitary event with that of a mixed population; therefore, the alpha bursts in the EEG were scanned for single waves or coherent sequences.

3. In an analysis of single waves, three kinds of coherent waves were found: a diphasic positive–negative complex (Figure 5a); a monophasic negative wave (Figure 5b); and a triphasic positive–negative–positive sequence (Figure 5c). All waves of each type were then superimposed by line drawing so that closeness of fit might be estimated visually. For each trace, the corresponding intracellular record is shown on line 2. Parts a, b, and c of Figure 5 are each from different cells. When displayed in this manner it became clear that there was a regular and coherent relationship between the potential fluctuations of a single cell and appropriately selected waves of the EEG. For the sequence in Figure 5a, the initial positivity was, on all occasions, associated with EPSPs and cell discharge, while the larger negative component was related to a prolonged IPSP. The monophasic negative wave (Figure 5b) correlated with purely excitatory events in the cell, i.e. EPSPs and spikes near the peak negativity. However, there was a curious lack of membrane fluctuation, despite the rather large sample size (about 15 superpositions), in the period just prior to the onset of the negative surface potential. It was as though the membrane had been briefly 'clamped' from without and then released as it was invaded by a depolarizing EPSP. This is probably the same event as was described by Creutzfeldt et al. (38, 39), which he termed 'synaptic silence'. The third sequence (Figure 5c) was characterized by a sharper and narrower peak negativity with a steep descending limb culminating in a third positive deflection. Excitatory, depolarizing activity prevailed throughout the initial positive and negative phases, while the late positivity corresponded to an abrupt intracellular IPSP.

The monophasic negative waves (Figure 5b) correspond to the type II waves described by Spencer and Brookhart (40a, b) and the type B waves of Calvet et al. (41). They are the result of

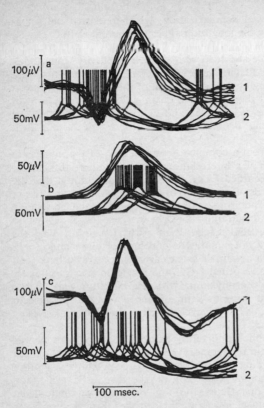

Figure 5. Superimposed line drawings of coherent wave-shapes (coherence judged by visual inspection) extracted from the surface record during spontaneous alpha bursts (channel 1) together with intracellular unit record (channel 2) corresponding to the EEG segment selected. Ten to twenty superpositions in each case. a, b, and c are three different cells. Further explanation in text. Negativity is up for channel 1 (surface record) and down for channel 2 (intracellular record) in this and in Figure 6

postsynaptic depolarizations mainly on the apical dendrites of pyramidal cells. Biphasic positive–negative waves (Figure 5a) are the result of postsynaptic depolarization near the pyramidal cell soma, probably by the terminals of specific afferent fibers, as seen from an electrode on the 'passive' end of the neuron in an electronic circuit, followed immediately by a more prolonged IPSP.

A more prolonged depolarization, which outlasted the soma-dendrite delay in the longitudinal electrotonic spread of activity, would first be seen as a 'reversed' potential by an electrode on the dendritic pole and then as a surface negativity (Figure 5c). The subsequent IPSP (Figure 5c) would then be seen as a surface positivity, as long as the polarization of the apical dendrites was less pronounced than that of the soma. The fields for both of these latter waves (Figures 5a and c) correspond with the Type 1 of Spencer and Brookhart (40a, b) and type A of Calvet *et al.* (41).

Quite apart from a complete interpretation of the manner in which these complex interrelationships sum and finally emerge as the surface-recorded EEG, there can be little doubt that the synaptic potentials of nerve cells are the elements that give rise to brain rhythms. The firmness of this conclusion stands in striking contrast to the uncertainty of early workers (42–5) who were limited to extra-cellular records of cortical neurons. That the slow waves were not simply the envelope of all-or-none CNS single-unit action potentials was clearly demonstrated by Li and Jasper (42), who recorded EEG and single units extracellularly and found that with asphyxia and with deep barbiturate anesthesia, all units stopped firing at a time when it was still possible to record spontaneous EEG waves as well as slow potentials evoked by thalamic shock.

We have had the opportunity to obtain intracellular records from nerve cells in the temporal cortex in one additional patient who was undergoing deep barbiturate narcosis with a new, ultra short-acting barbiturate as part of the diagnostic evaluation of the temporal-lobe seizures (46). The procedure was undertaken after implantation of intracranial electrodes through burr holes in the skull and, on this occasion, the microelectrode was inserted through the small burr hole. Intracellular recording was obtained in one cell maintained in 'healthy' condition (stable membrane potential of 65 millivolts) for 20 minutes. During this time, simultaneous EEG and intracellular recordings were made (Figure 6) before the intravenous introduction of methohexital (Figure 6a), during induction that was carried to the point of EEG silence (Figures 6b, c, d), and after a substantial amount of recovery (Figure 6e). The entire induction and recovery occupied less than 15 minutes. We observed, as others have (47), that action potentials disappeared at levels where EEG waves could still be detected (Figure 6c). However, the EEG waves were invariably associated with slow synaptic potentials in the cell soma.

When the EEG became isoelectric (Figure 6d), synaptic potentials failed also. Infusion of the drug was immediately stopped and within 20 seconds there was recurrence of EEG waves; within 5 minutes (Figure 6e) cellular discharge reappeared.

From this and from observations in many other laboratories

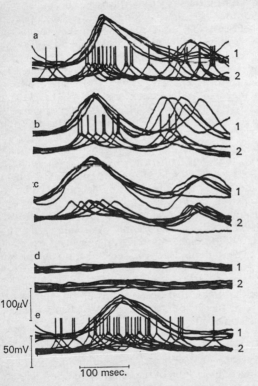

Figure 6. Superimposed line drawings of coherent wave-shapes in the EEG of another patient (channel 1) and the corresponding intracellular unit records from a microelectrode (channel 2). In this case a, b, c, d, e are all from the same cell (membrane potential 69 mV.; action potential 73 mV.) continuously held for 20 minutes during intravenous administration of methohexital. a illustrates the relationship between intracellular activity and EEG wave-shape before administering drug; b after approximately 200 mgm, c after 400 mgm, d after 500 mgm. Infusion of drug was then stopped and the tracing labeled e was obtained 5 minutes later. Unit spikes in this and the preceding figure have been retouched and truncated where necessary for clarity of photographic reproduction. Further explanation in text

on experimental animals (see Purpura, this volume [not included here] 48–52) a consensus is emerging that regards the slow oscillations of the EEG as the algebraic sum of hundreds of thousands of synaptic potentials in the many thousands of neurons which lie within the 'field' of a gross-recording electrode.

The detailed electrophysiology of cortical neurons under study in many laboratories has already gone far to substantiate the original model of Eccles (53) based upon the spinal motor neuron. Given what is now known of the biophysical properties of cortical pyramidal cells and the differential localization on the membrane surface of inhibitory and excitatory synapses from specific, unspecific, and intracortical terminals, as well as the careful analysis of intracortical potential fields by Spencer and Brookhart (40a, b) and Calvet et al. (41), it is now possible to explain in detail the mechanisms that generate most of the wave shapes contributing to the EEG. The 'pacing' of mean cortical neuronal firing and of EEG frequencies depends mainly on pacemaker cells in thalamic nuclei (52), although it is also clear that recurrent inhibition also exists in cortex (54, 48) and may contribute to the roughly 100-millisecond cycle of excitability. The model proposed for the thalamus by Andersen and Eccles (52), in which the firing of each afferent axon simultaneously excites via recurrent collaterals a widespread, IPSP-mediated, 'surround' inhibition lasting approximately 100 milliseconds, fits the available data extremely well. It is wise to be cautious, however, remembering that investigators thus far have succeeded in impaling only that one per cent of cortical neurons with the largest cell soma. Nevertheless, it is particularly exciting to see that observations on the human nervous system are in such good accord with that being obtained from animal experimentation.

There is now sufficient evidence to indicate that the terms 'synchrony' and 'desynchrony' are no longer merely plausible assumptions of the electroencephalographer. The assumptions have been confirmed by direct observation of the behavior of nerve cells and the intercorrelation of their activities with the concurrent EEG.

EEG and Sensory Coding

Two important conclusions relevant to the problem of sensory coding may be adduced from the evidence thus far. The first is that the most reliable sign of active neuronal processing of sensory information is differentiation and diversification of cellular firing patterns, as expressed by desynchronization of the EEG. Diversity, in fact, is the hallmark of cortical nerve cells. Even under most extreme drives – such as epileptic discharge, which itself imposes brain wave synchrony (Plate 4, channel 1) – two simultaneously monitored cells (Plate 4, channels 2 and 3), less than 100 microns apart may show oppositely directed behavior (43).

The second major conclusion takes cognizance of the ubiquity of brain waves, the narrow range of frequencies they occupy throughout all species, and now the mechanism of recurrent inhibition (52) responsible for their timing. Collectively, these facts argue for the operation of genetically determined mechanisms and render it extremely unlikely that specific sensory coding has anything to do with the frequency of brain waves. Changes in EEG frequency relate more to the balance between cellular synchrony and desynchrony than to the specific information content of a signal. If recorded with adequate resolution, they may indicated *where the action is*, but not *what* the action is all about. These comments apply only to the gross frequency of the spontaneous EEG. We have shown in the previous section that selected wave shapes are, in fact, highly correlated with the graded synaptic activity in particular cells. Creutzfeldt *et al.* (38) and Landau (this volume [not included here]) point out that such high correlations are also found for evoked potentials. It is quite possible, therefore, that stimulus-bound or time-locked wave shapes extracted in some way (averaging, autocorrelation, etc.) from the ongoing EEG may be related to information coding. (More is said on this subject by E. R. John, this volume [not included here]).

Sensory Coding in Single Neurons

The mammalian visual system is especially well suited for an analysis of sensory coding. The elementary details of stage-by-stage connectivity have been intensively studied (55–66). An extraordinary degree of order and specificity has been found not only at lower levels but also extending into the cortical regions and even beyond the primary receiving area (67). Single cells have been shown to be extremely selective in their stimulus preferences, and the required stimuli are generally quite complex (66, 67). Multisensory interactions at single units have been shown by Jung and co-workers (68) and by Murata *et al.*, (69) to be a very common and pervasive feature of visual physiology.

Our investigation was designed to provide information on the following three questions:

1. Do cells that respond to specific and complex stimuli exhibit equally specific response patterns, which constitute a neural signature for that stimulus?

2. In cells that respond to more than one stimulus configuration or more than one sensory modality, are there detectable differences in response pattern for each stimulus?

3. Are response patterns completely fixed or can they be modified as a result of experience?

The experimental animal was the curarized, unanesthetized cat. Prior to the experiment, the animals were fitted with an implanted nylon receptacle that could be opened, when necessary, for insertion of the microelectrode, and with a cap of dental cement attached to the skull and specially molded to receive the ear bars of the stereotaxic instrument. The receptacle was 5 to 6 millimeters in diameter and extended from the interaural line (Horsley–Clarke 0) anteriorly over the lateral gyrus. Thus, all penetrations were made in the zone designated as visual area III by Hubel and Wiesel (67). This area is considered analogous to Brodmann area 19 or parastriate cortex in man. During experimental sessions, an endotracheal tube was inserted for artificial respiration and the animal was immobilized with Flaxedil. The head was securely fixed in the stereotaxic apparatus by means of the cement cap, the body was kept warm and supported by elastic bands, and all injections were made through an indwelling femoral cannula. Thus, there were no pressure points, and great care was taken to assure that the procedure involved no stress for the animal. A one-diopter contact lens was fitted to each eye to assure a fixed focus and to protect the cornea from drying. Pupils were dilated with atropine.

Single-unit records were obtained with tungsten microelectrodes (70). After suitable amplification, the records were monitored on an oscilloscope and fed to a tape recorder for later playback and analysis.

All visual stimuli were projected on a viewing screen located 30 centimeters in front of the eyes. Stimuli could be delivered to each eye separately. Stimulus duration was always 50 milliseconds. Acoustic stimuli were 10-millisecond clicks repeated for 50 milliseconds; tactile stimuli consisted of weak electrical shocks to the contralateral hind limb. All stimuli were delivered on a random schedule with a mean intertrial interval of 22·5 seconds. A prepulse was put on tape 50 milliseconds before each stimulation.

Data analysis was performed on a LINC computer. It was programmed to compute and display summed post-stimulus-time

(PST) histograms (binwidth manually selectable) out to 250 milliseconds after stimulus onset or 300 milliseconds after the prepulse.

These experiments were carried out over a five-year period. During that time there were changes in experimental technique, recording apparatus, and even in strategy. Furthermore, each cell had a unique preferential or adequate stimulus (or stimuli), as well as a unique response pattern. Such particular preferences were sought out by the experimenters and were determining factors in the design of each experiment. Finally, variations in our ability to hold on to the unit and to maintain it in 'normal' condition determined the duration of each experiment and the number of replications and controls that were possible in each case. Taken together, all these factors resulted in a lack of strict standardization of procedure from one experiment to the next. Nevertheless, as will be shown, every effort was made to provide internal controls with which experientially determined changes in response pattern might be compared.

Response characteristics

Receptive fields were carefully plotted for each cell encountered and the 'preferred' stimulus configuration was determined. The latter were usually complex, consisting of edges, bars, or lines of various lengths and orientations. When the optimal stimulus was used, the mean cellular response was usually quite stable (as measured by PST histograms of sums of 20 trials), even though there was considerable trial-to-trial variability and scatter of latencies and sometimes omission of some components. Figure 7 illustrates the first 12 trials out of the total of 20 used to compute the histogram shown in the lower part of the figure. Two bursts of activity are evident when the tracings are displayed in this way and, of course, two peaks in the histogram. By examination of single tracings, the early burst would not have been detected in trials 3, 5, 8, and perhaps 7.

A more complex response is shown in Figure 8, where trial-to-trial differences in latency are prominent. An inhibitory interval may be recognized in the histogram; after the first burst, the activity drops below the baseline of 'spontaneous' activity (-50 milliseconds).

A total of 890 cells of visual area III responded to 'preferred' stimuli in the manner shown. A change of stimulus configuration – from only contralateral eye to both eyes simultaneously, or a change in the orientation of a line – resulted in a different response

trials

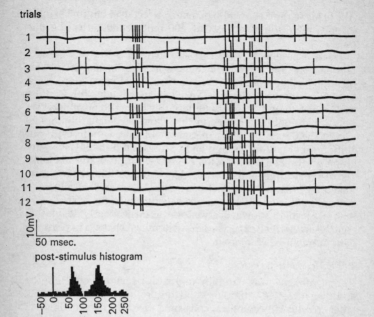

50 msec.

post-stimulus histogram

time in milliseconds

Figure 7. Single unit extracellular records of the first successive 12 trials of the 20 trials which were summed to form the PST histogram illustrated in the lower half of this figure. Each sweep triggered by onset of stimulus. Preferred stimulus for this cell was a dark bar on a light background oriented on a line from 5 : 00 to 11 : 00, 'stopped' on the left but extending out of the receptive field on the right. It was 4 mm. wide. Duration was 50 msec. Tracings were displayed on a storage oscilloscope by stepping down the vertical beam for each trial and were then photographed. The PST histogram displayed below was triggered by the pre-pulse which had been placed on the tape recording 50 msec. before stimulus onset. It, therefore, illustrates the pre-stimulus level of activity (−50 msec. to 0) as well as the cellular response to stimulation. When displayed simultaneously in this manner it is evident that there are two distinct bursts of activity (perhaps corresponding to onset and cessation of stimulation) which are reflected in the two peaks of the histogram. However, if the single traces had been examined separately, the early component might have been missed on trials 3, 5, 8, and, possibly, 7. Binwidth equals 5 msec. in this and all other histograms displayed in this paper. The calibration bar at time zero in this and all other histograms equals 20 spikes

pattern. Eight hundred seventy-one of these cells also responded to tactile and/or acoustic stimuli with response patterns different from those elicited by visual stimuli. The 'preferred' visual stimulus was then combined with other visual or other sensory stimuli,

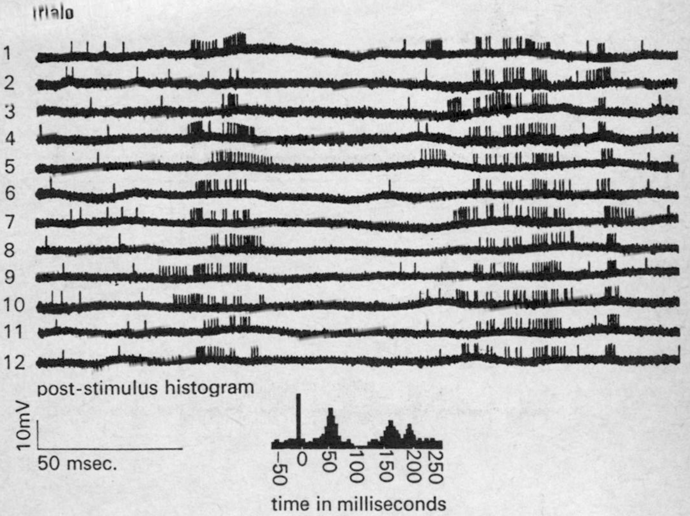

Figure 8. Single unit extracellular records of the first successive 12 trials of the 20 trials which were summed to form the PST histogram illustrated in the lower half of this figure. Three peaks are recognizable in the single tracings (except trial 2) although the 'latency' varies from trial to trial. The 'scatter' of these 'latencies' may be visualized as the width or negatively accelerated slope of the histogram peaks. Note also how the histogram displays an inhibitory interval between the first and second peaks. The stimulus in this case was a dark corner in the right upper quadrant of the visual field

yielding histograms having an extremely complex form rarely attributable to a simple linear summation of the firing pattern for each separate stimulus. Following this procedure (usually 2 blocks of 20 trials each), the original visual stimulus (test stimulus) was again presented alone. In the great majority of cells, response patterns were identical with those elicited prior to the paired-trial experience. However, in 102 well-studied cells, the subsequent test stimulus evoked stable response patterns with a marked resemblance to those elaborated by the combined stimuli.

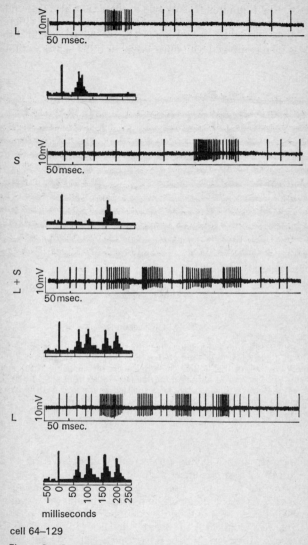

L

10mV

50 msec.

S

10mV

50 msec.

L + S

10mV

50 msec.

L

10mV

50 msec.

-50 0 50 100 150 200 250

milliseconds

cell 64–129

Figure 9.   See caption opposite

Response modification in 'polymodal' cells

Figure 9 demonstrates the histograms along with single-trace examples of the response to the visual stimulus (Figure 9, L), to a shock to the contralateral hind limb (Figure 9, S), to the two stimuli combined (Figure 9, L + S), and to the visual stimulus alone after the paired trials (Figure 9, L, lower). An appreciation of the true time course of this effect may be gained by viewing histograms of each successive sum of 20 trials for the entire stimulated output of a nerve cell throughout the period of its observation. Cell 63–294 delivered a moderately high-frequency, rather prolonged burst to a light line at about 2.00 in its receptive field (Figure 10, trials 1 to 20). A second sum of 20 trials (trials 21 to 40) gives some indication of the stability of the histogram. The cell also responded to acoustic stimulation with a brief burst peaking somewhat earlier than the peak of the light-evoked discharge (trials 41 to 80). Stimulation with the light line was then resumed; the resultant histogram (Figure 10, trials 81 to 100) showed that neither the interposition of acoustic stimulation alone nor of time itself had modified the response to light. Next, the light and click stimuli were presented simultaneously for two blocks of 20 trials each (trials 101 to 140), yielding PST histograms of very different composition from those for either stimulus individually. A reorganization or a completely new organization of response pattern emerged. Note that it took time; there are differences between the first (trials 101 to 120) and second (trials 121 to 140) sums of 20 trials of paired stimulation. Furthermore, following this 'experience', the light alone elicited a complex patterned discharge very similar to that elaborated by the combined stimuli (Figure 10, trials 141 to 200). The reorganization thus established did not persist indefinitely but began to decay during trials 201 to 220. An attempt to re-establish it by interposing a series of click stimulation alone (trials 221 to 240) was

Figure 9. Experientially-induced modification of response pattern. Cell responded to a dark horizontal bar at 3 : 00 (L) and also to electric shock to the contralateral hindlimb (S). Combining these two stimuli (L + S) resulted in a histogram very different from that which might occur from simple linear addition of the two separate responses. Furthermore, after 40 trials of such paired stimuli, the original visual stimulus (L) was presented alone. It elicited a pattern much more like that elaborated by paired stimulation than like that which it produced prior to pairing. The histograms are, again, sums of 20 trials. The single traces are those most representative of the overall pattern in each group of 20

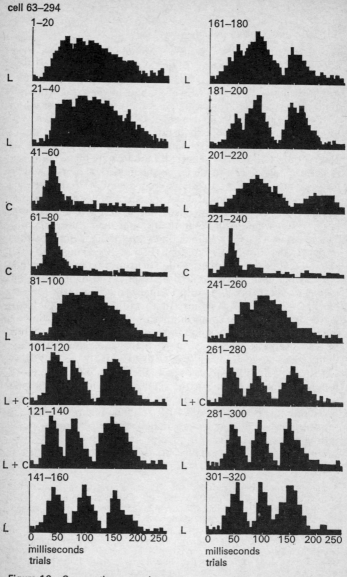

cell 63–294

1–20
L
21–40
L
41–60
C
61–80
C
81–100
L
101–120
L + C
121–140
L + C
141–160
L
161–180
L
181–200
L
201–220
L
221–240
C
241–260
L
261–280
L + C
281–300
L
301–320
L

0 50 100 150 200 250
milliseconds
trials

0 50 100 150 200 250
milliseconds
trials

Figure 10. See caption opposite

unsuccessful, the subsequent testing with light (trials 241 to 260) yielding a histogram indistinguishable from that of the original response to light (trials 1 to 20). Note also that the response pattern to click (trials 221 to 240) was unchanged from that in the control period (trials 41 to 60). However, a series of 20 trials of combined light *and* click stimulation (trials 261 to 280) did have the effect of restoring the modified pattern, which then was persistently elicited by light alone (trials 281 to 320) for as long as the cell could be held.

Response modification when nonpreferred stimulus is ineffective

Figure 11 illustrates sequential PST histograms in a cell that responded only to illumination of its receptive field in the contralateral eye (Figure 11, trials 1 to 20) with a brief burst followed by an inhibitory interval. Ipsilateral eye stimulation (trials 21 to 60) produced no alteration in spontaneous firing rate or pattern. Yet, when the two eyes were stimulated simultaneously (trials 61 to 100), a reorganization of firing pattern occurred, consisting mainly of the appearance of two late peaks and perhaps some increased scatter of the early component, such that it encroached upon, and thereby shortened, the inhibitory interval. Now, however, when the 'preferred' stimulus to the contralateral eye was reintroduced, the response pattern retained the two additional components contributed by or elaborated during paired stimulation (Figure 11, trials 101 to 140). The new pattern began to decay during the third postpairing block (trials 141 to 160) and was gone by the fourth block (trials 161 to 180). Stimulation of the right eye alone was still ineffective (trial 181 to 200), and did not result in restoration of the modified response to the left, or contralateral-eye stimulus (trials 201 to 220). Stimulation of both eyes simultaneously again generated a complex histogram containing the two late components (Figure 11, trials 221 to 240). Following this 'reinforcement', stimulation of the contralateral eye alone reproduced the modified pattern for the unusually long period of

Figure 10. Response modification in a polymodal cell. 'Preferred' visual stimulus (L) for this cell was a light line at 2 : 00 in its receptive field. Click stimulus (C), 30 db. above human auditory threshold in open field conditions, was also effective although with a different pattern. This figure illustrates the PST histograms obtained throughout the entire course of observation of this cell. L + C indicates 'preferred' visual and acoustic stimuli combined. Kind of stimulus is indicated on the left and trial numbers to the right of each histogram in this and all subsequent figures. Further explanation in text

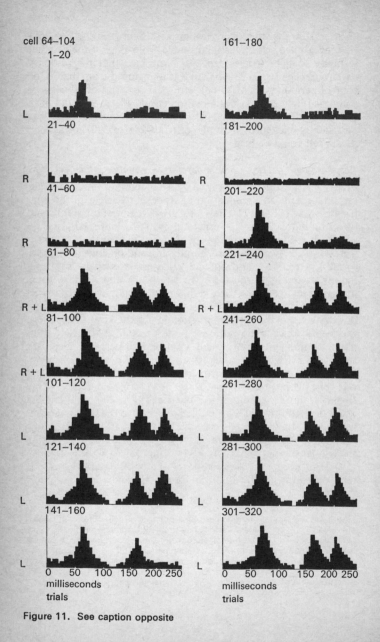

Figure 11. See caption opposite

about 40 minutes comprising four successive blocks of 20 trials each (trials 241 to 320) before the cell was lost.

The cells in Figures 10 and 11 both illustrate a differential specificity for the combined stimulus configuration. Stimulation by the nonpreferred member of the pair, whether it itself elicited a response, as in the case of the click (Figure 10), or did not, as in the case of ipsilateral eye stimulation (Figure 11), was not effective either in producing the response pattern caused by paired stimulation or of restoring the capacity of the 'preferred' stimulus to elicit the modified response.

Further differential specificity

Another cell affords a striking example of differential specificity. PST histograms of cell 64–107 are shown in Figure 12. This cell had a response repertoire that was more varied than most. It responded best to a vertical bar, 3.6 centimeters long, moving from left to right or right to left across its receptive field. It also responded transiently to diffuse illumination of the room. But the most important characteristic of the cell was that response patterns to the vertical bar moving to the right and to the left, respectively, were different, depending on whether the testing was done in the dark or in a dimly lighted room. Thus, one could distinguish four stimulus configurations to which the cell was differentially responsive:

(i) visual stimulus moving to the right in the dark (VR–D);
(ii) visual stimulus moving to the left in the dark (VL–D);
(iii) visual stimulus moving to the right in the light (VR–L); and
(iv) visual stimulus moving to the left in the light (VL–L).

The corresponding histograms are illustrated in Figure 12, VR–D, trials 1 to 20; VL–D, trials 21 to 40; VR–L, trials 61 to 80; VL–L, trials 81 to 100. The cell also responded to an electric shock delivered to the contralateral hind limb (Figure 12,

Figure 11. Response modification in the case where the non-preferred stimulus was ineffective. This cell responded to a light line 2 mm. wide and 3 cm. long only when the stimulus was presented to the left eye (L); stimulation of the corresponding receptive field area with the same stimulus to the right (ipsilateral) eye caused no alteration of spontaneous firing pattern, (R, trials 21 to 60). However, simultaneous binocular stimulation produced a response pattern (trials 61–100) different from that to left eye alone (trials 1 to 20). PST histograms of successive sums of 20 trials are shown. Further explanation in text

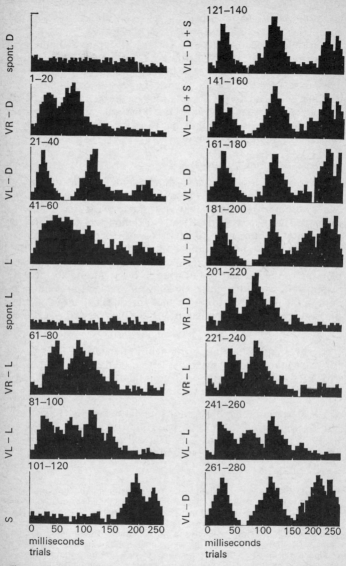

Figure 12. See caption opposite

S, trials 101–120) with a long latency. One of these four configurations, VL–D, was paired with the shock for two blocks of 20 trials each (trials 121 to 160). Following this 'experience', the VL–D-elicited response histogram was modified by the addition of a late component, which resembled that contributed by shock stimulation (Figure 12, trials 161 to 200). Testing of each of the other stimuli was then carried out. VR–D, trials 201 to 220, may be compared with its control, trials 1 to 20; VR–L, trials 221 to 240, may be compared with VR L, trials 61 to 80; VL–L, trials 241 to 260, with VL–L, trials 81 to 100. Finally, it was possible to restimulate with VL–D, trials 261 to 280, and note that the histogram modification was still present as compared with the control VL–D, trials 21 to 40. In this instance, the modification persisted for 60 minutes after pairing, of which 30 minutes were devoted to testing other stimuli and therefore not to stimulating with VL–D. It seems possible that the shorter duration of the effect seen in most cells (*circa* 20 to 30 minutes) may be a consequence of continuous testing, which, since it is 'reinforced', may result in a process analogous to extinction.

Some controls

Cell 64-126 (Figure 13) responded to acoustic (Figure 13 C, trials 21 to 40), as well as to visual stimulation (Figure 13 L, trials 1 to 20). Combining the two stimuli resulted in a complex, rather rhythmic histogram, which was certainly more than a linear transformation or addition of the two independent responses (Figure 13, trials 41 to 80). Upon testing with the 'preferred' stimulus alone, the modified or new response persisted for some time (Figure 13, trials 81 to 120) and then began to decay (Figure 13, trials 121 to 140 and 141 to 160). After it had decayed, it was

---

Figure 12. Further differential specificity. This cell had an extraordinarily rich response repertoire. It gave different response histograms to each of the following stimuli: a vertical bar 3.6 cm. in length moving from left to right in a dark room (VR–D), the same stimulus moving in the opposite direction (VL–D), same stimulus moving from left to right with the room lights on (VR–L), and the same stimulus moving from right to left with the room lights on (VL–L). The cell also responded simply to diffuse illumination of the room (L) and to an electric shock to the contralateral hindlimb (S). One of these stimulus configurations (VL–D) was paired with shock (S). The others served as controls for specificity. Histograms labeled 'spont. D' and 'spont. L' represent sums of randomly chosen, 250 msec. segments of record when the cell was unstimulated either in the dark room (D) or with the room lighted (L). See text for further explanation

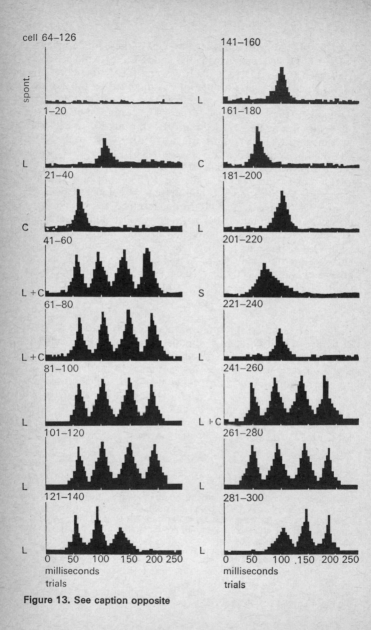

Figure 13. See caption opposite

not restored by exposure to the non-preferred stimulus (Figure 13, trials 161 to 180 and 181 to 200), nor by exposure to an electric shock (Figure 13, trials 201 to 220) introduced here as a novel stimulus, even though the shock succeeded in evoking a response from the cell. Again, only the specific pairing of the two stimuli restored the effect (Figure 13, trials 241 to 260), which then persisted as long as the cell could be held.

In contrast, cell 65–203 fell into what we now designate as a 'sensitization' group. It responded best to a light line directed toward 7:00 o'clock ('preferred' stimulus), but also to an electric shock to the contralateral hind limb (Figure 14 S, trials 21 to 60). Combining the two stimuli yielded response histograms (Figure 14, trials 61 to 100), which indeed seemed nothing more than a linear addition of the two independent responses. Nevertheless, the new response persisted when stimulation was resumed with the 'preferred' stimulus alone (Figure 14, trials 101 to 160). The usual response decrement occurred to a level even lower than that of the control or original response. However, upon presentation of the shock alone, *not paired stimulation*, and even though the shock alone did not elicit the response pattern of the paired stimuli (Figure 14, trials 181 to 200), there was restoration of the modified response pattern when tested by light stimulation alone (Figure 14, trials 201 to 240).

Discussion

The 102 cells that generated records of the type illustrated herein stand in striking contrast to the great majority of 769 cells wherein multimodal responses were also demonstrated. In this latter group, the response pattern elicited by pairing did not show any persistence whatsoever when tested with either preferred or non-preferred stimuli. Their response patterns were surprisingly constant, and did not even show habituation or any appreciable variation over long time periods of several hours and many hundreds of stimulations, at least as measured by PST histograms of sums of 20 trials.

The complexity and specificity of the stimulus required to

Figure 13. Cell was responsive to visual (L), acoustic (C), and tactile (S) stimulation. Illustrates PST histograms over the duration of experiment. Electric shock was used late in the experiment as a 'novel' stimulus and did not result either in 'dishabituation' or response restoration. Note that each of the three modalities of stimulation produced a different histogram. See text

cell 65–203

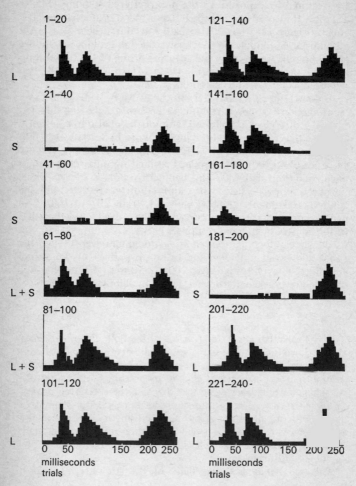

Figure 14. 'Sensitization' cell. This cell was responsive to a light line directed toward 7:00 o'clock (L) but also to electric shock (S). The experiment differs from previous examples in that following decay of the modified response pattern (trials 101 through 180), presentation of shock alone, *without pairing,* resulted in restoration of the modified response histogram. See text

excite all of these cells, their receptive field patterns, ocular-dominance distribution, and columnar organization emphatically confirm the observations of Hubel and Wiesel (67). The latter workers did not report a testing of multisensory convergence, but our observations on that score are in accord with those of Murata *et al.* (69) and Jung (68). In fact, Murata *et al.* (69) even examined their results by means of PST histograms, although apparently they did not look for evidence of modifiability.

The general stability of cellular responses in visual cortex makes those cells exhibiting response modification stand out clearly. In fact, there was never any ambiguity over which cells would and which would not exhibit this property. The phenomenon was either clearly present or the cell manifested no sign of modification, even after hundreds of trials.

The distribution of modifiable cells was not random; it was quite specific. The cells were almost always encountered in groups, and such groups were invariably found in columnar penetrations of the microelectrode.

Given the data already on hand concerning multisensory convergence (see also Horn, 71), it is not really surprising that stimulation from other modalities might modify the response to 'preferred' visual stimuli, although at best this might be expected in only a minority of cells, or there would not be as much constancy to our visual world as common observation insists there is.

Yet we have no way of judging whether the proportion we have found (roughly 10 per cent) represents a realistic estimate of that portion of the population having 'plastic' properties. There are, indeed, several reasons to consider that this estimate may be erroneously low. Thus, the recognition of pattern required the summed PST histogram method of data analysis. This, in turn, required that the same cell be held for several hours to provide all the necessary controls and comparisons. Needless to say, we may not have hit upon the appropriate or adequate stimulus in many cells. Moreover, if we lost a cell before adequate controls had been established, it was placed in the unmodified category. Hence, only cells in which adequate controls had been established were included in the modifiable group.

However tempting it may be, we do not yet believe it is wise or useful to label this phenomenon with the term 'conditioning', even though many of the criteria for conditioning are met and many of the subsidiary terms used in behavioral conditioning, e.g. extinction, may be appropriate. We understand the phenomenon described herein as a transient modification of response pattern that is specific to a particular past experience. The duration is limited, but is of the same order of magnitude as the 'consolidation' time (72), or short-term memory, and the heterosynaptic facilitation found by Kandel and Tauc in *Aplysia* (73). Behavioral conditioning requires the laying down of a permanent memory trace, and we particularly do not have evidence that the microstructure of a cellular firing pattern is the physical substrate of enduring memory. It is quite unlikely that recognition or recall requires the cellular re-creation of these temporal patterns of discharge. Recognition and recollection do not require 250 milliseconds of time, as anyone who has worked with tachistoscopic presentation of signals can testify, and as Lindsley *et al.* (74) has shown in an elegant physiological experiment.

These experiments have, however, provided answers to the questions set forth at the beginning of this section. There are clearly substantive differences in the response pattern of each single cell when it is activated by different stimuli. Thus, a cell may be responsive, for instance, both to a visual and to an acoustic stimulus, but this does *not* mean that modality information is lost. These cells must have their connectivity arranged in highly specific and organized ways, so that fibers carrying acoustic information to two different cells in visual cortex may modify the output of the cells differentially. Similarly, Figure 13 illustrates that a single cell, even though capable of activation by visual, acoustic, and tactile stimuli, maintains stimulus-specific discharge patterns. These findings allow strong inference that the microstructure of the response as exhibited in PST histograms does, in fact, constitute the neural code for that particular experience. On the other hand, it is also true that the histograms exhibit varying degrees of 'scatter' about the mode. On any single trial the response of a particular cell is probabilistic rather than absolutely deterministic with respect both to timing (see Figure 8) and pattern (note omission of the early component in some trials illustrated in Figure 7). Therefore, on any given trial, the response pattern of a single cell cannot uniquely specify the nature of an experience.

In relating these observations at the cellular level to the behavior of an organism, one must bear in mind the probability that information is processed in parallel in thousands of cells, so that the organism need not depend on the reliability of any single element for identification of an experience. These parallel chains need not all carry exactly the same information and, strictly speaking, therefore may not necessarily be redundant. It is only necessary that the nervous system receive enough information about an experience to identify it even if some aspects are left out or are distorted. Furthermore, it is likely that on first exposure to a stimulus, the nervous system specifies it less precisely than after many exposures. Ultimately, as was noted above, the code must be transformed from one based upon a discharge pattern through time to one that is more stable, i.e. immune to electrical interference (75), more disseminated, and susceptible of very much faster readout.

The term 'probabilistic' is used herein merely to describe the nature of the observed relationship between input and output. It does not imply any particular conclusion about the fundamental nature of the 'noise' in the system. It is quite possible that a completely deterministic system, but one in which many variables are unknown, would appear probabilistic to the limited viewpoint of a microelectrode sampling the output of one single cell. Nor, of course, do these considerations exclude the possibility of some fundamental stochastic property operating on the process of synaptic transmission. All that can be said at this stage is that it is not necessary to introduce any fundamental indeterminacy in the system to account for all the available data.

At first glance it seems especially appropriate that cells exhibiting 'plasticity' should be found in these higher reaches of the visual system. Such cells all receive inputs from hypercomplex cells and are higher-order hypercomplex, to use the terms introduced by Hubel and Wiesel (67). As they were not randomly scattered, but were organized quite specifically on a columnar plan, these cells would be in a position to make use of all the detailed information built into the connectivity of the visual system. They simply add another stage of complexity onto the levels already described by Hubel and Wiesel.

Certain other considerations lead us to question the proposition that 'plasticity' might be a property evolved only in higher-order cells. Thus, Chow and Lindsley (76), have observed similar transient modifications of firing pattern in lateral geniculate neurons. This occurred in approximately the same proportion of total cells sampled, i.e. 10 per cent, and the cells were also grouped together. Similar observations have been made by Yoshii and Ogura (77) in reticular formation and by Kamikawa, McIlwain, and Adey (78) in the thalamus. Moreover, Weingarten and Spinelli (79) have shown changes in the receptive fields of retinal ganglion cells as a result of auditory and somatic stimulation, and Adkins, Morse, and Towe (80) have reported analogous observations in cuneate cells.

These related findings suggest rather that 'plasticity' may be built in all along the neuraxis. There may be a specifically organized system of cells, developed during maturation, having a genetic endowment for the appropriate connectivity for inter-modality interaction and short-term maintenance of change.

Whether the permanent traces that underlie learning take place in these cells or in still other more specialized ones with which these are presumably connected, is a matter for future investigation.

Summary

We have reviewed some aspects of the electrical activity of the brain with respect to what relevance they might have for the problem of sensory coding. Discussion included the intrinsic rhythms of the EEG, what is known of their control, and the influence of sensory input upon them. Next, in the context of an opportunity to record intracellularly from human nerve cells, the relationship between synaptic potentials in single units and the grossly recorded EEG was defined and work from other laboratories reported. All these led to the conclusion that the EEG does indeed represent the summed synaptic potentials of the hundreds of thousands of neurons within the 'field' of a recording electrode. Current notions concerning the timing or pacing of brain waves were reviewed, and the conclusion reached that it was most unlikely that brain rhythms themselves were used in sensory coding. Finally, the problem of sensory coding in single neurons of the visual system was directly approached with a relatively prolonged monitoring system, and a small subsystem of cells was identified. This subsystem had an exceedingly rich repertoire of responses and response patterns that could be modified by past experience. Some implications of these observations were discussed.

References

1. M. B. RHEINBERGER and H. H. JASPER, 1937. Electrical activity of the cerebral cortex in the unanesthetized cat, *Am. J. Physiol.*, vol. 119, pp. 186–96.
2. D. B. LINDSLEY, 1960. Attention, consciousness, sleep and wakefulness, in *Handbook of Physiology* (J. Field, H. W. Magoun, and V. E. Hall, editors), Washington, D.C., American Physiological Society, section I, volume III, pp. 1553–94.

3. F. MORRELL and L. K. MORRELL, 1965. Computer aided analysis of brain electrical activity, in *Symposium on the Analysis of Central Nervous System and Cardiovascular Data using Computer Methods* (L. D. Proctor and W. R. Adey, editors), Washington, D C, National Aeronautics and Space Administration N P 72, pp. 441–78.

4. D. B. LINDSLEY J. II. SCHREINER, W. B. KNOWLES, and H. W. MAGOUN, 1950. Behavioral and EEG changes following chronic brain stem lesions in the cat, *Electroencephalog. Clin. Neurophysiol.*, vol. 2, pp. 483–98.

5. P. B. BRADLEY and J. ELKES, 1957. The effects of some drugs on the electrical activity of the brain, *Brain*, vol. 80, pp. 77–117.

6. W. DEMENT and N. KLEITMAN, 1957. Cyclic variations in EEG during sleep and their relation to eye movements, body motility, and dreaming, *Electroencephalog. Clin. Neurophysiol.*, vol. 9, pp. 673–90.

7. H. II. JASPER, 1954. Electrophysiology and experimental epilepsy, in *Epilepsy and the Functional Anatomy of the Human Brain* (W. Penfield and H. Jasper, editors), Boston, Little, Brown, pp. 183–238.

8. M. A. B. BRAZIER, 1960. *The Electrical Activity of the Nervous System*, New York, Macmillan, 2nd edition.

9. M. A. B. BRAZIER, 1961. *A History of the Electrical Activity of the Brain: The First Half-Century*, New York, Macmillan.

10. D. P. PURPURA, 1959. Nature of electrocortical potentials and synaptic organizations in cerebral and cerebellar cortex, *Intern. Rev. Neurobiol.*, vol. 1, pp. 48–163.

11. F. BREMER, 1958. Cerebral and cerebellar potentials, *Physiol. Rev.*, vol. 38, pp. 357–88.

12. E. D. ADRIAN and B. H. C. MATTHEWS, 1934. The interpretation of potential waves in the cortex, *J. Physiol. (London)*, vol. 81, pp. 440–71.

13. E. D. ADRIAN and B. H. C. MATTHEWS, 1934. The Berger rhythm: potential changes from the occipital lobes in man, *Brain*, vol. 57, pp. 355–85.

14. G. MORUZZI and H. W. MAGOUN, 1949. Brain stem reticular formation and activation of the EEG, *Electroencephalog. Clin. Neurophysiol.*, vol. 1, pp. 455–73.

15. H. H. JASPER, 1954. Functional properties of the thalamic reticular system, in *Brain Mechanisms and Consciousness* (J. F. Delafresnaye, editor), Springfield, Illinois, Charles C. Thomas, pp. 374–401.

16. H. H. JASPER, 1961. Thalamic reticular system, in *Electrical Stimulation of the Brain* (D. E. Sheer, editor), Austin, Texas, University of Texas Press, pp. 277–87.

17. H. GASTAUT, 1958. Some aspects of the neurophysiological basis of conditioned reflexes and behavior, in *Neurological Basis of Behavior* (G. E. W. Wolstenholme and C. M. O'Connor, editors), Boston, Little, Brown, pp. 255–72.

18. L. G. VORONIN and E. N. SOKOLOV, 1960. Cortical mechanisms of the orienting reflex and its relation to the conditioned reflex, *Electroencephalog. Clin. Neurophysiol., Suppl. 13*, pp. 335–46.

19. F. MORRELL and H. H. JASPER, 1956. Electrographic studies of the formation of temporary connections in the brain, *Electroencephalog. Clin. Neurophysiol.*, vol. 8, pp. 201–15.

20. K. L. CHOW, W. C. DEMENT, and E. R. JOHN, 1957. Conditioned electrocorticographic potentials and behavioral avoidance response in cat, *J. Neurophysiol.*, vol. 20, pp. 482–93.

21. F. MORRELL. 1958. Some electrical events involved in the formation of temporary connections, in *Reticular Formation of the Brain* (H. H. Jasper, L. D. Proctor, R. S. Knighton, W. C. Noshay, and R. T. Costello, editors), Boston, Little, Brown, pp. 545–60.

22. K. L. CHOW, W. RANDALL, and F. MORRELL, 1966. Effect of brain lesions on conditioned cortical electropotentials, *Electroencephalog. Clin. Neurophysiol.*, vol. 20, pp. 357–69.

23. C. E. WELLS, 1959. Modification of alpha-wave responsiveness to light by juxtaposition of auditory stimuli. *A. M. A. Arch. Neurol.*, vol. 1, pp. 689–94.

24. C. E. WELLS, 1963. Alpha wave responsiveness to light in man, in *EEG and Behavior* (G. H. Glaser, editor), New York, Basic Books, pp. 27–59.

25. L. MORRELL and F. MORRELL, 1962. Non-random oscillation in the response-duration curve of electrographic activation, *Electroencephalog. Clin. Neurophysiol.*, vol. 14, pp. 724–30.

26. F. MORRELL, 1961. Electrophysiological contributions to the neural basis of learning, *Physiol. Rev.*, vol. 41, pp. 443–94.

27. L. K. MORRELL, 1966. Some characteristics of stimulus-provoked alpha activity, *Electroencephalog. Clin. Neurophysiol.*, vol. 21, pp. 552–61.

28. E. N. SOKOLOV. 1963. *Perception and the Conditioned Reflex*, New York, Pergamon Press.

29. S. SHARPLESS and H. JASPER, 1956. Habituation of the arousal reaction, *Brain*, vol. 79, pp. 655–80.

29a. E. R. JOHN and K. F. KILLAM, 1959. Electrophysiological correlates of avoidance conditioning in the cat, *J. Pharmacol. Exp. Therap.*, vol. 125, pp. 252–74.

30. H. GASTAUT, A. JUS, C. JUS, F. MORRELL, W. STORM VAN LEEUWEN, S. DONGIER, R. NAQUET, H. REGIS, A. ROGER, D. BEKKERING, A. KAMP, and J. WERRE, 1957. Étude topographique des reactions électroencéphalographiques conditionnées chez l'homme, *Electroencephalog. Clin. Neurophysiol.*, vol. 9, pp. 1–34.

31. C. E. WELLS, 1963. Electroencephalographic correlates of conditioned responses, in *EEG and Behavior* (G. H. Glaser, editor), New York, Basic Books, pp. 60–108.

32. E. R. JOHN, 1961. High nervous functions: brain functions and learning, *Ann. Rev. Physiol.*, vol. 23, pp. 451–84.

33. K. L. CHOW, 1961. Brain functions, *Ann. Rev. Psychol.*, vol. 12, pp. 281–310.

34. S. POLYAK, 1957. *The Vertebrate Visual System*, Chicago, University of Chicago Press.

35. H. JASPER and W. PENFIELD, 1949. Electrocorticograms in man: effect of voluntary movement upon the electrical activity of the precentral gyrus, *Arch. Psychiat. Nervenkrankh.*, vol. 183, pp. 163–74.

36. H. GASTAUT, 1954. The brain stem and cerebral electrogenesis in relation to consciousness, in *Brain Mechanisms and Consciousness* (J. F. Delafresnaye, editor), Springfield, Illinois, Charles C. Thomas, pp. 249–83.

37. F. BREMER, 1953. *Some Problems in Neurophysiology*, London, Athlone Press.

38. O. D. Creutzfeldt, S. Watanabe, and H. D. Lux, 1966. Relations between EEG phenomena and potentials of single cortical cells. I. Evoked responses after thalamic and epicortical stimulation, *Electroencephalog. Clin. Neurophysiol.*, vol. 20, pp. 1–18.

39. O. D. Creutzfeldt, S. Watanabe, and H. D. Lux, 1966. Relations between EEG phenomena and potentials of single cortical cells. II. Spontaneous and convulsoid activity, *Electroencephalog. Clin. Neurophysiol.*, vol. 20, pp. 19–37.

40a. W. A. Spencer and J. M. Brookhart, 1961. Electrical patterns of augmenting and recruiting waves in depths of sensorimotor cortex of cat. *J. Neurophysiol.*, vol. 24, pp. 26–49.

40b. W. A. Spencer and J. M. Brookhart, 1961. A study of spontaneous spindle waves in sensorimotor cortex of cat, *J. Neurophysiol.*, vol. 24, pp. 50–64.

41. J. Calvet, M. C. Calvet, and J. Scherrer, 1964. Étude stratigraphique corticale de l'activité EEG spontanée, *Electroencephalog. Clin. Neurophysiol.*, vol. 17, pp. 109–25.

42. C. L. Li and H. Jasper, 1953. Microelectrode studies of the electrical activity of the cerebral cortex in the cat, *J. Physiol. (London)*, vol. 121, pp. 117–40.

43. F. Morrell, 1961. Microelectrode studies in chronic epileptic foci, *Epilepsia*, vol. 2, pp. 81–8.

44. R. P. Schmidt, L. B. Thomas, and A. A. Ward, Jr., 1959. The hyperexcitable neurone. Microelectrode studies of chronic epileptic foci in monkey, *J. Neurophysiol.*, vol. 22, pp. 285–96.

45. O. Creutzfeldt, 1963. Activité neuronique du système nerveux central de quelques aspects de l'activité neuronique unitaire corticale et de ses rapports avec l'électroencéphalogramme, in *Problèmes de Base en Electroencéphalographie* (H. Fischgold *et al.*, editor), Paris, Masson, pp. 34–60.

46. F. Morrell and C. Whitcher, in press. Use of deep barbiturate narcosis in the diagnostic study of epilepsy, *Electroencephalog. Clin. Neurophysiol.*

47. C. L. Li, H. McLennan, and H. Jasper, 1952. Brain waves and unit discharge in cerebral cortex, *Science*, vol. 116, pp. 656–7.

48. C. Stefanis and H. Jasper, 1964. Recurrent collateral inhibition in pyramidal tract neurons, *J. Neurophysiol.*, vol. 27, pp. 855–77.

49. D. P. Purpura, J. G. McMurty, C. F. Leonard, and A. Malliani, 1966. Evidence for dendritic origin of spikes without depolarizing prepotentials in hippocampal neurons during and after seizure, *J. Neurophysiol.*, vol. 29, pp. 954–79.

50. D. A. Prince, 1966. Modification of focal cortical epileptogenic discharge by afferent influences, *Epilepsia*, vol. 7, pp. 181–201.

51. O. Creutzfeldt, H. D. Lux, and S. Watanabe, 1966. Electrophysiology of cortical nerve cells, in *The Thalamus* (D. Purpura and M. Yahr, editors), New York, Columbia University Press, pp. 209–36.

52. P. Andersen and J. Eccles, 1962. Inhibitory phasing of neuronal discharge, *Nature*, vol. 196, pp. 645–7.

53. J. C. Eccles, 1964. *The Physiology of Synapses*, New York, Academic Press.

54. C. G. Phillips, 1959. Actions of antidromic pyramidal volleys on single Betz cells in the cat, *Quart. J. Exp. Physiol.*, vol. 44, pp. 1–25.

55. S. POLYAK, 1927. An experimental study of the association callosal, and projection fibers of the cerebral cortex of the cat, *J. Comp. Neurol.*, vol. 44, pp. 197–258.

56. S. A. TALBOT and W. H. MARSHALL, 1941. Physiological studies on neural mechanisms of visual localization and discrimination, *Am. J. Ophthalmol.*, vol. 24, pp. 1255–64.

57. J. M. THOMPSON, C. N. WOOLSEY, and S. A. TALBOT, 1950. Visual areas I and II of cerebral cortex of rabbit, *J. Neurophysiol.*, vol. 13, pp. 277–88.

58. S. W. KUFFLER, 1953. Discharge patterns and functional organization of mammalian retina, *J. Neurophysiol.*, vol. 16, pp. 37–68.

59. M. H. CLARE and G. H. BISHOP, 1954. Responses from an association area secondarily activated from optic cortex, *J. Neurophysiol.*, vol. 17, pp. 271–7.

60. R. W. DOTY, 1958. Potentials evoked in cat cerebral cortex by diffuse and by punctiform photic stimuli, *J. Neurophysiol.*, vol. 21, pp. 437–64.

61. E. F. VASTOLA, 1961. A direct pathway from lateral geniculate body to association cortex, *J. Neurophysiol.*, vol. 24, pp. 469–87.

62. R. OTSUKA and R. HASSLER, 1962. Über Aufbau und Gliederung der corticalen Sehsphäre bei der Katze, *Arch. Psychiat. Nervenkrankh.*, vol. 203, pp. 212–34.

63. E. H. POLLEY and J. M. DIRKES, 1963. The visual cortical (geniculocortical) area of the cat brain and its projections, *Anat. Record*, vol. 145, p. 345 (abstract).

64a. D. H. HUBEL and T. N. WIESEL, 1959. Receptive fields of single neurones in the cat's striate cortex, *J. Physiol. (London)*, vol. 148, pp. 574–91.

64b. D. H. HUBEL and T. N. WIESEL, 1961. Integrative action in the cat's lateral geniculate body, *J. Physiol. (London)*, vol. 155, pp. 385–98.

65. D. H. HUBEL and T. N. WIESEL, 1962. Receptive fields, binocular interaction and functional architecture in the cat's visual cortex, *J. Physiol. (London)*, vol. 160, pp. 106–54.

66. D. H. HUBEL and T. N. WIESEL, 1963. Shape and arrangement of columns in cat's striate cortex, *J. Physiol. (London)*, vol. 165, pp. 559–68.

67. D. H. HUBEL and T. N. WIESEL, 1965. Receptive fields and functional architecture in two nonstriate visual areas (18 and 19) of the cat, *J. Neurophysiol.*, vol. 28, pp. 229–89.

68. R. JUNG, 1961. Neuronal integration in the visual cortex and its significance for visual information, in *Sensory Communication*, (W. A. Rosenblith, editor), M.I.T. Press, Cambridge, pp. 627–74.

69. K. MURATA, H. CRAMER, and P. BACH-y-RITA, 1965. Neuronal convergence of noxious, acoustic, and visual stimuli in the visual cortex of the cat, *J. Neurophysiol.*, vol. 28, pp. 1223–39.

70. D. H. HUBEL, 1957. Tungsten microelectrode for recording from single units, *Science*, vol. 125, pp. 549–50.

71. G. HORN, 1965. The effect of somaesthetic and photic stimuli on the activity of units in the striate cortex of unanesthetized, unrestrained cats, *J. Physiol. (London)*, vol. 179, pp. 263–77.

72. J. A. DEUTSCH, 1962. Higher nervous functions: the physiological bases of memory, *Ann. Rev. Physiol.*, vol. 24, pp. 259–86.

73. E. R. KANDEL and L. TAUC, 1965. Heterosynaptic facilitation in neurones of the abdominal ganglion of *Aplysia depilans*, *J. Physiol.* (*London*), vol. 181, pp. 1–27.

74. D. B. LINDSLEY, L. G. FEHMI, and J. W. ADKINS, in press. Visually evoked potentials during perceptual masking in man and monkey, *Electroencephalog. Clin. Neurophysiol.*

75. F. MORRELL, 1963. Information storage in nerve cells, in *Information Storage and Neural Control* (W. S. Fields and W. Abbott, editors), Springfield, Illinois, Charles C. Thomas, pp. 189–229.

76. K. L. CHOW and D. B. LINDSLEY, unpublished observations.

77. N. YOSHII and H. OGURA, 1960. Studies on the unit discharge of brainstem reticular formation in the cat. I. Changes of reticular unit discharge following conditioning procedure, *Med. J. Osaka Univ.*, vol. 11, pp. 1–17.

78. K. KAMIKAWA, J. T. MCILWAIN, and W. R. ADEY, 1964. Response patterns of thalamic neurons during classical conditioning, *Electroencephalog. Clin. Neurophysiol.*, vol. 17, pp. 485–96.

79. M. WEINGARTEN and D. N. SPINELLI, 1966. Retinal receptive field changes produced by auditory and somatic stimulation, *Exptl. Neurol.*, vol. 15, pp. 363–76.

80. R. J. ADKINS, R. W. MORSE, and A. L. TOWE, 1966. Control of somatosensory input by cerebral cortex, *Science*, vol. 153, pp. 1020–22.

4 S. Tower

Pain: Definition and Properties of the Unit for Sensory Reception

S. Tower, 'Pain: definition and properties of the unit for sensory reception',
Pain, Williams and Wilkins, 1943, pp. 16–43.

That the receptive mechanism for pain is contained in a plexiform arrangement of nerve fibers with free nerve endings, has long been accepted. This is the only type of sensory innervation having the almost ubiquitous distribution of the pain sense. Ramifying fibers and free nerve endings may also serve other senses; in the skin, perhaps touch; and in the viscera, more obscure sensory functions; but there is general agreement that some part, at least, of these structures responds to stimuli causing pain. When, however, one presses the inquiry: what is the receptor for pain? there is no further agreement. Looking at the skin, the answer has usually been in terms of pain 'spots'. And Strughold (1924) has presented extensive quantative data on their density. Looking into or beneath the skin, however, no neatly wrapped up portions of terminal tissue, nor even concentrations of it, correspond with the spots as the various encapsulated endings tend to do, more or less, for the other modalities, while the individual free nerve terminal is too minute and often too questionable an object, as well as too numerous, to serve the purpose. In this dilemma thinking has drifted into what is probably the correct line, assuming the terminal ramification together with its free terminals to be, altogether, the sensory receptor, and by-passing the issue of the spot. Indeed, some thinking has gone so far as to abolish the separation between neuron and neuron, considering the entire plexiform arrangement as a syncytium in which neurons lose their individuality. Yet such a viewpoint is as unfounded on anatomical demonstration as the contrary supposition of individual discreteness, and considerably less acceptable, *a priori*, because of the validity of the neuron doctrine in the embryological development of this afferent innervation together with the rest of the nervous system.

With the application of vacuum tube amplification and oscillographic recording to analysis of function in the nervous system, and especially to the recording of activity in single nerve fibers isolated in peripheral nerves, a method became available whereby the terminal distribution of an individual afferent fiber could be disentangled from those of its associates, identified as a unit, and so examined. This terminal, together with its fiber, cell body, and central processes could be considered the sensory equivalent of the neuromotor unit; the neurosensory unit. Whether or not this neuron unit would also be acceptable as the unit for sensory reception, the receptor, would then depend on whether or not its properties conformed with functional attributes. This technique has now been applied (Tower, 1935, 1940) to the study of the sensory receptive mechanism for pain.

Setting largely aside the older controversies concerning pain reception, whose status has been so ably reviewed recently by Walshe (1942) and by Dallenbach (1939), the object of the present paper will be to review and correlate the anatomical and physiological evidence bearing on the definition and properties of a unit for pain reception; a receptor in a full sense. This done, the further attempt will be made to apply the concept thus arrived at to the relation between the reception of pain and that of other modalities, and between pain and the nocifensor system. Finally, the status of the punctiform concept of cutaneous sensibility will be reviewed in the light of this concept, and a new theory of spatial analysis developed, more in line with current concepts of function in the nervous system.

The Locus of Pain Reception in the Skin and Cornea

Throughout the body plexiform arrangements of nerve fibers are found, bearing free nerve terminals in the form of simple terminal twigs, end knobs, loops, brushes, or minute skeins. These are very rich both within and beneath the epidermis of the skin and cornea, but they are also present in the mucous membranes and in many deeper tissues, somatic and visceral, though not in all. The terminal portions of this ramification are in all sites, unmyelinated, but farther back, myelinated or unmyelinated fibers may enter into it. For the skin and cornea, with which I shall be chiefly concerned, it was thought until fairly recently that all of this plexiform arrangement of nerve fibers served pain reception; touch reception being assigned as the function of specialized endings such as Merkel's discs, endings about hair follicles, and Meissner's corpuscles.

Two fairly recent studies have put the relation between pain and touch reception, and free nerve terminals in a new light, without necessarily changing the status of the more elaborate nerve-endings mentioned as also touch receptors. The first of these studies, by Waterston (1933a) laid in part the design for both. By carefully slicing off layers of his own skin to varying depths, working by preference in a region of fairly thick skin such as the front or side of the terminal part of a finger, he showed that so long as the slices took only epidermis, only touch sensation was excited in their removal; never pain. Moreover, touch remained the sensation elicitable from the cut surface, although in this the touch was more prickly than that from the intact skin. Gold chloride preparations made of these shavings of skin showed the presence in them of nerve fibers in the stratum mucosum, terminating in loops and fine, arborescent figures on the surface of epithelial cells. In a second paper Waterston (1933b) further showed that pain can be elicited from the corium, and from many deeper tissues as well. He concluded that within the twofold structure of the skin there is a division of sensory function, the epidermis being the organ of touch, the corium, that of superficial pain.

The second study, by Woollard, Weddell, and Harpman (1940), culminating a series of studies by the senior author (Woollard, 1935, 1936, 1937), combined various physiological approaches to the problem of cutaneous pain with excellent histological technique. Whereas these authors agree with Waterston that no pain is aroused by shaving off as much epidermis as may be removed with a razor without causing bleeding, nevertheless this is not the entire story. When the two successive pains, which were long ago recognized as resulting from a single stimulus in some skin areas, were separately examined for the depth at which they are excited, by marking and measuring on the stimulating needle the depth of penetration at which each was felt and correlating this with the structure of the skin in that area, they found that the first pain is excited in the epidermis, and the second pain subepidermally. Both the epidermis and dermis are, therefore, organs for pain reception, though perhaps for pain of different quality.

Gasser has argued convincingly (see his paper in this volume [*Pain*]) that the two pains result from conduction over two sets of pain fibers of different conduction velocity, at the extreme, myelinated and unmyelinated. Lewis and Pochin (1937) hold a similar opinion. In the experiments of Woollard and his collaborators, as in those of their predecessors, this was suggested by the fact that the time interval between the two pains was generally longer the more distal the stimulation. The new point for the present exposition is that the different depth at which the two pains are excitable further implies that the fast-conducting and slow-conducting pain fibers are differently distributed in the skin; the fast in the epidermis, the slow in the dermis. Moreover, when these two pains were sought in the hypoalgesic border between normal skin and the area of anesthesia produced by novocain block of either the medial or the lateral cutaneous nerve to the forearm, superficial pain was found to extend farther into the affected area than deep pain, suggesting that the fast, and presumably large fibers have more widely distributed terminals than the slow fibers.

The fact that some areas of the body surface yield these two pain sensations in temporal sequence whereas others do not (according to Woollard *et al.*, the back and abdomen do not while the face, in spite of its shorter route to the central nervous system, does) suggests that less sensitive areas of the body surface may receive only, or predominantly one type of pain innervation, and that, the slow variety. One wonders if the thick skin examined by Waterston was supplied in this fashion. Unfortunately Woollard did not examine whether or not the pain over the back and abdomen is excited epidermally or subepidermally, or both. Nor do we have any knowledge of differences in the fiber constitution of the cutaneous nerves to such different areas to support or contradict this surmise, although such evidence could be easily had. A carefully planned investigation of variability from part to part of the human body of (1) the presence or absence of each of the two types of pain; (2) the existence and length, if found, of a time interval between the two pains, correlated with the distance of the site from the central nervous system; (3) the type of pain excited epithelially, and subepithelially in each site; and (4) the fiber constitution of cutaneous nerves to the part should clear up many of the discrepancies existing in current accounts and lay the basis for a new understanding of the role of fast and slow fibers in the mediation of pain.

It is only fair to add that Woollard and his co-workers reject the interpretation of the two pains as representing conduction in two systems of nerve fibers of different rate. Nor did their histological study bring to light any evidence that myelinated and unmyelinated trunk fibers are differently distributed throughout the depth of the skin. Previously, however, Kuntz and Hamilton (1938) had already described, from study of silver preparations of the skin of man and cats, how the intraepidermal fiber terminations are connected with myelinated fibers of relatively large caliber, whereas the free nerve terminals in the corium derive from smaller fibers.

There is much more to Woollard, Weddell, and Harpman's study which will be considered later, but on the point now in question, the location in the skin of the pain-receptive mechanism, these authors conclude: 'Pain can be aroused from the deeper layers of the epidermis and the superficial layers of the dermis.'

The central portion of the cornea, and probably also the tympanic membrane of the ear, are sites of peculiar interest for the problem under consideration for in each of these there is but one type of sensory innervation present, and but one sense perceived. With more than threshold stimulation this is unequivocally pain. The quality of the threshold sensation, whether contact or pain, is in dispute, as it is for the skin in general; but this problematical relationship will be considered later. No one, however, has asserted that the cornea has any other type of sensory innervation than the plexiform ramification with free nerve terminals, except around the sclerocorneal junction where both Krause's end-bulbs and cold sensibility are added.

The innervation of the cornea has been described by numbers of investigators among whom Cohnheim (1867), Dogiel (1890), Cajal (1909), Attias (1912), and Boeke (1935) are, perhaps, outstanding. The nerve fibers described as entering into this innervation are in large part myelinated as they enter the corneal connective tissue layer circumferentially from the sclera, but lose their myelin sheaths as they pass from the periphery toward the center of the cornea. The unmyclinated ramifications of these fibers then form a plexus in the connective tissue with terminal twigs or knobs or loops or brushes or fine skeins, and branches of this plexus penetrate into the epithelium where they may form a second plexus with free terminals. These terminals have been variously described as inter- and intra-cellular, with more emphasis on the former. Cajal states that the free nerve terminals are found in the intercellular cement substance from the deepest to the most superficial parts of the epithelium. The cornea, therefore, contains a ramifying sensory innervation concerned wholly with the reception of pain, which is distributed both beneath and within the epithelial layer, and throughout the depth of the latter. Here, then, as Woollard, Weddell, and Harpman claimed for the surface of the body in general, both epithelial and subepithelial innervations are organs or sites of pain reception.

Isolation and Physiological Properties of the Neuron Unit for Pain Reception

Since the advent of unitary analysis of activity in the nervous system, heralded by Adrian and Bronk's (1928) paper recording the impulses carried by single nerve fibers isolated in peripheral nerves, the technique of amplifying and recording action potentials in single fibers has been applied to the study of the mechanism of sensory end organs in many sites (Bronk, 1935), and in a number of instances neuron units of sensory innervation have been determined.

The plexiform or ramifying type of sensory innervation with free nerve terminals, has been subjected to such analysis in four sites. Adrian, Cattell, and Hoagland (1931) have outlined on the frog's skin areas of terminal distribution of single afferent neurons sensitive to touch which Rubin and Syrocki (1936) later identified with free nerve endings in the epidermis. The areas defined ranged from 4 to 100 sq. mm., but actually, since the demonstration depended on bifurcation of sensory axons close to the dorsal root ganglion, the two branches then diverging into different divisions of the spinal nerve, the terminal field outlined for one branch was presumably only a portion of the fiber's total field. In the frog's viscera the terminal distributions of single afferent fibers have been worked out by myself (Tower, 1933). Some of these were surprisingly large, often covering 2 or 3 sq. cm. and not infrequently twice that area. In contrast, the fields of presumed touch fibers in the cat's tongue examined cursorily by Pfaffmann (1939) were fairly small, ranging around 5 mm. in diameter. Because the sensory innervation of the frog's viscera is capable, under proper stimulation, of giving rise to nociceptive reactions, presumably some of the afferent units examined, most likely those yielding smaller impulses, were units for pain reception. But to bring an uncomplicated and unquestioned receptive mechanism for pain under examination the cat's cornea was used (Tower, 1935, 1940). Since the reactions of laboratory mammals to stimulation in this field recapitulate those of the human, and since the sensibility there present in the human is pain, it may be inferred that in laboratory mammals the sensibility involved is likewise pain.

The mammalian cornea exposes for examination an uncomplicated field of the ramifying or plexiform type of innervation, and except around the sclero-corneal junction, no other. Within this plexiform arrangement of nerve fibers there is no anatomical cue to the neuron units. The nerve fibers entering into this innervation are derived from the ophthalmic division of the Vth cranial nerve via the long ciliary nerves. These penetrate the eyeball in variable number around the optic nerve, and run foreward in the sclera to enter the cornea circumferentially around the sclero-corneal junction. The further organization within the cornea has already been described. To isolate and identify the neurosensory units in this innervation, arrangements were made to amplify and record the action potentials in the long ciliary nerves of de-cerebrated cats in conjunction with stimulation of the cornea. For lead, fine filaments of long ciliary nerves were used when present; otherwise the nerves were cut down until only 2 or 3 fibers remained active. Vacuum tube amplification and oscillo-graphic recording were used, and photographic records made. The stimulators employed included a set of von Frey needles, a corresponding set of hairs, a mechanical stimulator delivering a prick of variable but controllable intensity, and blunt glass rods.

The nerve impulses from receptors in the cornea constituted a graded series from moderately large to quite small. All were spikes, and by comparison with Zotterman's (1939) records of C-fiber activity from stimulation of the cat's skin, all probably represented activity in medullated fibers. The responses obtained using the different stimulators were essentially similar; a train of impulses of rapidly diminishing frequency, or occasionally, with threshold stimulation, a single impulse only. Initial frequency and duration of the discharge were both functions of the intensity of the stimulus when this was very brief. With continued stimula-tion, the same held, but the discharge steadily diminished, some-times to cease entirely in a few seconds, sometimes to establish a level of activity sustained for as long as the stimulation lasted. Removing the stimulus after adaptation had begun, commonly caused a second small outburst. It was notable that some fiber terminals adapted rapidly and completely to a given stimulus while others did not.

Isolated thus by attack on the nerve, one fiber of the type yielding fairly large impulses was found to be distributed over roughly a quadrant of the cornea and usually over the adjacent sclera and conjunctiva. Within this large area were parts not supplied by the fiber in question, but perhaps in a 2-fiber prepara-tion by the second of the survivors. When many fibers remained active the territories of a number of these, seemingly a very large number, interlocked or overlapped inextricably. Low threshold and slow adaptation characterized the central regions of the terminal fields of individual fibers, and rapid adaptation more than high threshold, the peripheral parts. Fibers of small impulse size appeared, in general, to have less extensive terminals than those of larger impulse size, though it was difficult to be certain of the individual with these small impulses. Plate 5 (central inset) shows some of the features of this activity.

Within the terminal ramification of one nerve fiber local conditions influenced both the initial frequency and the duration of discharge resulting from a given stimulation, and at best, adjacent parts of a fiber's field were rarely equally responsive. Adaptation and fatigue were spatially restricted processes. Thus a series of stimuli which rapidly produced fatigue if directed to one spot in a fiber's field, failed to do so if spaced over the territory. Similarly, when, with continued stimulation, adaptation was complete, a second stimulus directed perhaps no more than a millimeter from the first in the same terminal, provoked a fresh, vigorous discharge over the same nerve fiber.

Yet the separate regions of one nerve terminal were not entirely independent. From time to time preparations were obtained in which a nerve fiber, or some part of its terminal, discharged spontaneously and rhythmically 1 to 8 times a second, sometimes for hours. Stimulation in the corneal field of such a fiber elicited the usual outburst of impulses, but thereafter the spontaneous firing slowed or ceased, sometimes for many seconds. Plate 6 shows this phenomenon. Stimulation anywhere within the extensive field of such a fiber produced this effect, and in proportion only to the intensity of the discharge called forth, while excitation of other fibers within the area was quite without such result. A similar effect was reported by Cattell and Hoagland (1931) for the frog's tactile receptors; impulses fired antidromically into the terminal over the trunk fiber reduced the excitability of all parts of the receptor.

Putting these facts together, the nerve ending in the cornea emerges as all the terminal ramifications of one nerve fiber. This is a unit, activity in any part of which conditions the whole. Moreover there is no evidence that activity in this unit influences in any way the activity of other spatially interlocked units. Functionally, the corneal sensory receptive mechanism is an aggregate of units and not a continuum. Nevertheless, within the neuron terminal there are differences between center and periphery such that the frequency, duration, and rate of adaptation of the train of impulses conducted to the central nervous system is determined, not alone by the intensity of stimulation but also by the site. This functional differentiation, which may well have a structural basis, introduces a new factor into the central evaluation of peripheral stimulation which may permit of central analysis of peripheral locus on other than a one site : one fiber relationship, and more in line with current thinking about function in the nervous system. Before developing this theory of spatial discrimination, however, the relevant anatomical data should be presented.

Morphology of Pain Innervation in Relation to Pain Sensibility in the Skin

Since the work on the cornea was done, delimiting the unit of pain reception by physiological procedure, the anatomical groundwork has, as it were, been laid under it by the painstaking researches of Woollard and his collaborators, and, following his untimely death, by Weddell and his. Some of the methods and results of this work have already been presented : those bearing on the problem of the locus of pain reception in the skin. In these studies, both human skin and skin of various animals has been examined, using as histological technique largely intravital methylene blue.

Approaching the problem of the constitution of the sensory plexuses in the skin phylogenetically, Weddell (1941a) found that a cutaneous nerve plexus in which stem fibers dichotomize, and interlock, and give rise to free nerve terminals or terminal nets beneath and in the deeper epithelial layers, is common to both ends of the scale – to the elasmobranch fish and to man. In the elasmobranch this is the only type of cutaneous innervation present. The rabbit, monkey, and man possess additional sets of nerve fibers and types of ending.

To follow the ramification of individual stem fibers in these cutaneous innervations to their endings, both to the free type and to some of the more specialized forms, Woollard and his coworkers, and after him Weddell and his, examined specimens of skin from areas of partial innervation produced either by severing a cutaneous nerve, or as found in the margins of artificially produced skin ulcers. In skin from such areas in rabbits, either from the margins of ulcers on the ears, or from the thoracic areas of overlap following avulsion of intercostal nerves, Woollard, Weddell, and Harpman (1940) found that ramifying fibers from the adjacent innervated area extended into the partially denervated area for variable distances, averaging 1 mm. in the ear and as much as 3 to 5 mm. over the thorax. These fibers supplied free nerve terminals to both the deeper epidermal and subepidermal tissues. Stimulation of these nerve fibers or terminals in lightly anesthetized animals gave rise to struggling. Similar examination of human skin taken distal to an ulcer on the forearm, skin which had previously been shown to be sensitive only to pain, likewise contained only fine fibers giving rise to subepidermal and intra-epidermal nerve endings.

Substantiating this work Weddell (1941a), and Weddell, Guttmann, and Gutmann (1941) found that the number of nerve fibers and nerve terminals diminished progressively throughout a marginal zone from innervated to denervated territory until isolated terminals only could be found. The isolated free terminal nets, stimulation of which Woollard *et al.* had previously shown gave rise to nociceptive responses in the rabbit, invariably extended farther into the area of denervation than did terminals about hairs.

Both Woollard and Weddell agree that individual nerve fibers never anastomose in their terminal distributions (reversing Woollard's previous opinion, 1937); that is, they are never syncytial. Contrarily, the terminal net of a single fiber may show frequent anastomosis.

Another feature of cutaneous sensory innervation stressed by Weddell (1941a, b, and c) is the multiple innervation of every part by separate neurons bearing similar terminals. In the plexiform ramifications this is accomplished by overlapping and interlocking of the separate ramifying unit terminals, a feature which was outstanding in the physiological study of the corneal innervation. Correspondingly, each hair follicle is innervated by branches of from 2 to 7 stem fibers, while each stem fiber is distributed to a number (up to 300 on the rabbit's ear) of follicles. With encapsulated endings such as those of Krause or Meissner a similar result is achieved by clustering the end organs, each of which is supplied by a separate trunk fiber. Moreover, the stem fibers to any given territory approach from various directions, sometimes running recurrent courses of considerable length in small nerve trunks, thus offering a basis for the fact that small incisions in the skin rarely denervate any area. This anatomical demonstration of multiple or overlapping innervation as a general feature of cutaneous innervation, which Boring[1] long ago

1. 'A more satisfactory theory is one which assumes that single sensory spots are innervated by more than one nerve fiber, that the multiple innervation is projected upon the central nervous system as multiple excitations. . . .' Boring, 1916, p. 99.

suspected, disposes finally of the one spot: one fiber concept of cutaneous innervation, and at once raises the question what is the basis of the 'spot' as a cutaneous sensory phenomenon. On this point Woollard and his associates (1940 p. 428), correlating their histological and physiological findings, had already written:

In the rabbit, the nerve fibers presumably subserving pain dichotomize repeatedly, innervating relatively large areas of skin. The extent to which the fibers in question overlap towards denervated areas is also indicative of the relatively large area of skin supplied by the terminals of one such fiber. In man, the distance to which the nerve fibers and endings subserving pain overlap those subserving other cutaneous sensations is of the same order as the minimum distance at which two simultaneously applied stimuli arousing pain of equal intensity are perceived individually. This distance is as much as 1–1·2 cm. on the forearm. The facts suggest that, in man, a nerve fiber subserving pain derived from one dorsal root ganglion cell supplies a considerable area of skin. Thus, although cutaneous sensation has been found to be punctate, this does not imply that each spot contains a receptor derived from a separate neurone.

Weddell (1941a) has subsequently contributed more quantitative data on the size of the net terminating an individual fiber. On the back of the hand in man it covers an area of approximately 0·75 cm. greatest diameter, which is about the limen of two-point discrimination for pain in that region. On the monkey's thumb it is only 1·5 mm. in diameter, slightly smaller than the limen of two-point discrimination in this region in man.

Pain Reception in Deep Tissues

Although sensory mechanisms in the deeper somatic tissues and in the viscera have been extensively investigated both histologically and by impulse recording technique, little of this work relates to pain mechanism, and the unit of pain reception has nowhere been worked out. In my study (1933) of the action potentials elicited by stimulation of frog's viscera, slow impulses were found to be excited by harmful stimuli such as crushing, burning, and tearing. Moreover, such stimuli, when applied to decerebrate or despinal frogs evoked nociceptive reflexes, both somatic and visceral. But the areal distribution of the small fibers conducting these impulses was in no case accurately determined. There is, however, not much doubt that visceral pain is served by ramifying nerve fibers with free terminals, such as were found in the frog's viscera in this study, and have been repeatedly described elsewhere.

For the deeper somatic tissues Weddell and Harpman (1940) have described in methylene blue preparations of human deep fascia and periosteum interlocking terminal nerve nets deriving from fine medullated and from non-medullated nerve fibers, in conjunction with a study of the pain sensations which may be evoked from human deep tissues. The pain is of two sorts, prick pain, fairly well localized though with some misreferences, and a diffuse and very unpleasant aching. Working, apparently, with this latter pain, Mendelson (data reported by Bazett, 1934) found a mean value for the conduction velocity of the sensory impulses involved of 6 meters per second; definitely a slow mechanism, but still not slow enough for the non-medullated, or C group. However, such a mean figure cannot assure the type of fiber concerned, for a mixture of medullated and non-medullated fibers in proper proportion could be, and probably is behind it. Kellgren (1938) previously had described the sharply localized quality of pain from fascia and tendon, in contrast with pain from skeletal muscle which is diffuse and often referred in a characteristic segmental pattern.

Obviously much work remains to be done on the pain receptive mechanism of deeper tissues, but it seems likely that differences between superficial and deep pain sensibility will result more from differences in the central analyser mechanism than from fundamental differences in the peripheral receptor.

Bearing of the Anatomical and Physiological Evidence Presented on the Border Zone Produced by Peripheral Nerve Lesions

Following lesions of peripheral nerves in man, the border zone between innervated and denervated territory is an area of peculiar sensibility. There are many discrepancies in the accounts of the peculiarities given by different observers; Rivers and Head (Head; 1920), Trotter and Davies (1909), Boring (1916), and Lanier, Carney, and Wilson (1935). Some of these discrepancies may represent differences in technique of examination; some, of viewpoint. The histological and physiological evidence presented previously in this paper has a definite bearing on some of the problems involved.

Obviously the fact that the freely ramifying cutaneous innervation serving pain reception extends farther from an area of innervation into the territory of a cut nerve than other types of cutaneous innervation underlies the outstanding phenomena of the border zone which is the retention of pain sensibility, however modified. Moreover, in the disagreement which exists between Head and Rivers on the one hand, and Trotter and Davies and Boring on the other, the former workers describing the border zone as an area of dissociated sensibility, pain alone remaining, whereas the latter two groups of workers describe it as a zone of progressively deepening hypoaesthesia to all forms of sensibility, the histological evidence presented, and physiological evidence as well, fits better with the first view. Actually, Weddell, Guttmann, and Gutmann's (1941) description of such a zone in the rabbit, showing hair follicle terminals disappearing first, and free terminals later, splits the difference between the two views. Both sensory supplies, and presumably both touch and pain sensibility overlap somewhat, but the large neuron units for pain reception overlap more generously than do the presumably smaller units serving touch. Unfortunately Weddell, Guttmann, and Gutmann (1941) did not say over what extent of rabbit's skin the 300 hair follicles innervated by one nerve fiber might be distributed, and there is little data on the actual size of any touch units. Pfaffmann (1939), as previously mentioned, gave them as about 5 mm. in diameter on the cat's tongue. Touch units in the frog's skin (Adrian, Cattell, and Hoagland, 1931) may measure 100 sq. mm. For man, there is no accurate data – only prejudice in favor of a small unit.

The physiological and anatomical evidence is not without its discrepancies, however. Adrian (1931) demonstrated that slow fiber innervation carried by the ulnar nerve in cats, overlaps the territory of the median nerve extensively, whereas fast fiber innervation stops abruptly at the median axis of the foreleg. Hogg (1935) similarly showed that in the frog's skin the slow fibers carried by a dorsal cutaneous nerve are distributed more extensively than the fast fibers. Generally speaking, the slow fibers in question provoke pain reactions, though not exclusively such, and the fast fibers, touch reactions. Yet, in Woollard's (1940) study it was superficial pain, which is first and fast, which overlapped the border farthest. In the cat's cornea also (Tower, 1940), where the overlap between the fields of the medial and lateral long ciliary nerves is 2 to 3 mm. in the vertical meridian, the most conspicuous overlap was made by the terminals of the fibers of largest impulse size. The resolving factor in these apparent discrepancies may be that where a fast fiber pain mechanism is present, as it certainly is in the human skin and in the cat's cornea, this has the most extensive overlap, whereas where no such fast pain mechanism is in evidence, as in Adrian's work on the cat's foreleg and Hogg's on the frog's skin, one measures only the overlap of the slow system. In Woollard's (1940) experiments on the border zone on his own forearm between medial and lateral cutaneous nerves, the total width of the zone was 2 cm. Deep pain was elicited in diminishing intensity over slightly more than the first centimeter, superficial pain over the entire breadth, whereas touch stopped abruptly at the median line, apparently without much previous diminishment. Although these observations open up questions for further investigation, nevertheless the total picture presented by this new work puts the border zone on a firmer anatomical and physiological foundation.

In contrast with the progress which seems to have been made in interpreting the border zone resulting from peripheral nerve lesions, the reverse condition which follows on dorsal root lesions, in which the area of insensibility to touch is larger than that to pain, still remains one of the most perplexing problems in the field of cutaneous innervation. Histological examination of skin from such territories should be most illuminating for the light it would throw on the underlying anatomical conditions, but unfortunately such examinations do not seem to have been made.

Problems of Relation Between Pain Reception and Reception of Other Modalities

Foremost among these problems is the controversy long standing between von Frey and Goldscheider: Is pain a sensation, *sui generis*, or does it develop from a threshold sensation which is tactile or contact or pressure in quality? Von Frey (1894) expounded the view that pain is an independent modality; Goldscheider, that it is part of a pressure–pain continuum of experience. The cornea was one site where these, and other contenders took a stand, von Frey insisting that corneal sensation is wholly painful; Goldscheider (1920), that it has an underlying pressure quality. With the development of Sjöqvist's operation for relief of trigeminal pain, cutting the descending root of the Vth nerve in the medulla, the reality of this underlying sensation has been demonstrated. The cornea is then, after tractotomy, insensitive to pain, but retains some touch sense. A number of investigators have now established this fact, beginning with Rowbotham (1939). Grant and Weinberger (1941) report that in a majority of cases even with complete analgesia of the ophthalmic division of the

101

Vth nerve the blink reflex is elicitable. A similar relation between a threshold touch sensation and pain has been insistently claimed for the skin in general. Indeed, Heinbecker, Bishop, and O'Leary (1934) go so far as to state 'Sensibility of the skin consists of four fundamental modalities – touch, pricking touch, warmth and cold. Pain is the affective quality resulting from a more than threshold stimulation of the pricking touch group.' The interpretation of the threshold response must be, finally, a function of the central nervous system. The problem for us is: how is it peripherally conditioned?

Single induction shocks applied to the free nerve endings are felt. Both Heinbecker and Bishop (1935) and Lewis and Pochin (1937) agree to this. But Heinbecker and Bishop, with their orientation to the problem of the threshold experience had the experience of threshold contact, while Lewis and Pochin, with their interest in the two pains, observed that the pain was 'first pain' only. Here may be a clue.

Turning now to some casual statements of both Gad and Goldscheider (1892) and Lewis and Pochin (1937) concerning the double pain response from skin on which their investigations were focused: the first response, they say, may be touch or pain, and is easily passed over as pain, whereas the second is unequivocally pain at all times. If one considers that these two pains, epithelial and subepithelial, may represent activity in separate pain receptive mechanisms, the first served by fairly good-sized, medullated, 'fast' nerve fibers, the second by unmedullated or by quite small medullated and 'slow' fibers, and if one considers, furthermore, that the sensory innervation of the cornea, and indeed, the sensory division of the Vth cranial nerve as a whole including its descending root is characterized by a greater proportion of myelinated to unmyelinated nerve fibers than sensory innervation elsewhere over the body, a possible correlation begins to emerge. The fast fiber system to skin, together with the myelinated pain innervation to the cornea which also ends intraepithelially, seem to have the threshold touch or contact quality. Indeed, were the problem reinvestigated, correlating the threshold sensation and the course of adaptation with the superficial or deep locus of excitation of the sensation, and with the fast or slow character of the mediating nerve fibers, much of the confusion might be cleared up. My suspicion is that 'first pain', 'superficial pain', and 'fast pain' have a contact quality at threshold and during adaptation, whereas deep, slow, second pain does not. In line with this Goldscheider himself (1920, p. 17) admitted that some pain spots did not have a threshold pressure sensation, and in these the pain appeared only after a latent period, that is, late.

Another, longstanding, but still unsettled controversy concerns whether or not overstimulation of other modalities than pain, of the specific receptors for touch, cold, warmth, and perhaps for light and sound registers as painful. Pain in this relation might be considered the affective quality resulting from much more than threshold stimulation of such receptors.

With respect to the specific touch receptors including hairs the evidence is various and fairly conclusive. Cattell and Hoagland (1931) stimulated tactile receptors of frogs with an interrupted jet of air at frequencies as high as 250–300 per second without eliciting any pain reaction. This, for the frog, is close to the top rate of conduction possible to nerve fibers. Similarly, stimulating the hairs of a cat by a vibrating rod never produced evidence of pain no matter how great the frequency (Adrian, 1931). A similar demonstration could very easily be made with man, and more conclusively, but I cannot find that it has been. Nevertheless, over-stimulation in itself does not appear to be a condition inevitably resulting in pain.

The pain associated with intense heat or cold stimulation, especially when these are applied as radiant heat or cold, avoiding contact or mechanical concomitants, raises questions more in line with the trend of this paper's discussion. To begin with, Dallenbach, in conjunction with two of his students (Stone and Dallenbach, 1934, for heat; and Edes and Dallenbach, 1936, for cold) showed that from slowly increasing degrees of warm and hot, or cool and cold, pain gradually emerges, grows in intensity, remains at a high degree for a time, and then gradually subsides into decreasing degrees of hot and warm or cold and cool. In their view pain culminates the temperature experience. Some other investigators, Trotter and Davies (1909) for example, believe that hot and cold are themselves combined experiences respectively, of warm and pain and cool and pain. With increasing intensity, then, the temperature sensation disappears and only burning pain remains.

Possible neurohistological bases for these phenomena invite consideration. There has been a natural suspicion that the fine accessory fibers sometimes found in encapsulated organs such as Krause's end bulbs or Meissner's corpuscles, fibers which Lavrenko (1938) recently showed to be of somatic, not sympathetic derivation, might serve pain reception, and the main fibers the specialized sense. Woollard, Weddell, and Harpman (1940) commented on the similarity of the accessory fibers and endings to the fibers and free nerve endings of the subepidermal plexus. Similarly, fine fibers in hair follicles might serve pain reception, as well as fine nerve fibers in muscle spindles and other deeply situated receptors. These need not necessarily be separate fibers. There is no reason why a branch of a fiber, or a portion of a terminal supplying the general vicinity should not be included in the specialized receptor to serve its pain reception. If this be true, the individual nerve fiber is still specific in that it mediates one sense only, but the end organ as a whole is compound. This presupposes that pain fibers respond to a wide range of stimuli, including mechanical and thermal disturbances, which is certainly the case for the frog's skin (Adrian, 1931). Against this as a generality, is Nafe and Wagoner's (1937) demonstration that the corneal sensory mechanism of man is insensitive not only to heat but also to the pain of excessive temperature stimulation; evidence that pain terminals are not, in themselves, everywhere sensitive to heat. Are there, possibly, various pain endings differentially responsive to different stimuli? Where specialized end organs for temperature reception are concerned, the vascular and connective tissue arrangements of these may serve in some unknown fashion to make both the main nerve fiber, which registers as warm, and the accessory fiber, which registers as pain, discharge under the same stimulating conditions.

In the light of these speculations it is interesting to reconsider briefly Head's well-known triangle of epicritic sensibility; an area on his wrist produced by section of a cutaneous nerve, which was devoid of pain sensibility and of sensibility to hot and cold, though touch, warm and cool were appreciated. Being devoid of pain innervation, it might be thought that no 'accessory' pain fibers would be incorporated in, or related to the specific temperature receptors. In consequence while warm and cool could be appreciated, it might be expected that hot and cold could not. An anatomical check on the nerve endings in the skin in such an area should show the correctness or the error of this hypothesis. Five of Head and Sherren's patients had similar areas of dissociated sensibility (Head, 1920, pp. 112, 113, 156, 158, 218); and dorsal root lesions show it over much more extensive areas.

The Pain Receptor and the Nocifensor System

The experimental work of Sir Thomas Lewis and his colleagues on pain is of such a quality, and the enlargement of our concepts resulting from it so great, that one regrets having to attack the total structure at any point. Nevertheless it has fathered an anatomical monstrosity in the 'nocifensor' system. Lewis (1936, 1942) and his group have, to my mind, unquestionably demonstrated that there is distributed in the skin a system of nerve fibers deriving from the dorsal roots, having an arborescing pattern of terminal distribution and not forming a syncytium. This system he has called the 'nocifensor' system, considering it to have no afferent function relative to the central nervous system, but to be concerned with the spread of cutaneous hyperalgesia. Anatomists, in general, have not accepted the concept of the nocifensor system for there is nothing in their experience to validate it. Woollard, Weddell, and Harpman (1940) come out unequivocally: ' "Nocifensor" reactions are mediated by the nerve apparatus subserving pain.' Nevertheless anatomists, and objecting physiologists also, have not faced some of the implications of their rejection.

Lewis' (1936, pp. 400–1) arguments for separating the nocifensor and pain systems is briefly put. The grounds are classical.

Hyperalgesia such as we are discussing may reasonably be conceived to be the ultimate result of a reduction in the threshold of sensory nerves subserving pain; but such a conception should not be allowed to mislead us into believing that pain nerves form the system through which the local state underlying hyperalgesia is provoked. Consideration will indeed show that the nerves in question cannot be those concerned with the conveyance of pain impressions from the skin, for these, as is indicated by observations recorded in an appendix, are accurately located by the subject, which could not be the case if the corresponding impulse entered a system of branching axons connecting to a wide area of skin.

Turning to the appendix (p. 414 [not included here]) the accuracy of this localization is given as 1 cm. or less on the fingers and hand. It was to preserve a theory of spatial discrimination then, that the nocifensor system was postulated. If spatial discrimination could be put on a basis whereby it is not a function of individual neuron units, not its limen dependent on their size, then the concept of a nocifensor system would no longer be required to protect an outmoded theory. The demonstration of overlap as a striking and general feature of innervation of both skin and cornea permits, and very nearly requires a new theory of spatial discrimination based on analysis of a pattern of activity in overlapping neuron units. Such a theory was developed for the corneal innervation (Tower, 1940) when the size of the neuron units and their extensive overlap was first appreciated.

If the nocifensor concept be abandoned, and the fiber system to which it is applied be recognized as identical with the pain receptive mechanism, and if, further, Lewis' reconstruction of the system be accepted as correct, that the neuron units with terminal ramification are not syncytial, and that spread throughout the system is by nerve pathways, then it follows that the maximal areas of hyperalgesic spread give us data on the size of the largest pain terminals, or neuron units for pain reception in any area under investigation. In an experiment in which cutaneous hyperalgesia is produced by pinching or faradizing or otherwise injuring the skin in a small area, assuming that every pain terminal which overlaps the spot of origin becomes hyperalgesic throughout its full extent, then the diameters of the largest pain units will be represented by the radii from the spot where the hyperalgesia was excited to the boundaries of its maximal spread. From the data presented, some of these unit neuron terminals on the human forearm must be 9 to 12 cm. long by 3 to 4 cm. wide if spread is confined to neurons innervating the site of initiation. Alternatively, the hyperalgesia-producing substance presumed to be liberated in this spread may activate, and thus recruit additional neuron units. Knowing what we now do of the intricate interlocking of the terminals of separate neurons, this is not difficult to imagine, though no form of interaction between the units has yet been demonstrated. It is more difficult to imagine, were this recruitment to take place, what could then stop the spread of hyperalgesia over the entire body.

The question is, can we conceive of sensory receptive units of this order of magnitude on the basis of present evidence? The largest units yet demonstrated are those in the frog's viscera, 6 sq. cm. in area, and on the frog's skin, 1 sq. cm., the latter, however, representing only part of a fiber's field. I have already pointed out that the largest neuron units in the cat's cornea were never fully explored in their spread over the conjunctiva and sclera. Neuron units of the size contemplated would quite defy histological identification even by such painstaking technique as Woollard and Weddell have developed. Lewis' evidence must be accepted as the most unassailable yet offered. However, experiments to determine whether or not units of this size do exist, should not be difficult. Leading from few-fiber preparations of cutaneous nerves in cats, monkeys, chimpanzees, or even possibly man, the total field of unit terminals could be fully explored and outlined. If these extended over the border zone, moreover, one could be virtually certain that the terminals in question served pain. Furthermore, a correlation of these terminals with the presumed nocifensor system might be possible by repeating the procedures productive of hyperalgesia. The chimpanzee's forearm, a relatively hairless area, would be excellent for such studies. Until these experiments are done, however, it will probably be only the bold or foolhardy who think of neuron units of pain reception of such magnitude, and perhaps only myself.

The Pain Receptor in Relation to the Punctiform Concept of Cutaneous Sensibility

The punctate concept of cutaneous sensory innervation has been one of those ambiguous formulations which is right enough to have survived, and yet never clear-cut. Yet this very ambiguity has stimulated, and continues to stimulate much good anatomical and physiological work, especially in pursuit of the receptor presumed to underlie the spot. At the time the punctate concept was established, by Blix (1884–5) first, and after him by von Frey and his students chiefly, it was thought that the single spot, or at most the group of spots involved in the limit of spatial discrimination, the circle of Weber, was innervated by a single nerve fiber which, in turn, made connection with other nerve fibers ascending the neural axis in chain formation finally to reach the cerebral cortex, where a disturbance initiated at the cutaneous end of this chain would be interpreted and localized. It was never clearly formulated that the 'spot' makes its appearance only at this level; that it is an aspect of consciousness.

As neurophysiological technique and thinking have developed it has become increasingly clear that by and large the nervous system does not operate in a simple chain fashion. Rather, it operates on the principle of analysis or synthesis of constellations of activity in many nerve cells and fibers. This is becoming increasingly apparent in studies of motor function such as those of Lorente de Nó on the oculo-motor mechanism and of Lloyd on the spinal cord, but it has been most clearly demonstrated in the sensory field in Talbot and Marshall's (1941) brilliant work on the visual system. In this development the chains have been largely replaced by reverberating circuits. Even the spinal cord under some conditions backfires into the peripheral afferent system after receipt of a volley of incoming sensory impulses.

That the spot is an entity in consciousness I shall not question.

It does not follow, however, that the spot need be an element in peripheral innervation. And the current status of the anatomical and physiological evidence bearing on the pain mechanism certainly gives no indication of spot organization in the periphery. The pain spot now becomes a sensory concept, along with hot and cold as previously discussed, and according to Bazett (1934), also cutaneous pressure; all at one time thought to be entities in the periphery. Consciousness may be imagined to synthesize the sensory impressions coming in over the multiplicity of fibers innervating any normal area of skin into the concept of a point which is then projected onto the periphery for the specific purpose of localization. The automatic treatment of a painful stimulus, after withdrawal, is quite different. An area is rubbed, and as everyone experiences, once the spot is located, the feeling tends to irradiate.

That the cortex does indeed, for purposes of localization, operate with a concept of the surface of the body composed of a mosaic of points is indicated in current work by Bishop (personal communication) using a high voltage spark as stimulus, without touching the skin. With this form of excitation some points are easier to stimulate than others, and pain much easier than touch, but so far, points on areas up to over a centimeter across seem all to be referred to the same locus and have the same properties.

In this connection it is, perhaps, significant that Hardy, Wolff, and Goodell (1940) have shown for the pain of radiant heat that threshold is independent of spatial summation, leaving spatial summation available for other interpretation. This is not the case with the heat sensation, itself. And heat is also that one of the four accepted modalities least clearly localized in spots.

A New Theory of Spatial Analysis in the Pain Receptive Mechanism

When it became clear in studying the corneal sensory mechanism (Tower, 1940) that wide distribution of a neuron unit terminal, and extensive overlapping of many such units, were the elements of design of this peripheral sensory innervation, a new theory of spatial analysis was constructed taking advantage of these newly established conditions even though the cornea is itself an area of poor spatial localization. On this basis, locus discrimination, and probably also two point discrimination and areal analysis, could be carried out in any area innervated as is the cornea, provided, of course, the central nervous system were organized for, and trained in such analysis for the peripheral innervation in question. The theory is based in the periphery on both physiological and anatomical considerations.

In discussing the action of the sense organs Adrian (1932, pp. 28–9) pointed out that with intense stimulation the frequency of discharge from a sensory organ can be made to rise to a value very little below the maximum frequency for nerve, and on this basis suggested that rapid and slow discharges may not arise from the same point. There may be a gradual transition from nerve fiber to nerve ending with a gradual slowing of time relations, and an intense stimulus may take effect at a point where recovery is rapid. Applying this to the corneal innervation: If the unit terminal is an arborization wherein a stem fiber, which may or may not be myelinated, divides into branches successively finer out to the ultimate free terminal or closed mesh, with or without mesh connections in the previous orders of branching, then a strong stimulus near the point of entrance of the trunk fiber into its terminal ramification might be expected to push frequency to the limit permitted by the refractory properties of that fiber. The maximal frequency of about 500 per second in the response from the cornea suggests such a limitation. On the other hand, since the nerve fiber begins to divide fairly deeply, the deformation of a feeble stimulus at that site could not be expected to affect the trunk fiber, but only the more strategically situated and finer superficial ramifications. If fineness imposes slowness, the slow train in response to a weak stimulus is accounted for. On the periphery of a fiber's field, even intense stimulation could be expected to affect only the fringe of the arborization, again presumably fine and of slow properties. Correspondingly, stimulation on such a periphery in the cornea, no matter how intense, provoked a brief, widely spaced train of impulses or one impulse only, like threshold or contact stimulation in the center of the fiber's field. If the individual arborization becomes intraepithelial both superficially and at the periphery, a point on which there is as yet no evidence for the cornea but suggestive evidence for the skin in Woollard, Weddell, and Harpman's (1940) finding that superficial pain extends farther into a hypoanesthetic area than deep pain, this might account for the similar rapid adaptation in these two sites in contrast with the slow or incomplete adaptation in the central area. For Hoagland (1936) has related the rapid adaptation of the frog's touch fibers, by comparison with the slow adaptation of deeper lying fibers which presumably serve pain to the rapid liberation of large amounts of potassium by deformed epithelial cells and not by the deeper tissues when similarly stimulated.

These possibilities of correlated structural and functional differentiation within the neuron unit terminal whereby the frequency of the train of impulses conducted to the central nervous system is determined not alone by the intensity of stimulation but also by the site, might, in a field of overlapping unit terminals, be made the basis of locus discrimination in the following fashion. By central analysis of a pattern of excitation wherein fibers excited minimally encircle fibers more strongly excited, localization might well be arrived at, yet the frequency of discharge in the individual fiber or fibers most strongly excited still serve to indicate the intensity of the stimulation as has hitherto been assumed. Moreover, with destruction of the patterns of overlapping fibers in areas of partial denervation, the basis for such spatial analysis would be disordered, or even eliminated. For an area of partial innervation with some overlap remaining, the central analysing mechanism including the cerebral cortex would have to come to its interpretations on incomplete data, as judged by normal standards. That the judgments should be less acute and often in error is therefore not surprising. And were overlap eliminated or virtually so, no localization should be possible.

This concept of locus discrimination, and of its impairment in areas of partial denervation, is equally applicable to any modality of sensation where the terminal distribution of unit neurons overlaps, regardless of whether the overlap be of large or small free ramifications, or of the multiple supply of a number of hair follicles or Krause's end bulbs or other encapsulated end organs, or even of hair cells in the organ of Corti, or rods or cones in the retina. It is in fact, in relation to the visual receptors that Talbot and Marshall (1941) have given us some insight into how the central nervous system might carry out analysis of the pattern of stimulation in the overlapping units.

Heretofore this paper has attempted to draw together relevant anatomical and physiological observations to create a working concept of a sensory receptive mechanism for pain. The glaring inadequacies and inconsistencies in the fabric of evidence have not been disguised, but neither have they been stressed. In attempting to apply the theory of spatial analysis as a general theory one is made acutely aware of these deficiencies. To begin with the evidence on the size of the single pain terminal is far from complete. Even in the cornea the larger terminals were not fully outlined in their spread onto the sclera and conjunctiva. In neurohistological work, one does not know how many branchings a given fiber may have undergone before it enters the field of microscopic observation. We know that nerve fibers branch even in the main nerve trunks, though probably not extensively. Several long-reach axon reflexes which are physiological evidence of such branching in the sensory system, have been discussed in the paper on the cornea. Only Lewis' work on the spread of hyperalgesia seems to hold out a measure of the largest pain terminals. On the other hand, not all pain units, at least in the cornea, are large. And we are not forced to consider spatial analysis solely on the basis of overlap in the largest endings. The finer the grain, so to speak, of the overlapping pattern, presumably the finer the analysis which would be arrived at. The greater accuracy of spatial analysis with touch than with pain presumably depends on just such anatomical difference.

Before we can arrive at a judgment whether or not the theory of spatial discrimination developed in this paper could be generally valid for cutaneous sensibility, a great deal more evidence is required. First of all the uncertainty should be settled for the three main aspects of spatial analysis: localization of one point, discrimination and localization of 2 points simultaneously applied, and areal estimation or analysis of many points: which of the modalities permit of, or cooperate in such analysis. There are discrepancies of observation between Head, and Trotter and Davies, and Boring, especially with regard to 2-point discrimination, which should be reinvestigated. The paucity of quantitative data on the size of the neurosensory units for touch has been pointed out. For heat and cold there is no such data. Without underestimating the desirability of new information bearing on the relations between morphologically specific nerve endings and the reception of specific modalities of sensibility, neuroanatomy, with neurophysiology, has now entered a phase in which quantitative as well as qualitative considerations must be taken into account if working concepts of function in the nervous system are to develop further.

Summary

Anatomical and physiological studies currently have converged to establish, for the peripheral sensory receptive mechanism for pain, that the element or unit in this organization is, not a spot innervated by a particular nerve fiber, but an area of terminal distribution of a unit neuron of variable extent but of much more than spot dimensions; to be measured in square millimeters or centimeters. This terminal, together with its fiber, cell body, and central processes constitutes a neurosensory unit for the modality in question. In any area of normally innervated skin or cornea many such unit terminals overlap and interlock intricately, but there is no fusion. Indeed, evidence of any form of interaction is still lacking. In such a widespread and overlapping peripheral sensory innervation, spatial analysis, and especially localization ceases to be conceivable on the basis of local concentration of the terminals of a single fiber. Alternatively, analysis of the pattern of responses in the overlapping fibers offers a new possibility of spatial analysis more in line with current concepts of function in the nervous system.

Discussion

Dr Joseph C. Hinsey (New York, N.Y.): I would like to state my admiration for these critical studies which Dr Tower has carried out in this most difficult field. It is very surprising and gratifying to see the way that the physiological and the anatomical studies have converged in this problem. I should like to ask whether or not, in Dr Tower's opinion, pain is conducted by fibers of large size. She spoke of myelinated fibers but didn't denote their size. She spoke of the potentials as being large potentials, but she didn't give the velocity of conduction. I don't know whether it was possible for her to measure that. But thinking back of the long discussion with regard to the functional significance of the unmyelinated fibers and of the work that Dr Ranson did over a period of years, it would be interesting to have Dr Tower's impression after the work she has done. It should be remembered that the content of unmyelinated sensory fibers in the fifth nerve in the cat is smaller than one finds in the peripheral nerves like the saphenous and other sensory nerves, and it may mean that small myelinated fibers and possibly larger ones are concerned with pain conduction there. I think we have to admit, too, that fibers of different sizes are concerned with pain conduction in other parts of the body, but I believe that this method and the observations that Dr Tower has made may throw light upon that problem.

President Wolff: Dr Tower, would you care to respond to that?

Dr Sarah S. Tower: Yes. Dr Hinsey has brought out, I think, one of the main points; that the cornea receives a fairly large proportion of myelinated nerve fibers to unmyelinated for its local innervation. Moreover, in work such as this, that is dissecting out single nerve fibers, one inevitably ends up with one of the larger fibers available; so that what I have been examining is the function of the larger fibers; fibers around seven μ according to Windle. There was a good deal of evidence that many smaller fibers were active, but anyone who has had experience with the method knows that the action potentials in very small fibers are so small that even though one has cut the nerve down until only a few fibers remain, one can't do this type of analysis accurately.

Dr R. Lorente de Nó (New York, N.Y.): There is one question I would like to ask Dr Tower. Do you have any evidence bearing on where the fibers are stimulated in the cornea? I know it is a very difficult question to answer, but in your experiments do you have any evidence whether those fibers would be stimulated all along their course or only the fine branches where the stimulation occurs, although there is no particular pain ending in the cornea. Were particular parts of the fiber more sensitive than the others? Would you care to make a correlation of this type?

Closing discussion

Dr Sarah S. Tower: I have done considerable thinking on that. Direct experimentation is difficult. I would hold with Adrian in what he has said in his little book on the mechanism of nervous action. With the contact stimulus, just a mere touch, one must believe that that part of the ramification responding is in the epithelium. The frequency of that response is always quite slow, perhaps 10 to 40 per second, and there may be not more than one impulse. But with more intense stimulation one can push the frequency up to perhaps 500 per second; that is to about the maximum frequency of the trunk fiber as it comes into such a terminal ramification, if it is a fairly good sized fiber with fast properties. If one can infer the fineness of the ramification that one is stimulating from the frequency of the response, one would judge that the contact stimulus was operating superficially where the nerve fibers are very fine, and the stronger stimulation, closer and closer to the main trunk fiber until probably the frequency of the main trunk fiber imposed the limiting factor on the frequency of response. But there is an indirect argument and not experimental evidence.

References

ADRIAN, E. D. (1931), 'The messages in sensory nerve fibers and their interpretation', *Proc. Roy. Soc. B.*, vol. 109, pp. 1–18.

ADRIAN, E. D. (1932), *The Mechanism of Nervous Action*, Univ. Penn. Press, Philadelphia.

ADRIAN, E. D., and BRONK, D. W. (1928), 'The discharge of impulses in motor nerve fibres', *J. Physiol.*, vol. 66, pp. 81–101.

ADRIAN, E. D., CATTELL, McK., and HOAGLAND, H. (1931), 'Sensory discharges in single cutaneous nerve fibres', *J. Physiol.*, vol. 72, pp. 377–91.

ATTIAS, G. (1912), 'Die Nerven der Hornhaut des Menschen', *Graefes Arch. Ophthal.*, vol. 83, pp. 207–77.

BAZETT, H. C. (1934), 'Methods of investigation of sensation in man and the theoretical value of the results obtained', *Res. Publ. Ass. Nerv. Ment. Dis.*, vol. 15, pp. 83–93.

BISHOP, G. H. (1943), Personal communication.

BLIX, M. (1884), 'Experimentelle beiträge zur Lösung der Frage über die specifische Energie der Hautnerven', *Z. Biologie*, vol. 20, pp. 141–56.

BLIX, M. (1885), 'Experimentelle Beiträge zur Lösung der Frage über die specifische Energie der Hautnerven', *Z. Biologie*, vol. 21, pp. 145–60.

BOEKE, J. (1935), 'Innervationsstudien. VIII. Zur Innervation der Cornea bei Säugern. Die Innervierung des Bindegewebes der Cornea bei Macasus rhesus'. *Z. Mikr.-Anat. Forsch.*, vol. 38, pp. 594–618.

BORING, E. G. (1916), 'Cutaneous sensation after nerve-division', *Quart. Jour. Exp. Physiol.*, vol. 10, pp. 1–95.

BRONK, D. W. (1935), 'The mechanism of sensory end organs', *Res. Publ. Ass. Nerv. Ment. Dis.*, vol. 15, pp. 60–82.

CAJAL, S. R. (1909), '*Histol. du Système Nerveux de l'Homme et des Vertébrés*' vol. I, pp. 461–4, Maione, Paris.

CATTELL, McK., and HOAGLAND, H. (1931), 'Response of tactile receptors to intermittent stimulation', *J. Physiol.*, vol. 72, pp. 392–404.

COHNHEIM, J. (1867), 'Uber die Endigung der Sensiblen Nerven in der Hornhaut', *Arch. Path. Anat., Physiol., Klin. Med.*, vol. 38, pp. 343–86.

DALLENBACH, K. M. (1939), 'Pain: history and present status', *Amer. J. Psychol.*, vol. 52, pp. 331–47.

DOGIEL, A. S. (1890), 'Die Nerven der Cornea des Menschen', *Anat. Anz.*, vol. 5, pp. 483–94.

EDES, B., and DALLENBACH, K. M. (1936), 'The adaptation of pain aroused by cold', *Amer. J. Psychol.*, vol. 48, pp. 307–15.

FREY, M. V. (1894), 'Beiträge zur Physiologie des Schmerzsinns', *Ber. Sachs. Ges. (Akad.) Wiss.*, vols. 46, 47, pp. 185–200.

GAD, J., and GOLDSCHEIDER, A. (1892), 'Ueber die Summation von Hautriezen', *Z. Klin. Med.*, vol. 20, pp. 339–73.

GOLDSCHEIDER, A. (1920), *Das Schmerzproblem*, Julius Springer, Berlin, 91 pp.

GRANT, F. C., and WEINBERGER, L. M. (1941), 'Experiences with intramedullary tractotomy. IV. Surgery of the brain stem and its operative complications', *Surg. Gynec. Obstet.*, vol. 72, pp. 747–54.

HARDY, J. D., WOLFF, H. G., and GOODELL, H. (1940), 'Studies on pain. A new method for measuring pain threshold: Observations on spatial summation of pain', *J. Clin. Invest.*, vol. 19, pp. 649–57.

HEAD, H. (1920), *Studies in Neurology*, 2 vols., Henry Frowde, Hodder and Stoughton Ltd, London.

HEINBECKER, P., and BISHOP, G. H., (1935), 'The mechanism of painful sensation', *Res. Publ. Ass. Nerv. Ment. Dis.*, vol. 15, pp. 226–38.

HEINBECKER, P., BISHOP, G. H., and O'LEARY, J., (1933), 'Pain and touch fibers in peripheral nerves', *Arch. Neurol. Psychiat.*, vol. 29, pp. 771–89.

HEINBECKER, P., BISHOP, G. H., and O'LEARY, J. (1934), 'Analysis of sensation in terms of the nerve impulse', *Arch. Neurol. Psychiat.*, Chicago, vol. 31, pp. 34–53.

HOAGLAND, H. (1936), 'On the mechanism of adaptation (peripheral sensory inhibition) of mechanoreceptors', *Cold Spr. Harb. Monogr.*, vol. 4, pp. 347–57.

HOGG, B. M. (1935), 'Slow impulses from the cutaneous nerves of the frog', *J. Physiol.*, vol. 84, pp. 250–8.

KELLGREN, J. H. (1930), 'Observations on referred pain arising from muscle', *Clin. Sci.*, vol. 3, pp. 175–90.

KUNTZ, A., and HAMILTON. J. W. (1938), 'Afferent innervation of the skin', *Anat. Rec.*, vol. 71, pp. 387–400.

LANIER, L. H., CARNEY, H. M., and WILSON, W. D. (1935), 'Cutaneous innervation. An experimental study', *Arch. Neurol. & Psychiat.*, vol. 34, pp. 1–60.

LAVRENKO, V. V. (1938), 'Participation of sympathetic nerve fibres in the structure of sensory nerve endings', *Bull. Biol. Méd. Exp.*, vol. 5, pp. 37–8.

LEWIS, T. (1936), 'Experiments relating to cutaneous hyperalgesia and its spread through somatic nerves', *Clin. Sci.*, vol. 2, pp. 373–423.

LEWIS, T. (1942), *Pain*, Macmillan Co., New York, 192 pp.

LEWIS, T., and POCHIN, E. E. (1937), 'The double pain response of the human skin to a single stimulus', *Clin. Sci.*, vol. 3, pp. 67–76.

NAFE, J. P., and WAGONER, K. S. (1937), 'The insensitivity of the cornea to heat and pain derived from high temperatures', *Amer. J. Psychol.*, vol. 64, pp. 631–5.

PFAFFMANN, C. (1939), 'Afferent impulses from the teeth due to pressure and noxious stimulation', *J. Physiol.*, vol. 97, pp. 207–19.

ROWBOTHAM, G. F. (1939), 'Observations on the effects of trigeminal denervation', *Brain*, vol. 42, pp. 364–80.

RUBIN, M. A., and SYROCKI, B. J. (1936), 'On the mechanism of adaptation of free ending tactile receptors in frog skin', *J. Cell. Comp. Physiol.*, vol. 9, pp. 29–35.

STONE, L. J., and DALLENBACH, K. M. (1934), 'Adaptation to the pain of radiant heat', *Amer. J. Psychol.*, vol. 46, pp. 229–42.

STRUGHOLD, H. (1924), 'Über die Dichte und Schwellen der Schmerzpunkte der Epidermis in den verschiedenen Körperregionen', *Z. Biol.*, vol. 80, pp. 367–80.

TALBOT, S. A., and MARSHALL, W. H. (1941), 'Physiological studies on neural mechanisms of visual localization and discrimination', *Amer. J. Ophth.*, vol. 24, pp. 1255–63.

TOWER, S. S. (1933), 'Action potentials in sympathetic nerves elicited by stimulation of frog's viscera', *J. Physiol.*, vol. 78, pp. 225–45.

TOWER, S. S. (1935), 'Nerve impulses from receptors in the cornea', *Proc. Soc. Exp. biol.*, *N.Y.*, vol. 32, pp. 590–2.

TOWER, S. S. (1940), 'Units for sensory reception in cornea; with notes on nerve impulses from sclera, iris and lens', *J. Neurophysiol.*, vol. 3, pp. 486–500.

TROTTER, W., and DAVIES, H. M. (1909), 'Experimental studies in the innervation of the skin', *J. Physiol.*, vol. 38, pp. 134–246.

WALSHE, F. M. R. (1942), 'The anatomy and physiology of cutaneous sensibility: A critical review', *Brain*, vol. 65, pp. 48–112.

WATERSTON, D. (1933a), 'Observations on sensation. The sensory functions of the skin for touch and pain', *J. Physiol.*, vol. 77, pp. 251–7.

WATERSTON, D. (1933b), 'On pain', *Lancet*, vol. 1, pp. 943–6.

WEDDELL, G. (1941a), 'The pattern of cutaneous innervation in relation to cutaneous sensibility', *J. Anat.*, vol. 75, pp. 346–67.

WEDDELL, G. (1941b), 'The multiple innervation of sensory spots in the skin', *J. Anat.*, vol. 75, pp. 441–6.

WEDDELL, G. (1941c), 'The clinical significance of the pattern of cutaneous innervation', *Proc. Roy. Soc. Med.*, vol. 34, pp. 776–8.

WEDDELL, G., GUTMANN, L., and GUTMANN, E. (1941), 'The local extension of nerve fibres into denervated areas of skin', *J. Neurol. Psychiat.*, vol. 4, pp. 206–25.

WEDDELL, G., and HARPMAN, J. A. (1940), 'The neurohistological bases for the sensation of pain provoked from deep fascia, tendon and periosteum', *J. Neurol. Psychiat.*, vol. 3, pp. 319–28.

WOOLLARD, H. M. (1935), 'Observations on the terminations of cutaneous nerves', *Brain*, vol. 58, pp. 352–67.

WOOLLARD, H. M. (1936), 'Intra-epidermic nerve endings', *J. Anat.*, vol. 71, pp. 54–60.

WOOLLARD, H. M. (1937), 'Continuity in nerve fibers', *J. Anat.*, vol. 71, pp. 480–91.

WOOLLARD, H. H., WEDDELL, G., and HARPMAN, J. A. (1940), 'Observations on the neurohistological basis of cutaneous pain', *J. Anat.*, vol. 74, pp. 413–40,

ZOTTERMAN, Y. (1939), 'Touch, pain and tickling: an electrophysiological investigation on cutaneous sensory nerves', *J. Physiol.*, vol. 95, pp. 1–28.

5 L. Kruger and F. Michel

Reinterpretation of the Representation of Pain Based on
Physiological Excitation of Single Neurons in the
Trigeminal Sensory Complex

L. Kruger and F. Michel, 'Reinterpretation of the representation of pain
based on the physiological excitation of single neurons in the trigeminal
sensory complex', *Exp. Neurol.*, vol. 5 (1962), pp. 157–78.

The stimulus modality required to excite single neurons was studied in
the different portions of the trigeminal sensory complex. Regional preponderance of different modalities could be related to the mediolateral
arrangement at all levels, but there was no apparent differentiation of
the rostrocaudal axis with respect to modality, receptive field size, or
adaptive properties. The directional sensitivity of neurons innervating
specialized structures such as vibrissae and teeth is described. The few
neurons which were excited by noxious stimuli were primarily isolated
outside the morphological limits of the sensory V complex. It is concluded that virtually all trigeminal neurons can be excited by delicate
tactile stimuli in the present experimental conditions. While presumably
all tactile neurons can be influenced by painful stimuli, present evidence
favors the absence of neurons uniquely sensitive to noxious stimuli.
The representation of pain is interpreted as involving tactile neurons
excited by small tactile fibers which are known to convey pain sensations under a variety of stimulus conditions.

Introduction

Functional subdivision of the sensory trigeminal (V) nuclear complex has long been apparent for several independent reasons. The
preservation of tactile sensibility together with a marked interference of pain and temperature sensation following the trigeminal tractotomy procedure introduced by Sjöqvist (40), is
probably the most decisive evidence for modality segregation
within this grouping. It is also clear that fiber components of
different caliber enter different portions of the complex, and several authors have suggested various subdivisions based on its
cytoarchitecture. The present study constitutes a systematic attempt to identify the nature of the stimulus required to elicit the
discharge of every element encountered in different portions of the
trigeminal complex. Since at least the caudal portion of the spinal
V nucleus can be implicated in painful sensations in man, and

117

because of the failure in previous experiments to identify 'pain' neurons in this region in deeply anesthetized cats (23), these experiments have been performed on decerebrate cats prepared under special circumstances. Evidence is presented demonstrating that few, if any, neurons in the entire trigeminal sensory complex cannot be excited by discrete stimuli of a non-noxious character.

Methods

Most of the details concerning the experimental methodology employed have been discussed in previous publications (21, 23). The present report is based upon an analysis of 788 units isolated in 174 electrode penetrations which were identified histologically and were influenced by trigeminal stimulation. Other neurons isolated which did not meet these criteria, or which were studied in anesthetized preparations, will not be considered here. The distribution of the needle tracks and the somatotopic pattern have been presented in the preceding paper (21).

In order to avoid any possible blocking effects caused by anesthetic agents, all experiments were performed on decerebrate cats. In preliminary experiments the entire operative procedure was performed in a single stage under ether anesthesia, but the blood loss and depressive effects resulting from cerebellectomy in this anesthetic condition resulted in rapid deterioration of the preparation when performed in conjunction with decerebration. Therefore, the day before each acute experiment, the cat was anesthetized with sodium pentobarbital (30 mg./kg., i.p.), and only the posterior fossa was exposed. The entire cerebellum was removed on one side with a fine suction tip, and the wound was sutured. By keeping the animal warm and administering penicillin, the animal was usually awake within a few hours. The following day it was anesthetized with ether, and the suture rapidly opened. A blunt spatula was then inserted into the rostral end of the posterior fossa transecting the brain stem at the intercollicular level. The entire procedure, including insertion of a tracheal cannula and placing carotid loops, requires less than 10 min. after which ether was discontinued, and the animal recovered rapidly. In this manner an animal with active trigeminal reflexes can be maintained in a stable condition for long periods of time. Rectal temperature was maintained by circulating hot water through a regulated pad. The exposed medulla was bathed with warm saline at irregular intervals, but it may be presumed that its temperature could frequently have fallen below normal.

Physiological stimuli were always applied manually. Because most units encountered could be readily driven by hair displacement, the approximate region of representation was usually apparent by listening to the background activity by means of a loud-speaker. When an isolated unit was not driven by hair displacement, other stimuli were tested in the vicinity of the last driven unit, or more frequently the region from which background activity could be excited. In most cases, light touch or pressure stimuli were found to be effective within the expected distribution. When these stimuli failed to elicit a reaction, coarser stimuli such as hard tapping, pinching, pin prick, hot matches, or ice cubes were at times employed. However, it should be noted that most units which were difficult to drive by cutaneous stimulation displayed signs of injury and were 'lost' (i.e. presumably destroyed) before a definite decision could be made concerning their modality. A majority of these units which were apparently driven by noxious stimuli were almost certainly excited by mechanical displacement of the brain with relation to the electrode. A similar irritation effect has already been pointed out by Perl and Whitlock (35) for units in the posterior group of the thalamus which they could excite with noxious stimuli. The few examples of neurons which may be considered to be driven exclusively by localized noxious stimuli are discussed in some detail below. In two cases in which neurons were driven by mechanical displacement of a tooth, a hole was drilled through the enamel and dentine so that a pin could be inserted into the pulp. The cornea was routinely tested whenever the electrode entered the ophthalmic division representation. The thermal sensitivity of tactile units described by Gentry, Whitlock, and Perl (9) was not tested. The numerals on figures refer successively to the numbers of the animal, electrode penetration, and single neuron isolated for that puncture.

Results

The introduction of the electrode tip into the trigeminal complex was almost invariably readily detected by continuously stroking all portions of the face while the electrode was being advanced. The rare instances in which histological evidence indicated that the electrode had reached the trigeminal complex without our detecting trigeminal activity were largely confined to the interior of the buccal cavity where it is easier to overlook the appropriate receptive field. The consistency of an orderly dorsoventral sequence of trigeminal divisions (21, 23), however, made it relatively

easy to concentrate detailed attention to the part of the integu-
mentary surface which would be represented at any given point.
The wealth of tactile activity at virtually all points in the trigeminal complex also made it easy to determine the approximate
region represented even when a single unit was not clearly isolated. This factor is of particular importance because it was the
specific aim of this study to identify and characterize those
neurons which might be presumed to be concerned with painful
stimulation by applying coarse pressure, pinching, or thrusting a
needle point into the region represented. The majority of units
isolated which displayed stable discharges long enough for careful
study, were readily classified in terms of modality, receptive field,
and adaptive properties.

Tactile neurons

The present paper will deal solely with those units which were
influenced by actual stimulation of the peripheral distribution of
the trigeminal nerve and for which the recording site was histologically identified. In all, 788 units were isolated which fulfilled
these criteria, and all but 53 of these fell into one of three modality
categories which we have classified as tactile, the remaining 53
will be dealt with in detail below. It is apparent from Table 1 that

Table 1

Modality Classification of Trigeminal Neurons ($n = 788$)

Modality	Adaptation		Total
	Fast	Slow	
Hair	398	39	437
Touch	86	26	112
Pressure	90	99	189
Other ('noxious')	43	7	50

the largest group of neurons can be activated by hair displacement, and these were usually identified by directing a weak puff
of air across the skin on the same side. Over 90 per cent of these
neurons were found to be fast adapting. Most units driven by touch
did not possess receptive fields in hairy skin. The remaining
tactile units were driven by somewhat heavier mechanical displacement of the integument, but were clearly not noxious in
character and are most easily characterized as pressure units. The
distinction between touch and light pressure tends to be somewhat

120

arbitrary, and some errors of classification are not unlikely for these categories. The column marked 'other' in Table 1 includes all other trigeminal units, some of which are also probably tactile but are considered separately because of special circumstances.

There is a decided tendency for modality skewing in different portions of the trigeminal complex as might be expected from its spatial organization (21). Thus, most of the hair neurons were

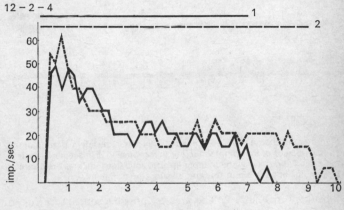

Figure 1. Plot of rate of impulse discharge of a slowly adapting neuron in the medial part of the principal trigeminal nucleus responding to pressure on the ipsilateral gum. The solid and dotted lines at the top denote the period of stimulus application

isolated in the lateral half of the nucleus where the skin of the face is most heavily represented, and a large proportion of the touch and pressure neurons were isolated in the medial portion. This is at least partly a reflection of the medial representation of the buccal cavity. Touch neurons were most commonly found to have receptive fields on hairless regions: the lips, nostril, and teeth. Pressure neurons were also most commonly found when stimulating structures within the mouth. It may also be noteworthy that touch neurons innervating the gums and palate were relatively rare, but these regions were most commonly represented by pressure neurons of the slowly adapting variety (Figure 1).

The adaptive properties of most neurons are clearly defined but can occasionally be ambiguous for neurons which respond with a large train of impulses to a rapidly applied transient. In general, slowly adapting neurons can be characterized as discharging throughout the duration of stimulus application and often briefly for a short period after stimulus application as in Figures 1 to 4. Some neurons which we have classified as fast adapting also discharge longer than the duration of the stimulus, as in the case of the vibrissa unit in Figure 4, but do not continue to discharge if the vibrissa remains displaced, as in the case of the lip hair neuron

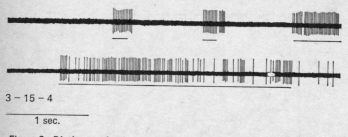

3 – 15 – 4

1 sec.

Figure 2. Discharge of a slowly adapting neuron in the lateral portion of the caudal nucleus of the spinal V nucleus in response to displacement of a few hairs overlying the ipsilateral upper lip. The solid line indicates the duration of stimulus application in this and all subsequent figures

illustrated in Figure 2. The greatest possible source of error in classification here lies in the uncertainty of whether the maintained bending of the hair is sufficiently steady so as not to provide a continual stimulus. Undoubtedly the distinction between fast and slowly adapting hair neurons which are sensitive to very small angular displacement would be highly uncertain at times, and to some extent our classification of adaptation is probably determined by the apparent sensitivity of the neuron studied.

The innervation of some specialized structures in the trigeminal nerve distribution is of particular interest. The teeth appear to be well represented throughout the entire medial portion of the entire trigeminal nuclear complex, and the majority of units representing the teeth are excited by light touch (Figure 3). All tooth touch units appear to display directional sensitivity so that an apparent receptive field can be plotted on each tooth, but this is almost certainly due to the direction of displacement necessary to excite receptors at the base of the tooth in the periodontal membrane (22, 32, 36). Neurons representing the teeth were always driven exclusively from one tooth, and in terms of number of neurons per tooth the canines would appear to be most extensively represented if our small sample is significant. A few neurons were excited by tapping on a given tooth and will be considered below since they were not classified as tactile.

13 – 10 – 1

1 sec.

Figure 3. Discharge of a slowly adapting neuron in the spinal trigeminal nucleus excited by light touch of the labial face of the ipsilateral lower molar tooth

The vibrissae are clearly the most extensively represented structures, and it is rare to find a neuron excited by displacement of more than a single vibrissa. Vibrissa neurons also possess remarkably precise directional sensitivity as was noted previously for trigeminal fibers by Fitzgerald (7), and usually discharge high-

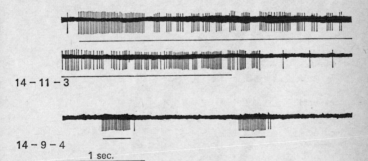

14 – 11 – 3

14 – 9 – 4

1 sec.

Figure 4. Impulse discharge of two neurons in the spinal V nucleus responding to displacement of a single vibrissa. A slowly adapting (upper) and rapidly adapting (lower) neuron are illustrated

frequency fast-adapting bursts to vibrissa displacement in the appropriate direction (Figure 4). The ease in delineating the receptive field of vibrissa neurons afforded an ideal opportunity for studying the influence of displacement of adjacent hairs outside of the excitatory receptive field. Although carefully investigated, we have failed to find a single example of the 'surround inhibition' noted for some cortical neurons by Mountcastle (31) either for vibrissa neurons which are especially easy to study or for other regions of the face.

It should be noted that neurons representing only one vibrissa were encountered in the lateral half of the trigeminal complex at all rostrocaudal levels studied (Figure 5). Actually, a far greater number of such neurons were isolated, but not studied, a point of particular relevance in considering the sampling of receptive fields

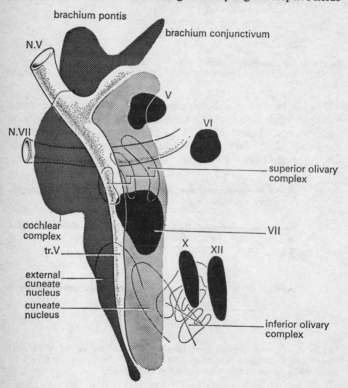

Figure 5. A dorsal view reconstruction of the brain-stem trigeminal sensory complex and adjacent structures used as landmarks in reconstructing the position of needle tracks. The sites at which neurons were isolated which were excited uniquely by one vibrissa are indicated by dots. When more than three such neurons were isolated in a single electrode penetration, the point is indicated by a cluster of dots. Motor nuclei and nerves are indicated with roman numerals

for size comparisons. Obviously the proportion of vibrissa units studied at a given level can enormously skew the mean receptive field size. It is clear from our findings that the number of units with different fields sampled is far too few for comparing mean receptive field size in different portions of the trigeminal nuclear complex. The problem could be clarified by limiting the comparison to restricted regions of the skin rather than pooling hetero-

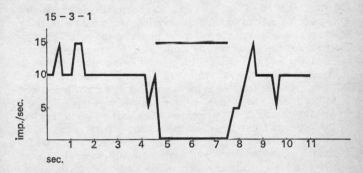

Figure 6. Plot of rate of impulse discharge for a spontaneously firing neuron of the spinal trigeminal nucleus inhibited by light touch of the ipsilateral mandibular gum

geneous data, but our findings for the vibrissae and for a large number of mandibular hair units suggest that the size of the receptive field does not vary with site of recording and is probably only related to peripheral innervation density. In this connection it may be relevant to note that only two tactile units representing the cornea were encountered, and one of these was lost before it could be studied carefully. However, for this region, the difficulty in isolating 'pain' neurons may be as relevant as the apparent scanty innervation of the cornea.

Finally, it should be noted that tactile neurons rarely displayed spontaneous activity, and when they did it could usually be interpreted as a sign of damage, because they could not be studied for long periods of time. However, for two units it was found possible to inhibit the steady discharge by applying light pressure or touch to a restricted receptive field (Figure 6). An excitatory zone for both of these neurons could not be found. One exceptional neuron (not included in Table 1) displayed a central fast-adapting field and a slowly adapting surround.

Nontactile neurons

It became rapidly apparent during the course of the present experiments that neurons of this category are quite rare, and their receptive fields exceedingly difficult to delimit. After histological examination of the electrode tracks, it was found that a large number of these neurons were not isolated within the sensory trigeminal nuclear complex, but were in nearby structures including motor nuclei. These included eight neurons in the motor nucleus of V, seven of which were driven by scratching or pricking inside the mouth, and the other by pinching the upper lip with forceps. Another nine similar units were located in the facial nucleus. On the basis of location alone it would seem fruitless to consider these neurons as related to the transmission of painful impulses from the face, since they can be more simply interpreted as motor reflex discharges to painful stimuli.

Another group of neurons influenced by noxious stimuli applied to the face were found to be located in various parts of the reticular formation. We will not here consider neurons of the nuclei reticularis gigantocellularis and pontis caudalis, since these were all driven from virtually anywhere on the body and are, therefore, not specifically trigeminal. However, it might be noteworthy that these neurons were never excited by tactile stimuli, and the discharges elicited by strong pinching or needle prick were generally poor and clearly less stable than those encountered in the tactile trigeminal region. There were also eight neurons in the nucleus reticularis parvocellularis, and five in the nucleus reticularis lateralis which were influenced by noxious stimuli localized to the head of the animal. We shall not discuss these in detail since there was no consistent pattern in the few examples studied, and because it is unclear whether this region should be regarded as related to afferent impulse conduction or to reflex motor integration.

The remainder of nontactile neurons deserve particular attention because they were located within the limits of the sensory trigeminal complex, and seven neurons near its medial edge in the region of the nucleus of the fasciculus solitarius, all of which were driven from within the mouth, or squeezing the tongue. There were six neurons in the principal or sensory nucleus of V, of which four were driven by hard pressure or scratching on the gums, one by tapping on the maxillary molar teeth, and one by tapping on the maxillary periosteum (Figure 7). In all cases, the discharges were not very securely driven compared to tactile neurons, and the receptive fields were difficult to delimit. It would seem quite possible that at least in some of these cases, a true tactile field difficult to locate within the buccal cavity was being poorly driven by mechanical transmission of the crude stimulus employed.

The situation for the spinal trigeminal complex is equally difficult to interpret. Out of twenty neurons in this complex driven by nontactile stimuli, ten were driven by a tap over the fascial sheet overlying the orbit, jaw, the edge of the lip, or the bridge of the nose (Figure 7), the last region being innervated solely by free

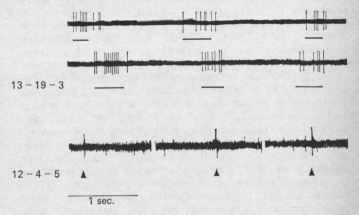

13 – 19 – 3

12 – 4 – 5

1 sec.

Figure 7. Upper record is from a neuron in the spinal trigeminal nucleus which responded to scratching of the gum surrounding the lower canine. The lower record is from a neuron in the oral part of the spinal V nucleus which responded to mild tapping (triangles) on the periosteum over the bridge of the nose

nerve endings (12). While it could be argued that the stimulus used here is not pleasant when applied to ourselves, it becomes even more difficult to argue that it is of necessity noxious in character. For two neurons driven by tapping on the nose, the receptive field could be located in the tissue underlying the skin by dissecting the skin free, and a somewhat weaker stimulus was needed to excite the exposed fascia or periosteum. Two other units were driven by hard pinching of the supraorbital skin and ear, one by coarse mechanical displacement of the cornea, and one was inhibited by pinching the skin virtually at any part of the face on either side. It might be noted parenthetically that most of the 'other' neurons referred to in Table 1 were only excited from the ipsilateral side of the face. The remaining possibly 'noxious' neurons were excited by scratching, pricking, or hard tapping of the gums, palate, and teeth. For two neurons excited by tapping on a tooth, a hole was drilled through the enamel with a dental drill in order to expose the dentine and pulp, but in neither case could the unit be clearly affected from the interior of the tooth.

It is, of course, possible that some of these examples may represent true 'pain' neurons, but the present findings are open to several serious criticisms. Firstly, it should be noted that the neurons under consideration here did not predominate in the caudal portion of the spinal V nucleus and indeed were also present in the main sensory nucleus. The occasional difficulty in identifying the true receptive field of a neuron (especially when located inside the mouth) may lead to its being poorly excited by transmission mechanically from a crudely stimulated adjacent region. Furthermore, with an open head preparation it should be easy to produce pulsation of the brain stem and a pronounced elevation of blood pressure with noxious stimulation as noted by Perl and Whitlock (35). Although the head was rather rigidly mounted, it is also not inconceivable that hard scratching on the gums or tapping over a body ridge might displace the whole head by a few microns and elicit an irregular discharge by a pure mechanical artifact. An observed alteration in spike height in a few examples might easily be explained in this manner. All of these factors taken together tend to cast serious doubt on whether these experiments have revealed any substantial evidence whatever concerning the presence or properties of 'pain' neurons. From a conservative point of view it would seem necessary to conclude that we have not successfully isolated the neurons concerned uniquely with pain transmission. Should this interpretation prove to be correct, one can either conclude that such neurons systematically have not been sampled, or that specific 'pain' neurons do not exist. The former interpretation would imply that some factor such as electrode size may account for failing to record from neurons of a certain size, an argument difficult to support histologically; or that even this especially favorable means of preparing a decerebrate animal may lead to deleterious effects which could lead to a selective block of one category of neurons.

Discussion

The means of excitation for neurons in the trigeminal sensory complex is of particular interest because of the well-substantiated dissociation of cutaneous modalities within this grouping revealed by clinical findings. It is generally assumed that the principal sensory nucleus of V is concerned primarily with relaying tactile impulses (10, 41) and that the spinal nucleus of V, or at least its caudal portion, constitutes the relay for pain and temperature, because following the Sjöqvist procedure (40) of sectioning the descending root of V there is a marked analgesia of the face and a preservation of tactile sensibility over the same distribution. However, it should be emphasized that careful examination of such patients reveals that touch is mildly impaired and that there is not a complete loss for any modality (44, 48). The patient can still distinguish hot from cold and the head from the point of a pin.

The presence of a tactile projection to the spinal nucleus of V in the cat (5, 11, 13, 23, 25) is well established, but the mild tactile defect following tractotomy would imply that the tactile projection should not predominate, a prediction which the present experiments would superficially appear to contradict. This would seem to be morphologically self-evident, however, since all authors appear to agree with Ramón y Cajal's (38) original observation that the vast majority of trigeminal fibers bifurcate, sending a fine branch to the principal nucleus of V and a larger branch to the spinal nucleus. Unless one wishes to argue as Gerard (10) suggested, that the two branches of the same parent fiber conduct different modalites, it is inevitable to conclude that there must be at least as many tactile neurons in the spinal nucleus as found in the principal nucleus. In fact, the extensive branching of the descending root would imply the presence of far more tactile neurons in the spinal nucleus. Although it is not unreasonable to suggest that different branches of a given fiber may have different functional roles, it would seem difficult to believe that each branch would not conduct the same physiological activity evoked in the parent fiber.

There appears to be ample evidence that the fibers in the descending tract of V are appreciably smaller at the level of the caudal nucleus of spinal V. Sjöqvist (40) reported that below the level of the inferior olive in the monkey, 92 per cent of the fibers in the tract are less than 4 μ. Gerard's (10) figures for the cat show the same trend although with somewhat different values. Thus, in simplest terms, the basic problem appears to resolve itself between a choice of two most likely alternatives. Either the large number of small fibers, most of which can be presumed to be tactile, confer upon the caudal nucleus of spinal V its specialized role in pain and temperature sensation, or the nonbifurcating trigeminal fibers clearly demonstrated in fetal and early postnatal material (2, 51), which are by no means numerous, must bear the total burden of conducting impulses conveying these sensations.

It should be emphasized that the morphological dichotomy of the trigeminal complex into a principal and spinal portion has a remarkably constant phyletic history (4, 43, 53), and it is clear that the spinal nucleus is activated by tactile stimuli with a similar somatotopic pattern in reptiles (24). A partial explanation for the differentiation of the trigeminal complex has been offered on developmental grounds by Humphrey (15). She emphasizes that the neural tube closes in a cervico-rostral direction in time, and since nerve fibers are attracted to regions of most intense mitotic activity, the first trigeminal fibers to establish contact and arborize extensively are those in the caudal nucleus of spinal V, forming a conspicuously distinctive fine fiber network not duplicated in the later developing portions which appear to receive collaterals of these fibers (40).

Previous electrophysiological studies of the sensory trigeminal nuclear complex appear to be in essential agreement with respect to somatotopic pattern, and there is no disagreement concerning a tactile projection to at least some portion of the spinal V nuclear complex (5, 11, 13, 17, 18, 23, 24, 25, 29). There have been suggestions that the late response evoked in the spinal nucleus may be concerned with pain, although its threshold is the same as for the activation of touch fibers (17–19) and there is evidence of a late response to tooth-pulp stimulation which may be presumed to be painful (3), but the specificity and localization of these responses as well as evidence for specific pain neurons has not yet been documented. While it must be admitted that all tactile fibers can presumably be excited by more intense noxious stimuli, recording methods have failed to reveal why a dissociation of sensations can be obtained following the Sjöqvist (40) tractotomy procedure.

The level of section required to produce analgesia and thermanesthesia is of particular interest in providing a clue to the functional differentiation of the spinal V complex. The literature on this point is too extensive for review here, but there seems to be essential agreement that a section only a few millimeters rostral to the obex is effective in producing analgesia in man and in eliminating the corneal reflex in the cat (10), thus clearly indicating that only a portion of the spinal nucleus need be disconnected to produce sensory dissociation. If Sjöqvist (40) is correct in his opinion that the rostral portions of spinal V (nuclei oralis and interpolaris of Olszewski, 34) receive only collaterals of fibers of the descending tract, it becomes exceedingly difficult to explain the modality dissociation on the basis of different modalities of afferent fibers.

Perhaps the best clue concerning pain sensation is its clear implication of small fiber activity. It is well known that with asphyxial block of a peripheral nerve in which only C fibres are conducting, touch is lost but pain sensations remain (27). The absence of touch in this condition is critical because there have long been reports of C-fiber activation by light mechanical displacement of hairs (6, 14, 16, 54), and the excellent single unit studies of Iggo (16) indicate that the vast majority are excited by gentle tactile stimuli applied within very small receptive fields. The implication is clearly that tactile activity in C fibers is not interpreted as touch and indeed can be interpreted as painful. Is it therefore possible that specific 'pain' fibers and neurons in the peripheral nervous system are not required to elicit a sensation of pain?

Proving that pain fibers and neurons do not exist is virtually impossible, since negative findings must of necessity be tentative, and there are some scanty positive findings which must be considered even in the present experiments. The positive findings within the trigeminal complex, however, require especially careful scrutiny because of several weaknesses. First, it should be emphasized that a certain amount of carelessness on the part of the investigators is inevitable. On numerous occasions we have had difficulty in determining the limits of a receptive field for a neuron driven by pinching or tapping hard on the skin only to find that we had missed a true tactile receptive field at a distance which was being excited by mechanical transmission. The difficulty of access to some receptive fields, especially those on the mucous membrane linings, might well account for many of those few neurons in the trigeminal sensory complex which required 'noxious' stimuli in order to elicit a discharge. There are also a few units driven by tapping on the bridge of the nose or rim of the orbit which possess definable receptive fields, and in some instances we were able, by dissecting through the skin, to identify a receptive field on the deep tissue over the bridge of the nose. Most of these units excited by deep or hard pressure were distributed in the region innervated by the nasociliary nerve or on the gums. While it is difficult to argue that the stimulus in these instances would not be painful, on the basis of our own reaction to similar stimuli applied to ourselves, it would seem even more precarious to insist that these constitute noxious stimuli. Finally, it should be re-emphasized that a certain number of units were probably excited by mechanical injury of the neuron resulting from small movements of the brain when crude stimuli are applied, some of which may be due to vascular pulsation (35). Such mechanically excited units contribute an artifact which is difficult to classify because they are usually driven by distinctly noxious stimuli and are usually 'lost' with a terminal injury discharge.

Perhaps one of the most striking positive findings is the remarkable rarity of units which were not driven by light touch or pressure. Unless the electrode employed by virtue of its size and impedance, does not randomly sample neurons of all sizes, it must be concluded that almost all neurons in all regions of the sensory trigeminal complex explored are activated by tactile stimuli.

However, there are other regions for which there is some evidence of unit activity being driven only by noxious stimuli. For reasons discussed above we shall consider the 'pain' units isolated in the motor nuclei of V and VII as irrelevant for any sensory function, but those units within the reticular formation can be reasonably regarded as related to the 'spinothalamic' afferent system (8, 30). Trigeminal afferents to the reticular formation have been noted on the basis of Golgi preparations (38), Nauta degeneration (42), and electrophysiological findings (26), but there are many authors who have denied their presence, and there is little agreement concerning their distribution. The present findings provide some evidence that some reticular neurons can be influenced by noxious stimuli applied within the peripheral trigeminal distribution, but in most instances, stimuli applied to other parts of the body were also effective, and no receptive field could be delimited. None of these neurons could be activated by tactile stimuli, in our experience, and similar single unit findings have been reported for the presumed thalamic projection of this region of the brain stem (1, 20, 35, 50).

Some recent evidence has been adduced for a spinothalamic projection to the posterior nuclear group of the thalamus (20, 30, 37, 49, 50), and some units responding uniquely to noxious stimuli have been described (37, 49), but Perl and Whitlock (35) have recently emphasized that in their experience mechanical injury artifacts, especially of a vascular nature, could account for the excitation by noxious stimuli of every neuron in this region studied carefully. This difficulty should be considered in interpreting all apparently 'noxious' units regardless of site of recording, especially when a receptive field cannot be readily ascertained. This may not be applicable to units in the internal medullary lamina and centrum medianum (1, 35), but since these regions appear to be only collaterally related to the main 'pain pathway' the role of these neurons will be deferred and considered elsewhere.

The general thesis we wish to propose is that all tactile neurons can obviously be influenced by noxious stimuli, and there is ample anatomical as well as excellent electrophysiological evidence (35, 37, 45) that the spinothalamic ('pain') pathway converges upon, and indeed projects extensively upon, the tactile system (39). The idea that the pain pathway is intimately related to the activity of tactile neurons would not appear to be completely unreasonable if the dissociation of sensation could be explained, and we believe this is possible on the basis of long known findings.

It is clear that tactile activity in the smallest fibers do not evoke the sensation of touch, but rather that of pain, at least if excited in sufficient quantity and in the absence of A-fiber activity. Herein would lie the simplest explanation of the pathological conditions of hyperpathia where the gentlest tactile stimulus may provoke severe pain. The numerous experiments on section of human peripheral nerves provides another important clue, because it is well known that the borders of the resulting anesthetic zone become hypersensitive, and tactile stimuli in this zone can produce pain. It is also known that this border zone is filled with growing fibers of small caliber from adjacent nerve trunks before the regrowth of regenerating cut fibers (46). A variety of phenomena related to pain can be explained on the basis of creating a condition for excessive small fiber activity. For example, Noordenbos (33) has recently shown that in post-herpetic trigeminal neuralgia there is a marked shift in the fiber spectrum toward the small fiber end on the affected side of the trigeminal nerve. It is our belief that the same principle can be applied to numerous observations concerning pain, including pathological conditions of central origin and we will deal with this more comprehensively elsewhere. However, there still remains the difficulty of explaining the constant relationship of pain representation and thermal sensitivity. Here again there is excellent evidence that tactile neurons in the dorsal horn (45), nucleus gracilis (9), ventrobasal complex, and posterior group of the thalamus (35, 37) are sensitive to thermal stimuli. This does not imply that there is no fiber specificity, since there is evidence of specific large thermosensitive fibers, but that in the absence of small fiber activity, thermal sensitivity is impaired. It should also be noted that following the Sjöqvist trigeminal tractotomy procedure, despite the impairment of thermal sensitivity associated with analgesia, the patient can still distinguish hot from cold (44).

It follows from the above interpretation that the functional dissociation within the trigeminal complex would not be determined on the basis of specific pain afferents but rather on a disproportion of small tactile fiber activity associated with the caudal nucleus of the spinal V complex. An analogous situation exists for the rest of the body where the dorsal horn of the spinal cord (the presumed homologue on morphological grounds) contributes far more small fibers to the somatic pathway than the dorsal funicular-lemniscal pathway. The strikingly similar dense small fiber plexus in the substantia gelatinosa of the dorsal horn and caudal nucleus of spinal V would appear to provide an excellent basis for the homology of these structures and for their being implicated with central small fiber activity. As discussed elsewhere (21), there also are excellent reasons to homologize the principal nucleus of V with the dorsal column nuclei.

Previous interpretations of the nature of trigeminal pain transmission have recognized the role of tactile fibers in eliciting painful sensations because of the striking ease with which a delicate tactile stimulus can trigger an enduring pain in trigeminal neuralgia. An excellent attempt to analyse this problem has been made by King and his co-workers (17 to 19). They have shown that the late response induced by nerve stimulation is markedly enhanced in cats who have been rendered experimentally hyperesthetic by injecting alumina gel into the caudel portion of the spinal V nuclear complex. Although they have adduced evidence for antidromic firing of the trigeminal nerve to explain trigeminal neuralgia, this would appear to be unlikely in pathological circumstances, and a simpler interpretation of their findings may exist if one accepts the idea that excessive activity in the very dense small fiber system of the caudal nucleus of spinal V will produce pain even if activated by a tactile stimulus, as in trigeminal hyperpathias. The exaggerated late response in their experimentally hyperpathic animals could well be a reflection of increased small fiber activity, and it should be emphasized that their findings also indicate that the late response has the same threshold as the fast 'touch' response. A similar explanation might be invoked to explain the tactile hyperpathia in other circumstances. List and Williams (28) have reviewed the evidence implicating vascular complications which are often acute episodes in many (but not all) cases of trigeminal neuralgia, and Wolff (52) has suggested that an episodic ischemic nerve injury occurs in many of these cases. Assuming that trigeminal ischemia mimics the well-known experiments on ischemic block of peripheral nerve (e.g. Landau and Bishop, 27) the disproportionately large amount of small fiber activity in the absence of large fiber activity could produce a situation where touch stimuli cannot be interpreted as touch sensation, and only pain results.

This interpretation, therefore, implies that pain sensation results when a large number of small caliber tactile fibers excite neurons of the tactile thalamus (ventrobasal complex) which is known to be the principal termination of the spinothalamic ('pain') tract. The more potent depolarizing action of large tactile fiber activity presumably renders these same thalamic neurons capable of discharge in a pattern which the organism interprets as a tactile sensation and can thus obscure and thereby inhibit a pattern which might be interpreted as painful in the absence of large fiber effects. Although other factors, such as a true inhibitory influence of large fibers, may also be operative in this mechanism, it would seem fruitless to speculate further at present. It can only be emphasized that both anatomical and physiological findings continue to provide little support for a true dichotomy of pain and tactile fiber systems. In retrospect this should long have been evident by virtue of the numerous examples in which tactile stimuli are experienced as painful. The presence of 'tactile activity' in neuronal groupings known to be concerned with pain would appear to be a logical necessity. It is for this reason that touching the cornea is painful, but after tractotomy which disconnects the small fiber central path, the patient reports touch for the same stimulus.

The evidence adduced by Weddell and his co-workers (47) for implicating at least the free nerve endings in the skin with the representation of more than one modality appears to be irrefutable, at least in some regions lacking specialized end organs. While the specificity of nerve fibers and some receptors is equally certain, it would appear to be a logical necessity for the small fiber system to be involved in the transmission of both touch and pain activity. A relatively isolated excitation of the small fiber central pathway arising in the caudal portion of the spinal V nucleus can be expected to elicit a pattern of thalamic activity which causes a sensation of pain regardless of the stimulus. Under physiological circumstances it is assumed that a noxious stimulus is capable of exciting fast repetitive discharge of small caliber fibers which possess free nerve endings in the skin and which outlasts the effects of the short train of impulses arising from specialized endings that are conducted via nerves of large caliber.

References

1. ALBE-FESSARD, D., and L. KRUGER, Dualité des réponses des cellules du centre médian du thalamus à des stimulations naturelles ou électriques. *Compt. rend.* 248:299–301, 1959.
2. ÅSTRÖM, K. E., On the central course of afferent fibres in the trigeminal, facial, glossopharyngeal, and vagal nerves and their nuclei in the mouse. *Acta Physiol. Scand.* 29, Suppl. 106:209–320, 1953.
3. BROOKHART, J. M., W. K. LIVINGSTON, and F. P. HAUGEN, Functional characteristics of afferent fibers from tooth pulp of cat. *J. Neurophysiol.*, 16:634–42, 1953.
4. CROSBY, E. C., and R. E. YOSS, The phylogenetic continuity of neural mechanisms as illustrated by the spinal tract of V and its nucleus. *Research Publ., Assoc. Research Nervous Mental Disease* 33:174–208, 1954.
5. DARIAN-SMITH, I., and G. MAYDAY, Somatotopic organization within the brain stem trigeminal complex of the cat. *Exp. Neurol.* 2:290–309, 1960.
6. DOUGLAS, W. W., and J. M. RITCHIE, The sensory functions of the nonmyelinated afferent nerve fibres from the skin. *Ciba Study Group Paper*, No. 1:26–39, 1959.
7. FITZGERALD, O., Discharges from the sensory organs of the cat's vibrissae and the modification of their activity by ions. *J. Physiol. London* 98:163–78, 1940.
8. FRENCH, J. D., M. VERZEANO, and H. W. MAGOUN, An extralemniscal sensory system in the brain. *A.M.A. Arch. Neurol. Psychiat.* 69:505–18, 1953.
9. GENTRY, J. R., D. G. WHITLOCK, and E. R. PERL, Tactile projection to nucleus gracilis of cat. *Federation Proc.* 20:349, 1961.
10. GERARD, M. W., Afferent impulses of the trigeminal nerve. *A.M.A. Arch. Neurol. Psychiat.* 9:306–38, 1923.
11. GORDON, G., S. LANDGREN, and W. A. SEED, Responses of single cells in the caudal part of the spinal nucleus of the trigeminal nerve of the cat. *J. Physiol. London* 153:12–13, 1960.
12. HARPMAN, J. A., Specificity of sensory nerve endings. *Brit. Med. J.* 2:497–8, 1951.
13. HARRISON, F., and K. B. CORBIN, Oscillographic studies on the spinal tract of the fifth cranial nerve. *J. Neurophysiol.* 5:465–82, 1942.
14. HOGG, B. M., Slow impulses from the cutaneous nerves of the frog. *J. Physiol. London* 84:250–58, 1935.
15. HUMPHREY, T., The trigeminal nerve in relation to early human fetal activity. *Research Publ., Assoc. Research Nervous Mental Disease* 33:127–54, 1954.
16. IGGO, A., A single unit analysis of cutaneous receptors with C afferent fibers. *Ciba Study Group Paper*, No. 1:41–56, 1959.
17. KING, R. B., and J. C. BARNETT, Studies of trigeminal nerve potentials. Overreaction to tactile facial stimulation in acute laboratory preparations. *J. Neurosurg.* 14:617–27, 1957.

18. KING, R. B., and J. N. MEAGHER, Studies of trigeminal nerve potentials. *J. Neurosurg.* 12:393–402, 1955.

19. KING, R. B., J. N. MEAGHER, and J. C. BARNETT, Studies of trigeminal nerve potentials in normal compared to abnormal experimental preparations. *J. Neurosurg.* 13:176 83, 1066.

20. KRUGER, L., and D. ALBE-FESSARD, The distribution of responses to somatic afferent stimuli in the diencephalon of the cat under chloralose anesthesia. *Exp. Neurol.* 2:442–67, 1960.

21. KRUGER, L., and F. MICHEL, A morphological and somatotopic analysis of single unit activity in the trigeminal sensory complex of the cat. *Exp. Neurol.* 5:139–56, 1962.

22. KRUGER, L., and F. MICHEL, A single neuron analysis of the buccal cavity representation in the sensory trigeminal complex of the cat. *Arch. Oral Biol.*, in press.

23. KRUGER, L., R. SIMINOFF, and P. WITKOVSKY, Single neuron analysis of dorsal column nuclei and spinal nucleus of trigeminal in cat. *J. Neurophysiol.* 24:333–49. 1961.

24. KRUGER, L., and P. WITKOVSKY, A functional analysis of neurons in the dorsal column nuclei and spinal nucleus of the trigeminal in the reptile (*Alligator mississippiensis*), *J. Comp. Neurol.* 117:97–105, 1961.

25. KUHN, R., Topographical pattern of cutaneous sensibility in the dorsal column nuclei of the cat. *Tr. Am. Neurol. Assoc.* 74:227–30, 1949.

26. LAMARCHE, G., J. M. LANGLOIS, and M. HÉON, Unit study of the trigeminal projections in the reticular formation of the medulla oblongata in the cat. *Can. J. Biochem. and Physiol.* 38:1163–6, 1960.

27. LANDAU, W., and G. H. BISHOP, Pain from dermal, periosteal and fascial endings and from inflammation. Electrophysiological study employing differential nerve blocks. *A.M.A. Arch. Neurol. Psychiat.* 69:490–504, 1963.

28. LIST, C. F., and J. R. WILLIAMS, Pathogenesis of trigeminal neuralgia. A review. *A.M.A. Arch. Neurol. Psychiat.* 77:36–43, 1957.

29. MCKINLEY, W. A., and H. W. MAGOUN, The bulbar projection of the trigeminal nerve. *Am. J. Physiol.* 137:317–24, 1942.

30. MEHLER, W. R., M. E. FEFERMAN, and W. J. H. NAUTA, Ascending axon degeneration following anterolateral cordotomy. An experimental study in the monkey. *Brain* 83:718–50, 1960.

31. MOUNTCASTLE, V. B., Modality and topographic properties of single neurons of cat's somatic sensory cortex. *J. Neurophysiol.* 20:408–34, 1957.

32. NESS, A. R., The mechanoreceptors of the rabbit mandibular incisor. *J. Physiol. London* 126:475–93, 1954.

33. NOORDENBOS, W. *Pain*, Elsevier, Amsterdam, 1959.

34. OLSZEWSKI, J., On the anatomical and functional organization of the spinal trigeminal nucleus. *J. Comp. Neurol.* 92:401–13, 1950.

35. PERL, E. R., and D. G. WHITLOCK, Somatic stimuli exciting spinothalamic projections to thalamic neurons in cat and monkey. *Exptl. Neurol.* 3:256–96, 1961.

36. PFAFFMAN, C., Afferent impulses from the teeth due to pressure and noxious stimulation. *J. Physiol. London* 97:207–19, 1939.

37. POGGIO, G. F., and V. B. MOUNTCASTLE, A study of the functional contributions of the lemniscal and spinothalamic systems to somatic sensibility. *Bull. Johns Hopkins Hosp.* 106: 266–316, 1960.

38. S. RAMÓN Y CAJAL, *Histologie du Système Nerveux de l'Homme et des Vertébrés*, vol. 1, Consejo Superios de Investigaciones Cientificas, Madrid, 1955, pp. 839–88.

39. ROSE, J. E., and V. B. MOUNTCASTLE, Touch and kinesthesis. *Handbook Physiol. Sect. 1, Neurophysiol.* 1:387–429, 1959.

40. SJÖQVIST, O., Studies on pain conduction in the trigeminal nerve. A contribution to surgical treatment of facial pain. *Acta Psychiat. Neurol. Scand.* (suppl.) 17:1–139, 1938.

41. SMYTH, G. E., The systematization and central connections of the spinal tract and nucleus of the trigeminal nerve. *Brain* 62:41–87, 1939.

42. TORVIK, A., Afferent connections to the sensory trigeminal nuclei, the nucleus of the solitary tract and adjacent structures. An experimental study in the rat. *J. Comp. Neurol.* 106:51–141, 1956.

43. VAN VALKENBURG, C. T., Zur kenntnis der radix spinalis nervi trigemini. *Monatschr. Psychiat. Neurol.* 29:407–37, 1911.

44. WALKER, A. E., Anatomy, physiology and surgical considerations of the spinal tract of the trigeminal nerve. *J. Neurophysiol.* 2:234–48, 1939.

45. WALL, P. D., Cord cells responding to touch, damage and temperature of skin. *J. Neurophysiol.* 23:197–210, 1960.

46. WEDDELL, G., L. GUTTMANN, and E. GUTMANN, The local extension of nerve fibers into denervated areas of skin. *J. Neurol. Psychiat.* 4:206–25, 1941.

47. WEDDELL, G., E. PALMER, and D. TAYLOR, The significance of the peripheral anatomical arrangements of the nerves which serve pain and itch. *Ciba Study Group Paper*, No. 1:3–10, 1959.

48. WEINBERGER, L. M., and F. C. GRANT, Experiences with intramedullary tractotomy. III. Studies in sensation, *A.M.A. Arch. Neurol. Psychiat.* 48:355–381, 1942.

49. WHITLOCK, D. G., and E. R. PERL, Afferent projections through ventrolateral funiculi to thalamus of cat. *J. Neurophysiol.* 22:133–48, 1959.

50. WHITLOCK, D. G., and E. R. PERL, Thalamic projections of spinothalamic pathways in monkey. *Exp. Neurol.* 3:240–55, 1961.

51. WINDLE, W. F., Non-bifurcating nerve fibers of the trigeminal nerve. *J. Comp. Neurol.* 40:229–40, 1926.

52. WOLFF, H. G. *Headache and Other Head Pain*, Oxford University Press, New York, 1948.

53. WOODBURNE, R. T., A phylogenetic consideration of the primary and secondary centers and connections of the trigeminal complex in a series of vertebrates. *J. Comp. Neurol.* 65:403–501, 1936.

54. ZOTTERMAN, Y., Touch, pain and tickling: an electrophysiological investigation on cutaneous sensory nerves. *J. Physiol. London* 95:1–28, 1939.

6 R. Melzack and P. D. Wall

Pain Mechanisms: a New Theory

R. Melzack and P. D. Wall, 'Pain mechanisms: a new theory', *Science*, vol. 150 (1965), pp. 971–9.

Introduction

The nature of pain has been the subject of bitter controversy since the turn of the century (1). There are currently two opposing theories of pain: (i) specificity theory, which holds that pain is a specific modality like vision or hearing, 'with its own central and peripheral apparatus' (2), and (ii) pattern theory, which maintains that the nerve impulse pattern for pain is produced by intense stimulation of nonspecific receptors since 'there are no specific fibers and no specific endings' (3). Both theories derive from earlier concepts proposed by von Frey (4) and Goldscheider (5) in 1894, and historically they are held to be mutually exclusive. Since it is our purpose here to propose a new theory of pain mechanisms, we shall state explicitly at the outset where we agree and disagree with specificity and pattern theories.

Specificity Theory

Specificity theory proposes that a mosaic of specific pain receptors in body tissue projects to a pain center in the brain. It maintains that free nerve endings are pain receptors (4) and generate pain impulses that are carried by A-delta and C fibers in peripheral nerves (6) and by the lateral spinothalamic tract in the spinal cord (2) to a pain center in the thalamus (7). Despite its apparent simplicity, the theory contains an explicit statement of physiological specialization and an implicit psychological assumption (8, 9). Consider the proposition that the skin contains 'pain receptors'. To say that a receptor responds only to intense, noxious stimulation of the skin is a physiological statement of fact; it says that the receptor is specialized to respond to a particular kind of stimulus. To call a receptor a 'pain receptor', however, is a psychological assumption: it implies a direct connection from the receptor to a brain center where pain is felt (Figure 1), so that stimulation of the receptor must always elicit pain and only the sensation of pain. This distinction between physiological specialization and psychological assumption also applies to peripheral fibers and central projection systems (9).

The facts of physiological specialization provide the power of specificity theory. Its psychological assumption is its weakness.

Figure 1. Descartes' (76) concept of the pain pathway. He writes: 'If for example fire (A) comes near the foot (B), the minute particles of this fire, which as you know move with great velocity, have the power to set in motion the spot of the skin of the foot which they touch, and by this means pulling upon the delicate thread CC, which is attached to the spot of the skin, they open up at the same instant the pore, d e, against which the delicate thread ends, just as by pulling at one end of a rope one makes to strike at the same instant a bell which hangs at the other end'

As in all psychological theories, there is implicit in specificity theory the conception of a nervous system; and the model is that of a fixed, direct-line communication system from the skin to the brain. This facet of specificity theory, which imputes a direct, invariant relationship between stimulus and sensation, is examined here in the light of the clinical, psychological, and physiological evidence concerning pain.

Clinical evidence

The pathological pain states of causalgia (a severe burning pain that may result from a partial lesion of a peripheral nerve), phantom limb pain (which may occur after amputation of a limb), and the peripheral neuralgias (which may occur after peripheral nerve infections or degenerative diseases) provide a dramatic refutation of the concept of a fixed, direct-line nervous system.

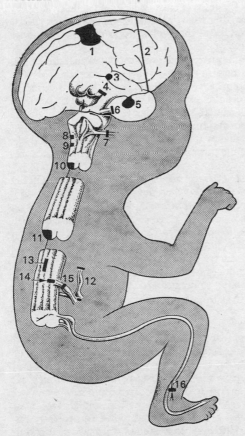

Figure 2. MacCarty and Drake's (77) schematic diagram illustrating various surgical procedures designed to alleviate pain: 1, gyrectomy; 2, prefrontal lobotomy; 3, thalamotomy; 4, mesencephalic tractotomy; 5, hypophysectomy; 6, fifth-nerve rhizotomy; 7, ninth-nerve neurectomy; 8, medullary tractotomy; 9, trigeminal tractotomy; 10, cervical chordotomy; 11, thoracic chordotomy; 12, sympathectomy; 13, myelotomy; 14 Lissauer tractotomy; 15, posterior rhizotomy; 16, neurectomy

Four features of these syndromes plague patient, physician, and theorist (8, 10).

1. Surgical lesions of the peripheral and central nervous system have been singularly unsuccessful in abolishing these pains permanently, although the lesions have been made at almost every level (Figure 2). Even after such operations, pain can often still be elicited by stimulation below the level of section and may be more severe than before the operation (8, 10).

2. Gentle touch, vibration, and other nonnoxious stimuli (8, 10) can trigger excruciating pain, and sometimes pain occurs spontaneously for long periods without any apparent stimulus. The fact that the thresholds to these stimuli are raised rather than lowered in causalgia and the neuralgias (10), together with the fact that referred pain can often be triggered by mild stimulation of normal skin (8), makes it unlikely that the pains can be explained by postulating pathologically hypersensitive 'pain receptors'.

3. The pains and new 'trigger zones' may spread unpredictably to unrelated parts of the body where no pathology exists (8, 11).

4. Pain from hyperalgesic skin areas often occurs after long delays, and continues long after removal of the stimulus (10). Gentle rubbing, repeated pin pricks, or the application of a warm test tube may produce sudden, severe pain after delays as long as 35 seconds. Such delays cannot be attributed simply to conduction in slowly conducting fibers; rather, they imply a remarkable temporal and spatial summation of inputs in the production of these pain states (8, 10).

Psychological evidence

The psychological evidence fails to support the assumption of a one-to-one relationship between pain perception and intensity of the stimulus. Instead, the evidence suggests that the amount and quality of perceived pain are determined by many psychological variables (12) in addition to the sensory input. For example, Beecher (13) has observed that most American soldiers wounded at the Anzio beach-head 'entirely denied pain from their extensive wounds or had so little that they did not want any medication to relieve it' (13, p. 165), presumably because they were overjoyed at having escaped alive from the battlefield (13). If the men had felt pain, even pain sensation devoid of negative affect, they would, it is reasonable to assume, have reported it just as lobotomized patients (14) report that they still have pain but it does not bother them. Instead, these men 'entirely denied pain'. Similarly,

Pavlov's (15, 16) dogs that received electric shocks, burns, or cuts, followed consistently by the presentation of food, eventually responded to these stimuli as signals for food and failed to show 'even the tiniest and most subtle,' (17, p. 30) signs of pain. If these dogs felt pain sensation, then it must have been nonpainful pain (17), or the dogs were out to fool Pavlov and simply refused to reveal that they were feeling pain. Both possibilities, of course, are absurd. The inescapable conclusion from these observations is that intense noxious stimulation can be prevented from producing pain, or may be modified to provide the signal for eating behaviour.

Psychophysical studies (18) that find a mathematical relationship between stimulus intensity and pain intensity are often cited (2, 13, 18, 19) as supporting evidence for the assumption that pain is a primary sensation subserved by a direct communication system from skin receptor to pain center. A simple psychophysical function, however, does not necessarily reflect equally simple neural mechanisms. Beecher's (13) and Pavlov's (15) observations show that activities in the central nervous system may intervene between stimulus and sensation which may invalidate any simple psychophysical 'law'. The use of laboratory conditions that prevent such activities from ever coming into play reduces the functions of the nervous system to those of a fixed-gain transmission line. It is under these conditions that psychophysical functions prevail.

Physiological evidence

There is convincing physiological evidence that specialization exists within the somesthetic system (9), but none to show that stimulation of one type of receptor, fiber, or spinal pathway elicits sensations only in a single psychological modality. In the search for peripheral fibers that respond exclusively to high-intensity stimulation, Hunt and McIntyre (20) found only seven out of 421 myelinated A fibers, and Maruhashi et al. (21) found 13 out of several hundred. Douglas and Ritchie (22) failed to find any high-threshold C fibers, while Iggo (23) found a few. These data suggest that a small number of specialized fibers may exist that respond only to intense stimulation but this does not mean that they are 'pain fibers' – that they must always produce pain, and only pain, when they are stimulated. It is more likely that they represent the extreme of a continuous distribution of receptor-fiber thresholds rather than a special category (24).

Similarly, there is evidence that central nervous system

pathways have specialized functions that play a role in pain mechanisms. Surgical lesions of the lateral spinothalamic tract (2) or portions of the thalamus (25) may, on occasion, abolish pain of pathological origin. But the fact that these areas carry signals related to pain does not mean that they comprise a specific pain system. The lesions have multiple effects. They reduce the total number of responding neurons; they change the temporal and spatial relationships among all ascending systems; and they affect the descending feedback that controls transmission from peripheral fibers to dorsal horn cells.

The nature of the specialization of central cells remains elusive despite the large number of single-cell studies. Cells in the dorsal horns (24, 26) and the trigeminal nucleus (27) respond to a wide range of stimuli and respond to each with a characteristic firing pattern. Central cells that respond exclusively to noxious stimuli have also been reported (28, 289). Of particular interest is Poggio and Mountcastle's (28) study of such cells in the posterior thalamus in anesthetized monkeys. Yet Casey (30), who has recently confirmed that posterior thalamic cells respond exclusively to noxious stimuli in the drowsy or sleeping monkey, found that the same cells also signalled information in response to gentle tactile stimulation when the animal was awake. Even if some central cells should be shown unequivocally to respond exclusively to noxious stimuli, their specialized properties still do not make them 'pain cells'. It is more likely that these cells represent the extreme of a broad distribution of cell thresholds to peripheral nerve firing, and that they occupy only a small area within the total multidimensional space that defines the specialized physiological properties of cells (9). There is no evidence to suggest that they are more important for pain perception and response than all the remaining somesthetic cells that signal characteristic firing patterns about multiple properties of the stimulus, including noxious intensity. The view that only the cells that respond exclusively to noxious stimuli subserve pain and that the outputs of all other cells are no more than background noise is purely a psychological assumption and has no factual basis. Physiological specialization is a fact that can be retained without acceptance of the psychological assumption that pain is determined entirely by impulses in a straight-through transmission system from the skin to a pain center in the brain.

Pattern Theory

As a reaction against the psychological assumption in specificity theory, new theories have been proposed which can be grouped under the general heading of 'pattern theory'. Goldscheider (5), initially one of the champions of von Frey's theory, was the first to propose that stimulus intensity and central summation are the critical determinants of pain. Two kinds of theories have emerged from Goldscheider's concept; both recognize the concept of patterning of the input, which we believe (9) to be essential for any adequate theory of pain, but one kind ignores the facts of physiological specialization, while the other utilizes them in proposing mechanisms of central summation.

The pattern theory of Weddell (31) and Sinclair (3) is based on the earlier suggestion, by Nafe (17), that all cutaneous qualities are produced by spatiotemporal patterns of nerve impulses rather than by separate modality-specific transmission routes. The theory proposes that all fiber endings (apart from those that innervate hair cells) are alike, so that the pattern for pain is produced by intense stimulation of nonspecific receptors. The physiological evidence, however, reveals (9) a high degree of receptor-fiber specialization. The pattern theory proposed by Weddell and Sinclair, then, fails as a satisfactory theory of pain because it ignores the facts of physiological specialization. It is more reasonable to assume that the specialized physiological properties of each receptor-fiber unit – such as response ranges, adaptation rates, and thresholds to different stimulus intensities – play an important role in determining the characteristics of the temporal patterns that are generated when a stimulus is applied to the skin (9).

Other theories have been proposed, within the framework of Goldscheider's concept, which stress central summation mechanisms rather than excessive peripheral stimulation. Livingston (8) was perhaps the first to suggest specific neural mechanisms to account for the remarkable summation phenomena in clinical pain syndromes. He proposed that intense, pathological stimulation of the body sets up reverberating circuits in spinal internuncial pools, or evokes spinal cord activities such as those reflected by the 'dorsal root reflex' (32), that can then be triggered by normally non-noxious inputs and generate abnormal volleys that are interpreted centrally as pain. Conceptually similar mechanisms were proposed by Hebb (33) and Gerard (34), who suggested that hypersynchronized firing in central cells provides the signal for pain.

Related to theories of central summation is the theory that a specialized input-controlling system normally prevents summation from occurring, and that destruction of this system leads to pathological pain states. Basically, this theory proposes the existence of a rapidly conducting fiber system which inhibits synaptic transmission in a more slowly conducting system that carries the signal for pain. These two systems are identified as the epicritic and protopathic (7), fast and slow (35), phylogenetically new and old (36), and myelinated and unmyelinated (10) fiber systems. Under pathological conditions, the slow system establishes dominance over the fast, and the result is protopathic sensation (7), slow pain (35), diffuse burning pain (36), or hyperalgesia (10). It is important to note the transition from specificity theory (7, 35, 36) to the pattern concept: Noordenbos (10) does not associate psychological quality with each system but attributes to the rapidly conducting system the ability to modify the input pattern transmitted in the slowly conducting, multisynaptic system.

The concepts of central summation and input control have shown remarkable power in their ability to explain many of the clinical phenomena of pain. The various specific theoretical mechanisms that have been proposed, however, fail to comprise a satisfactory general theory of pain. They lack unity, and no single theory so far proposed is capable of integrating the diverse theoretical mechanisms. More important, these mechanisms have not received any substantial experimental verification. We believe that recent physiological evidence on spinal mechanisms, together with the evidence demonstrating central control over afferent input, provides the basis for a new theory of pain mechanisms that is consistent with the concepts of physiological specialization as well as with those of central summation and input control.

Gate Control Theory of Pain

Stimulation of the skin evokes nerve impulses that are transmitted to three spinal cord systems (See Plate 7, central inset): the cells of the substantia gelatinosa in the dorsal horn, the dorsal-column fibers that project toward the brain, and the first central transmission (T) cells in the dorsal horn. We propose that (i) the substantia gelatinosa functions as a gate control system that modulates the afferent patterns before they influence the T cells;

(ii) the afferent patterns in the dorsal column system act, in part at least, as a central control trigger which activates selective brain processes that influence the modulating properties of the gate control system; and (iii) the T cells activate neural mechanisms which comprise the action system responsible for response and perception. Our theory proposes that pain phenomena are determined by interactions among these three systems.

Gate control system

The substantia gelatinosa consists of small, densely packed cells that form a functional unit extending the length of the spinal cord. The cells connect with one another by short fibers and by the longer fibers of Lissauer's tract (37, 38), but do not project outside the substantia gelatinosa. Recent evidence (39) suggests that the substantia gelatinosa acts as a gate control system that modulates the synaptic transmission of nerve impulses from peripheral fibers to central cells.

Figure 3 shows the factors involved in the transmission of impulses from peripheral nerve to T cells in the cord. Recent studies (39–41) have shown that volleys of nerve impulses in large fibers are extremely effective initially in activating the T cells but that their later effect is reduced by a negative feedback mechanism. In contrast, volleys in small fibers activate a positive feedback mechanism which exaggerates the effect of arriving impulses. Experiments (37, 39, 41) have shown that these feedback effects are mediated by cells in the substantia gelatinosa. Activity in these cells modulates the membrane potential of the afferent fiber terminals and thereby determines the excitatory effect of arriving impulses. Although there is evidence, so far, for only presynaptic control, there may also be undetected postsynaptic control mechanisms that contribute to the observed input–output functions.

We propose that three features of the afferent input are significant for pain: (i) the ongoing activity which precedes the stimulus, (ii) the stimulus-evoked activity, and (iii) the relative balance of activity in large versus small fibers. The spinal cord is continually bombarded by incoming nerve impulses even in the absence of obvious stimulation. This ongoing activity is carried predominantly by small myelinated and unmyelinated fibers, which tend to be tonically active and to adapt slowly, and it holds the gate in a relatively open position. When a stimulus is applied to the skin, it produces an increase in the number of active receptor-fiber units as information about the stimulus is transmitted toward the brain.

Since many of the larger fibers are inactive in the absence of stimulus change, stimulation will produce a disproportionate relative increase in large-fiber over small-fiber activity. Thus, if a gentle pressure stimulus is applied suddenly to the skin, the afferent volley contains large-fiber impulses which not only fire the T cells but also partially close the presynaptic gate, thereby shortening the barrage generated by the T cells.

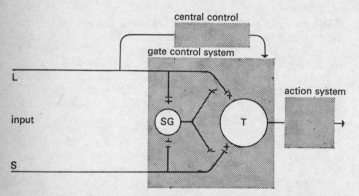

Figure 3. Schematic diagram of the gate control theory of pain mechanisms : L, the large-diameter fibers ; S, the small-diameter fibers. The fibers project to the substantia gelatinosa (SG) and first central transmission (T) cells. The inhibitory effect exerted by SG on the afferent fiber terminals is increased by activity in L fibers and decreased by activity in S fibers. The central control trigger is represented by a line running from the large-fiber system to the central control mechanisms ; these mechanisms, in turn, project back to the gate control system. The T cells project to the entry cells of the action system. +, excitation ; −, inhibition (see text)

If the stimulus intensity is increased, more receptor-fiber units are recruited and the firing frequency of active units is increased (9, 24). The resultant positive and negative effects of the large-fiber and small-fiber inputs tend to counteract each other, and therefore the output of the T cells rises slowly. If stimulation is prolonged, the large fibers begin to adapt, producing a relative increase in small-fiber activity. As a result, the gate is opened further, and the output of the T cells rises more steeply. If the large-fiber steady background activity is artificially raised at this time by vibration or scratching (a maneuver that overcomes the tendency of the large fibers to adapt), the output of the cells decreases.

Thus, the effects of the stimulus-evoked barrage are determined by (i) the total number of active fibers and the frequencies of nerve impulses that they transmit, and (ii) the balance of activity in large and small fibers. Consequently, the output of the T cells may differ from the total input that converges on them from the peripheral fibers. Although the total number of afferent impulses is a relevant stimulus parameter, the impulses have different effects depending on the specialized functions of the fibers that carry them. Furthermore, anatomical specialization also determines the location and the extent of the central terminations of the fibers (24, 41, 42).

There are two reasons for believing that pain results after prolonged monitoring of the afferent input by central cells. First, threshold for shock on one arm is raised by a shock delivered as long as 100 milliseconds later to the other arm (43). Second, in pathological pain states, delays of pain sensation as long as 35 seconds after stimulation cannot be attributed to slow conduction in afferent pathways (10). We suggest, then, that there is temporal and spatial summation or integration of the arriving barrage by the T cells. The signal which triggers the action system responsible for pain experience and response occurs when the output of the T cells reaches or exceeds a critical level. This critical level of firing, as we have seen, is determined by the afferent barrage that actually impinges on the T cells and has already undergone modulation by substantia gelatinosa activity. We presume that the action system requires a definite time period for integrating the total input from the T cells. Small, fast variations of the temporal pattern produced by the T cells might be ineffective, and the smoothed envelope of the frequency of impulses – which contains information on the rate of rise and fall, the duration, and the amplitude of firing – would be the effective stimulus that initiates the appropriate sequence of activities in the cells that comprise the action system.

Central control trigger

It is now firmly established (44) that stimulation of the brain activates descending efferent fibers (45) which can influence afferent conduction at the earliest synaptic levels of the somesthetic system. Thus it is possible for central nervous system activities subserving attention, emotion, and memories of prior experience to exert control over the sensory input. There is evidence (44) to suggest that these central influences are mediated through the gate control system.

The manner in which the appropriate central activities are triggered into action presents a problem. While some central activities, such as anxiety or excitement, may open or close the gate for all inputs at any site on the body, others obviously involve selective, localized gate activity. Men wounded in battle may feel little pain from the wound but may complain bitterly about an inept vein puncture (13). Dogs that repeatedly receive food immediately after the skin is shocked, burned, or cut soon respond to these stimuli as signals for food and salivate, without showing any signs of pain, yet howl as normal dogs would when the stimuli are applied to other sites on the body (16). The signals, then, must be identified, evaluated in terms of prior conditioning, localized, and inhibited *before* the action system is activated. We propose, therefore, that there exists in the nervous system a mechanism, which we shall call the central trigger, that activates the particular, selective brain processes that exert control over the sensory input (Figure 3). There are two known systems that could fulfil such a function, and one or both may play a role.

The first is the dorsal column–medial lemniscus system. The largest and most rapidly conducting A fibers which enter the spinal cord send short branches to the substantia gelatinosa, and long central branches directly to the dorsal column nuclei. Fibers from these nuclei form the medial lemniscus, which provides a direct route to the thalamus and thence to the somato-sensory cortex. The striking characteristics of this system are that information is transmitted rapidly from the skin to the cortex, that separation of signals evoked by different stimulus properties and precise somatotopic localization are both maintained throughout the system (46), and that conduction is relatively unaffected by anesthetic drugs (47). Traditionally, the dorsal column system is supposed to carry two-point discrimination, roughness discrimination, spatial localization, tactile threshold, and vibration (48). Complex discrimination and localization, however, are not a modality; they represent decisions based on an analysis of the input. Indeed, the traditional view is questionable in the light of Cook and Browder's (49) observation that surgical section of the dorsal columns produced no permanent change in two-point discrimination in seven patients.

The second candidate for the role of central control trigger is the dorsolateral path (50), which originates in the dorsal horn and projects, after relay in the lateral cervical nucleus, to the brain stem and thalamus. This system has small, well-defined receptive fields (51) and is extremely fast; in spite of having one additional relay, it precedes the dorsal column–medial lemniscus volley in the race to the cortex (52).

Both these systems, then, could fulfil the functions of the central control trigger. They carry precise information about the nature and location of the stimulus, and they conduct so rapidly that they may not only set the receptivity of cortical neurons for subsequent afferent volleys but may, by way of central-control efferent fibers, also act on the gate control system. Part, at least, of their function, then, could be to activate selective brain processes that influence information which is still arriving over slowly conducting fibers or is being transmitted up more slowly conducting pathways.

Action system

Pain is generally considered to be the sensory adjunct of an imperative reflex (53). Pain, however, does not consist of a single ring of the appropriate central bell, but is an ongoing process. We propose, then, that once the integrated firing-level of T cells exceeds a critical preset level, the firing triggers a sequence of responses by the action system.

Sudden, unexpected damage to the skin is followed by (i) a startle response; (ii) a flexion reflex; (iii) postural readjustment; (iv) vocalization; (v) orientation of the head and eyes to examine the damaged area; (vi) autonomic responses; (vii) evocation of past experience in similar situations and prediction of the consequences of the stimulation; (viii) many other patterns of behavior aimed at diminishing the sensory and affective components of the whole experience, such as rubbing the damaged area, avoidance behavior, and so forth.

The perceptual awareness that accompanies these events changes in quality and intensity during all this activity. This total complex sequence is hidden in the simple phrases 'pain response' and 'pain sensation'. The multiplicity of reactions demands some concept of central mechanisms which is at least capable of accounting for sequential patterns of activity that would allow the complex behavior and experience characteristic of pain.

The concept of a 'pain center' in the brain is totally inadequate to account for the sequences of behavior and experience. Indeed, the concept is pure fiction, unless virtually the whole brain is considered to be the 'pain center', because the thalamus (7, 25), the limbic system (54), the hypothalamus (55), the brain-stem reticular formation (56), the parietal cortex (57), and the frontal cortex (14) are all implicated in pain perception. Other brain areas are obviously involved in the emotional and motor features of the behavior sequence. The idea of a 'terminal center' in the brain which is exclusively responsible for pain sensation and response therefore becomes meaningless.

We propose, instead, that the triggering of the action system by the T cells marks the beginning of the sequence of activities that occur when the body sustains damage. The divergence of afferent fibers going to the dorsal horns and the dorsal column nuclei marks only the first stage of the process of selection and abstraction of information. The stimulation of a single tooth results in the eventual activation of no less than five distinct brain-stem pathways (58). Two of these pathways project to cortical somatosensory areas I and II (59), while the remainder activate the thalamic reticular formation and the limbic system (60), so that the input has access to neural systems involved in affective (54) as well as sensory activities. It is presumed that interactions occur among all these systems as the organism interacts with the environment.

We believe that the interactions between the gate control system and the action system described above may occur at successive synapses at any level of the central nervous system in the course of filtering of the sensory input. Similarly, the influence of central activities on the sensory input may take place at a series of levels. The gate control system may be set and reset a number of times as the temporal and spatial patterning of the input is analysed and acted on by the brain.

Adequacy of the Theory

The concept of interacting gate control and action systems can account for the hyperalgesia, spontaneous pain, and long delays after stimulation characteristic of pathological pain syndromes. The state of hyperalgesia would require two conditions: (i) enough conducting peripheral axons to generate an input that can activate the action system (if, as in the case of leprosy, all components of the peripheral nerve are equally affected, there is a gradual onset of anesthesia), and (ii) a marked loss of the large peripheral nerve fibers, which may occur after traumatic peripheral-nerve lesions or in some of the neuropathies (61), such as post-herpetic neuralgia (10). Since most of the larger fibers are destroyed, the normal presynaptic inhibition of the input by the gate control system does not occur. Thus, the input arriving over the remaining myelinated and unmyelinated fibers is transmitted through the unchecked, open gate produced by the C-fiber input.

Spatial summation would easily occur under such conditions. Any nerve impulses, no matter how they were generated, which converge on the central cells would contribute to the output of these cells. These mechanisms may account for the fact that non-noxious stimuli, such as gentle pressure, can trigger severe pain in patients suffering causalgia, phantom limb pain, and the neuralgias. The well-known enhancement of pain in these patients during emotional disturbance and sexual excitement (62) might be due to increased sensory firing as a result of an increased sympathetic outflow (63, 64) which is unchecked by presynaptic inhibition. Conversely, the absence of small fibers in the dorsal roots in a patient with congenital insensitivity to pain (65) suggests that the mechanisms for facilitation and summation necessary for pain may be absent.

Spontaneous pain can also be explained by these mechanisms. The smaller fibers show considerable spontaneous activity, which would have the effect of keeping the gate open. Low-level, random, ongoing activity would then be transmitted relatively unchecked (because of the predominant loss of A fibers), and summation could occur, producing spontaneous pain in the absence of stimulation. This is a possible mechanism for the pains of anesthesia dolorosa and the 'spontaneous' pains which develop after peripheral nerve and dorsal-root lesions. Because the total number of peripheral fibers is reduced, it may take considerable time for the T cells to reach the firing level necessary to trigger pain responses, so perception and response are delayed. This same mechanism can also account for post-ischemic pressure-block hyperesthesia and for the delays in sensation of as much as 10 seconds which occur when the large peripheral fibers fail to conduct (66).

We propose that the A-fiber input normally acts to prevent summation from occurring. This would account for Adrian's (67) failure to obtain pain responses in the frog from high-frequency air blasts which fired peripheral nerves close to their maximum firing rate, in an experiment meant to refute the view that summation of the effects of noxious stimuli is important for pain. It is now clear that the air blasts would tend to fire a high proportion of the low-threshold A fibers, which would exert presynaptic inhibition on the input by way of the gate control system; thus the impulses would be prevented from reaching the T cells where summation might occur. The double effect of an arriving volley is well illustrated by the effects of vibration on pain and itch. Vibration activates fibers of all diameters, but activates a larger proportion of A fibers, since they tend to adapt during constant stimulation, whereas C-fiber firing is maintained. Vibration therefore sets the gate in a more closed position. However, the same impulses which set the gate also bombard the T cell and therefore summate with the inputs from noxious stimulation. It is observed behaviorally (26, 68) that vibration reduces low-intensity, but enhances high-intensity, pain and itch. Similar mechanisms may account for the fact that amputees sometimes obtain relief from phantom limb pain by tapping the stump gently with a rubber mallet (69), whereas heavier pressure aggravates the pain (8).

The phenomena of referred pain, spread of pain, and trigger points at some distance from the original site of body damage also point toward summation mechanisms, which can be understood in terms of the model. The T cell has a restricted receptive field which dominates its 'normal activities'. In addition, there is a widespread, diffuse, monosynaptic input to the cell, which is revealed by electrical stimulation of distant afferents (41). We suggest that this diffuse input is normally inhibited by presynaptic gate mechanisms, but may trigger firing in the cell if the input is sufficiently intense or if there is a change in gate activity. Because the cell remains dominated by its receptive field, anesthesia of the area to which the pain is referred, from which only spontaneous impulses are originating, is sufficient to reduce the bombardment of the cell below the threshold level for pain. The gate can also be opened by activities in distant body areas, since the substantia gelatinosa at any level receives inputs from both sides of the body and (by way of Lissauer's tract) from the substantia gelatinosa in neighboring body segments. Mechanisms such as these may explain the observations that stimulation of trigger points on the chest and arms may trigger anginal pain (70), or that pressing other body areas, such as the back of the head, may trigger pain in the phantom limb (11).

The sensory mechanisms alone fail to account for the fact that nerve lesions do not always produce pain and that, when they do, the pain is usually not continuous. We propose that the presence or absence of pain is determined by the balance between the sensory and the central inputs to the gate control system. In addition to the sensory influences on the gate control system, there is a tonic input to the system from higher levels of the central nervous system which exerts an inhibitory effect on the sensory input (44, 71). Thus, any lesion that impairs the normal downflow of impulses to the gate control system would open the gate. Central nervous system lesions associated with hyperalgesia and spontaneous pain (7) could have this effect. On the other hand, any central nervous system condition that increases the flow of descending impulses would tend to close the gate. Increased central firing due to denervation supersensitivity (72) might be one of these conditions. A peripheral nerve lesion, then, would have the *direct* effect of opening the gate, and the *indirect* effect, by increasing central firing and thereby increasing the tonic descending influences on the gate control system, of closing the gate. The balance between sensory facilitation and central inhibition of the input after peripheral-nerve lesion would account for the variability of pain even in cases of severe lesion.

The model suggests that psychological factors such as past experience, attention, and emotion influence pain response and perception by acting on the gate control system. The degree of central control, however, would be determined, in part at least, by the temporal-spatial properties of the input patterns. Some of the most unbearable pains, such as cardiac pain, rise so rapidly in intensity that the patient is unable to achieve any control over them. On the other hand, more slowly rising temporal patterns are susceptible to central control and may allow the patient to 'think about something else' or use other stratagems to keep the pain under control (73).

The therapeutic implications of the model are twofold. First, it suggests that control of pain may be achieved by selectively influencing the large, rapidly conducting fibers. The gate may be closed by decreasing the small-fiber input and also by enhancing the large-fiber input. Thus, Livingston (74) found that causalgia could be effectively cured by therapy such as bathing the limb in gently moving water, followed by massage, which would increase the input in the large-fiber system. Similarly, Trent (75) reports a case of pain of central nervous system origin which could be brought under control when the patient tapped his fingers on a hard surface. Conversely, any manipulation that cuts down the sensory input lessens the opportunity for summation and pain, within the functional limits set by the opposing roles of the large- and small-fiber systems. Second, the model suggests that a better understanding of the pharmacology and physiology of the substantia gelatinosa may lead to new ways of controlling pain. The resistance of the substantia gelatinosa to nerve-cell stains suggests that its chemistry differs from that of other neural tissue. Drugs affecting excitation or inhibition of substantia gelatinosa activity may be of particular importance in future attempts to control pain.

The model suggests that the action system responsible for pain perception and response is triggered after the cutaneous sensory input has been modulated by both sensory feedback mechanisms and the influences of the central nervous system. We propose that the abstraction of information at the first synapse may mark only the beginning of a continuing selection and filtering of the input. Perception and response involve classification of the multitude of patterns of nerve impulses arriving from the skin and are functions of the capacity of the brain to select and to abstract from all the information it receives from the somesthetic system as a whole (7–9). A 'modality' class such as 'pain', which is a linguistic label for a rich variety of experiences and responses, represents just such an abstraction from the information that is sequentially re-examined over long periods by the entire somesthetic system.

References

1. K. M. DALLENBACH, *Amer. J. Physiol.* 52, 331 (1939); K. D. KEELE, *Anatomies of Pain*, Blackwell, Oxford, 1957.
2. W. H. SWEET, *Handbook Physiol.* 1, 459 (1959).
3. D. C. SINCLAIR, *Brain* 78, 584 (1955).
4. M. VON FREY, *Ber. Kgl. Sächs. Ges. Wiss.* 46, 185 (1894); *ibid.*, p. 283.
5. A. GOLDSCHEIDER, *Ueber den Schmerz in physiologischer und klinischer Hinsicht*, Hirschwald, Berlin, 1894.
6. G. H. BISHOP, *Physiol. Rev.* 26, 77 (1946); A-delta fibers are the smallest myelinated fibers and C fibers are the unmyelinated fibers, in the peripheral nerve.
7. H. HEAD, *Studies in Neurology*, Keegan Paul, London, 1920.
8. W. K. LIVINGSTON, *Pain Mechanisms*, Macmillan, New York, 1943.
9. R. MELZACK and P. D. WALL, *Brain* 85, 331 (1962).
10. W. NOORDENBOS, *Pain*, Elsevier, Amsterdam, 1959.
11. B. CRONHOLM, *Acta Psychiat. Neurol. Scand. Suppl.* 72, 1 (1951).
12. W. K. LIVINGSTON, *Sci. Amer.* 88, 59 (1953); R. MELZACK, *ibid.* 204, 41 (1961); T. X. BARBER, *Psychol. Bull*, 56, 430 (1959).
13. H. K. BEECHER, *Measurement of Subjective Responses*, Oxford Univ. Press, New York, 1959.
14. W. FREEMAN and I. W. WATTS, *Psychosurgery in the Treatment of Mental Disorders and Intractable Pain*, Thomas, Springfield, Ill., 1950.
15. I. P. PAVLOV, *Conditioned Reflexes*, Milford, Oxford 1927.
16. I. P. PAVLOV, *Lectures on Conditioned Reflexes*, International Publishers, New York, 1928.
17. J. P. NAFE, in *Handbook of General Experimental Psychology*, C. Murchison, ed., Clark Univ. Press, Worcester, Mass., 1934.
18. J. D. HARDY, H. G. WOLFF, H. GOODELL, *Pain Sensations and Reactions*, Williams and Wilkins, Baltimore, 1952.

19. C. T. MORGAN, *Introduction to Psychology*, McGraw-Hill, New York, 1961.
20. C. C. HUNT and A. K. McINTYRE, *J. Physiol. London* 153, 88, 99, (1960).
21. J. MARUHASHI, K. MIZAGUCHI, I. TASAKI, *ibid.* 117, 129 (1952).
22. W. W. DOUGLAS and J. M. RITCHIE, *ibid.* 139, 385 (1957).
23. A. IGGO, *ibid.* 143, 47 (1958).
24. P. D. WALL, *J. Neurophysiol.* 23, 197 (1960).
25. V. H. MARK, F. R. ERVIN, P. I. YAKOVLEV, *Arch. Neurol.* 8, 528 (1963).
26. P. D. WALL and J. R. CRONLY-DILLON, *ibid.* 2, 365 (1960).
27. P. D. WALL and A. TAUB, *J. Neurophysiol.* 25, 110 (1962); L. KRUGER and F. MICHEL, *Exp. Neurol.* 5, 157 (1962).
28. G. F. POGGIO and V. B. MOUNTCASTLE, *Bull. Johns Hopkins Hosp.* 106, 226 (1960).
29. G. M. KOLMODIN and C. R. SKOGLUND, *Acta Physiol. Scand.* 50, 337 (1960); G. GORDON, S. LANDGREN, W. A. SEED, *J. Physiol. London* 158, 544 (1960); J. S. EISENMAN, S. LANDGREN, D. NOVIN, *Acta Physiol. Scand. Suppl.* 214, 1 (1963).
30. K. L. CASEY, *A Search for Nociceptive Elements in the Thalamus of the Awake Squirrel Monkey*, paper read at the 16th Autumn meeting of the American Physiological Society, Providence, R.I., 1964.
31. G. WEDDELL, *Annu. Rev. Psychol.* 6, 119 (1955).
32. D. H. BARRON and B. H. C. MATTHEWS, *J. Physiol. London* 92, 276 (1938).
33. D. O. HEBB, *The Organization of Behavior*, Wiley, New York, 1949.
34. R. W. GERARD, *Anesthesiology* 12, 1 (1951).
35. T. LEWIS, *Pain*, Macmillan, New York, 1942.
36. G. H. BISHOP, *J. Nerv. Ment. Dis.* 128, 89 (1959).
37. P. D. WALL, *Progr. Brain Res.* 12, 92 (1964).
38. J. SZENTAGOTHAI, *J. Comp. Neurol.* 122, 219 (1964).
39. P. D. WALL, *J. Physiol. London* 164, 508 (1964); L. M. MENDELL and P. D. WALL, *ibid.* 172, 274 (1964).
40. P. D. WALL, *J. Neurophysiol.* 22, 205 (1959); *J. Physiol. London* 142, 1 (1958).
41. L. M. MENDELL and P. D. WALL, *Nature* 206, 97 (1965).
42. D. G. WHITLOCK and E. R. PERL, *Exp. Neurol.* 3, 240 (1961).
43. A. M. HALLIDAY and R. MINGAY, *Quart. J. Exp. Psychol.* 13, 1 (1961).
44. K. E. HAGBARTH and D. I. B. KERR, *J. Neurophysiol.* 17, 295 (1954).
45. H. G. J. M. KUYPERS, W. R. FLEMING, J. W. FARINHOLT, *Science* 132, 38 (1960); A. LUNDBERG, *Progr. Brain Res.* 12, 197 (1964).
46. V. B. MOUNTCASTLE, in *Sensory Communication*, W. A. Rosenblith, ed., Massachusetts Institute of Technology, Cambridge, 1961.
47. J. D. FRENCH, M. VERZEANO, W. H. MAGOUN, *A.M.A. Arch. Neurol. Psychiat.* 69, 519 (1953); F. P. HAUGEN and R. MELZACK, *Anesthesiology* 18, 183 (1957).
48. T. C. RUCH and J. F. FULTON, *Medical Physiology and Biophysics*, Saunders, Philadelphia, 1960.

49. A. W. COOK and E. J. BROWDER, *Arch. Neurol.* **12**, 72 (1965).
50. F. MORIN, *Amer. J. Physiol.* **183**, 245 (1955).
51. E. OSWALDO-CRUZ and C. KIDD, *J. Neurophysiol.* **27**, 1 (1964).
52. U. NORRSELL and P. VOERHOEVE, *Acta Physiol. Scand.* **54**, 9 (1962).
53. C. S. SHERRINGTON, in *Textbook of Physiology*, E. A. Schäfer, ed., Pentland, Edinburgh, 1900.
54. J. V. BRADY, *Handbook Physiol.* **3**, 1529 (1960).
55. W. R. HESS, *Diencephalon: Autonomic and Extrapyramidal Functions*, Grune, New York, 1954.
56. J. M. R. DELGADO, *J. Neurophysiol.* **18**, 261 (1955); R. MELZACK, W. A. STOTLER, W. K. LIVINGSTON, *ibid.* **21**, 353 (1958).
57. P. SCHILDER and E. STENGEL, *A.M.A. Arch. Neurol. Psychiat.* **25**, 598 (1931).
58. D. I. B. KERR, F. P. HAUGEN, R. MELZACK, *Amer. J. Physiol.* **183**, 253 (1955).
59. R. MELZACK and F. P. HAUGEN, *ibid.* **190**, 570 (1957).
60. W. J. H. NAUTA and H. G. J. M. KUYPERS, in *Reticular Formation of the Brain*, H. H. Jasper *et al.*, ed., Little, Brown, Boston, 1958.
61. W. BLACKWOOD, W. H. MCMENEMEY, A. MEYER, R. M. NORMAN, D. S. RUSSELL, *Greenfield's Neuropathology*, Arnold, London, 1963.
62. W. R. HENDERSON and G. E. SMYTH, *J. Neurol. Neurosurg. Psychiat.* **11**, 88 (1948).
63. K. F. CHERNETSKI, *J. Neurophysiol.* **27**, 493 (1964).
64. J. DOUPE, C. H. CULLEN, G. O. CHANCE, *J. Neurol. Neurosurg. Psychiat.* **7**, 33 (1944).
65. A. G. SWANSON, G. C. BUCHAN, E. C. ALVORD, *Arch. Neurol.* **12**, 12 (1965).
66. D. C. SINCLAIR and J. R. HINSHAW, *Brain* **74**, 318 (1951).
67. E. D. ADRIAN, *The Basis of Sensation: The Action of Sense Organs*, Christophers, London, 1928.
68. R. MELZACK, P. D. WALL, A. Z. WEISZ, *Exp. Neurol.* **8**, 35 (1963); R. MELZACK and B. SCHECTER, *Science* **147**, 1047 (1965).
69. W. R. RUSSELL and J. M. K. SPALDING, *Brit. Med. J.* **2**, 68 (1950).
70. H. COHEN, *Trans. Med. Soc. London* **64**, 65 (1944).
71. A. TAUB, *Exp. Neurol.* **10**, 357 (1964).
72. G. W. STAVRAKY, *Supersensitivity Following Lesions of the Nervous System*, Univ. of Toronto Press, 1961; S. K. SHARPLESS, *Annu. Rev. Physiol.* **26**, 357 (1964).
73. R. MELZACK, A. Z. WEISZ, L. T. SPRAGUE, *Exp. Neurol.* **8**, 239 (1963).
74. W. K. LIVINGSTON, *Ann. N.Y. Acad. Sci.* **50**, 247 (1948).
75. S. E. TRENT, *J. Nerv. Ment. Dis.* **123**, 356 (1956).
76. R. DESCARTES, 'L'Homme' (Paris, 1644), M. FOSTER, transl., in *Lectures on the History of Physiology during the 16th, 17th and 18th Centuries*, Cambridge Univ. Press, Cambridge, England, 1901.
77. C. S. MACCARTY and R. L. DRAKE, *Proc. Staff Meetings Mayo Clinic* **31**, 208 (1956).

7 G. F. Poggio and V. B. Mountcastle

A Study of the Functional Contributions of the Lemniscal and Spinothalamic Systems to Somatic Sensibility

Excerpt from G. F. Poggio and V. B. Mountcastle, 'A study of the functional contributions of the lemniscal and spinothalamic systems to somatic sensibility', *Bull. Johns Hopkins Hospital*, vol. 106 (1960), pp. 283–316.

[. . .]

The results obtained [to experiments described in the omitted section of this article] are epitomized by a description of the observations made in one penetration of PO. This track is reconstructed to the left of Figure 1, which shows that the electrode passed through the posterior third of the area. The symbols indicate that the electrode first traversed a region in which cells activated by sound and those sensitive to somatic sensory stimulation were mixed, more or less indiscriminately. In the lowest $550\,\mu$ of the passage only cells of the latter type were encountered. The figurine drawings to the right of Figure 1 show the peripheral fields of the cells sensitive to somatic stimulation. It is clear that these cells may be driven by diverse types of stimuli, that their receptive fields are very large, and that there is no clear pattern of representation of the body form in this region. We will describe these properties in more detail, as well as others not illustrated by the results of this particular penetration.

The Modality Properties of PO Neurons

One characteristic feature of the cells of PO is that a majority of them can be activated only by peripheral stimuli which may reasonably be regarded as destructive of tissue. The stimuli employed were such as to produce withdrawal-escape or vigorous attack in waking animals, active flexion, and respiratory reflexes in lightly anesthetized cats, and overt pain in humans. Seventy-one of the 123 neurons sensitive to somatic stimulation which we have studied were of this class (see Table 1). Some of these responded to pin-pricks or shallow cuts of the skin, but to no form of reasonably gentle mechanical stimulation, delivered to the same skin areas. Other neurons which we have classified as nociceptive responded only to heavy compressions of the limbs, or to kneading of the periosteum, and were not activated by any form of stimulation – mechanical or noxious – delivered to the

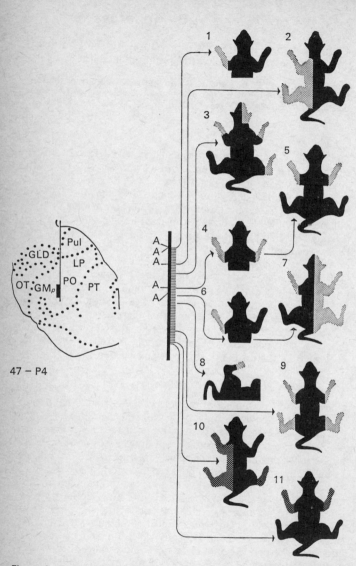

47 – P4

Figure 1. See caption opposite

skin. We have never observed a PO neuron which responded to gentle rotation of a joint, a property characteristic of a large group of VB neurons. The remaining 52 PO neurons could be activated by gentle displacement of hairs, or by light skin pressure. In this property they resembled VB neurons. However, only 8 of the 52 were related to restricted and specific contralateral peripheral receptive fields, in the VB manner. As Table 1 indicates, 23 of the 52 had stocking-like fields on one or both contralateral limbs, and the remaining 21 could be driven by stimuli to either side of the body.

A second and very striking feature of PO neurons is that the adequate driving stimulus is in many cases not specific, as are those for the cells of VB. In 12 instances we studied cells which could be activated by light mechanical stimulation of one part of the peripheral receptive field, and only by destructive stimuli to another part, and this phenomenon has been observed for many other cells not sufficiently well isolated for study. Neuron 48-2 provides a typical instance. Its peripheral receptive fields are shown in Figure 5 (48-cc). The cell could be activated by hair movement or light skin pressure from stocking-like receptive fields on each of the four extremities. These response patterns are illustrated in Figure 2. On the ipsilateral side, as the stimulus was moved upward beyond the proximal edges of the mechanoreceptive field, it was found that forceps pinches and pin-pricks were potently effective in producing responses of the cell, while brush movements or air jets were no longer adequate. This is illustrated by the records and charts of Figure 3.

Figure 1. Representation of the data obtained in a microelectrode penetration which passed through the posterior nuclear group of the thalamus (47–P4). The reconstruction of the penetration, made from study of the serial sections, is depicted by the drawing to the left. In the region marked by the heavy line active and drivable neurons were observed which displayed the 'posterior group properties' described in the text. The responsive region is indicated by the expanded scale (20 μ intervals) shown to the right. As indicate levels at which neurons were isolated which were activated only by sound. Figurine drawings 1 through 9 show (light chequered shading) the peripheral receptive fields of cells which were activated by light mechanical stimuli delivered to the body surface, whereas the cells whose receptive fields are shown (dark chequered shading) by drawings 10 and 11 could be activated only by stimuli which were destructive of tissue. It is important to note that here the sequence of receptive fields composes no topographical pattern. In other penetrations of the posterior group the auditory, nociceptive, and mechanoreceptive cells were indiscriminately mixed in the dorso-ventral direction

Table 1

The Location and Extent of the Excitatory Peripheral Receptive Fields for Cells of the Posterior Nuclear Group of the Thalamus, Correlated with the Optimal Driving Stimulus for Each

	Skin TP	Skin NC	Deep NC	Totals
Contralateral receptive fields				
Contra forelimb, stocking-like	19	0	4	23
Contra hindlimb, stocking-like	1	0	9	10
Contra limbs, with some parts of body or face	3	0	0	3
Contra fields, restricted and specific	8	1	0	9
Totals	31	1	13	45
Ipsilateral receptive fields				
Ipsi forelimb, stocking-like	0	1	2	3
Ipsi hindlimb, stocking-like	0	1	1	2
Ipsi limbs, and part of ipsi body or face	0	1	3	4
Totals	0	3	6	9
Bilateral receptive fields				
All four limbs, with or without body parts	14	14	17	45
Symmetrical pairs of limbs, with or without face or body	5	3	8	16
One entire side, and one limb of the other side	1	1	1	3
Tail only	1	0	4	5
Totals	21	18	30	69
Overall Totals	52	22	49	123

TP—Touch-Pressure; NC—Nociceptive.

Not only are many PO cells polyvalent with respect to such different forms of somatic sensory stimuli, but some can be activated by auditory or vibratory stimuli as well. It was a common observation that neurons responsive to either noxious or light mechanical stimuli to the skin of the body were also activated

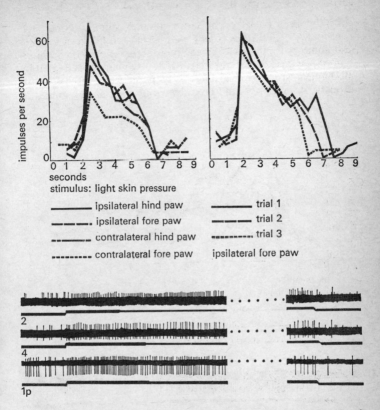

Figure 2. The data presented here were obtained during the study of neuron 48cc–2, which was located in the posterior nuclear group of the thalamus. Its receptive field is indicated by a figurine drawing shown in Figure 5. The cell could be driven by light mechanical stimulation of each of the four limbs and by nociceptive stimulation of the ipsilateral trunk, body, and proximal limbs, at which sites light mechanical stimulation was ineffective. The family of impulse frequency v. time curves to the left plots the responses evoked by steady light skin pressure to each of the four limbs; the stimulation periods are indicated by the lines above. The records obtained during stimulation of the two forelimbs are reproduced below (records 2 and 4). The family of curves to the right plots the responses to three steady stimuli delivered to the ipsilateral forepaw, at intervals of 5 minutes. They illustrate the remarkable reproducibility of response pattern observed for this cell. After a period of observation, the spike potential of this cell reversed its initial sign, as shown by the lowest record, 1p, but showed no other change in its properties. The neuron was observed for 40 minutes

either by brief clicks or by more complex sounds. Nine such neurons were studied in some detail. Occlusion between somatic and auditory inputs was the common observation, and summation of response occurred rarely. Many PO neurons activated by mechanical stimuli of distant body parts were insensitive to acoustic stimuli but could be activated by mechanical stimuli to

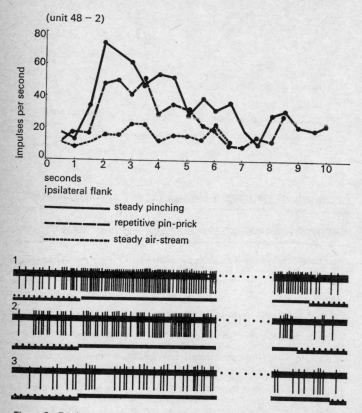

Figure 3. Further study of neuron 48cc–2. Records 1 and 2, shown below, were obtained during nociceptive stimulation of the ipsilateral flank. Record 3 was obtained during stimulation of the same body region with a steady stream of air. The impulse frequency v. time charts shown above indicate that the neuron was responsive to the first but not to the second form of stimulation. The neuron was sensitive to light mechanical stimuli delivered to other portions of its receptive field (see Figure 5)

the bone of the head (and frequently only on one side) which suggests, with of course no proof, that vestibular activation was effective in producing the responses. Finally, many neurons located within the confines of P O were sensitive *only* to acoustic stimuli, and we have studied 24 of them in some detail. These were frequently intermingled in an almost random fashion with those responding only to somatic stimuli and with those responding to both.

Table 2

Correlations Between the Modality Types, the Receptive Fields, and the Anatomical Locations of Neurons of the Posterior Group of Nuclei

	I	II	III	Totals		Skin TP	Skin NC	Deep NC	Totals		Skin TP	Skin NC	Deep NC	Totals
A	11	0	8	19	A	4	4	11	19	I	31	1	13	45
B	18	9	38	65	B	16	14	35	65	II	0	3	6	9
C	16	0	23	39	C	32	4	3	39	III	21	18	30	69
Totals	45	9	69	123		52	22	49	123		52	22	49	123

A, B, and C are the three arbitrary A–P divisions of the posterior group of nuclei.
I, II, and III are the three types of receptive fields described in Table 2.
Skin TP, Skin NC, and Deep NC refer to the three modality types described in the text.

These forms of modality interaction were not the only ones observed. While we have not yet employed discrete thermal stimuli delivered to the skin, in the absence of a simultaneous mechanical stimulation, we have observed a remarkable effect of skin temperature upon the excitability of P O neurons. We have observed a drop in skin temperature, with a steady deep core temperature of 38°C., to produce a profound reduction in the spontaneous activity of P O cells, and a complete loss of their drivability by somatic stimuli. Both forms of activity then reappear upon warming the skin. We have so far not made a quantitative study of this phenomenon. It can be interpreted as a central effect produced by the changing frequency of discharge of thermosensitive cutaneous afferents, or as a sign of a peripheral effect upon other cutaneous receptors. In either case it suggests again the unspecific modality properties of P O neurons.

The figures of Table 2 indicate that the property of response to nociceptive stimuli is strongly correlated with large bilateral receptive fields, and that neurons sensitive to light mechanical stimuli which are not noxious in nature are more likely to be found in the posterior third of the region.

In summary, whereas the cells of VB are responsive to highly specific mechanical stimuli delivered to the skin, those of P O are in the majority sensitive to noxious stimuli. While VB neurons are modality specific, those of P O may be responsive to very diverse types of stimuli, and frequently the same cell may respond to light mechanical stimulation of one part of its receptive field, to noxious stimulation of another part of the field, and to auditory or vibratory stimuli as well. P O neurons are *not modality specific*, and they frequently are responsive to stimuli which, when applied in man, are provocative of pain.

Topographic Properties of P O Neurons

The lack of topographic representation illustrated by Figure 1 is typical of our total experience, and in no single one of the penetrations of P O have we observed an orderly sequence of the receptive fields of its neurons. In fact, it is a common event to observe two cells, whose action potentials are present simultaneously in the record, to be related to receptive fields that are very widely separated on the body. An example is given in Figure 4, which shows the receptive fields of two adjacent cells. Neuron 50-7 was polyvalent, responding to light mechanical stimuli to the ipsilateral forepaw, and to noxious stimuli over a larger field covering most of the foreleg. Neuron 50–8, on the other hand, was unaffected by such ipsilateral foreleg stimuli, but was sensitive to light mechanical stimulation of the postaxial side of the contralateral hindleg, and the base of the tail. No interactions of any kind were observed.

The data of Table 1 indicate the great variety of the locations and extents of the receptive fields of PO neurons. Of the 123 cells, 69 had receptive fields covering parts of both sides of the body, and 45 of these fields extended to all four limbs. Forty-five other cells had fields restricted to the contralateral side of the body, yet only 9 of these had restricted and specific fields of the V B type. Thirty-three of these 45 had stocking-like fields covering one entire contralateral limb, and 3 of these covered both of the contralateral limbs. Only 9 cells were observed whose receptive fields were restricted to the ipsilateral side of the body. Each field described is the maximal extent of the field for each unit which was determined while it was under observation. How the receptive fields may change in size is indicated below.

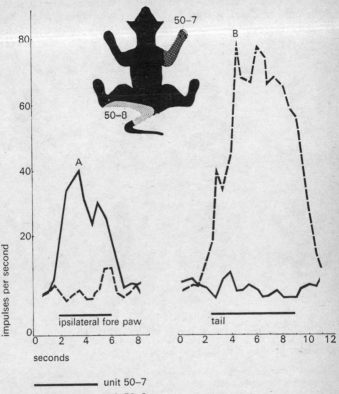

Figure 4. The electrical signs of the impulse discharges of neurons 50–7 and 50–8 were observed simultaneously, at the same recording position within the posterior nuclear group. The first was responsive to light mechanical stimulation of the preaxial side of the ipsilateral forepaw (white), and to noxious stimulation delivered to a much larger field covering most of the ipsilateral foreleg (dark chequered shading). The second cell, however, was activated by light mechanical stimuli delivered to the base of the tail and the postaxial side of the contralateral hip and hindleg (light chequered shading). The graphs indicate the response patterns of the two cells when stimuli were delivered first to the ipsilateral forefoot (A), and then to the other receptive field (B). No interaction was observed. The very wide separation of the two receptive fields illustrates the lack of topographical pattern of representation of the body surface within the posterior group of nuclei

Eight examples of bilateral receptive fields are shown in Figure 5. Each of these neurons was activated by stimulation of the skin: 5 by light mechanical stimuli, 2 by noxious stimuli, and 1 was responsive to either, with different receptive fields for each form of stimulation. In 4 of the cases shown the receptive fields were

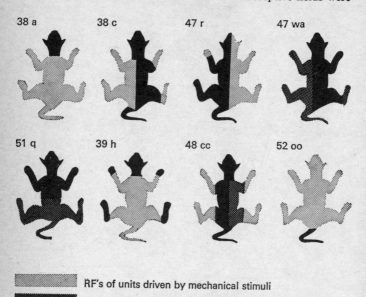

RF's of units driven by mechanical stimuli

RF's of units driven by noxious stimuli

Figure 5. A representative sample of the receptive fields of neurons of the posterior nuclear group of the thalamus. Five of these cells (38a, 38c, 47r, 39h, and 52oo) were activated by light mechanical stimuli. Two were responsive only to noxious stimuli (47wa, 51q), while one (48cc) was responsive to either form of stimulation but the receptive fields for the two forms were not identical. The ipsilateral side of the body is indicated to the right of the figurine drawings

discontinuous in distribution, and this has been a common observation. In contrast, we have never observed a discontinuous receptive field for a cell of VB. The figures of Table 2 indicate that (a) such large bilateral, frequently discontinuous, receptive fields are positively correlated with the nociceptive modalities, and (b) are found for cells distributed throughout the full extent of PO.

In one other aspect the cells of PO are so different from those of VB as to deserve special comment. That is, their extreme susceptibility to the conditions of the experiment. Some mention has been made of the effect of skin temperature upon the excitability of PO neurons. However, it is in relation to the depth of anesthesia that the most extreme variability is observed. With very slight changes in anesthetic level very wide receptive fields may shrink, for example, from one covering the entire body to one covering but a single limb. On the other hand, we have frequently seen the reverse. That is, units which when first isolated subtend limited receptive fields may, with the passage of time and lightening anesthesia, become responsive to stimuli delivered within very large and frequently bilateral receptive fields. It is because of this effect of anesthesia, in reducing field size, that we suggest that in the unanesthetized state a large percentage of PO neurons are likely to be drivable from any place on the body. This variability may be due to oscillating levels of supraspinal control of synaptic transmission at the segmental level.

It is not only the topography of receptive field that is so affected by the anesthetic agent, for we have commonly observed polyvalent neurons to lose their multiplicity of responsiveness with further small injections of thiopental. Such an injection may wipe out entirely the nociceptive field and shrink the mechanoreceptive one. Further, such injections render many PO neurons completely undrivable. It is for these reasons that we think it possible that in the unanesthetized state a large majority of PO neurons may be brought to action by nociceptive stimuli.

Response Properties of PO Neurons

Responses to brief stimuli

Cells of PO related to the skin respond to brief supramaximal mechanical or electrical stimuli delivered to the skin with short high frequency trains of 2–7 impulses, much as do cells of VB (60). While some cells of PO may respond with latencies as brief as those of the cells of VB, others display latencies some 2–3 times longer. In a typical instance, a skin-nociceptive neuron whose receptive field covered the entire body responded as follows (averages of 15 trials each): contralateral foreleg, 20·7 msec.; contralateral hindleg, 28·4 msec.; ipsilateral foreleg, 23·4 msec.; ipsilateral hindleg, 37·8 msec.; contralateral face, 14·7 msec.; ipsilateral face, 24·4 msec. These are to be compared with latencies for cells of VB with these orders of magnitude: face, 3–4

169

msec.; foreleg, 8–11 msec.; hindleg, 11–14 msec.; all contralateral. In general the latencies lengthen as the stimulated site is moved caudally over the body.

A cell of VB responds with a maximal number of impulses when the stimulus is at or near the center of its receptive field.

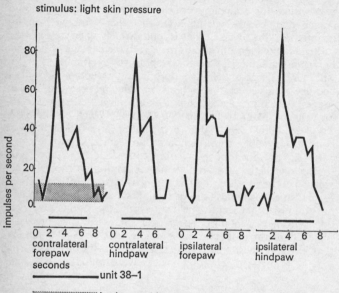

Figure 6. Graphs of the impulse frequency of neuron 38–1 which illustrate the similarity in degree and temporal pattern of the response of this cell to steady, light mechanical stimulation of the skin of each of the four paws. The bars at the bottom of each curve indicate the approximate time and duration of each stimulus. The shaded area indicates the 'spontaneous' rate of discharge of the cell in the absence of any stimulation. The results illustrate the uniformity of the projection of receptive fields upon some neurons of the posterior group of nuclei of the thalamus

The potency for excitation of a stimulus then decreases gradually as it is moved towards the edge of the field. PO neurons usually show a quite different relation. An example is given in Figure 6. It shows that neuron 38–1 responded in almost the same degree and temporal pattern to light skin pressure delivered to any one of the four limbs. Other neurons of this type may be less responsive to stimulation in one part of the field than in others, e.g. from one of the four limbs, but respond in the same degree to stimuli delivered anywhere else in the field. That is to say that the fields may be almost equipotential with respect to place in their capacity to excite the related PO cell, up to nearly the edge of the field. This has been observed for both steady physiological and brief electrical stimuli.

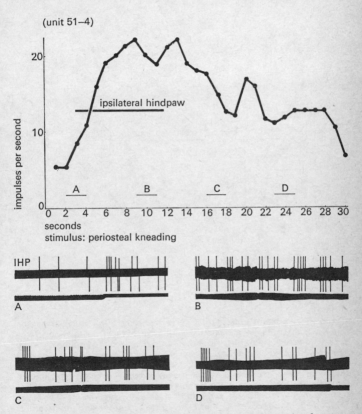

Figure 7. This figure presents data obtained during the study of neuron 51–4, which was activated only by noxious stimuli delivered to the deep tissues of any part of the body, except for the face. The graph indicates the slow recruitment of activity during periosteal kneading, and the prolonged after-discharge which followed it. Records A, B, C and D are samples taken at times indicated on the graph above

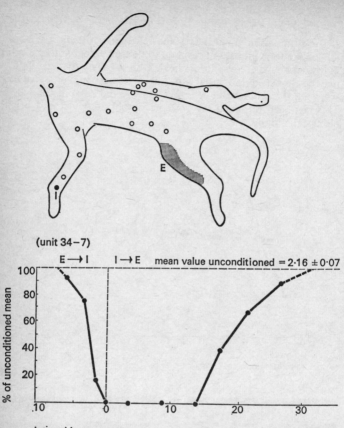

(unit 34—7)

E → I   I → E   mean value unconditioned = 2·16 ± 0·07

interval in msec.

Figure 8. This figure presents data obtained during the study of neuron 34—7, which could be activated by light mechanical stimulation of the preaxial side of the contralateral hindleg, as indicated in the figurine drawing. The neuron could be inhibited by similar stimuli delivered to any spot on a very large part of the remainder of the body surface, including the face. Inhibition was tested from the spots indicated by the circles on the figurine drawing. An inhibition (I)—excitation (E) series was done with electrical stimuli delivered to the skin at the spots marked on the drawing. The curve of inhibition and recovery from it is given below. In making the graph no allowance has been given for the presumed shorter latency of the inhibitory effect from the foreleg than the excitatory from the hindleg which accounts, we believe, for the fact that inhibition seemingly exists when the excitatory stimulus leads. Each point on the curve indicates the mean number of impulses per response (15 trials) for the conditioned response, expressed as a percentage of the unconditioned response to the excitatory stimulus

Responses to steady stimuli

Skin touch-pressure cells of PO may in some cases respond to steady stimuli with sharp high-frequency onset transients, decline to a steady frequency of discharge during continued application of the stimulus, and return suddenly to the resting rate when the stimulus is removed. Others may discharge only on and off transients. This behavior is quite typical for two classes of touch-pressure cells of VB. PO cells responding to noxious stimuli, however, may perform in quite a different way. An example is given by the charts and records of Figure 7. With onset of periosteal kneading the frequency of discharge increased slowly, reaching its peak only after 10 seconds of stimulation. The stimulation period was followed by a prolonged after-discharge of the cell, which continued for more than 15 seconds. This is the usual pattern, but some cells of this class may cease to discharge rather abruptly, as illustrated in Figure 3.

Inhibition

Afferent inhibition in the lemniscal system, at the cortical level, has been described in some detail (55) (57). In these cases the receptive field is surrounded by a limited area of skin within which stimuli will inhibit both the spontaneous and driven activity of the cell. This pattern is quite different for cells of PO. An example is given in Figure 8. While the excitatory receptive field in this case was unusually small for a cell of PO, the cell could be inhibited from the entire remainder of the contralateral side of the body, from a large area of the ipsilateral side, and from the face as well. The duration of the inhibition is indicated by the graph below. A more common pattern is for a cell of PO to be inhibited from a field that is located homologously on the opposite of the body from the excitatory one. An example is given by Figure 9. The inhibition of cells of PO has been observed in 16 instances.

Anatomico-Physiological Correlations

Reconstructions of 9 of the 27 electrode tracks which passed through the region of the posterior nuclear group are shown in Figure 10. These 9 have been selected and the tracings of the sections in which they occurred arranged to give an orderly display, in an oro-caudal sequence, of the results obtained. The

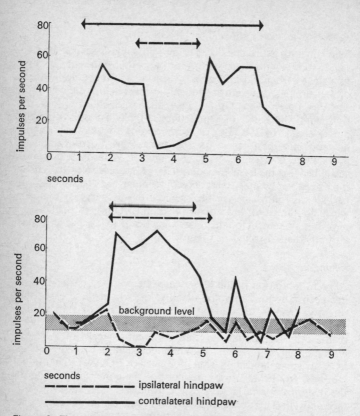

Figure 9. The graphs above present data obtained during the study of neuron 50–5. As the graphs indicate the cell was activated by stimulation of the contralateral hindpaw, and this driven activity was inhibited by the interpolation of a stimulus to the ipsilateral hindpaw. The adequate stimulus in each case was light mechanical in nature

observations made in the penetrations not shown in this figure differ in no qualitative way from those depicted.

Several points are evident from these reconstructions. In the first place, in penetrations passing through the most anterior part of PO the somatic sensory neurons with PO properties are found in that crescent-shaped anterior extension of PO which clasps the dorso-postero-lateral corner of VB (e.g. 50–P1, 52–P4). Secondly, in this region an electrode may pass through PO above and into

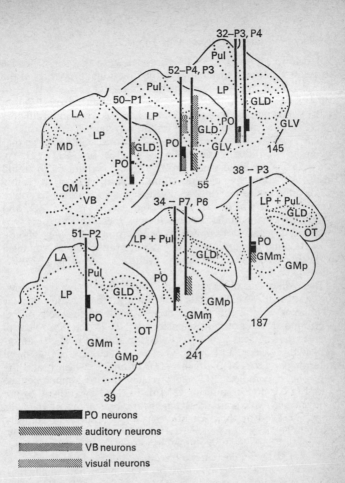

Figure 10. The drawings above represent the reconstructions of nine microelectrode penetrations of the thalamus. They were made from study of the serial sections of the experimental brains. The properties of the neurons observed in each penetration are indicated by the symbols. For a full description and discussion, see the text. CM – centre median; GLD – dorsal nucleus of the lateral geniculate body; GLV – ventral nucleus of the lateral geniculate body; GMm – magnocellular division of the medial geniculate body; GMp – principal division of the medial geniculate body; LA – the lateral anterior nucleus; LP – the lateral posterior nucleus: MD – the mediodorsal nucleus; OT – optic tract; PO – the posterior group of nuclei of the thalamus; Pul – pulvinar; VB – the ventrobasal nuclear complex of the thalamus

VB below (e.g. 52–P4, 32–P3). In each case there is a precise correlation between the change in the functional properties of the cells observed from those characteristic of PO above to those of VB below, and the movement of the electrode tip from PO into VB, as shown in the reconstructions. There is some intermingling of cells of the two types at this region of juncture.

The symbols of Figure 10 indicate, as one would expect, that when the electrode tip was within the confines of GLD or GMp, the neurons observed were sensitive to either light or to sound respectively, and to no other stimuli. What was not so readily predictable is the fact that many neurons responding to sound were observed which were distributed very widely in PO, and particularly in its caudal portion. Rarely, these were the only type of drivable neurons observed in a penetration of PO (e.g. 34–P6). More commonly, auditory neurons were randomly intermingled with those activated by somatic sensory stimuli (e.g. 34–P7, 38–P3).

From all of our observations it is possible to make the following statements, which relate our findings to previous nuclear terminology of this thalamic region. Somatic sensory cells of PO are found in the anterior extension of LP, in the more ventral part of that nucleus as it extends farther caudally, in the suprageniculate nucleus, and in the GMm, particularly in that more anterior part of GMm which is transitional between it and the ventrobasal complex. PO neurons sensitive to sound may be found in LP and in anterior GMm. In these locations they are intermingled with somatic PO neurons, and many of the cells may be excited by their somatic sensory, vibratory, or auditory stimuli. The more posterior part of GMm is more exclusively, though not completely, auditory in nature.

It should be added that we have not observed a cell with PO properties outside the confines of PO, as we have defined it. Four penetrations passed into PO and no cells of PO properties were observed, although in each case the electrode was recording well. We attribute these failures to the deteriorating condition of the animal.

Discussion

The physiological observations described above give support to the view that the posterior group of thalamic nuclei is a second thalamic transfer region of the somatic afferent system. In the cat it lies caudal and dorsal to the region of lemniscal transfer, the ventrobasal complex, and the two are joined by a region of morphological transition. It is our thesis that this posterior region receives its afferent input from elements of the anterolateral system of the spinal cord, and differs remarkably from the ventro-basal complex in its functional properties – subserving among other aspects of somatic sensibility the modality of pain. It projects upon a cortical region which includes the second somatic area.

The fact that fibers whose cells of origin lie in the dorsal column nuclei terminate wholly within the ventrobasal complex implies that the posterior region receives anterolateral column input. This has now been established by the anatomical studies of Mehler *et al.* (49), and is in agreement with the experimental findings of Whitlock and Perl (72), and with the results of our own series of preliminary experiments reported here. This posterior region is, however, but one of several oral destinations of the anterolateral system. Large numbers of small myelinated and unmyelinated fibers end in the reticular core of medulla and midbrain, and activity conducted in them is from thence relayed upward upon the more medial regions of the dorsal thalamus. A number of fibers of the anterolateral columns reach these intralaminar nuclei directly, a projection termed paleo-spinothalamic. A definite anterolateral projection to the ventrobasal complex exists in the cat. It increases at a great rate in monkey and chimpanzee (48), and reaches its greatest development in man. It is not known which component of the anterolateral system accounts for this increase in neo-spinothalamic projection, either from the standpoint of the fiber sizes, or the modalities served by them.

These very widespread projections of the anterolateral system, relaying activity evoked by somatic sensory stimuli upon many nuclear structures of the forebrain, suggest its importance in functions as equally varied. Our own experiments relate to but one of these areas of projection, the posterior group of nuclei. We wish to discuss the functional properties of the cells of this region, contrast these properties with those of the lemniscal component of the somatic system, and indicate the possible significance of this region in somatic sensibility, particularly with reference to the role it appears to play as a part of the central neural substratum for the perception of pain.

Physiological properties of the cells of the posterior group of nuclei of the thalamus

1. The mechanoreceptive function of PO. Large numbers of PO cells are activated by somatic sensory stimuli. While some 40 per

177

cent are sensitive to light mechanical disturbances of the body surface, other properties of these cells mark the region as different in many respects from the ventrobasal complex, many cells of which are sensitive also to such stimuli. The first difference is that *the mechanoreceptive cells of PO are not place specific:* there is no orderly projection of the body form within this region, and individual cells may subtend very wide and frequently bilateral receptive fields, which in some instances include the entire body surface. The second major difference is that *the cells of PO are not modality specific.* Many of those driven by light mechanical stimuli are sensitive also to vibratory or auditory stimuli. Others may respond to noxious stimuli delivered to skin areas outside their mechanoreceptive fields. Mode and space specificity are, on the other hand, the preminent qualities of the cells of the ventrobasal complex.

PO differs from VB in another way, for we have never observed any cells of this region which were sensitive to the gentle rotation of joints. By contrast, large numbers of cells of VB and of the first somatic cortical area are of this class, and are thought to constitute the essential neural substratum for position sense and kinesthesis (56).

In summary, so far as mechanoreceptive sensibility is concerned, no properties of PO indicate that it could serve the discriminative forms of somatic sensibility. The properties of the cells of VB, on the other hand, allow a very finely tuned capacity for temporal and spatial discriminations in the mechanoreceptive spheres of touch-pressure, position sense and kinesthesis.

2. *The nociceptive function of PO.* We are well aware of the difficulty one faces in labeling as painful any stimulus delivered to an experimental animal, for no introspective report is available. Nevertheless, when a stimulus is by nature destructive of tissue, provokes a defense or escape maneuver accompanied by signs of an appropriate emotional change in the normal waking animal, and evokes painful sensations when applied to man, it seems reasonable to regard the stimulus as *painful in nature to both animal and man.* To label such stimuli as 'tissue-destructive, escape-provoking, and emotion-changing' but not to call them painful, seems to us a semantic triviality. There is no *a priori* reason to suppose that in evolution the perception of pain appears as a wholly new sensory phenomenon in man.

Nearly 60 per cent of the PO neurons which we have observed could be activated only by such noxious stimuli. The fact that the cells of PO project upon the cerebral cortex suggests that this thalamocortical system plays a role in the conscious perception of pain. While it is clear that this system can transmit information signalling that a painful event has occurred, it is equally clear that it is not likely to provide data concerning the location of that event. The receptive fields of such neurons are always very large, for over half the fields covered parts of both sides of the body, and a considerable number covered the entire body surface. How then is the position of the painful stimulus determined? Two possibilities suggest themselves, and there are doubtless others. In the first place, the localization might depend upon the simultaneous activation of mechanoreceptors by the painful stimulus, and the relay of that activity over the topographically precise lemniscal system. Support for this view is given by the fact that in humans in whom lesions have interrupted the lemniscal system at any level, the capacity to localize a painful stimulus is very poor in those areas of the body deprived by the lesion of the discriminative forms of somatic sensibility. This implies that the correct localization of the painful stimulus requires a high-level integration of activity, combining qualitative information from the anterolateral system with data for discrimination from the lemniscal. A second possibility is that the component of the anterolateral system which projects upon the ventrobasal complex contains nociceptive elements which display the discriminative properties of the lemniscal system. The avalanching phylogenetic development of this component is suggestive that this may indeed be the case, and we are presently testing this hypothesis in a single unit analysis study of the ventrobasal complex in monkeys, after section of the dorsal columns. A report of a similar study has been made by Whitlock and Perl (73).

The fact that this system receives nociceptive afferents from both sides of the body offers an explanation, we believe, for certain observations in man regarding laterality. Several observers have reported, for example, that while hemispherectomy produces over the contralateral side of the body a severe deficit in the discriminative forms of sensation, a form of pain sensibility remains (7, 26, 35, 50, 76). In these patients noxious stimuli produce a diffuse, poorly localized, frequently radiating, painful sensation. It is just such a form of pain, devoid of a discriminative aspect, which would be served by the ipsilateral component of the anterolateral-posterior group–cerebral cortical pathway.

That an ipsilateral component of the anterolateral system exists is indicated by the retrograde degeneration which occurs in both dorsal horns following an anterolateral cordotomy, in both man and experimental animals (12, 43, 54). It is shown also by the slight increase in the pain threshold and decrease in the density of 'pain spots' which results on the side of the body ipsilateral to the cordotomy (31, 32). Very rarely, the ipsilateral component is the predominant one, for in a few cases hypalgesia occurs mainly on the ipsilateral side (34, 68). We have never observed a cat in which the projection to PO was not bilateral.

Evidence put fo ward by several investigators indicates that noxious stimuli activate cells in many parts of the brain stem and diencephalon. Collins and O'Leary discovered that a region of the mesencephalic tegmentum is activated by impulses carried in gamma- and delta-sized fibers of peripheral nerves (24). The responses survived dorsal column section, were eliminated by cutting the anterolateral columns, potentiated by noxious stimulation of the body surface, and were extremely sensitive to the depth of anesthesia. Magoun and McKinley showed some time ago that the center median could be activated by peripheral nerve volleys (46), and Albe-Fessard and Kruger have now found that the cells of the region are activated by stimuli which are destructive of tissue (1, 42). What the physiological implication of this very diverse activation of the diencephalon by noxious stimuli may be is uncertain. It appears to us, however, that the posterior group relay is likely to be concerned in the conscious perception of pain, for it is the only one of these regions which is known to project upon the cerebral cortex.[1] We will discuss the nature of that projection in the following section.

The nature of the stimuli required to excite the cells of PO, their very wide receptive fields, the lack of pattern within the area, and the prolonged after-discharge of the cells following noxious stimuli all suggest that the system may play a role in the genesis of symptoms in a very diverse group of clinical conditions which have in common the occurrence of *hyperpathia*. This is characterized by: (1) the long latent period between application of the noxious stimulus and the perception of pain, (2) the diffuse and particularly disagreeable nature of the pain evoked, and its powerful effect in provoking emotional reactions, (3) gross errors in localization, (4) usually elevated pain thresholds, and (5) the

1. Underlying this statement is the belief that the cerebral cortex plays an essential role in sensory perceptions. While this seems reasonable to us, and to fit with the facts which are available, it does not at all deny the importance for general perception of the widespread activation of some subcortical regions by sensory stimuli.

persisting painful sensation after removal of the stimulus. This syndrome appears after lesions located at any level of what we have termed the lemniscal component of the somatic afferent system: of the cerebral cortex, the ventrobasal thalamic nuclei, the dorsal columns of the spinal cord, or of the large myelinated fibers of peripheral nerves. It is an important observation that this disagreeable pain sensibility appears only in those regions of the body which are no longer represented in the lemniscal system – which are defective in the discriminative forms of sensation. It appears when the larger myelinated fibers of peripheral nerves are differentially blocked by asphyxia, leaving unmyelinated and probably the smaller myelinated fibers functionally intact (11). This hyperpathia appears also in the zones of transition in sensibility which surround an area rendered anesthestic by nerve section. The unbridled action of the anterolateral-posterior group system could account for these perverted sensations, which are at least occasionally eliminated in these cases by anterolateral cordotomy (33, 67). Can the normal level of activity in this system account also for the great exaggeration of pain sensibility which occasionally occurs, as in the thalamic syndrome? Consideration of their clinical observations led Head and Holmes (37) and others since them to postulate that activity evoked in the lemniscal system in some way prevents the full development of that occurring in the anterolateral system – an afferent inhibition cross-modal in nature. There seems to us to be much in this idea which fits some experimental findings. For example, observations made in the postcentral gyrus of the monkey conform with this hypothesis, for Mountcastle and Powell (57) found there some cells which were (a) excited by noxious stimulation of the skin, in a manner suggesting that the anterolateral system was responsible for their activation, and (b) inhibited by light mechanical stimulation, delivered to *exactly the same spot in the skin*. Such light mechanical stimuli activate most potently the lemniscal system, and it is possible that a lesion of this system would thus remove the inhibition of those postcentral cells excited by noxious stimuli. Whether a lemniscal lesion removes also some inhibition of the second somatic area, which we believe to be one of the principal projection areas of the posterior group of nuclei, is unknown.

3. The polysensory nature of PO. Many cells of PO respond to more than one form of somatic stimulation, and to vibratory and auditory stimuli as well. Not only are some individual cells heterogeneous in this respect, but the region as a whole is, for

181

many other cells of PO which respond only to auditory stimuli are intermingled with both strictly somatic and with heterogeneous ones. There is good reason to conclude from the work of Meyer and Woolsey (51), Rose and Woolsey (61), and Neff *et al.* (21, 58), that the region transmits to the cortex information useful in making discriminations in the auditory sphere. For example, animals with only this auditory portal to the cortex can be trained to discriminate between two frequencies, but not between two simple sequences of tones (28). This indicates that the capacity for auditory discrimination of cats with only this region remaining is rudimentary in comparison with that of an animal with an intact principal portion of the medial geniculate. The difference is to be compared with that between PO and VB in the sphere of somatic sensory discriminations. Other cells of PO are uniquely sensitive to vibratory stimuli, which conforms with the finding of Mickle and Ades that a region medial to GMp is activated by vestibular nerve volleys (53).

That PO is a region of convergence and interaction of afferent activity provoked by noxious and by auditory stimuli is of interest in relation to some recent observations in humans. For example, Benjamin has shown that the threshold for hearing can be significantly raised by painful stimuli (8).

The pulvinar-posterior group as a whole must now be considered as receiving a very diverse sensory input. Buser and his colleagues have shown that parts of it are activated by visual and others by auditory stimuli, and that complex interactions occur (18, 19). These investigators have also produced evidence that this region projects upon the 'association' areas of the cortex, via pathways which are independent of the primary sensory areas (15, 16, 17, 18, 20), which gives physiological confirmation of a well-established anatomical fact.

What the general functional significance of this sensory polyvalence of the pulvinar posterior group may be is uncertain.

The cortical projection of the posterior group of nuclei of the thalamus

The experimental anatomical evidence we have reviewed above indicates that the posterior group of nuclei is a cortical dependency, and that the second somatic area is included in its field of projection. This agrees with the suggestion of Knighton, who found that electrical stimulation in a region which we interpret to have been in or close to the posterior group, evoked responses confined to the second somatic area (41). The study of Rose and

Woolsey (61) provided evidence that this projection is sustaining in nature, for a removal of portions of the adjacent auditory areas must be combined with a lesion of the second somatic to produce its total retrograde degeneration. It is of interest to compare what is known of the functional natures of the relevant thalamic and cortical centers.

There is evidence that the second somatic area of the cortex possesses functional properties characteristic of both the lemniscal and the anterolateral systems. A number of investigators have shown, using the evoked potential method, that the body form is represented there in a way as nearly detailed as in the postcentral gyrus (9, 36, 74, 75). Corollary to this, Carreras and Levitt found in a single unit analysis that many cells of the region are both mode and place specific, as are those of the first somatic area (23). These are lemniscal properties. Other functional characteristics of this region are, however, similar to those of the posterior group of nuclei. Tunturi and Bremer have both shown that a part of the anterior ectosylvian gyrus is activated by auditory stimuli, and that this region overlaps in considerable part the second somatic area (14, 66). In this regard, Berman demonstrated an interaction between the responses to auditory and somatic stimuli which was most marked at the region of transition between the somatic and auditory areas (9). This interaction has now been observed at the single unit level by Carreras and Andersson, and these latter investigators have observed other cells of the region which were activated only by noxious stimuli to the periphery, and which were related to very wide and frequently bilateral receptive fields (22). These are anterolateral properties. The overlapping proximity of the vestibular cortical area (39, 52, 69) and the position of the vestibular thalamic area within the posterior thalamic group (53) gives further support to the hypothesis that there is an intimate relation between this thalamic region and the region of the anterior ectosylvian gyrus of the cortex.

On the other hand, the cortical cells with properties similar to those of the posterior thalamic group are not confined to the second somatic field. Mountcastle and Powell observed a small percentage of the cells of the postcentral gyrus of the monkey which possessed anterolateral properties: they were activated only by noxious stimuli, from very wide receptive fields (57). There few cells appeared to be indiscriminately placed in the midst of an overwhelming majority with lemniscal properties.

These observations lead to the following tentative generalization. That is, that while the first and second somatic areas are in the main expressive of the functional natures of the lemniscal and anterolateral ascending systems, respectively, that they are not exclusively so. Each possesses to a certain extent the properties of the other. Whether this indicates that essential projections exist from VB and PO to the first and second somatic cortical areas, respectively, and that there are sustaining projections from VB to SII and from PO to SI is not established, but this hypothesis fits the facts which are available at present. From a broader point of view one can consider the ventrobasal complex and the geniculate bodies, together with their essential cortical projection areas as the essential cores of the somatic, visual and auditory systems. Surrounding them at both thalamic and cortical levels, and fusing between them, are areas which are less specific with regard to local sign and modality served, in which complex sensory interactions occur, and which are thought to subserve sensory integrative actions. The observations of Albe-Fessard, of Buser, and their colleagues (1–5, 13, 15–20, 42, 45), and of Amassian (6), that the pulvinar-posterior and the more medial regions of the thalamus such as the center median, and the cortical association areas as well, receive complex and multiple sensory inputs, support this point of view.

Our observations indicate that PO and its cortical projection to an area which includes the second somatic are concerned in a special way with pain sensibility. This does not imply that pain does not project upon the postcentral gyrus also; indeed some experimental evidence obtained in monkeys suggests that it does so (57). Many reviewers have, we believe, overemphasized negative observations obtained in man, citing reports that electrical stimulation of the postcentral gyrus does not often evoke painful sensations in waking humans, and that removal of the postcentral gyrus may not produce a contralateral analgesia. There are, however, many reports that under certain circumstances stimulation of the postcentral gyrus does evoke sensations of pain (25, 30, 38 44, 71). The facts that pain relating to the skin is likely to be concentrated in area 3 (59), which is buried deep in the human central sulcus, and that pain elements are likely to require special parameters of the exciting electrical stimuli, suggest an explanation, we believe, for the negative observations. Removals or injury of the postcentral gyrus may, in fact, be quite effective in eliminating certain types of pain, particularly when the lesion extends or the intentional removal is carried to the very depths of the central sulcus (27, 29, 30, 40, 44, 47, 63, 65). From what is known of the cortical projection of pain one would predict that a certain form of pain sensibility would, however, remain after postcentral removal, and indeed that this remaining form might even under certain conditions be exaggerated. On the other hand, one would expect lesions of the second somatic area and of adjacent areas of the lower parietal convolutions to produce very complex disturbances in the perception of pain. These expectations seem to fit closely with a number of clinical observations (10, 62, 64, 70).

Summary

[. . .] In a series of animals, single unit analysis studies were made of these two thalamic regions. The functional properties of their cells may be contrasted as follows:

1. The body surface is represented in an orderly topographic manner in VB, and the cells of this region are related to small and quite specific receptive fields on the contralateral side of the body. On the other hand, no topographic pattern of representation was observed in PO, and its cells may be activated from very large receptive fields, which may be contralateral, ipsilateral, or both, and which in the limit cover the entire body surface. The cells of PO are not place specific.

2. The cells of VB are modality specific, and any given cell may be activated by one or another form of mechanical stimulation, but not by more than one, and many are activated by the gentle rotation of joints. In contrast, the cells of PO are in many instances polyvalent with respect to the adequate stimuli which activate them, some being responsive to light mechanical stimuli and to stimuli which are destructive of tissue, as well as to sound and to vibrations. Other cells of PO may be sensitive only to sound. These auditory neurons are intermingled with those sensitive to somatic sensory stimuli, but are more concentrated in the posterior part of the magnocellular portion of the medial geniculate body. No cells of PO were activated by the gentle rotation of joints. The cells of PO are not modality specific.

3. No cells of VB were observed to be activated by noxious stimuli. The majority of the cells of PO, however, were sensitive to stimuli which were destructive of tissue, stimuli which produced avoidance and respiratory reflexes, and which evoke in conscious man the perception of pain. Such nociceptive neurons were commonly related to very large and usually bilateral receptive fields. These cells were frequently polyvalent, responding to light mechanical stimuli to parts of their receptive fields, and to auditory and vibratory stimuli as well. Nociceptive neurons,

during continued stimulation, frequently show a slow recruitment of activity, and prolonged after-discharges after removal of the stimulus.

In the discussion a capitulation is given of the functional properties of the first and second somatic areas of the cerebral cortex, and these are compared with those of the two thalamic regions studied. These facts, correlated with experimental anatomical evidence regarding thalamo-cortical projections, lead to the conclusion that while the first and second somatic areas of the cortex are in the main expressive of the functional attributes of the lemniscal and spinothalamic components of the somatic system, they are not exclusively so, and each shares to a certain degree the physiological properties of the other. Particular reference is made to the role of the spinothalamic-posterior group system in the central nervous mechanism subserving pain sensibility.

References

1. D. ALBE-FESSARD and L. KRUGER, 'Dualité des réponses des cellules du centre médian du thalamus à des stimulations naturelles ou électriques', *Compt. Rend. Acad. Sc.*, vol. 248 (1959), p. 299.
2. D. ALBE-FESSARD and A. ROUGEUL, 'Activités bilatérales tardives évoquées sur le cortex du chat sous chloralose par stimulation d'une voie somesthésique', *J. Physiol.*, vol. 47 (1955), p. 69.
3. D. ALBE-FESSARD and A. ROUGEUL, 'Relais thalamiques d'afférences somesthésiques aboutissant à certaines régions localisées du cortex associatif du chat', *J. Physiol.*, vol. 48 (1956), p. 370.
4. D. ALBE-FESSARD and A. ROUGEUL, 'Activités d'origine somesthésique évoquées sur le cortex non-spécifique du chat anesthésié au chloralose: rôle de centre médian du thalamus', *Electroencephalog. clin. Neurophysiol.*, vol. 10 (1958), p. 131.
5. D. ALBE-FESSARD, A. ROUGEUL, and S. TSOULADZE, 'Etude comparée, à l'échelle neuronique, des activités évoquées dans un relais somesthésique primaire et un relais somesthésique secondaire', *Compt. rend. Acad. Sc., Paris*, vol. 245 (1957), p. 573.
6. V. E. AMASSIAN, 'Evoked single cortical unit activity in the somatic sensory areas', *Electroencephalog. clin. Neurophysiol.*, vol. 5 (1953), p. 415.
7. E. BELL, JR., and L. J. KARNOSH, 'Cerebral hemispherectomy. Report of a case ten years after operation', *J. Neurosurg.*, vol. 6. (1949), p. 285.
8. F. B. BENJAMIN, 'The effect of pain on simultaneous perception of nonpainful sensory stimulation', *J. appl. Physiol.*, vol. 8 (1956), p. 630.
9. A. L. BERMAN, 'Somatic and auditory interaction in the anterior ectosylvian gyrus of the cerebral cortex of the cat', *Ph.D. Thesis*, The Johns Hopkins University, 1957.
10. A. BIEMOND, 'The conduction of pain above the level of the thalamus opticus', *A.M.A. Arch. Neurol. Psychiat.*, vol. 75 (1956), p. 231.

11. N. BIGELOW, I. HARRISON, H. GOODELL, and H. G. WOLFF, 'Studies on pain: quantitative measurements of two pain sensations of the skin, with reference to the nature of the "hyperalgesia of peripheral neuritis"', *J. clin. Invest.*, vol. 24 (1945), p. 503.

12. S. T. BOK, 'Das rückenmark', in *Handbuch der mikroscopischen anatomie des menschen* ed by J. von Möllendorf, Springer, Berlin, 1920, pp. 378.

13. P. BORENSTEIN, J. BRUNER and P. BUSER, 'Organisation neuronique et convergences hétérosensorielles dans le complex lateral posterior "associatif" du thalamus chez le chat', *J. Physiol.*, Paris, vol. 51 (1959), p. 413.

14. F. BREMER, 'Analyse oscillographique des réponses sensorielles des encorces cérébrale et cérébelleuse', *Rev. Neurol.*, vol. 87 (1952), p. 65.

15. P. BUSER and P. BORENSTEIN, 'Variations caractéristiques des réponses sensorielles "associatives" du cortex cérébral du chat en fonction du degré général d'activation corticale', *Compt. Rend. Acad. Sc., Paris*, vol. 93 (1956), p. 243.

16. P. BUSER and P. BORENSTEIN, 'Données sur la répartition des réponses sensorielles corticales (somesthésiques, visuelles, auditives) chez le chat curarisé non anesthésié', *J. Physiol.*, Paris, vol. 48 (1956), p. 419.

17. P. BUSER and P. BORENSTEIN, 'Observations sur les réponses corticales visuelles recueillies dans le cortex associatif suprasylvien chez le chat sous chloralose', *J. Physiol.*, Paris, vol. 48 (1956), p. 422.

18. P. BUSER and P. BORENSTEIN, 'Réponses somesthésiques, visuelles et auditives recueillies au niveau du cortex "associatif" suprasylvien chez le chat curarisé non anesthésié', *Electroencephalog. clin. Neurophysiol.*, vol. 11 (1959), p. 285.

19. P. BUSER, P. BORENSTEIN, and J. BRUNER, 'Étude des systèmes "associatifs" visuels et auditifs chez le chat anesthésié au chloralose', *Electroencephalog. clin. Neurophysiol.*, vol. 11 (1959), p. 305.

20. P. BUSER and G. HEINZE, 'Effets d'une association des stimuli périphériques hétérogènes sur l'activité de certaines aires corticales chez le chat', *J. Physiol.*, Paris, vol. 46 (1954), p. 284.

21. R. A. BUTLER, I. T. DIAMOND, and W. D. NEFF, 'Role of auditory cortex in discrimination of changes in frequency', *J. Neurophysiol.*, vol. 20 (1957), p. 108.

22. M. CARRERAS and S. A. A. ANDERSSON, Personal communication, 1959.

23. M. CARRERAS and M. LEVITT, 'Microelectrode analysis of the second somatosensory cortical area in the cat', *Fed. Proc.*, vol. 18 (1959), p. 24.

24. W. F. COLLINS and J. L. O'LEARY, 'Study of a somatic evoked response of midbrain reticular substance', *Electroencephalog. Clin. Neurophysiol.*, vol. 6 (1954), p. 619.

25. H. CUSHING, 'A note upon the faradic stimulation of the postcentral gyrus in conscious patients', *Brain*, vol. 32 (1909), p. 44.

26. W. E. DANDY, 'Physiological studies following extirpation of the right cerebral hemisphere in man', *Bull. Johns Hopkins Hosp.*, vol. 53 (1933), p. 31.

27. J. Dejerine and J. Mouzon, 'Un nouveau type de syndrome sensitif cortical observé dans un cas de monoplégie corticale dissociée', *Rev. Neurol.*, vol. 28 (1915), p. 1265.

28. I. T. Diamond and W. D. Neff, 'Ablation of temporal cortex and discrimination of auditory patterns', *J. Neurophysiol.*, vol. 20 (1957), p. 300.

29. D. H. Echols and J. A. Colclough, 'Abolition of painful phantom foot by resection of the sensory cortex', *J. Amer. Med. Ass.*, vol. 134 (1947), p. 1476.

30. T. C. Erickson, W. J. Bleckwenn, and C. N. Woolsey, 'Observations on the postcentral gyrus in relation to pain', *Tr. Am. Neurol. A.*, vol. 77 (1952), p. 57.

31. O. Foerster, 'Symptomatologie der Erkrankungen des Rückenmarks and seiner Wurzeln', *Handbuch der Neurologie*, edited by O. Bumke, and O. Foerster, Springer, Berlin, 1936, vol. 5, pp. 1–403.

32. O. Foerster and O. Gagel, 'Die Vorderseitenstrangdurchschneidung beim menschen', *Ztschr. f.d. ges. Neurol. Psychiat.*, vol. 138 (1932), p. 1.

33. C. H. Frazier, F. H. Lewy, and S. N. Rowe, 'The origin and mechanism of paroxysmal neurologic pain and the surgical treatment of central pain', *Brain*, vol. 60 (1937), p. 44.

34. L. A. French and W. T. Peyton, 'Ipsilateral sensory loss following cordotomy', *J. Neurosurg.*, vol. 5 (1948), p. 403.

35. W. J. Gardner, L. J. Karnosh, C. C. McClure, Jr., and A. K. Gardner, 'Residual function following hemispherectomy for tumour and for infantile hemiplegia', *Brain*, vol. 78 (1955), p. 487.

36. T. P. Hamuy, R. B. Bromiley, and C. N. Woolsey, 'Somatic afferent areas I and II of dog's cerebral cortex', *J. Neurophysiol.*, vol. 19 (1956), p. 485.

37. H. Head and G. Holmes, 'Sensory disturbances from cerebral lesions', *Brain*, vol. 34 (1911), p. 102.

38. G. Horrax, 'Experiences with cortical excisions for the relief of intractable pain in the extremities', *Surgery*, vol. 20 (1946), p. 593.

39. W. H. Kempinsky, 'Cortical projection of vestibular and facial nerves in the cat', *J. Neurophysiol.*, vol. 14 (1951), p. 203.

40. K. Kleist, *Handbuch der Ärzlichen Erfahrungen im Weltkriege*, ed. by O. von Schjerning, Barth, Leipzig, 1934, vol. 4, part 2, p. 1416.

41. R. S. Knighton, 'Thalamic relay nucleus for the second somatic sensory receiving area in the cerebral cortex of the cat', *J. comp. Neurol.*, vol. 92 (1950), p. 183.

42. L. Kruger and D. Albe-Fessard, 'Dualité des réponses observées dans le centre médian lors de stimulations somatiques. Types d'afférences et voies spinales', *J. Physiol.*, Paris, vol. 51 (1959), p. 501.

43. M. Kuru, *Sensory Paths in the Spinal Cord and Brain Stem of Man*, Sogensya, Tokyo and Osaka, 1949, 39 pp.

44. W. Lewin and C. G. Phillips, 'Observations on partial removal of the postcentral gyrus for pain', *J. Neurol. Neurosurg. Psychiat.*, vol. 15 (1952), p. 143.

45. S. Libouban, 'Exploration électrophysiologique, sous contrôle stéréotaxique, des noyaux thalamiques répondant à la somesthésie chez le rat', *J. Physiol.*, Paris, vol. 51 (1959), p. 517.

46. H. W. MAGOUN and W. A. McKINLEY, 'The termination of ascending trigeminal and spinal tracts in the thalamus of the cat', *Am. J. Physiol.*, vol. 137 (1942), p. 409.

47. J. MARSHALL, 'Sensory disturbances in cortical wounds with special reference to pain', *J. Neurol., Neurosurg. Psychiat.*, vol. 14 (1951), p. 187.

48. W. R. MEHLER, 'The mammalian "pain tract" in phylogeny', *Anat. Rec.*, vol. 127 (1957), p. 332.

49. W. R. MEHLER, M. E. FEFERMAN and W. J. NAUTA, 'Ascending axon degeneration following anterolateral cordotomy. An experimental study in the monkey', *Brain*, vol. 83 (1960), pp. 718–50.

50. I. N. MENSH, H. G. SCHWARTZ, R. G. MATARAZZO, and J. D. MATARAZZO, 'Psychological functioning following hemispherectomy in man', *A.M.A. Arch. Neurol. Psychiat.*, vol. 67 (1952), p. 787.

51. D. R. MEYER and C. N. WOOLSEY, 'Effects of localized cortical destruction upon auditory discriminative conditioning in the cat', *J. Neurophysiol.*, vol. 15 (1952), p. 149.

52. W. A. MICKLE and H. W. ADES, 'A composite sensory projection area in the cerebral cortex of the cat', *Am. J. Physiol.*, vol. 170 (1952), p. 682.

53. W. A. MICKLE and H. W. ADES, 'Rostral projection pathway of the vestibular system', *Am. J. Physiol.*, vol. 176 (1954), p. 243.

54. F. MORIN, H. G. SCHWARTZ, and J. L. O'LEARY, 'Experimental study of spinothalamic and related tracts', *Acta Psychiat. Neurol. Scand.*, vol. 26 (1951), p. 371.

55. V. B. MOUNTCASTLE, 'Modality and topographic properties of single neurons of cat's somatic sensory cortex', *J. Neurophysiol.*, vol. 20 (1957), p. 408.

56. V. B. MOUNTCASTLE and T. P. S. POWELL, 'Central nervous mechanisms subserving position sense and kinesthesis', *Bull. Johns Hopkins Hosp.*, vol. 105 (1959), p. 173.

57. V. B. MOUNTCASTLE and T. P. S. POWELL, 'Neural mechanisms subserving cutaneous sensibility, with special reference to the role of afferent inhibition in sensory perception and discrimination', *Bull. Johns Hopkins Hosp.*, vol. 105 (1959), p. 201.

58. W. D. NEFF, J. F. FISHER, I. T. DIAMOND, and M. YELA, 'Role of auditory cortex in discrimination requiring localization of sound in space', *J. Neurophysiol.*, vol. 19 (1956), p. 500.

59. T. P. S. POWELL and V. B. MOUNTCASTLE, 'Some aspects of the functional organization of the cortex of the postcentral gyrus of the monkey: a correlation of findings obtained in a single unit analysis with cytoarchitecture', *Bull. Johns Hopkins Hosp.*, vol. 105 (1959), p. 133.

60. J. E. ROSE and V. B. MOUNTCASTLE, 'Activity of single neurons in the tactile thalamic region of the cat in response to a transient peripheral stimulus', *Bull. Johns Hopkins Hosp.*, vol. 94 (1954), p. 238.

61. J. E. ROSE and C. N. WOOLSEY, 'Cortical connections and functional organization of the thalamic auditory system of the cat', in *Biological and Biochemical Bases of Behavior*, University of Wisconsin Press, 1958, pp. 127–150.

62. J. L. RUBINS and E. D. FRIEDMAN, 'Asymbolia for pain', *A.M.A. Arch. Neurol. Psychiat.*, vol. 60 (1948), p. 554.

63. W. R. RUSSELL, 'Transient disturbances following gunshot wounds of the head', *Brain*, vol. 68 (1945), p. 79.

64. P. SCHILDER and E. STENGEL, 'Das Krankheitsbild der Schmerzasymbolie', *Ztschr. f. d. ges. Neurol. Psychiat.*, vol. 129 (1930), p. 250.

65. T. T. STONE, 'Phantom limb pain and central pain; relief by ablation of portion of posterior central cerebral convolution', *A.M.A. Arch. Neurol. Psychiat.*, vol. 63 (1950), p. 739.

66. A. R. TUNTURI, 'Further afferent connections to the acoustic cortex of the dog', *Am. J. Physiol.*, vol. 144 (1945), p. 389.

67. F. TURNBULL, 'Cordotomy for thalamic pain. A case report'. *Yale J. Biol. Med.*, vol. 11 (1939), p. 411.

68. H. C. VORIS, 'Ipsilateral sensory loss following chordotomy: report of a case', *A.M.A. Arch. Neurol. Psychiat.*, vol. 65 (1951), p. 95.

69. E. M. WALZL and V. B. MOUNTCASTLE, 'Projection of vestibular nerve to cerebral cortex of the cat', *Am. J. Physiol.*, vol. 159 (1949), p. 595.

70. E. A. WEINSTEIN, R. L. KAHN, and W. H. SLOTE, 'Withdrawal, inattention, and pain asymbolia', *A.M.A. Arch. Neurol. Psychiat.*, vol. 74 (1955), p. 235.

71. J. C. WHITE and W. H. SWEET, *Pain: Its Mechanisms and Neurosurgical Control*. Charles C. Thomas, Springfield, Ill., 1955, 736 pp.

72. D. G. WHITLOCK and E. R. PERL, 'Afferent projection through ventrolateral funiculi to thalamus of cat', *J. Neurophysiol.*, vol. 22 (1959), p. 133.

73. D. G. WHITLOCK and E. R. PERL, 'Peripheral stimuli effective in activating thalamic elements via ventrolateral spinal tracts', *Anat. Rec.*, vol. 133 (1959), p. 351.

74. C. N. WOOLSEY, 'Organization of somatic sensory and motor areas of the cerebral cortex', in *Biological and Biochemical Bases of Behavior*, University of Wisconsin Press, 1958, pp. 63–81.

75. C. N. WOOLSEY and D. FAIRMAN, 'Contralateral, ipsilateral, and bilateral representation of cutaneous receptors in somatic areas 1 and II of the cerebral cortex of pig, sheep and other mammals', *Surgery*, vol. 19 (1946), p. 684.

76. R. ZOLLINGER, 'Removal of left cerebral hemisphere. Report of a case', *A.M.A. Arch. Neurol. Psychiat.*, vol. 34 (1935), p. 1055.

8 V. B. Mountcastle, G. F. Poggio and G. Werner

The Relation of Thalamic Cell Response to Peripheral Stimuli Varied over an Intensive Continuum

V. B. Mountcastle, G. F. Poggio and G. Werner, 'The relation of thalamic cell response to peripheral stimuli varied over an intensive continuum', *J. Neurophysiol.*, vol. 26 (1963), pp. 807–34.

Introduction

The aim of our present studies is to quantitate neural events in successively more centrally located projection regions of the somatic afferent system, events which begin with the activation of peripheral receptors by physical stimuli. It is expected that such investigations will yield results permitting one to recognize laws governing the transformations intervening between peripheral sensory and central neural events. Studies of this kind deal with two quantifiable variables: a stimulus continuum measured in physical units, and a continuum of neural activity measured in some units deemed appropriate to the nature of the neural response. The task is, then, to assign numbers to observations in such a way that one can perform numerical operations which establish the quantitative relation between the two continua of measurement.

While the measurement scale for the stimulus input is set by its physical value, it is not at all obvious in what way the neural response should be scaled. A primary concern, therefore, in the quantitation of neural responses, is to select scales which will set different neural responses in a meaningful functional relation to the stimuli of differing intensities which evoke them. Thus the selection of scales for measuring neural responses is guided by pragmatic criteria, is not intrinsically determined, and is, therefore, open to exploration. What is required for a first-order definition are scales of measurement which permit mapping of ordered relations of 'greater' and 'smaller' in the stimulus domain into corresponding relations in the domain of the neural response. More exacting analyses would require that the numerical values on the neural response scale increase monotonically as the stimulus intensity increases, for then certain algebraic operations on one would be paralleled by similar operations in the other. Should this prove possible, it would be of interest to inquire which quantitative aspects of the neural response tally with psychophysical measurements.

The observations to be reported in this paper are based upon studies of the activity of single neurons. When some principles of sampling are observed, such data provide also an adequate appreciation of the performance of populations of neurons under those circumstances so far open to experimental control. Previous studies (5, 6, 7, 8) suggested that of the different components of the dorsal column–medial lemniscal system it is that concerned with the position and movement of the limbs which would lend itself most easily to quantitative treatment. It has been shown that first-order fibers innervating the joints and the cells to which they are centrally linked at successive stages of the system are sensitive indicators of the steady-state positions and the movements of the limbs (1, 2, 4, 7, 12). It is this component of the system which we have chosen as a prototype for study.

Several problems are raised by experimental aims such as those indicated. First, anesthetic agents are likely to exert an effect upon the actual level of central cell discharge evoked by a peripheral stimulus, and to produce abnormally rapid rates of 'adaptation' of that response to a steady stimulus. We have met this first problem by using a deafferented-head preparation, described in the preceding paper (9). While this preparation allows experiment without anesthesia or pain, a neuromuscular blocking agent is required. These animals vary between a state of light somnolence and one of alertness during the experiment.

Second, the stimulus must be precisely controlled. This requirement has, we believe, been met by using the joint-rotator machine described below. Third, the record obtained should include the electrical signs of every impulse discharged by the nerve cell under observation. Whether this requirement is met by the use of a microelectrode whose tip is located extracellularly and some distance (e.g. 50–200 μ) from the neuron soma is, we believe, not certain. Arguing from first principles and from the observations made in other locales using intracellular recording, we must assume that as the degree of depolarization, and thus the frequency of discharge of a cell, increases, the site of impulse initiation may advance from axon hillock to, e.g. the first node of Ranvier. Can one be certain, then, that there is full retrograde invasion of the soma by each and every impulse which is also propagated, in the other direction, down the axon? And if a certain percentage of those impulses which are propagated down the axon should produce in the soma only the so-called 'A' spike, will these be recorded above noise level by the extracellular electrode located some distance from the soma? It should be clearly understood that quantitative analyses such as those given in this and later papers (10, 17) are made with the assumption that the electrical signs of every impulse discharged are recorded, and that this is not absolutely certain.

In the fourth place is the matter of the variability of central cell responses. It has been our experience, and that of other investigators as well, that the frequency of cell discharge varies in the course of the application of a stimulus. One component of this response variation is associated with the onset of the stimulus and thus is clearly recognized as a time-dependent transient. In addition, time-independent variations of considerably smaller magnitude occur in what appears to be a random fashion during the continued application of a constant peripheral stimulus. Responses to such steady-state stimulation also vary to some extent between consecutive applications of what are thought to be identical stimuli. Therefore, measurements of cell responses to steady-state stimulation require examination of their validity from the statistical point of view.

In this paper we describe the relation between the frequency of discharge of thalamic joint neurons and limb position. Changes in the latter are treated as variations along an intensive continuum, from threshold to a position evoking the maximum response. Here only the relation of thalamic cell discharge to steady limb position is described; the relation of transient response to joint movement will be considered in a later paper.

Methods

The results described in this paper were obtained in the course of 35 experiments upon deafferented-head macaque monkeys. The description of the surgical preparation of these animals is given in the preceding paper (9), which contains also an account of our method of recording with microelectrodes from an extracellular position, in a hydraulically closed head, the electrical signs of the impulse discharge of single cells of the ventrobasal nuclear complex of the thalamus. A given unit was classified as a 'joint neuron' if the following criteria were met: (i) the cell could not be activated by mechanical stimulation of hairs, the skin, or by more intense mechanical stimuli sufficient under other circumstances to activate those thalamic neurons related to receptors of the deep fascia or the periosteum, (ii) the cell could be activated by gentle rotation of a joint, and (iii) the more or less steady-state discharge of the cell could be graded by positioning the limb at a series of steps through the excitatory angle. Confusion arose only in the case of those neurons related to deep fascial or periosteal fields located near a joint. Such cells may be activated by extreme flexion or extension of a joint; they are not sensitive to its gentle rotation, however, and their discharge rates cannot be graded by a serial positioning of that joint.

Method of stimulation

Once a neuron was identified as a true joint neuron, by our criteria, arrangements were made to rotate the limb at that joint by means of a machine designed for this purpose. First, the center of rotation of the instrument was positioned in line with the natural axis of rotation of the joint, with the aid of a guide sleeve. The proximal, nonmoving part of the extremity was fixed with sandbags and padded clamps as solidly as was compatible with the unanesthetized state of the animal. The distal or moving portion of the limb was then grasped in a padded clamp which was in turn attached to the rotating arm of the instrument. The rotation produced can thus be arranged to occur in the natural plane of rotation of the joint.

The instrument can be set to produce rotations at any one preset velocity between 4°/sec. and 45°/sec., and between angular limits which can be preset to within 2° of arc. In the automatic mode of operation nearly sinusoidal rotations are produced between the limits set, at the velocity chosen. In the triggered mode of operation a pulse at the instrument's input initiates a single rotation. This may be allowed to proceed fully to the preset limit or stopped and started again at any time desired; the limb then reaches the final preset limit via a series of steps each of which can be made of any duration.

The block diagram of Figure 1 illustrates the circuitry used in the automatic mode of operation. The rotator's drive shaft, to which the limb is fixed by a lateral arm, drives potentiometer R1. The voltage at the arm of R1 is therefore proportional to the angle through which the joint has been rotated, and is available at the monitor terminals. V1 and V2 are conventional comparators arranged to operate with relays K1 and K2 to cause the drive shaft to rotate in either direction depending upon the relative state of the comparators. R2 and R3 set the discharge thresholds of the comparators and thus determine the limits of rotation. When either limit is reached the action of relay K1 reverses the direction of the shaft's rotation by altering the polarity of the voltage applied to the motor's armature. This reciprocating motion continues until power is removed from the rotator.

The circuitry used in the triggered mode of operations is identical, with the addition of the further components shown in Figure 1. V5 is a flip-flop alternately energizing and de-energizing relay K3 in response to successive impulses at the rotator's trigger input terminals. For a given state of K3 there is but one state of K1 that will permit application of power to the drive motor; when this condition is met the motor

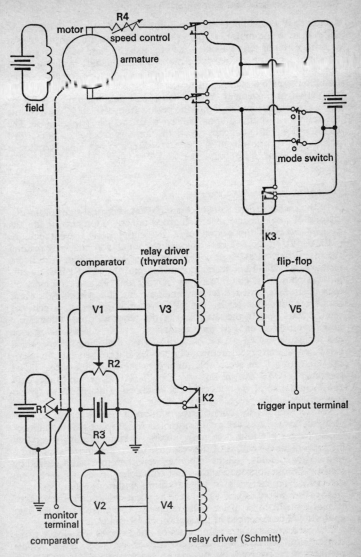

Figure 1. Block diagram of circuits controlling movements of a device used for rotating the limbs at their joints. Details are given in the text under 'Methods'

rotates to its preset limit, whereupon K1 reverses its state to that deny-ing power to the motor, stopping the shaft's rotation. An impulse at the trigger input terminals may then reverse the state of K3, restoring power of the proper polarity to move the drive shaft in the opposite direction. Thus successive trigger pulses initiate single traverses of the limb in alternate directions, provided the trigger interval is longer than the period of movement between the preset angular limits. A trigger pulse arriving before the end of the period stops the shaft's movement; the rotation is resumed upon the arrival of the next trigger pulse. The motion stops automatically when the limit is reached, as described above, and the movement in the return direction may also be made in a series of steps, if desired.

Data processing and analysis

In the earlier experiments of this series the electrical signs of the dis-charges of single neurons were recorded directly upon moving film, as was on occasion the output of a sequential period event counter (SPEC) (9). In the first case, frequency counts were made by reading the film projected at $15 \times$, with counting periods ranging in different instances for 200–1,000 msec. For measurements with SPEC, its out-put was photographed upon slowly moving film (9), and each mark on each upstroke counted, after film enlargement, thus yielding the event count per unit time set by the SPEC counting interval, which was usually 200 msec. In the latter half of the series all observations were initially recorded on FM analog magnetic tape. These analog tape recordings were then played back through a digitizing system which permitted accurate measurement of intervals and conversion of numeri-cal values to a form acceptable for processing by a high-speed digital computer (IBM 7090); in this way EPUT (events per unit time) data and their statistical analyses could be obtained. This reduction system is described in the preceding paper (9).

For determining the quantitative relation of neural activity to joint position, it was necessary to take into account the fact that the number of discharges per unit time may undergo certain seemingly random fluctuations in the course of the response to the continued application of a steady stimulus. Neural responses were therefore characterized by statistical estimators the validity and confidence limits of which were determined on the basis of the variations within any one period of steady stimulation, as well as between applications at different times of stimuli thought to be of the same intensity. These aspects of the data analysis will be described in the section on 'Results'.

The estimations of the parameters of fitted curves were made using conventional methods and desk calculators, or, when larger sample numbers were involved, by automatic computation (IBM 7090). The goodness of fit of functional relations between independent and de-pendent variables was determined by the analysis of variance.

Results

Once the electrical signs of impulse discharge of a thalamic neuron had been isolated from those of its neighbors, and the cell identified as a joint neuron, we sought to determine what we define as the receptive or excitatory angle for the cell, i.e. that portion of the angle of rotation of the relevant joint within which the steady position of the limb evokes a sustained discharge of the neuron at a rate significantly above its prestimulus or spontaneous level. In every case, we found joint neurons to be maximally activated at an extreme of the range of movement of a joint. For example, neurons driven by rotation of the contralateral elbow reach their highest rates at either full flexion or full extension, and never at any intermediate position. Less extreme positions evoke successively lower frequencies of discharge, until the threshold position is reached. Further displacements produce no further changes in rate of discharge. The excitatory angle as depicted by this relation of frequency to angle is a continuous, monotonic, and thus single-ended function.

Experimental observations defining the excitatory angle

Such an excitatory angle study was made upon thalamic neuron 36–7, a cell activated by flexion of the contralateral knee. A continuous plot of the frequency of this cell's discharge throughout the study is given in Figure 2. The plot begins just as a step-movement crossed threshold, which is between 120° and 90°. Each successive step-movement toward full flexion at 25° evoked a marked but transient increase in frequency which, while the limb was held in each new position, declined to a more or less steady rate of discharge, which was successively higher after each successive step. Each step-movement in the reverse direction produced a marked but transient decrease in frequency, which slowly recovered toward a more or less steady rate, which was successively lower for each successively more extended position of the limb, until the edge of the excitatory angle was passed once again.

The graph of Figure 2 shows that comparable angular positions on the ascending and descending phases of the movement produced roughly comparable rates of cellular discharge. In this regard neuron 36–7 was unusual, for some hysteresis was commonly observed for other cells. For the analyses described below, whenever such a hysteresis was observed, only data obtained upon the ascending phase of excitatory angle studies were used.

Information of a somewhat similar nature was obtained in a slightly different experiment. In this case the joint was positioned initially well outside the edge of the excitatory angle, and then rotated to a given position within the angle, held there for a period of time, and rotated once again to the starting position.

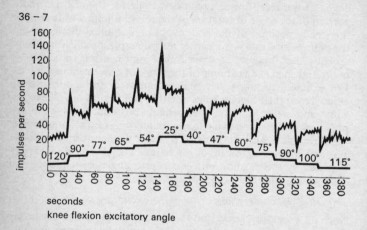

Figure 2. Graph plotting, continuously, impulses per second versus time for the excitatory angle study of neuron 36–7, a ventrobasal thalamic cell sensitive to flexion of the contralateral knee. For a statistical analysis of homogeneity the counting period used was 200 msec. Analyses of variance between successive 5-sec. periods of the last 15 sec. of each plateau showed that the populations were homogenous

When this is done for a series of positions over the range of the excitatory angle, the results define the relation of cell response to stimulus intensity, as these have been described above. The graphs of Figure 3 plot the results obtained for four of the eight angles tested in this way for neuron 23–1.

The results obtained in these two types of study have been found commensurable, and in the analyses which follow they have been treated as a common body of data for each cell for which both are available.

The question immediately arises whether the steady-state rates of discharge shown by graphs such as those of Figure 3 are functions not only of angular position, but perhaps also of the velocity with which the joint is moved to that position. It is clear from all our data that this is not the case, for while the peak

198

frequency during the transient phase is sometimes determined by the rate of movement, the final steady rate is independent of it, and is a function – so far as peripheral events are concerned – of

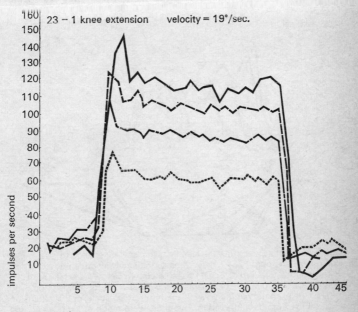

Figure 3. Graphs illustrating, in part, the results obtained during the 'one speed to several angles' experiment for neuron 23–1, a ventrobasal thalamic cell driven by extension of the contralateral knee. For each angle, five trials were made, and the data listed in terms of impulses per 200-msec. counting period. The five lists were then oriented correctly in time, averaged and summed for each second, and finally plotted, as shown here, as impulses per second. It was shown (see Figure 5) that the averaged populations were homogeneous during the last two thirds of each plateau. The knee was rotated for a position well outside the excitatory angle to true joint angles of, from above downward, 180°, 125°, 100° and 80°, respectively. Movements toward extension were begun at the 7th sec., and those toward flexion at the 35th sec

the steady angular position alone. Evidence supporting this statement is obtained in a third type of experiment: setting the angle of movement from without to some position within the excitatory angle as a constant, and then varying from trial to trial the velocity of movement, as well as its phases of acceleration and deceleration. The results of such an experiment upon neuron 23–7, one driven by extension of the contralateral wrist, are shown by the graphs of Figure 4. It is clear from these that the peak

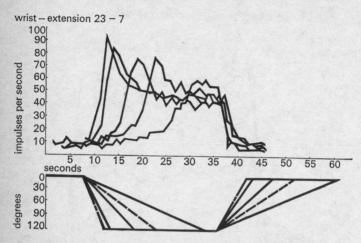

wrist – extension 23 – 7

Figure 4. Graphs illustrating the results of the 'several speeds to one angle' experiment for neuron 23–7, a ventrobasal thalamic cell driven by extension of the contralateral wrist. Scale for angle shown below, is arbitrary: 120° on this scale equals 85° extension of the wrist from its midposition. The edge of the excitatory angle was 55° on this arbitrary scale, or 20° extension of the wrist from its midposition. Five trials were made at each speed, the results oriented in time and averaged, and the averages are plotted as the curves shown here. Angular velocities were 23, 19, 11, 7·5, and 4 degrees per second, respectively, for the curves with peaks successively from left to right, as indicated by identical lines above and below

transient changes in a regular manner with changes in the rate of movement, but that the final steady-state frequency of discharge is a function of position alone.

Measurement and scaling

It will be clear from the observations just described, we believe, that it is permissible to regard the movement of a limb at a joint through the range of the excitatory angle for a thalamic cell as a variation of a sensory stimulus along an intensive continuum. We define the physical value of this stimulus in terms of the degrees of deflection (θ) of the joint away from the edge of the excitatory angle (θ_T) in the excitatory direction: thus, stimulus intensity $= (\theta - \theta_T)$. Although the independent variable, angle, is a quantity measured on an equal interval scale, the properties of a ratio scale are attained by the definition of a physiological zero (θ_1) in the manner just described.

The dependent variable, the frequency of nerve cell discharge, is one which varies along a ratio scale, but its value under any particular sensory drive is determined by the compounding of two factors which we believe to be additive: the prestimulus or spontaneous rate, and the increment in rate evoked by the specific sensory stimulus. Therefore, in order to measure on ratio scales the activity evoked by the stimulus it is appropriate to consider the rate of the spontaneous activity as a constant which defines a zero value for a scale of driven neural activity. Introduction of this constant, C, allows comparisons of the increments produced by different stimuli, yet preserves the ratio nature of the scale of the dependent variable. The response is defined as the observed discharge rate, F, measured in impulses per unit time, less the prestimulus or spontaneous rate, C: thus, response $= (F - C)$. Therefore

$$(F - C) = f(\theta - \theta_T)$$

and it is our purpose to define the function f.

The conversion to and preservation of ratio scales allows one to normalize the data obtained for a number of different neurons on percentile scales, a permissible transformation of ratio scales, and thus to describe the behavior of a population of cells in dimensions common to all.

The validity of measurement

Concern for the scaling of the independent and dependent variables is a prerequisite for the primary aim of this study, i.e. to determine a functional relation between a continuum of stimuli on the one hand, and one of neural response on the other. No less important is the validity of the measurement of neural activity. It is apparent in the plots in Figures 2, 3, and 4 that this estimation presupposes an examination of certain statistical properties of the EPUT values observed during periods of steady stimulation. In particular, it requires determining which statistical estimators are valid for characterizing the neural activity during periods of steady stimulation. For this purpose, the histograms of EPUT values over periods of 30–50 sec. of response during steady stimulation were determined for a sample of 11 units.

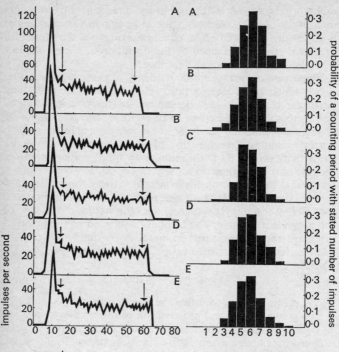

Figure 5. The five graphs to the left plot nerve impulse frequency per second for thalamic neuron 33–6, before, during, and after each of five movements of the contralateral knee through an angle of 74° at a velocity of 18°/sec. to a position of full flexion (A – E). After each flexion movement the limb was held steadily in the flexed position for about 1 min., and then rotated back to the initial position of about 100° joint angle, which was just on the extensor side of the excitatory angle for this cell. The five rotations were as identical in speed and extent as the rotation device would allow. At this velocity the initial transient responses are very large, relative to the plateau levels of discharge which persist during the periods in which the limb is held steadily in the fully flexed position. The portion of each record between the arrows was selected by eye as representing a more or less steady state. From these plateau periods, counts were made of the number of impulses per 200 msec. The histograms of the EPUT counts are shown to the right, appropriately labeled. Comparison of these histograms and their means and standard errors (see fourth column in table below) suggests that they represent samples drawn from a homogeneous population, which if true would permit pooling of the data obtained over a period of time and

From these histograms it was possible to ascertain that the distribution of EPUT values is either normal, or does not deviate from normality to an extent larger than seems permissible for employing the mean and the standard deviation as unbiased estimators (see the study illustrated in Figure 5). Furthermore, a comparison of the confidence limits of means over consecutive divisions within each period of steady driving, and over responses obtained in different applications of identical stimuli, revealed that samples of EPUT data generated in response to identical stimuli are representative of statistically homogeneous populations. For these reasons we believe that the means and the standard errors of the means determined from EPUT data and pooled in time and over repeated trials can be considered as valid statistical estimators of the neural responses to a given steady stimulus. The analysis described in Figure 5 illustrates the importance of determining that a steady state of response does exist.

Figure 5—*Continued:*

from several trials. Further examination revealed, however, that the transient response had not completely ended when these EPUT counts were begun at the time indicated by the first arrow over each graph to the left above. When the presumed steady states were divided into thirds and restudied, the first thirds showed significantly higher rates of discharge than those rates occurring during the next two-thirds of the record, as indicated by the means and SEs for each third, shown in the first three columns below. Comparison of these data for only the second and third segments indicates that these portions can, for all practical purposes, be regarded as samples drawn from a common and homogeneous population. This period of plateaus has been used to derive the mean values of discharge for all the neurons considered in the present study.

		I	*II*	*III*	*Over-all*
A	Mean	5·53	4·88	4·61	5·02
	SE	0·125	0·148	0·128	0·087
B	Mean	5·38	4·49	4·19	4·66
	SE	0·165	0·182	0·124	0·096
C	Mean	5·11	4·81	4·29	4·71
	SE	0·121	0·130	0·131	0·072
D	Mean	5·44	4·41	4·56	4·80
	SE	0·180	0·133	0·142	0·092
E	Mean	5·71	4·28	4·40	4·74
	SE	0·181	0·137	0·193	0·094

A, B, C, . . . refer to the five trials indicated above. *I*, *II* and *III* refer to consecutive thirds of the plateau periods. In each block the upper figure is the mean number of impulses per counting period of 200 msec., while the lower figure is the standard error of that mean.

The stimulus–response relation: the power law

The statistical analyses of the type illustrated in the preceding section give some confidence to our estimations of the mean level of neuronal activity, in a variety of nearly steady states. They indicate also the degree of variability which occurs in time during the steady response to a steady stimulus, as well as that which occurs from trial to trial for responses to identical stimuli. Figure 3 gives raw data plots of some of the data obtained during study of neuron 23–1, a ventrobasal thalamic cell activated by extension

23 – 1 knee extension

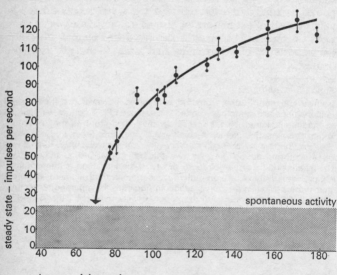

• — • — • = 0·005 confidence intervals

Figure 6. Plot of impulses per second in the steady state versus angle, for neuron 23–1, a ventrobasal thalamic neuron driven by extension of the contralateral knee. For each point populations were shown to be homogenous; the confidence with which the mean frequency was estimated is shown by lines and bars, which indicate the 0·005 level. The rate of spontaneous activity is the mean of many different records of it, obtained over a 3-hour period of study. The curve is one arbitrarily cast by eye; its intercept with the spontaneous activity level is defined as the threshold, or the edge of the excitatory angle, for the cell

of the knee. In all, records were obtained of the response of this cell at each of 13 angular positions, and for 5 trials for each of 8 of these. In addition, the activity of the neuron was recorded with the knee in the flexed or ~~nnnn n havory position~~ on a total of ~~12 occasions~~ during the more than 3 hours the neuron was held under study. The results obtained are plotted on the graph of Figure 6 which shows also the average level of prestimulus, or spontaneous, activity, as well as the confidence intervals for the estimate of each mean value. A line has been cast by eye through these points representing different levels of activity evoked by different joint positions, to an intercept with the spontaneous activity level. It is this intercept which we define as threshold, or the edge of the excitatory angle. The graph of Figure 7 plots the

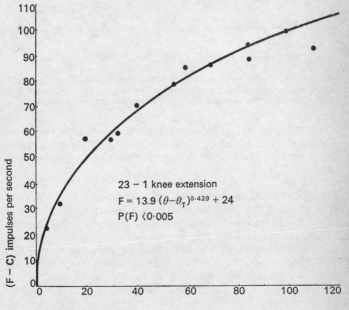

23 – 1 knee extension

$$F = 13.9 \, (\theta - \theta_T)^{0.429} + 24$$

$$P(F) \langle 0.005$$

$(F - C)$ impulses per second

$(\theta - \theta_T)$ – degrees

Figure 7. A replot of the data for 23–1 shown in Figure 6, but now the abscissa scale has been converted to a ratio scale by introduction of the threshold value, θ_T, as indicated, and frequency is expressed as the increment, over the spontaneous level, produced by a given angular position. The curve is the best-fitting power function of the form and with the constants indicated

same data, after transformation in the manner described above, i.e. F to (F — C) and θ to $(\theta - \theta_T)$, on ratio scales. The line plots the best-fitting power function of the form and with the constants given in the figure. In Figure 8 these same data are presented in logarithmic transformation, and the calculated regression line drawn in.

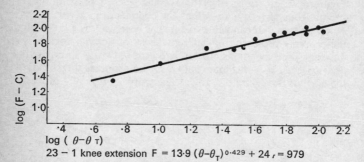

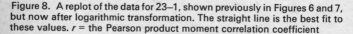

23 — 1 knee extension $F = 13.9 \, (\theta - \theta_T)^{0.429} + 24$, $r = 979$

Figure 8. A replot of the data for 23–1, shown previously in Figures 6 and 7, but now after logarithmic transformation. The straight line is the best fit to these values. r = the Pearson product moment correlation coefficient

The Pearson product moment correlation coefficient, $r = 0.979$, is indicative of a highly significant correlation. Thus it is possible to say that for this neuron a power function of the general form

$$R = KS^n$$

where R = response (i.e. F — C), S = stimulus (i.e. $\theta - \theta_T$) and K is a constant or proportionality, is adequately descriptive of the functional relation between the two variables under study.

Quantitative studies have been carried to some stage of completion for 72 of the 410 thalamic joint neurons observed in this investigation, and data sufficient for an analysis such as that illustrated are available for 25 of these. The results are given in Table 1. There it can be seen that the range of excitatory angles varies not only for different joints, but among those neurons related to the same joint as well. For example, the six neurons activated by knee flexion subtend peripheral angles which vary from 30° to 122°. The mean value of the exponent n is 0.73 ± 0.05, and only three cells of the entire group have values for the exponent which are greater than 1.0.

The question arises of how well the power function describes the relation between stimulus and response. Column 9 of Table 1 gives the extraordinarily high values obtained for the correlation coefficient r for the straight-line fits of the log–log transformations of the data, for each neuron. The mean value of this r is 0.96 ± 0.008. In addition, an analysis of variance was applied to

Table 1

Subject: $F = K(\theta - \theta_T)^n + C$

Unit	Joint	Movement	Excit. angle, deg.	No. pts	n	K	C	r	Total resid. var.	Resid. var. per point	Signif. level, $P(F)<$
19–1	Ankle	Ext.	72	8	0.56	3.64	5	0.99	21	3.9	0.005
19–2	Elbow	Ext.	70	6	0.41	2.59	6	0.87	12	2.0	0.10
22–4	Shoulder	Ext. rot.	85	7	0.67	2.11	5	0.99	39	5.8	0.005
23–1	Knee	Ext.	110	13	0.44	13.4	24	0.98	240	18.3	0.005
23–4–I	Elbow	Ext.	83	4	0.62	2.64	24	0.99	3	8.8	0.005
23–4–II	Elbow	Ext.	88	4	0.68	2.02	13	0.99	2	0.5	0.005
23–7	Wrist	Ext.	65	4	0.56	3.70	5	0.96	17	4.2	0.025
24–1	Meta.-Phal.	Ext.	30	3	1.15	0.60	8	0.98	6	2.0	0.10
24–4	Knee	Flex.	58	3	0.69	6.07	37	0.99	2	0.7	0.025
24–5	Shoulder	Ext. rot.	73	4	0.80	0.31	2	0.92	10	2.5	0.10
24–6	Meta.-Phal.	Ext.	90	6	0.30	14.6	2	0.90	99	16.5	0.025
26–1	Ankle	Ext.	76	4	0.78	1.15	1	0.95	28	7.0	0.10
26–2	Ankle	Ext.	75	5	0.47	7.4	3	0.93	46	9.2	0.025
27–1	Elbow	Flex.	40	5	0.75	3.85	0	0.99	27	5.4	0.005
30–1–I	Wrist	Ext.	55	7	1.16	0.76	10	0.99	10	1.4	0.005
30–1–II	Wrist	Ext.	55	4	0.68	5.59	10	0.99	81	20.2	0.025
31–1	Hip	Abd.	63	9	0.93	0.99	10	0.93	178	19.7	0.005
31–4	Hip	Abd.	95	9	0.99	0.88	10	0.98	86	9.6	0.005
31–5	Hip	Abd.	80	5	0.86	1.32	10	0.99	25	5.0	0.005
32–3	Shoulder	Ext. rot.	68	5	0.70	2.15	13	0.99	22	4.5	0.005
32–5	Elbow	Ext.	82	11	0.71	2.19	13	0.98	100	9.0	0.005
33–3	Knee	Flex.	40	7	1.60	0.836	20	0.90	186	26.6	0.005
33–6	Knee	Flex.	30	4	0.61	0.244	2	0.95	11	2.7	0.10
33–11	Knee	Flex.	122	6	0.65	1.64	10	0.98	63	10.5	0.01
35–1	Elbow	Ext.	68	6	0.69	1.60	5	0.98	39	6.5	0.005
35–2	Knee	Flex.	55	4	0.59	2.37	8	0.85	49	12.2	
36–7	Knee	Flex.	106	19	0.67	3.13	20	0.97	343	18.1	0.005

the ratio between the total variance and the variance remaining after the best power function fit. The values of column 12 of Table 1 give the results, for each neuron, and indicate with what probability an error would be made in rejecting the hypothesis that the reductions in variances (see columns 10 and 11) are not due to the fitted functions. For 24 of the 25 neurons this probability is 0.1 or less, and for 15 it is 0.005 or less.

Thus it is reasonable to conclude that a power function of the form given is adequately descriptive of the relation between stimulus and response for a number of thalamic neurons, and that this holds over a considerable number of joints, and regardless of the direction of the exciting movement.

Table 2

Total and Residual Variances

| Unit | No. pts | Total variance | Residual variances about best fit for functions | | | | | |
			A	B	C	D	E	F
19–1	8	1,092	88	31	65	82	108	170
19–2	6	470	8	12	44	28	7	29
22–4	7	1,030	62	39	119	48	244	115
23–1	13	6,735	230	240	225	1,457	521	5,862
23–4–I	4	514	10	2	331	132	113	67
33–4–II	4	338	2	3	61	9	129	77
23–7	4	461	14	17	31	7	17	152
24–1	3	299	19	6	153	84	151	82
24–4	3	1,453	3	2	987	405	571	173
24–5	4	76	11	10	30	22	45	14
24–6	6	462	172	99	141	372	163	681
26–1	4	169	143	28	148	25	93	231
26–2	5	763	259	46	261	106	233	171
27–1	5	2,160	27	88	38	52	52	35
30–1–I	7	1,294	472	10	723	557	1,928	168
31–3	9	1,662	888	178	253	195	597	180
31–4	9	4,675	80	84	1,016	441	2,196	259
31–5	5	1,341	17	25	124	76	415	63
32–3	5	607	12	22	9	32	117	83
32–5	11	3,380	312	100	332	171	950	162
33–3	7	1,125	383	183	418	413	774	338
33–6	4	90	3	11	6	11	12	14
33–11	6	444	210	61	49	35	180	169
35–1	6	511	55	39	70	46	153	128
35–2	4	174	47	49	50	50	78	74
36–7	19	6,234	213	343	667	181	808	1,703
Sum	168	37,559	3,740	1,674	6,464	5,033	10,655	11,201
Var/pt		224	22	10	40	30	63	67

A: $F = K(\theta - \theta_T)^n$

B: $F = K(\theta - \theta_T)^n + C$

C: $F = K \dfrac{\alpha(\theta - \theta_T)}{1 + \alpha(\theta - \theta_T)} + C$

D: $F = F_{max} 1 - e^{(\theta - \theta_T)} + C$

E: $F = K \log (\theta - \theta_T) + C$

F: $F = K(\theta - \theta_T) + C$

Are other functions descriptive of the stimulus–response relations?

Inspection of the data suggests the possibility that other negatively accelerating functions might fit as well as does the power law. To answer this question we have tested the fit, for each neuron, of several other monotonic functions. The results are given in Table 2. Function *B* is the power function used in the analyses described above. Function *C* is a form of the 'A over 1 plus *A*' law, *D* is an exponential relation, *E* the Fechnerian semi-logarithmic relation, and *F* the equation for a straight line. The lowest row of numbers indicates that function *B* surpasses its nearest competitor by a factor of 3 in the reduction of variance. It appears from these data that negatively accelerating functions other than the power law may be fitted to the observed data only poorly, and that they are less adequately descriptive of the stimulus–response relation.

23 – 4 elbow extension

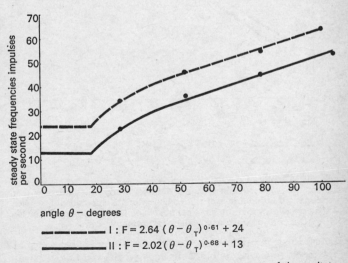

I : $F = 2.64 \, (\theta - \theta_T)^{0.61} + 24$

II : $F = 2.02 \, (\theta - \theta_T)^{0.68} + 13$

Figure 9. Graph showing results of two measurements of the excitatory angle for neuron 23–4, a ventrobasal thalamic cell driven by extension of the contralateral elbow. The two studies were made about 1 hour apart, and in this interval the 'spontaneous' activity level changed by a factor of 11 impulses/sec. The two curves are the best-fitting power functions of the form and with the constants shown

The role of spontaneous activity

The data of Table 2 show that on the average the introduction of the constant C to account for the prestimulus or spontaneous activity (function B) allowed an improvement in fit over a power function without such a constant (function A) by a factor of more than 2. This matter is, we believe, of importance for two

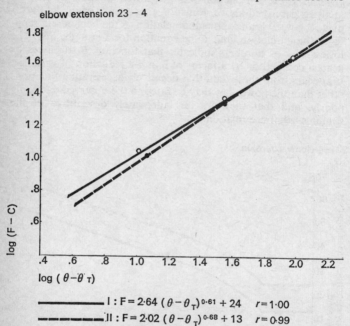

I : $F = 2.64 (\theta - \theta_T)^{0.61} + 24$ $r = 1.00$

II : $F = 2.02 (\theta - \theta_T)^{0.68} + 13$ $r = 0.99$

Figure 10. A replot of the data shown in Figure 9, now after logarithmic transformation. The straight lines are the best-fitting functions after this transformation. Introduction of the constant for the spontaneous activity in each case shows that the increments in impulse discharge produced by each angular position were nearly identical in the two cases

reasons. First, it validates the scaling of the dependent variable with respect to C, the spontaneous activity. Beyond this, it raises an important question. That is, does the central nervous system operate along intensive continua on an absolute scale, or is a given level of activity compared to the prestimulus rate? That introduction of a constant for spontaneous activity allows one to establish a more regular relation between values for responses obtained as the stimulus intensity is varied suggests that the latter is so. This idea is further supported, for example, by the observations made upon neuron 23–4, a thalamic cell driven by extension of the contralateral elbow, and subtending an excitatory angle of 83°. The lower curve of Figure 9 shows the results obtained during an initial study, at which time the neuron discharged on an average 13 impulses/sec. with the elbow at an angular position other than one within the excitatory angle. About 1 hour later this spontaneous rate had risen to 24/sec., and the study was repeated, with care taken to deliver, as precisely as possible, stimuli at angles identical with those used in the first study. The results are shown by the upper curve of Figure 9. Figure 10 shows the log–log transformations of these two sets of data, each with its appropriate value for the constant C for spontaneous activity. It is obvious that the increment in neural activity provoked by a stimulus is, in this case at least, independent of the prestimulus level. This suggests that whatever intracortical mechanism estimates position by use of this thalamocortical input must operate upon a differential scale, and thus compare any given increase against the background prestimulus level obtaining at that time.

Reconstruction of population behavior

That there is a relative similarity of the stimulus–response relation for different thalamic joint neurons is not at all certain from the data presented so far, for these neurons differ both in the width of the excitatory angle each subtends, i.e. in the range of the intensive continuum for each (see Table 1), and in the rate of discharge reached by each under maximal excitatory drive. The observations made upon different neurons can be compared and viewed as an ensemble after conversion, in each case, of the stimulus and response scales to per cents of maximum, a permissible transformation of ratio scales. This would be most telling if done for a large number of neurons related to the same joint. In lieu of observations on such a population, we have normalized the data for 14 neurons, each related to a 'hinge' joint, which are thought to be most comparable and for which our control of the stimulus is most precise. Data for the 91 angles for which steady-state responses were recorded in the course of study of these 14 neurons are shown on normalized scales in Figure 11. The fitted curve is the power function which reduced the residual variance to a minimum. The straight-line fit to the log–log transformation of these data is shown in Figure 12, and the correlation coefficient indicates that this fit is very good indeed. Moreover, it should be emphasized that a large share of the variability shown by the data of Figure 11 is due to variations of the constant K and the exponent n, from one neuron to another. This variability due to

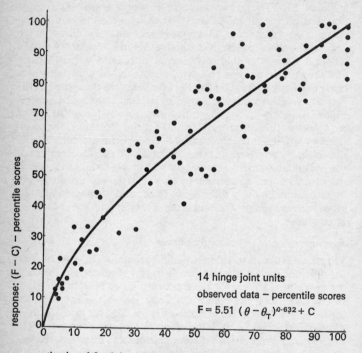

Figure 11. Plot of normalized data for studies of the relation between angle and frequency for 14 hinge-joint ventrobasal thalamic neurons. The curve is the best-fitting power function with the constants shown. Further discussion in text

constants alone is shown in Figure 13, where the calculated 'best fit' values for each angle for each neuron, estimated separately, are plotted together.

Thus the evidence available supports the statement that the response of any thalamic joint neuron to rotation of the relevant joint will be described by a power function, and that the constants for that function fall within a certain narrow range.

Signs of integrative action of the afferent pathway

Earlier studies of the first-order afferents from the knee joint of the cat showed that their receptive angles are usually some 20° in angular extent, and that while the maximal discharge rate for a given neuron may be at the extreme range of movement, i.e. at

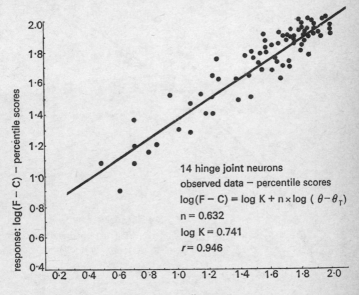

Figure 12. A replot of the data shown in Figure 11, after logarithmic transformations. The line is the best fitting function. r = Pearson product moment correlation coefficient

full flexion or full extension ('single-ended' excitatory angles), for many other afferents this position of maximal discharge is reached at some intermediate point, and the frequency of discharge drops rapidly when the limb is moved in either direction from the maximally excitatory position ('double-ended' excitatory angles) (1, 12). Third-order elements of the system (at least in the monkey) are remarkably different. Their excitatory angles are wider by an average factor of nearly 4 (see Table 1), and no single cell has ever been observed which was related to a double-ended excitatory angle, for all were excited maximally at one of the extremes of rotation of the relevant joint.

To represent these facts, the data for the same 14 neurons

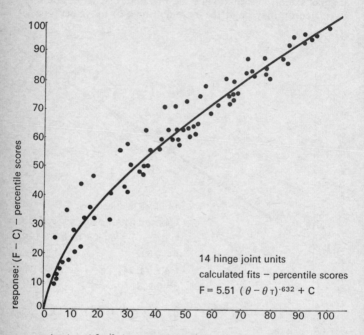

14 hinge joint units

calculated fits — percentile scores

$F = 5.51 \ (\theta - \theta_T)^{.632} + C$

response: $(F - C)$ — percentile scores

stimulus: $(\theta - \theta_T)$ — percentile scores

Figure 13. Plot of the calculated points determining the best-fitting power functions for the 14 hinge-joint ventrobasal thalamic neurons. The variability about the best fitted curve is due to variations in the constants n and K from neuron to neuron, as shown in Table 1. The variability of the data points about the best fitting curve in Figure 11 on the other hand, includes both the variability in constants and the 'error' or variability in measurement

described above have been used to reconstruct a synthetic population of thalamic neurons, as if they were related to the same joint. For the curves of Figure 14 the best fitted power function for each neuron is plotted in such a way that the angular scale of joint position is transformed to a percentile scale of the total possible rotation of a joint in either direction from its midpoint, thus normalizing the variation in extent of angular rotation which exists between different joints. It is apparent that a majority of the cells subtend angles greater than one-half the total range of angular movement possible, and that their response curves must therefore overlap in the middle range. This fact as well as the very

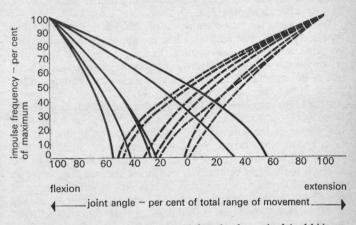

Figure 14. Plots of the best fitting power function for each of the 14 hinge-joint ventrobasal thalamic neurons. Abscissa scale normalized for different joints by correcting values for each to per cent of the maximal possible movement in either direction from a middle, or neutral position of the joint. Further discussion in text

great width of the excitatory angles of thalamic cells will be considered in the discussion as examples of transformations which may occur at subcortical relay stations of sensory systems, transformations which are thought to contribute to integrative action, regarded in its broadest sense.

Discussion

The experimental results we have described were obtained by study of a certain component of the somatic afferent system. It consists of first-order afferent fibers whose endings terminate in joint capsules and ligaments, their central extensions in the dorsal columns, and the groups of cells upon which they impinge, directly upon those of the dorsal column nuclei, and after successive relays upon cells at successive stages of the system: the thalamic ventrobasal nuclear complex and the postcentral gyrus of the cerebral cortex. The evidence, both experimental and clinical, that it is the dorsal column medial lemniscal system, and this cellular component in particular, which provides the neural input upon which the sensations of the position and movement of the limbs depend has been marshalled in another place (7) and can, we believe, be accepted.

We have chosen this component of the system for the studies reported here for two reasons. First, the appropriate stimulus can be delivered in a precise manner. Second, the cells of this component are in very large majority completely independent of peripheral inputs other than that arising from sensory endings in the joints. It has previously been shown (7), that very exceptionally such neurons may be inhibited by light tactile stimuli delivered to skin distal to the relevant joint. This type of inhibition has been looked for in the case of each thalamic neuron studied; it has been encountered rarely. When it was observed, stimuli within that skin area were avoided. It is our opinion, therefore, that the changes in thalamic cell activity described here are due, so far as peripheral inputs are concerned, to changes in afferent input in first-order nerve fibers produced by joint movement or steady position. We would like to emphasize that the joint afferent system possesses most potently those properties characteristic of the lemniscal system (6, 11). It is likely, therefore, that our findings will have some general significance.

The stimulus–response relation

Our main objective was to study the stimulus–response relation. The problems are immediately raised of the validity of measurement of the dependent variable, neural activity, as well as of the scale along which it should be measured. For the present study we have chosen the number of impulses per unit time – the average running frequency – as the measure of neural activity. Obviously, the sequential timing of the impulses may be a factor of informational importance, over and above the value of the running frequency, although direct evidence that this is true has yet to be adduced. For the present analyses this internal structure of the neural message has been ignored: it will be treated in later papers (10, 17). The data presented above show, we believe, that the levels of activity of thalamic cells can be measured with reliability, even though these levels vary from time to time.

We emphasize that the stimulus–response relation we have measured is one which varies along an intensive continuum. It is

not at all obvious from behavioral observations or from introspection that this should be so, and position sense is commonly
regarded as varying only extensively. The general point should
be made, however, that a given neuron can only change its rate
of firing, i.e. can only vary intensively, and this we have of course
found to be the case for thalamic neurons driven by joint rotation. It is clear that extensive variations of sensory stimuli, e.g.
change in position, must be signaled by variations in the spatial
patterns of activity in large groups of neurons. It seems paradoxical that position of the limbs is not one of these, but our
observations on this point are, we believe, certain. That is, that
of the thalamic nerve cells related to a given joint, some will be
driven by movement in one direction, some by the other. But of
those activated by a given movement, all will discharge along
monotonically increasing functions, reaching their maximal firing
rates at the limit of movement.[1] Which movement is made, e.g.
whether extension, flexion, rotation, etc., is signaled 'extensively' by the activation of different groups of cells for each,
while the degree of any movement is signaled 'intensively' by
the increasing rates of discharge in the relevant group of cells.
The matter under discussion is of more than theoretical interest,
for some evidence obtained from the study of the first-order
afferents suggests that the situation there is quite different. If this
is true, there must occur a remarkable transformation between
first- and third-order elements of the system. This change will be
discussed below.

The essential point we wish to make in this paper is that a
lawful relation obtains between stimulus and response, i.e. that
between the steady position of a limb at a joint and the rates of
discharge of the thalamic cells related via polysynaptic linkages
to primary afferents from that joint. We have presented evidence
that this relation is best described by a power function of the
general form

$$R = KS^n + C$$

where R the response is measured as frequency of nerve cell discharge, K is a constant of proportionality, S the physical value of
the stimulus, and C a constant whose value is the average rate of

1. This limit of movement is defined as complete but gentle flexion,
extension, etc. of a joint. Movement of the joint beyond this point produces
subluxation, in the monkey under neuromuscular block, and frequently a
decrease in the mean firing rate of the thalamic cell. This decrease is produced, we presume, by an excessive depolarization of and hence decreased
firing rates in first-order afferents.

firing of the neuron in the prestimulus period, i.e. the so-called spontaneous activity. Evidence was presented to show that other monotonically increasing functions are much less accurately descriptive of this relation.

That a power function is descriptive of this relation is of interest when related to recent psychophysical findings. Stevens and his colleagues (13, 14, 15, 16), and others as well (3), have found such a relation between the physical value of a stimulus and the human observer's estimate of that value. The power law holds for a large number of sensory modalities. The exponent n varies with sensory mode, being close to 1·0 for the mechano-receptive senses, which fits well with the average value of n obtained in these experiments. It is not so surprising to find that the behavioral estimation of intensities and the levels of activities of central nerve cells stand in a similar relation to the physical values of the responsible stimuli. What is of additional import-ance, we believe, is that this transformation has occurred so early as the thalamocortical stage of that long chain of successive neural transformation which must intervene between afferent sensory discharge and the behavioral response – in this case the estimation and verbal description of the physical value of one stimulus, as compared to that of others. This means, we believe, that these subsequent neural transformations may occur along linear coordinates, so far as the value 'intensity' is concerned.

Transformations and integrative action

It is one aim of studies such as this to provide data sufficient to allow detailed descriptions of the patterns of first-order afferent discharge evoked by a given stimulus, and of the full panorama of neural change evoked by that stimulus at each succeeding relay station of the system, into and through the cerebral cortex. Thus could one define the central reflection of the sensory event. For the joint afferent system nothing other than their presence is known about the relevant cells at the second-order level in the dorsal column nuclei. There have, however, been studies of the first-order afferents in the cat, and it is of interest to compare them with our present results obtained in a study at the third-order level.

All who have studied them have found the first-order fibers to be sensitive indicators of both position and movement of the joints (1, 2, 12). Movement into the relevant angular range pro-duces an onset transient discharge which, if the movement ends within the excitatory angle for the fiber, declines to a steady rate of discharge determined by position. For the knee joint of the cat, receptive angles for first-order fibers are about 20° in extent (1, 12). While many of these receptive angles are single-ended and monotonic, and thus placed at the extreme of the ranges of movement, other fibers are related to double-ended receptive angles. They are maximally activated with the limb in some midposition, and decrease their rates of discharge with movement of the limb away from that position, in either direction. Obviously, such elements must be regarded as signaling position of the limb along an extensive continuum, i.e. position could only be detected by determining which fibers of the total population were active. And for fibers with double-ended receptive angles, it is clear that any frequency of discharge save the maximal may be produced at either of two limb positions. The conclusion must be that changes of frequency cannot signal position, with certainty.

If these facts are true for the monkey, a subtle form of transformation occurs by the time of the third-order relay, one which we believe is an instance of integrative action in an afferent pathway. As the plots of Figure 14 show, the excitatory angles of thalamic cells are single-ended and always monotonic, and are wider by a factor of 4 than are those of the first-order elements. Thus each thalamic cell, by its varying rate of discharge with movement, provides a running spatial integral of the activity of a considerable number of first-order fibers which must, across two synaptic relays, converge upon it. In a sense a purely spatial pattern varying extensively is converted into one varying intensively in the domain of frequency, rather than of spatial location within a neural field. The value of that position within the neural field is retained to signal different movements, and not different degrees of the same movement.

The graphs of Figure 14 are of further interest, for they indicate that the receptive angles of large numbers of thalamic cells overlap in the middle range. Thus with a joint such as the elbow in or near the midposition, both 'extensor' and 'flexor' neurons will be discharging, at low rates. A small shift in one direction will increase the rates in one group and decrease those in the other. These changes will be very great in this middle range, for here are the most precipitous portions of the power functions. As the movement progresses to, for example, full flexion, extensor neurons will become silent and all available flexor neurons will be recruited to action. A subtle question then arises of whether the capacity to discriminate angular deflection will vary with angular position. In the middle range the reciprocal action of cells sensitive to antagonistically directed movements, and the rapid slopes of their frequency response curves, should provide for an exquisite discriminatory capacity. At the extremes of position, on the other hand, reciprocal action is no longer present, and the frequency response curves become flatter, but the successive recruitment of all the neurons activated by that particular movement may provide a compensating factor.

Our recent studies of first-order afferents related to the joints in the monkey (Mountcastle, Kidd, and Oswaldo-Cruz; unpublished observations, 1962) have served to emphasize another and potentially important transformation in the system. Under steady drive the first-order afferents discharge at extraordinarily steady rates – with, in the steady state, nearly constant intervals between successive impulses. Thalamic neurons, under the same conditions, discharge impulses which succeed one another at irregular intervals (10, 17) even though the over-all frequency may remain nearly constant. This loss of regularity poses important questions for study: where and how does it occur, and is it of intrinsic value for a cortical interpretive mechanism which can discriminate between total spatial and temporal patterns of input which differ only very slightly from one another?

Summary

Those cells of the ventrobasal nuclear complex of the thalamus which are responsive to the steady position and to movements of the joints have been studied by the method of single unit analysis, in unanesthetized, deafferented-head monkeys. These cells, their related peripheral afferents, and their intervening second-order cells form a system which functions to detect the angular positions of the joints, and which details by its thalamocortical discharge pattern and frequencies the direction and rate of movement, and the steady positions of the limbs.

The independent variable, joint angle, has been controlled with an instrument allowing independent variation of the speed of rotation and the extent of the angle turned, and scaled along true ratio scales. The zeros of these scales are set by the threshold, or edge of the excitatory angle, for each cell studied. Thalamic cell discharges were measured in terms of impulses per unit time, and the validity of measurement established.

The thalamic cell discharge varies as a monotonic function of joint position, one best described by a power function of the form $R = KS^n + C$, where R is the response in impulse per second, K a constant of proportionality, S the stimulus, and C a constant determined by the prestimulus level of activity. The exponent n averaged about 0·7 for a population of 25 neurons for each of which it was determined. The relation of this finding to recent psychophysical observations is discussed. Some evidence is adduced which suggests that in this sensory system the relevant response is the increment produced by the stimulus over and above the prestimulus level of activity.

The excitatory angles for thalamic cells were measured, and were found always to be monotonic, and thalamic cell discharge always reached a maximal rate at one or the other extreme range of movement. These angles averaged 73°. The differences between these and previous findings by others on the first-order afferents were considered as evidence of transformations at the synaptic relays of the system, and discussed from the standpoint of their role in integrative action.

References

1. ANDREW, F. L. and DODT, E. The deployment of sensory nerve endings at the knee joint of the cat. *Acta physiol. scand.*, 1953, *28*:287–96.
2. BOYD, I. A. and ROBERTS, T. D. M. Proprioceptive discharges from stretch receptors in the knee-joint of the cat. *J. Physiol.*, 1953, *122*:38–58.
3. EKMAN, G. Some aspects of psychophysical research. In *Sensory Communication*, edited by W. A. Rosenblith. Cambridge, Mass., and New York, Technology Press and John Wiley, 1961, pp. 35–47.
4. MOUNTCASTLE, V. B. Modality and topographic properties of single neurons of cat's somatic sensory cortex. *J. Neurophysiol.*, 1957, *22*:408–34.
5. MOUNTCASTLE, V. B. Duality of function in the somatic afferent system. In *Brain and Behavior*, edited by M. A. B. Brazier, Washington, D.C., American Institute of Biological Sciences, 1961, pp. 67–93.
6. MOUNTCASTLE, V. B. Some functional properties of the somatic afferent system. In *Sensory Communication*, edited by W. A. Rosenblith. Cambridge, Mass. and New York, Technology Press and John Wiley, 1961, chapt. 22.
7. MOUNTCASTLE, V. B. and POWELL, T. P. S. Central neural mechanisms subserving position sense and kinesthesis. *Johns Hopk. Hosp. Bull.*, 1959, *105*:173–200.
8. POGGIO, G. F. and MOUNTCASTLE, V. B. A study of the functional contributions of the lemniscal and spinothalamic systems to somatic sensibility. Central nervous mechanisms in pain. *Johns Hopk. Hosp. Bull.*, 1960, *106*:266–316.
9. POGGIO, G. F. and MOUNTCASTLE, V. B. The functional properties of ventrobasal thalamic neurons studied in unanesthetized monkeys. *J. Neurophysiol.*, 1936, *26*:775–806.

10. POGGIO, G. F. and VIERNSTEIN, L. J. Time series analysis of the discharge sequences of thalamic somatic sensory neurons. *J. Neurophysiol.*, in press.

11. ROSE, J. E. and MOUNTCASTLE, V. B. Touch and kinesthesia. In *Handbook of Physiology*, edited by J. Field and H. W. Magoun. Washington, D.C.: Am. Physiol. Soc., sect. 1, vol. 1, 1959, chapt. XVII.

12. SKOGLUND, S. Anatomical and physiological studies of knee joint innervation in the cat. *Acta. physiol. scand.*, 1956, *36*: Suppl. 124.

13. STEVENS, S. S. On the psychophysical law. *Psychol. Rev.*, 1957, *64*: 153–81.

14. STEVENS, S. S. Tactile vibration: dynamics of sensory intensity. *J. exp. Psychol.*, 1959, *57*: 210–18.

15. STEVENS, S. S. The psychophysics of sensory function. In *Sensory Communication*, edited by W. A. Rosenblith. Cambridge, Mass., and New York, Technology Press and John Wiley, 1961, pp. 1–33.

16. STEVENS, S. S. and GALANTER, E. H. Ratio scales and category scales for a dozen perceptual continua. *J. exp. Psychol.*, 1957, *54*: 377–411.

17. WERNER, G. and MOUNTCASTLE, V. B. The variability of central neural activity in a sensory system, and its implications for the central reflection of sensory events. *J. Neurophysiol.*, in press.

Part Two Sensory Processes and Perception: The Code

The foregoing articles make it likely that the sensory processes, in essence, construct an alphabet from the input, an alphabet that can then be utilized as a code to represent the input. From the results of these experiments arises the question regarding the size of the coded units at various levels in the system: e.g. whether at the retinal level characters or letters are the units. Another question is whether, at the receptive cortex, words are readied, or whether some more remote part of the brain is necessary. But the outlines of the problem have been given, as have the techniques with which to come to grips with it.

But, of course, there is more to the coding problem than determining the units out of which a code may be constructed. A different approach to the problem is detailed in the next group of papers. These are more directly concerned with the construction of the code or model, given the units with which to work.

9 E. N. Sokolov

Neuronal Models and the Orienting Reflex

Excerpts from E. N. Sokolov, 'Neuronal models and the orienting reflex', in M. A. B. Brazier (ed.), *The Central Nervous System and Behavior, Third Conference*, Josiah Macy, Jr., Foundation, 1960, pp. 187–212.

I would like to propose four general problems for discussion: the object study of sensory integration; the components of the orienting reflex; the neuronal model and the structure of the orienting reflex; and the application of the neuronal model to the explanation of the conditional reflex. [. . .]

The term *orienting reflex* was introduced by Pavlov in 1910 (2, 3). This reflex is characterized by two general properties: the first is that it is an unspecific reflex and is initiated by any increase, decrease, or qualitative change of a stimulus, independent of the modality of the stimulating agent. The second property is that it is subject to extinction or habituation on repeated presentation. This orienting reflex is a special functional system which can be differentiated from the other two general types of unconditioned reflexes – the adaptive reflex and the defensive reflex. The adaptive reflex is the reflex connected with the direction of a change of stimulus, and the defensive reflex is a general response of the organism when the stimulus is too strong for normal functioning.

For example, when we record the vascular response of the vessels of the head and of the finger simultaneously, as in Figure 1, we find with the orienting reflex, whether evoked by sound A, cold B, warmth C, or electrical shock D, that there is dilation of the vessels of the head and a simultaneous vasoconstriction of the vessels of the finger.

This reaction, and this is the important point, is produced only by the first few presentations of the stimuli. The response is unspecific, i.e. irrespective of the modality of stimulation. This is a sign of the orienting reflex. For example, after ten or fifteen presentations (Figure 1 A, center record), sound no longer produced an effect. Cold produced the adaptive reflex in the form of vasoconstriction in head and hand (B, center record). Warmth also produced a specific adaptive reflex but in the form of vasodilation in both head and hand (C, center record). Shock produced a special defensive reflex (D, center record).

When we aroused the subject by an additional loud sound, he could be brought back to the first stage of nonspecific orienting reflexes. Once again, sound, cold, warmth, and shock produced the same nonspecific effect. We can, therefore, differentiate the orienting nonspecific reflex (which can be extinguished) from the specific adaptive reflex, which is persistent in spite of repeated presentations. We can differentiate a defensive reflex, which is also stable in spite of repeated presentations (7).

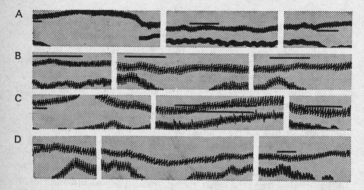

Figure 1. Orienting, adaptive, and defensive reflexes in man. Each upper trace represents vascular response in the head, and each lower trace vascular response in the finger. Upward deflections – vasodilation. Downward deflections – vasoconstriction. Horizontal lines = presentation of stimulus. (A) SOUND: Left, orienting response to new stimulus. Centre, habituation on repetition. Right, recovery of orienting reflex to sound after external stimulation. (B) COLD: Left, nonspecific orienting response. Center, specific adaptive response with vasoconstriction in both head and finger. Right, return of nonspecific orienting response after external stimulation. (C) WARMTH: Left, nonspecific orienting response. Center, specific adaptive vasodilation in both head and finger. Right, recovery of orienting response to warmth after external stimulation. (D) ELECTRIC SHOCK: Left, orienting response. Center, defensive reflex. Right, recovery of orienting response to shock after external stimulation.

Two different forms of orienting reflex can be distinguished: a generalized orienting and a localized orienting reflex. When we record simultaneously the occipital EEG, the EEG of the motor region, the skin galvanic response (SGR), muscle tension, eye movements, and respiration, the first presentation of tactile stimulation produces a generalized response (Figure 2).

After twenty-four presentations, the only effect is a slight depression of EEG in the motor region. The other components are inhibited. Therefore, during the course of repeated presentations, the generalized form of the orienting response, which includes a different analyser system, changes into a local form, which is a kind of activation of the specific analyser that is being stimulated.

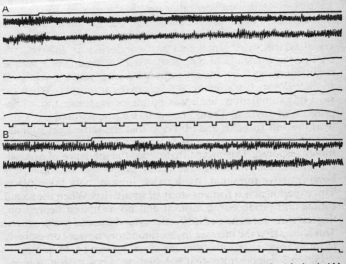

Figure 2. Change from generalized to local orienting reaction. In both (A) and (B), from top to bottom: signal; occipital EEG; EEG of motor region; SGR; EMG; eye movements; and respiration. (A) The first presentation of tactile stimulation of skin produced a generalized response in EEG, SGR, eye movements, and respiration. Muscle tension was not increased in this case. (B) After 24th presentation, the only response was a brief EEG change in the motor region. Excitation now localized only in the region of the analyser directly stimulated

It is important to recognize that the localized form of the orienting reaction in some degree became related to the modality of stimulation. If I use tactile stimulation or a change in proprioceptive stimuli, there is a localized response in the motor region. If I use light, the special localized response appears in the occipital EEG and the specific eye movements. The result depends on the modality of stimulation. [. . .]

To summarize the results of the first part of this report, the orienting reflex is a special functional system, which increases the discriminatory power of analysers. I believe there are two mechanisms for this: the first is a direct stimulation through the special descending pathways to the receptors from the reticular formation and from the cortex, which can change this discriminatory power, and the second mechanism is an indirect one, a change in the blood supply of the cortex and of the peripheral part of the analysers, which can indirectly change the excitability. The orienting reflex includes the cortical as well as the somatic mechanism of the increase in sensitivity of the visual system. These inferences can be studied in the form of a decrease in the threshold of the visual system. The experiment was conducted as follows. We studied the threshold of the visual system by means of test light stimulations such as are generally used in psychophysiological studies. We used a stimulus 0·8 below the threshold. When we gave this stimulation, there was no motor response and no depression of rhythm. Then, after a sound stimulation, we again used this test stimulus and observed that the same light stimulation now evoked an α-rhythm depression, and somewhat later, a motor response. This means that under the influence of arousal, the stimulation which was previously below the threshold now became above threshold. An increase in sensitivity takes place. This experiment is a form of study of sensitivity. When the sound stimulation produced no arousal and no α-rhythm depression, this test stimulus remained ineffective after the sound presentation. This shows that the increase in discriminatory power corresponds to an increase in sensitivity in the visual system (4, 6). [. . .]

Figure 3 demonstrates that habituation is not a drop in sensitivity. The stimulus is a light just above threshold in intensity, and presented after 40 minutes of dark adaptation. When habituation develops, there is no response in the occipital EEG and no SGR. When the intensity of light is changed, the orienting reflex returns. There is an SGR and a marked depression of α-rhythm.

The hypothesis is that under the influence of repeated presentations, a kind of neuronal model is elaborated in the cortex (8). What is meant by 'neuronal model'? The model postulates a chain of neural cells which preserve information about the intensity, the quality, the duration, and the order of presentation of the stimuli (5, 9).

We have studied this hypothesis by means of prolongation and by shortening of the duration of the stimulus. Figure 3 B shows that after a few presentations, each 5 seconds in length, the response disappeared; there was no SGR and no α-rhythm depression. But when the period of stimulation was shortened to only 2 seconds, an SGR and α-rhythm depression reappeared at the moment the stimulus was cut short (Figure 3 D).

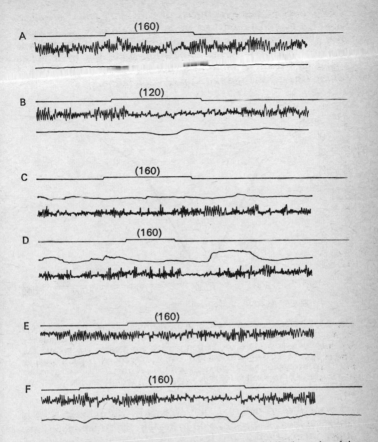

Figure 3. Reappearance of orienting reflex on diminishing intensity of the light stimulation. In (A) to (F), from top to bottom: signal of light in relative units, occipital EEG, and SGR. (A) After three sessions, complete habituation. (B) Diminishing light intensity from 160 to 120 relative units evokes a generalized reaction (α-depression and SGR). (C) Habituation to 160 relative units of intensity with a duration of 5 secs. (D) Decrease in duration evokes the orienting reflex at the moment when the light is cut short. (E) Habituation to 160 relative units and a duration of 5 secs. (F) Prolongation of the same intensity evokes the orienting reflex at the moment when the duration exceeds that of the standard stimulation

According to our hypothesis, the orienting reflex is evoked when the neuronal model set up in the brain does not coincide with all the parameters of the stimulus. The orienting reflex is produced not only by the stimulation itself, but by impulses arising as a result of noncoincidence between a certain cortical pattern (the model) and the applied stimulation. [...]

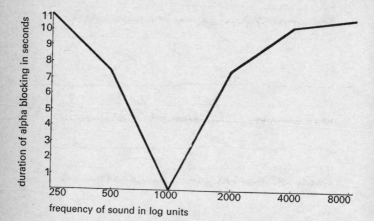

Figure 4. Characteristics of the filter in the neuronal model. It is evident that there is a selective filtering of the impulses to the habituated frequency and that the responses to other frequencies are greater, the greater the difference between them and that of the habituated sound. This is a negative filter, and it prevents the transmission of impulses from the applied stimulus to the neurons responsible for organizing the orienting reaction

I want first to describe, quite formally, the properties of a biological filter, and then go on to explain the structural scheme of the orienting reflex. In Figure 4, we measured the duration of the α-rhythm depression after habituation of the response to 1,000 cps. After habituation to the sound at 1,000 cps, the response to other frequencies is then greater in proportion to the difference between 1,000 cps and the frequency used as the new stimulus.

It is important to discuss the relationship between the neuronal model and the Pavlovian concept of a 'dynamic stereotype'. By a 'dynamic stereotype', is meant a special pattern of responses that is reproduced in accordance with previous experience. For example, light, sound, and tactile stimulation produced a different magnitude of reaction, but if, after each has been given, we present only one of these stimuli, we find that it alone reproduces the characteristic responses of the other stimuli.

This is what was called the dynamic stereotype, for there is a stereotyped reproduction of the reaction. 'Neuronal model' is a term which is used for the understanding of the *non*stereotyped orienting reflex for, in the orienting reflex, reaction is not stereotypically reproduced but is evoked only when there is a change of stimulus. I believe, however, that the neuronal mechanisms of these phenomena are the same, and a comparison between the orienting and the conditional reflex supports this view.

The next problem concerns the mechanism of this neuronal model. The most interesting results have been obtained in the drowsy state in man. In these experiments we used sounds, and on repetition in the waking state there was complete disappearance of the orienting reflex. When the background activity in man changed to that of a drowsy state with delta and theta waves instead of alpha, we observed a very interesting phenomenon. The orienting reflex, which had previously been inhibited during the waking state, reappeared and was not inhibited in spite of dozens

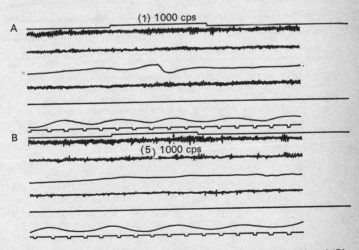

Figure 5. Habituation to sound (150 db, 1,000 cps): In both (A) and (B), from top to bottom: the signal, occipital EEG, EEG of motor region, SGR, EMG, eye movements, respiration, and time marker in seconds. After four presentations of this sound, all signs of the orienting reflex disappear

of presentations of the same sound stimulus while drowsiness lasted.

Figure 5 shows that in this subject, after the first presentation, there was an orienting reaction. This was a generalized response. After four presentations, no further response was observed. Then, after this habituation, a change in the state of the subject was observed and theta waves appeared in the EEG. As can be seen

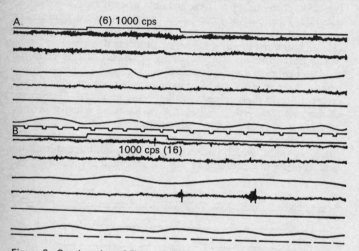

Figure 6. Continuation of Figure 5. (A) When an inhibitory state of cortex develops (note theta waves in EEG), there is a paradoxical recovery of orienting reflex (EEG change and SGR), indicating increased stimulation and decreased inhibitory control of impulse transmission. (B) Although in the awake state five presentations produced complete inhibition of orienting reflex in this subject, in the drowsy state there is no decrease even on the 16th presentation

from Figure 6, when there was a background of theta waves (in spite of the previous habituation of the orienting reflex in the fully waking state), the same stimulation produced return of α-rhythm, and also recovery of the SGR. This activation of a vegetative function indicates that, under the development of an inhibitory state of the cortex, some inhibitory control of this vegetative function is lost. [. . .]

In general, the latency is the same, in spite of the number of presentations. After four presentations when the subject was awake and in a state of excitation, the orienting reflex was inhibited. When he was drowsy, it was not inhibited; neither the SGR nor the EEG change habituated.

This suggests that habituation is the elaboration of an inhibitory conditional reflex regulating the transmission of impulses to the reticular formation. This hypothesis is supported by some data obtained in France by Benoit (1), who stimulated the reticular formation electrically and observed no habituation of arousal. Therefore, I believe that the block of impulses takes place somewhere between the collaterals from the specific pathway and the reticular formation.

We can explain it as follows: the beginning of stimulation in every case is one stimulus, and its prolongation acts as a second one. According to this hypothesis, the prolongation of stimulation produces an unconditioned inhibitory process which can develop during a sufficiently long presentation of each stimulus. We assume that this process arises between the collaterals and the reticular formation, probably by hyperpolarization of synaptic connections.

After repeated presentation of the same stimulation, the beginning of this stimulus becomes the conditioning stimulus for the prolongation which produces the inhibitory state. This conditioned inhibition of inflow into the reticular formation results in signals being transmitted via the specific pathways before the stimulation reaches the reticular formation and the nonspecific system; in this way, the specific transmission can regulate the transmission to the reticular formation through the mechanism of a conditional reflex.

When the cortex itself is in a state of inhibition (as in drowsiness), this active control of the subcortical level is excluded or diminished, and therefore impulses can reach the reticular formation in this state. [. . .]

References
1. O. BENOIT, 'Étude des variations de l'activation corticale provoquée par des stimulations réticulaires en expérience chronique', *J. Physiol.*, Paris, vol. 50 (1958), pp. 153–5.
2. I. P. PAVLOV, *Twenty Years of Experimental Study of the Higher Nervous Activity of Animals*, 6th edn, Moscow and Leningrad, 1938. (In Russian.)
3. I. P. PAVLOV, 'Studies of the action of the cerebral hemispheres', *Complete Collected Works*, vol. 4, 1947. (In Russian.)
4. E. N. SOKOLOV, *Perception and Conditional Reflexes*, Moscow University, 1958. (In Russian.)
5. E. N. SOKOLOV, 'Neuronal model of the stimulus. 1. The formation of a neuronal model by repeated representation of the stimulus', *Report Acad. Pedagog. Sc. U.S.S.R.*, vol. 4 (1959). (In Russian.)

6. R. P. STEKLOVA, 'Concerning the change of light sensitivity of the eye by action of auditory stimuli of different intensities', *The Orienting Reflex and Problems of Higher Nervous Activity*, Moscow, 1959. (In Russian.)

7. O. S. VINGRADOVA and E. N. SOKOLOV, 'The relation of vascular responses in the hand and in the head in some unconditioned reflexes in man', *Sechenov Physiol. Journal U.S.S.R.*, vol. 42 (1957), p. 1.

8. L. G. VORONIN and E. N. SOKOLOV, 'Cortical mechanisms of the orienting reflex and their relation to the conditional reflex', Proc. Internat. Conf. on EEG and Higher Nervous Activity, *EEG clin. Neurophysiol.*, Suppl. 13 (1960), pp. 335–44.

9. WAN TSIN, 'The neuronal model of the stimulus. 2. The neuronal model of the orienting reflex to light', *Rep. Acad. Pedagog. Sc. U.S.S.R.*, vol. 5 (1959). (In Russian.)

10 K. S. Lashley

The Problem of Cerebral Organization in Vision

K. S. Lashley, 'The problem of cerebral organization in vision', in H. Kluever (ed.), *Biological Symposia, vol. VII: Visual Mechanisms*, Jaques Cattell Press, Lancaster, 1942, pp. 301–22.

With the development of the cerebral cortex of mammals, many activities which are mediated by midbrain and thalamic structures in submammalian species are taken over, in part or wholly, by the new cerebral structures. After removal of the cerebral cortex or of the limited striate areas of the occipital lobes the capacity for visual responses is enormously reduced. In primitive mammals there remain only the pupillary and optokinetic reflexes, discrimination of intensities of light, and possibly some very crude remnants of detail vision, mediated by the tectum or pretectile region (Tsang, 1937; Marquis, 1934; Smith, 1933). The anthropoid apes have lost even such slight capacities for independent activity of the thalamus and midbrain as persist in lower mammals. The visual cortex of the primate brain is essential for any reaction to the spatial properties of a visual stimulus. Thus practically the entire repertoire of visual functions of mammals is dependent upon the activity of the occipital cortex.

Study of the integrative functions of the visual cortex plunges the investigator at once into definitely psychological problems. The adequate stimulus for an optic reflex can usually be described as a simple change in intensity of light, but the characteristic cerebral responses are based upon the distribution of intensities of light within the visual field. An analysis of the effective stimulus for such reactions regularly reveals a selective organization or abstraction of effective elements and a certain degree of generalization, even in the most primitive mammals. Thus for the rat, as for man, visual impressions consist of organized objects, seen against a less coherent background. Discriminative reactions, when analysed, are found to be based upon certain generalized features of the stimulus. Analysis of the properties of stimuli which determine reaction shows that in every case there is functional equivalence between a rather wide range of objects which have in common only certain general or relational characters which cannot be reduced to terms of stimulation of identical nervous elements (Lashley, 1938a, 1938b). Such perceptual generalization is typical of every differential response and may be traced by graduated steps, without change in fundamental principle, from the discriminative reactions of the rodent to the human insight which leads to important scientific generalizations.

The questions posed by such activities must be faced by the student of cerebral physiology. It has been customary to say that psychological processes of this sort are so complex that they defy immediate physiological analysis, and to hold to the faith that continued study of elementary nervous activities will eventually lead to an understanding of the complexities of organization. Generalization, insight, and reasoning have been regarded as aggregates of more elementary processes, built up by a combination of the activities of sensory fields brought about by transcortical association or by the activities of higher coordinating centers.

In contrast to such a view of intellectual functions as composites of simpler neurological processes, there is some reason for believing that generalization is one of the primitive, basic functions of organized nervous tissue. For example, the transposition of reactions along a stimulus dimension has been found in all organisms which are capable of differential response. That is, when an animal is trained to choose the larger or brighter of two objects and is then confronted with a still larger or brighter he chooses on the basis of relative size or brightness. Such generalizations, transpositional responses, are universal, from the insects to primates. They persist in the rat after total destruction of the striate cortex (Hebb, 1938) and thus seem to be as primitive as is discrimination.

In fact, the gross structural evolution of the nervous system may be largely disregarded when considered in relation to problems of sensory perception. The laws governing the organization of elements into coherent units of figure and ground, the determination of similarities for visual form, and the whole organization of the visual field is fundamentally the same for the bird, the rodent, and man, and it is very probable that the same general principles will be found to apply to insects and cephalopods, when these have been adequately studied. In spite of the enormous differences in structural arrangement of the visual systems of different animal classes, the functional activity seems essentially the same.

Visual tests for use with animals may be constructed to present a series of perceptual or logical relations of graded difficulty, after the manner of Thurstone's 'figure classification test' (Thurstone, 1938). The most difficult task of this character which it has been possible to teach a normal rat is that which I have called the 'conditional reaction', in which a positive or negative reaction to the same stimulus is required, according to the character of the background upon which it is displayed. Destruction of non-visual areas of the cortex or incisions along the margins of the striate areas, separating them from adjacent parts of the cortex, do not interfere with the establishment of this reaction. No part of the cerebral hemisphere except the visual area is essential for solution of any problem of this type which a normal animal can solve. In fact, if enough striate cortex remains to permit of any detail vision, that part seems able to mediate the most difficult perceptual generalization (Lashley, 1942). Transcortical association or control by higher intellectual centers seems to be ruled out by such experiments, which point to the conclusion that the receptive areas of the cortex are themselves capable of processes of generalization not fundamentally different from 'higher' intellectual activities.

Such facts as these indicate that the explanation of perceptual generalization is to be sought in the primitive organization of nervous tissue, rather than in any elaborate construction of transcortical associative connections or of higher coordinating centers. Every discriminative reaction involves a process which is basic for all generalization and intellectual functions; all imply a common neurological problem. This may be illustrated by equivalence of reactions in the so-called transposition experiment. The principle involved is that the reaction is determined by relations subsisting within the stimulus complex and not by association of a reaction with any definite group of receptor cells.

The same principle is inherent in the recognition of every visual object. Visual fixation can be held accurately for only a moment, yet, in spite of changes in direction of gaze, an object remains the same object. An indefinite number of combinations of retinal cells and afferent paths are equivalent in perception and in the reactions which they produce. This is the most elementary problem of cerebral functions and I have come to doubt that any progress will be made toward a genuine understanding of nervous integration until the problem of equivalent nervous connections, or as it is more generally termed, of stimulus equivalence, is solved. Therefore, rather than review the disconnected and somewhat unintelligible details of experimental studies on the visual cortex, I propose now to survey the possibilities of an explanation of stimulus equivalence in terms of present knowledge of the nervous system and with special reference to detail vision.

Neurologically, the problem is clear enough. The first experience of a stimulus excites a certain number of neurons in a definite pattern (Figure 1, bc–f). An associated reaction (y) is formed as a

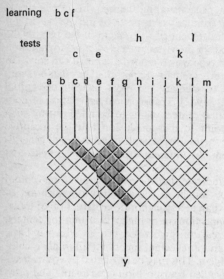

Figure 1. Diagram to illustrate the problem of stimulus equivalence. An association is formed with y by stimulation of receptor cells bc–f. Thereafter any similar pattern of receptors (ce–k) will excite reaction y. A fixed trace, as indicated by the heavy lines, fails to account for such equivalence

result of this stimulation. Thereafter, the excitation of any similar pattern of neurons (ce–k) will elicit the associated reaction. The later stimulation need not, and practically never does, involve the original combination of sensory cells. It preserves only certain proportions or relations among the elements of the stimulus pattern.

It must be assumed that the first stimulation leaves some trace in the nervous system which determines the subsequent reactions. The difficulty for neurological theory arises when an attempt is made to localize this trace. It cannot be restricted to the neurons originally excited or to their immediate connections, for they need not be reactivated in order to elicit the reaction again. It cannot be in any other restricted group of cells, for after a single experience, any part of the macular field can mediate the reaction. The memory trace somehow becomes a property of the whole system. This inference from the nature of stimulation is borne out by experimental and clinical studies which have uniformly failed to localize specific memories.

Here is the dilemma. Nerve impulses are transmitted over definite, restricted paths in the sensory and motor nerves, and in the central nervous system from cell to cell through definite intercellular connections. Yet all behavior seems to be determined by masses of excitation, by the form or relations or proportions of excitation within general fields of activity, without regard to particular nerve cells. It is the pattern and not the element that counts. What sort of nervous organization might be capable of responding to a pattern of excitation without limited, specialized paths of conduction? The problem is almost universal in the activities of the nervous system and some hypothesis is needed to direct further research.

Theories of Stimulus Equivalence

The possibility of any physiological explanation of stimulus equivalence has been denied by vitalists like Driesch and McDougall. An especially detailed analysis of the problem and criticism of physiological theories of association has been given by Becher (1911). The vitalistic approach has been valuable in emphasizing aspects of the problem which are ignored in the formulation of practically all biological theories of memory, but it should not lead us to abandon the search for the neurological basis of association.

Few students of nerve physiology have attempted to deal with the problem of stimulus equivalence in relation to memory but some half dozen different theories have been proposed to account for generalization of the stimulus. None of these has been developed in any detail. They appear rather as suggestions interpolated in discussion of other matters or merely by implication in general theories of nervous organization, so that I may be doing some injustice to their authors in elaborating such statements to fit these particular problems. However, the possibilities suggested must be considered.

Pavlov (1927) attempted an explanation of generalization based upon his theory of nervous irradiation. Briefly, he assumed that the effects of stimulation spread through the cortex from the point of primary excitation, so that adjacent points, as well as the primary one, become associated with the conditioned reaction. Figure 2 illustrates the theory as applied to the discrimination of two objects of different size. A field of positive association is formed around the excited field of the larger, and of negative association around that of the smaller. New objects of different size would elicit positive or negative reactions according to the relative areas of the two association fields which they excite. Obviously, however, the theory of irradiation completely fails to account for constancy of figure with changes in visual fixation and for transfer to similar figures differing in size, since simple irradiation generalizes the figure only for one retinal position. Some of Pavlov's followers have modified his theory by omitting its assumptions concerning the spatial spread of excitation and have assumed instead that irradiation is along dimensions of similarity (Spence, 1937; Hull, 1939); the conditioned reaction spreads to similar objects. This, of course, simply begs the question of the nature of the generalizing process, since it assumes that generalization is a function of similarity whereas similarity is an unexplained result of generalization.

A second suggestion has been derived by analogy with the selective switches of an automatic telephone system. The successive levels of nervous structure, constituting a series of relay stations between sense organ and muscle, seem adapted for some such action of selective switching. The idea has not been elaborated. I myself have not been able to work out a model on this principle without assuming definite localized memory traces which are contradicted by experimental facts; or assuming an innate exact reduplication of intercellular connections such as is precluded by the irregularities of nervous growth.

The possibility of chemical sensitization as a basis for memory has given rise to some speculations but, again, has not been elaborated. As applied to the problem of stimulus equivalence it would seem to require the assumption that each pattern of excitation gives rise to a specific chemical compound to which the final common path is sensitized; that a combination of excitations in the form of a triangle produces the same compound, no matter where it occurs; and that the degree of similarity of the compounds produced (proteins or what not) varies with the degree of similarity of the patterns of stimulation. Such results of stimulation seem impossible in the light of what is known concerning the chemistry of the nerve impulse.

240

Much of the recent experimental work on sensory equivalence and the organization of percepts has been carried out by members of the Gestalt school and has led to the formulation of the so-called field or vector theories. These assume that the pattern of sensory excitation in the cortex gives rise to a field of force, perhaps electrochemical in nature, for which generally the perimeter of the figure forms a boundary separating areas of different poten-

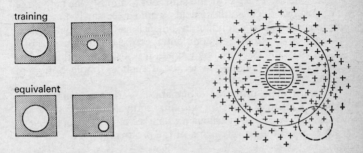

Figure 2. Diagram to illustrate the neurological implications of Pavlov's theory of generalization. Differential training with the large circle as a position stimulus is assumed to establish a cortical field of positive association for the larger, of negative for the smaller. Irradiation of the effects of stimulus constitutes generalization. Obviously any change in the point of fixation would render the mechanism inoperative

tials (Köhler, 1940). The behavior of elements in perception is interpreted in terms of the interplay of forces in a simple physical medium. The interrelations of figures in perception, the dominance of figure over background and the phenomena of illusions and apparent movement may be somewhat clarified by the theory. I suspect, however, that the success of field theory is more apparent than real. Its application to specific problems frequently involves specific, *ad hoc* assumptions, and its explanations turn out to be only elaborate tautologies.

No attempt has been made to deal with stimulus equivalence in terms of field theory. The assumption is implied that similar force-fields give rise to similar conscious experience and the theory has not been carried beyond this point. It seems still to be one of psycho-physical interaction. Interpreted in neurological terms it is subject to the same critic sm as was applied to Pavlov's conception of irradiation, since it assumes a brain field corresponding in its spatial characteristics to those of the sensory surface, with forces spreading according to the pattern of sensory excitation.

Some years ago I suggested that differential excitation might give rise to electrochemical gradients within the medium surrounding the neurons and that the latter might be so modified as to respond to the direction of the gradient (Lashley, 1929), thus making reaction dependent upon relative intensity of activity in different regions rather than upon specific nervous connections. It is doubtful, however, whether energies produced within such gradient fields, if they exist, are sufficient to modify the activity of the neurons.[1] Such gradient fields would necessarily be of considerable area, corresponding in dimensions to the striate cortex and in such a field the fall in potential across the dimensions of a single cell would be exceedingly small. It is also impossible to deal with complicated figures in terms of such a simple notion of gradients.

None of these proposed explanations is then adequate in its present form to account for stimulus equivalence, nor does any one of them suggest a mechanism which seems capable of development to meet the requirements of the problem.

Characteristics of Cerebral Activity

In seeking a more satisfactory hypothesis certain general considerations must be given weight.

1. Keith Lucas has written: '. . . we should inquire first with all care whether the elementary phenomena of conduction, as they are to be seen in the simple motor nerve and muscle, can give a satisfactory basis for the understanding of central phenomena; if they cannot, and in that case only, shall we be forced to postulate some new process peculiar to the central nervous system.' The statement of Lucas is a statement of the principle of parsimony, but direct studies of action currents within the brain have only confirmed the view that the transmission of nervous impulses from cell to cell forms the basis of all integration. Any hypothesis concerning the mechanism of generalization must start from the established facts of nerve conduction and must weave them into its texture.

2. The number of nervous elements activated by any stimulus

1. Gerard (1941) has shown that nervous activity in one region of the brain may start waves of potential change which traverse the cortex and excite nervous activity in other regions without transmission of impulses through intervening cells. The significance of these phenomena for integrated activity is not yet clear, but it is difficult to conceive that such potential differences can be characteristically different for different complicated visual patterns.

must be estimated in millions or hundreds of millions. The receptive layer of the visual cortex, in an animal even so primitive as the rat, contains half a million cells, all of which are subject to continuous excitation from the retina, and this half million serves only to initiate the chain of cerebral activities. In any such system the contribution of a single nerve cell can have little influence upon the whole. Behavior is essentially the statistical outcome of nervous activity. The memory traces upon which stimulus equivalence is based must involve the modification of large numbers of neurons.

3. With the best techniques available, students of the histology of the visual cortex have failed to demonstrate long transcortical connections between the striate areas and other architectonic fields, except the peristriate, nor are there long connections within the striate area itself (Clark, 1941). It is probable therefore that the integrative functions of the visual cortex are carried out by transmission over short internuncial fibers within the cortex.

4. The exact topographical projection of the retina and of the cutaneous surface upon the striate areas and the sensory cortex respectively has led to what may be an oversimplification in conceptions of the spatial relations of nervous activity underlying perception. Pavlov assumed an irradiation of excitation over a surface in the brain corresponding in its dimensions to the surface of the skin. Field theories, as developed by psychologists, postulate forces acting according to the geometry of the retina or of the objects in the visual field. Actually nothing is known of the functional significance of topographic projection of sensory surfaces on the cortex. The assumption that accurate projection of the cutaneous surface and the retina is important in providing a spatial reproduction of the sensory surfaces at an integrating level is rendered questionable by the fact that the anterior thalamic nuclei have an equally precise cortical projection for which no functional correlate is apparent (Lashley, 1941). Interconnections within the retina and the lateral geniculate nuclei may modify the sensory pattern profoundly before it reaches the cortex and within different cortical layers the effective pattern of organization may be reconstituted. There is no reason to believe that the effective integrative forces of the cortex act within a field which is a geometrical reproduction of the sensory surface. The geometry of nervous integration may be something quite different from the geometry of the stimulus.

5. The functional equivalence of different combinations of sensory fibers is paralleled by other natural phenomena: the

diffusion gradient, the formation of crystals, and the regeneration of form by living tissue. In each of these examples any part can exhibit the same functions as any other part within limits with which the reader is familiar. The parts are, in the terminology of Driesch, equipotential. In these analogous cases the substratum, or active substance, is a system composed of reduplicated structural elements: the distribution of molecules in the diffusion gradient, the reduplicated molecular structure in the crystal, and the identical chromosomal mechanisms in different cells of the organism. That is, in all instances of which we have knowledge the equipotential system appears to be a system composed of a number of identical elements. It is to be expected, therefore, that the memory trace is likewise reduplicated throughout the system (striate area, or what not) concerned in stimulus equivalence.

These considerations, especially the intercellular transmission of nervous impulses, the involvement of many elements, and the reduplication of functional mechanism as the basis of equivalence of parts, suggest probable characteristics of the memory trace. By what possible mechanisms might a pattern of stimulation, exciting one restricted group of nerve cells, set up a reproduction of itself, reduplicated throughout the whole cerebral area into which those nerve cells discharge?

Reduplication of Associative Mechanisms

The anatomic studies of Lorente de Nó (1934) have revealed a system of cross connections in the cortex which will permit the spread of excitation in any direction along the surface. Many adjacent neurons are capable of mutual excitation and the whole system is organized as a network, with loops of various lengths and complexity, capable of transmitting impulses from cell to cell across the cortex, or of reexciting initial points of stimulation by the action of return circuits having diverse characteristics.

From such a structural organization functional properties may be inferred with some confidence. Excitation started at any point must spread from that point throughout the system, since extinction (through building up of activity in reverberatory circuits) will occur only after the passage of the initial impulse. If the system is uniform throughout, a series of radiating waves should be produced, since the first wave of excitation will be followed by a wave of extinction, with excitation following again, either from successive volleys arriving over sensory pathways or by reexcitation at the retreating margin of the zone of extinction. The timing

244

of the waves should be uniform, since it is dependent upon the speed of conduction and the refractory periods of the elements of the system. With several or many points of excitation, interference patterns will be formed.[2]

Disregarding for the moment the effects of return circuits in order to get a simplified picture, the action should be somewhat analogous to the transmission of waves on the surface of a fluid medium. Interference of waves in such a system produces a pattern of crests and troughs which is characteristic for each spatial distribution of the sources of wave motion and which is reduplicated roughly over the entire surface. A somewhat similar patterning of excitations in the plane of the cortex is to be expected. Spatially distributed impulses reaching the cortex from the retina will not reproduce the retinal pattern of excitation in the cortex but will give rise to a different and characteristic pattern of standing waves, reduplicated throughout the extent of the functional area. An immediate objection is that the excitation of one part of the field may render that part refractory to impulses coming from other parts, and so block the formation of a uniform pattern. However, if the transcortical paths or reverberatory circuits are of random length, as they apparently are, not all in any region will be simultaneously in a refractory state and blocking will not occur.

The analogy with wave motion in a homogeneous liquid cannot be applied seriously to the cortical activity, since the cortical tissues have inherent characteristics as a transmitting mechanism quite different from those of a fluid. The analogy is presented only to give a conceptual picture of a reduplicated system which may serve as a starting point for a more adequate conception of the structure of the memory trace.

The cortex, built up as it is of millions of transmitting loops of various lengths and refractory periods, actually consists of an indefinite number of resonators. Each minute area may respond to any of a number of frequencies of excitation, establishing a resonance to that frequency and inhibiting momentarily the activity of other circuits of different characteristics. The effects of excitation at one point should spread through the cortex, activating successively circuits having the same characteristics as that initially excited. With the excitation of two or more points interference effects would change the pattern and establish dominant

2. The conception of interference patterns as the basis of integration has been suggested by Goldscheider (1906), Horton (1925), and others. These authors have not attempted to deal with the problem of stimulus equivalence and seem to have assigned the memory trace to a definite limited locus.

circuits having other characteristics than those elicitable from either point alone. Without more complete knowledge of the details of cortical structure and the characteristics of its reverberatory circuits than is now available, it is impossible to construct any clear picture of cortical activity, but it is not improbable that for any pattern of stimulation a stable resonance pattern, not unlike the interference effects of simple wave motion, would be established.

The problem of formation of intercellular connections is perhaps simplified by consideration of the fact that visual stimuli generally take the form of figures, that is, grouped masses of excitation of which the boundaries are the effective attributes for behavior. Interference patterns arising from such figures may have a simpler structure than those produced by a number of isolated points of excitation. Thus a linear stimulus should produce parallel waves throughout the excited area; neurons lying in parallel rows will be simultaneously excited and a sort of polarization of the area produced. Under such conditions, the associative connections required for a generalization of 'direction' in the visual field are quite simple. Simultaneously excited rows of neurons may acquire functional connections. It is perhaps significant that the reaction to the direction of lines is the visual association readily acquired by lower mammals.

It is futile at present to speculate concerning the interplay of more complicated patterns but certain of the simpler phenomena of visual perception can be predicted from such a theory of cerebral organization. For example, increase in frequency of excitation and increase in area of excitation produce similar changes in the interference pattern of spreading waves, corresponding to the fact that, under certain conditions, luminous intensity and surface area are equivalent for behaviour. The filling in of interrupted outlines and the completion of simple geometrical figures follow also from the characteristics of interference patterns.

Except for hypnagogic and after-images, which constitute a unique problem, the visual memory image is lacking in detail. After brief exposure of a nonsense figure, such as an ink blot or pattern of intersecting lines, memory of it is likely to consist only of a vague impression of direction of lines, or a single detail of intersecting lines (Woodworth, 1915). Memorization of the entire figure requires that it be broken up and learned piecemeal. Its recall will then consist, not of a concurrent reproduction of the whole, but a serial reconstruction of one part after another. Such facts, together with the visual behavior of lower mammals, indicate that primitive visual memory is a matter of fixation of a direction or combination of few directions in visual space. In other words, the pattern or organization of behavior at any given moment is a relatively simple element in the total temporal pattern of excitation. This fact has significance for the next stage of integration. I shall make no attempt here to deal with the temporal pattern or serial ordering of activities. That is a problem for which no clue is as yet provided by neurological research. The evidence suggests, however, that, at the receptive level of the cortex, the stimulus is integrated into a relatively simple pattern of excitation in which the dominant feature may be a directional association of elements, a sort of polarization. The structural organization of the cortex is such that the formation of a reduplicated pattern after the analogy of a wave interference pattern is not impossible, and such a reduplication of the memory trace seems to be the only postulate by which we can account for the phenomena of stimulus equivalence.

Transmission of Patterns to the Motor System

Such a theory of integration is still useless without some picture of the transition from the sensory pattern to the pattern of motor activity. What sort of connection from the sensory field to the neurons of the final motor path would permit of a constant reaction to the reduplicated patterns postulated in the theory? A reduplication of patterns throughout the sensory area, such as I have postulated, would permit the formation of similar associative connections within all parts of the area, since cells in definite spatial patterns would be simultaneously excited.[3] If efferent fibers from all parts of the sensory area play upon the final motor mechanism, equivalence of function of different parts of the sensory area would be provided. But such a mechanism of transmission is precluded by the plasticity and functional equivalence of motor reactions. Motor habits are no more rigidly restricted to a small number of specialized cellular elements than is sensory perception. The learned reaction is not a combination of just those movements which are exercised during the learning, but is an adaptive pattern, shifting from one to another group of

3. Temporal contiguity is the only one of the 'laws' of learning which approaches universality. Not all simultaneous activities of the nervous system become associated but apparently some temporal overlap is essential for association.

muscles according to the demands of the moment. The learned reaction can be described only as a sequence of movements in relation to the axes of the body. Movement is determined by direction in relation to the body and not by the training of specific muscles. This fact is well illustrated by handwriting which retains its essential characteristics, even when produced by combinations of muscles which have not before been employed for such purposes. Figure 3 shows the writing of two individuals, blindfolded,

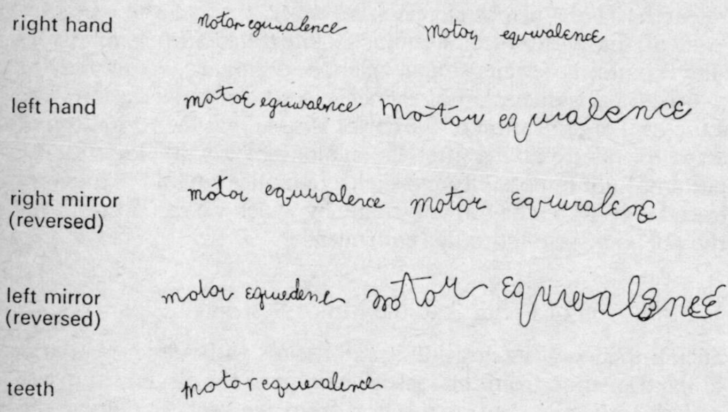

right hand

left hand

right mirror
(reversed)

left mirror
(reversed)

teeth

Figure 3. Writing of two blindfolded subjects with practiced and unpracticed groups of muscles. Mirror writing has been reversed for comparison with normal script

using right and left hands in various positions, as well as other muscle groups, unpracticed. In spite of clumsiness, the general features of the writing, individual differences in the forming of letters and the like, are characteristically maintained. The mechanics of writing is a sequence of movements in relation to bodily position, not a set pattern of special groups of muscles.

Usually the adaptive movements imply a still more general frame of reference; the coordinate system which constitutes the organism's orientation to its environment. When the rat learns the maze, he learns, not a stereotyped sequence of movements, but a series of distances and turns, which can be performed by unpracticed muscle groups, as when a cerebellar lesion forces him to roll through the maze. Maze performance is related to a system of coordinates still more plastic than the axes of the body. It is not unlike the achievement of the blindfolded chess player, who can rotate the board before his mind's eye, and play alternately from either side.

Not only is the equivalence of motor expressions a characteristic of behavior, but the motor control shows the same independence of limited conduction paths as does perception. The efferent path activating an adaptive pattern is no more restricted to specific fibers than is the recognition of a visual pattern dependent upon a single group of fibers in the optic nerve. In lower mammals double hemisection of the spinal cord does not preclude the performance of habitual manipulative acts and even in lower primates motor patterns survive the destruction of the pyramidal and other long spinal tracts (Brown, 1916).

The transition from the visual perceptual to the motor level thus appears to be, primitively, the translation of one system of space coordinates into another. Direction is dominant in visual memory and the reaction reduces to a sequence of directions of movement. Intervening between these is the system which constitutes spatial and postural orientation. Such a view of sensorimotor connections requires a revision of current conceptions of motor organization. The analyses of postural tonus made by Sherrington and by Magnus have shown that the tonic activity of each spinal motor center is influenced by almost every sensory stimulus to which the organism is subjected, including proprioceptive and cutaneous from all regions of the body, as well as vestibular and visual. The mechanism of this postural control is usually pictured in terms of specific connections from sense organ to muscle (Sherrington, 1911, p. 148). Such a conception implies the separate connection of every sensory cell with every motor center, although such interconnections have not been explicitly claimed. The effects of spinal lesions lead rather to the conclusion that the connections are more diffuse and it seems probable that the receptors pour their impulses into a common pool or network which acquires a more or less uniform polarization or dynamic pattern throughout and which in turn determines local reactions by the general characteristics of that organization. Cerebral influences may alter either the whole character of the pattern or produce local alterations through more direct paths. Local motor effects on activity of flexors and extensors may be exerted either through differential effects of the general interference pattern upon reciprocally connected motor centers or by more restricted interference in excitation of the many end buds on a single cell.

Obviously such a picture of nervous organization is almost as much oversimplified as were older diagrams of direct reflex arcs through the cortex. The dominance of one organization over others, as illustrated by the facts of attention, the mutual influences and distortions of perceptual forms which has been dealt with chiefly by field theories, and especially the temporal aspects of behavior apparent in the serial ordering of activities have not been touched upon.

The way seems open, however, for the extension of the same explanatory principles to such phenomena. A pattern of excitation in a cortical field may form a relatively stable and permanent foundation, modifying the effects of later excitation, as attention determines the selection of stimuli. That is, in cortical activity there must be postulated a persistent substratum of tonic innervation upon which are superimposed the fluctuating patterns resulting from current stimulation, in the same way that the innervation of voluntary movement is superimposed upon the spinal pattern of postural tonus. In the light of experimental evidence concerning the nature of nervous activity it seems most probable that the various patterns of integrated activity in successive levels of the nervous system have the form of tuned resonating circuits.

Such a speculative discussion is justified only by the prime importance of the problem of generalization and the inadequacy of current theories to deal with the problem. Bartley (1941) has recently contrasted the analytic approach which characterized studies of nervous transmission with the tendency to emphasize holistic concepts which is dominant in studies of perceptual organization, and has pointed out the need for some unifying principle which will bring these two opposed views together. The scheme of nervous organization which I have sketched makes no assumptions concerning elementary nervous activities beyond those established in studies of reflex conduction. It suggests a mechanism for action of the system as a whole which is also subject to analytic treatment in terms of nerve transmission. In this respect it is a substitute for field theory and, if of lesser immediate predictive value, is more consistent with elementary nerve physiology and is more open to experimental examination.

Details of the theory are of little immediate importance. But the principles of the establishment of interference patterns at successive levels in the nervous system, of the modification of these patterns by superimposed patterns from earlier stages in the series of levels, from retina to motor cells, and the reduplication of memory traces as a consequence of the properties of the interference pattern are, I believe, reasonable conclusions from the organization of behavior and the structure of the nervous system. The visual system is primarily concerned with spatial orientation and for it the transition from a sensory to motor pattern can be most adequately conceived as an interplay of polarized systems or of interweaving dynamic patterns in which the spatial properties of the visual stimulus are translated by integration at a series of levels into modifications of the general pattern of postural organization.

References

BARTLEY, S. H. (1941), *Vision*, New York.
BECHER, E. (1911), *Gehirn und Seele*, Heidelberg.
BROWN, T. G. (1916), *Quart. J. Exp. Physiol.*, vol. 10, pp. 103–43.
CLARK, W. E. LeGros (1941), *J. Anat.*, vol. 75, pp. 225–35.
GERARD, R. W. (1941), *Ohio J. Sci.*, vol. 41, pp. 160–72.
GOLDSCHEIDER, A. (1906), *Neurol. Zentralbl.*, vol. 25, p. 146.
HEBB, D. O. (1938), *J. Comp. Psychol.*, vol. 25, pp. 427–37.
HORTON, L. H. (1925), *The Dream Problem*, Philadelphia, pp. 115–69.
HULL, C. L. (1939), *Psychol. Rev.*, vol. 46, pp. 9–30.
KÖHLER, W. (1940), *Dynamics in Psychology*, New York, pp. 1–158.
LASHLEY, K. S. (1929), *Brain Mechanisms and Intelligence*, Chicago.
LASHLEY, K. S. (1938a), *Psychol. Rev.*, vol. 45, pp. 445–71.
LASHLEY, K. S. (1938b), *J. Gen. Psychol.*, vol. 18, pp. 123–93.
LASHLEY, K. S. (1941), *J. Comp. Neurol.*, vol. 75, pp. 67–121.
LASHLEY, K. S. (1942), *J. Genet. Psychol.*, vol. 60. pp. 197–221.
LORENTE DE NÓ, R. (1934), *J. f. Psychol. u. Neurol.*, vol. 46, pp. 113–77.
MARQUIS, D. G. (1934), *Assoc. Res. Nerv. Dis. Proc.*, vol. 13, pp. 558–92.
PAVLOV, I. P. (1927), *Conditioned Reflexes*, Oxford.
SHERRINGTON, C. S. (1911), *The Integrative Action of the Nervous System*, New Haven.
SMITH, K. U. (1933) *J. Genet. Psychol.*, vol. 53, pp. 251–72.
SPENCE, K. W. (1937), *Psychol. Rev.*, vol. 44, pp. 430–44.
THURSTONE, L. L. (1938), *Psychometric Monogr.*, no. 1.
TSANG, YÜ-CHÜAN. (1937), *J. Comp. Psychol.*, vol. 24, pp. 255–62.
WOODWORTH, R. S. (1915), *Psychol. Rev.*, vol. 22, pp. 1–27.

11 K. H. Pribram

Some Dimensions of Remembering: Steps Toward a Neuropsychological Model of Memory

Excerpt from K. H. Pribram, 'Some dimensions of remembering: steps toward a neuropsychological model of memory', in J. Gaito (ed.), *Macromolecules and Behavior*, Academic Press, 1966, pp. 166–73.

Experiencing Experience

Look at a friend, then look at his neighbor, and immediately you experience the difference. In the auditory mode, such transient, rapidly-paced recognition – of phrases in music, of phonemic combinations of speech, and so forth – are commonplace. Ordinary views of the memory mechanisms have considerable difficulty handling the immediacy, precision and apparent multidimensionality of the evanescent experience. Here a unique process must be in operation. What could it look like; how might it work?

Habit and Habituation

Let me begin by detailing a paradox concerning habit and habituation. If we are repeatedly in the same situation, in an invariant environment, two things happen. One is that if we have consistently to perform a similar task in that environment, the task becomes fairly automatic, i.e. we become more efficient. We say the organism (in this case, ourself) has learned to perform the task; he has formed *habits* regarding it. But at the same time the subject *habituates*, by which we mean that he no longer produces an orienting reaction; he no longer notices the events constant to this particular task in this environment. His verbal reports of introspection, his failure to move his head and eyes in the direction of the stimulus – electrophysiological measures such as galvanic skin response, plethysmography and EEG – all attest to the disappearance of orienting with repetition of unvarying input in an unvarying situation. Habituation, however, is *not* an indication of some loss of sensitivity on the part of the nervous system. Sokolov (1960), for example, has demonstrated that if he decreases the intensity of a tone which has been repeatedly given to a subject, orienting or alerting will recur. Further, if he again habituates the subject and then shortens the duration of the tone, orienting again will take place, but this time to the unexpected *silence*. These things led Sokolov to propose that a neural model of the environment is produced in the nervous system. This model would then constitute an expectancy, a type of memory mechanism against which inputs are constantly matched. The nervous system is thus continually tuned *by* inputs to process further inputs.

It is hardly necessary to state that the habitual performance of the organism is also due to neural activity. The point to be kept in mind is this: in the case of expectancy there is a diminution of neural activity with repetition, while in the case of performance, enhancement seems to occur. So the question is: What is the difference between these two kinds of neural activity that appear at first sight to be inversely related to each other? Neurophysiology provides us with some sound clues.

Graded potential changes at synapto-dendritic locations in nerve tissue, on the one hand, and nerve impulses on the other, are available as two kinds of processes which could function reciprocally. The channeling of nerve impulses obviously is related to performance. Graded neural events are therefore left as candidates to account for the orienting reaction of the organism and its habituation.

Further, a synapse does not work by itself. Nerve impulses arrive at many synapto-dendritic junctions simultaneously. In essence, such arrivals occur in patterns which generate stationary wave fronts. These, once established, can interact and produce patterns similar to moiré (Oster and Nishijima, 1963) or interference effects. These effects act as immediate analogue cross-correlation devices to produce new figures from which departure patterns of nerve impulses can be initiated. The orienting reaction could well be a function of such interference effects.

Subjectively, the orienting reaction is correlated with awareness, habituation with unawareness. What evidence do we have to suggest that the graded electrical activities of the central nervous system are involved in awareness? Kamiya (in preparation) at the University of California Medical School in San Francisco has shown, using instrumental-conditioning techniques, that people can be aware of whether their brains are producing alpha rhythms or not. Specifically, but briefly, the hypothesis reads that we are indeed able subjectively to tell one brain pattern of graded potential changes from another. My suggestion is, therefore, an old-fashioned one: that we experience some of the events going on in the brain, but not others. More experiments of the kind Kamiya has performed are urgently needed – the point is an important one. If accepted, it carries with it a corollary, viz. that nerve impulse patterns *per se* must be unavailable to awareness.

The Neural Hologram

But in order for recognition to be effected some more permanent alteration of substrate must act to influence the configuration of arrival patterns. If one looks at EEG records coming off an EEG machine for a number of hours during the day, and then goes home to try to sleep, what happens? The day's records go by in review; but note – they go by *in reverse*! This is known as the 'waterfall effect'.

Obviously, some neural change has taken place to allow the record to be re-viewed but also obvious is the fact that the re-viewing takes place from a different vantage point than did the original viewing. The record must therefore have 'stereo'-like properties that allow it to be examined now from this, now from that, standpoint. This re-viewing from various vantages must not lose its identity relative to the entire record: a familiar face gains, rather than loses, its familiarity and recognizable identity by being viewed from different angles.

Recently important new advances have been made in the study of interference effects. Moiré patterns, as mentioned above, have been explored and unexpected varieties of figures can be produced by the interaction of relatively simple grids. But even more startling in their similarity to perceptual processes are the results of a new photographic process which produces images by way of a record called a hologram (Leith and Upatnieks, 1965). The hologram does not visually resemble the original object – rather, it is a record of the wave patterns emitted or reflected from an object. As these authors say (p. 25), 'Such a record can be thought of as "freezing" of the wave pattern; the pattern remains frozen until such time as one chooses to reactivate the process, whereupon the waves are "read out" of the recording medium.' The process of producing an image from a hologram is called wave-front reconstruction photography.

Holograms are produced by virtue of interference effects. A photographic recording of these effects will yield a grating-like, grid-like structure that can be regarded as a two-dimensional analogue of the sinusoidal wave produced by an electric oscillator. The important point of this analogy is that just as an electric wave can be modulated to serve as a carrier of information, ... , so can the interferometrically produced wave pattern be modulated to serve as a carrier of information about the light waves that produced it (ibid., p. 27).

There are many startling attributes of holograms. Among these the following are of greatest interest to us in our search for the mechanism by which experience can be experienced.

First, the image which is seen by looking through the hologram is complete, three dimensional.

As the observer changes his viewing position the perspective of the picture changes, just as if the observer were viewing the original scene. Parallax effects are evident between near and far objects in the scene: if an object in the foreground lies in front of something else, the observer can move his head and look around the obstructing object, thereby seeing the previously hidden object ... In short, the reconstruction has all the visual properties of the original scene and we know of no visual test one can make to distinguish the two (ibid., p. 30).

Second, holograms have the property that

several images can be superimposed on a single plate on successive exposures, and each image can be recovered without being affected by other images. This is done by using a different spatial-frequency carrier for each picture ... The grating carriers can be of different frequencies ... and there is still another degree of freedom, that of angle (ibid., p. 31).

Finally, 'each part of the hologram, no matter how small, can reproduce the entire image; thus the hologram can be broken into small fragments each of which can be used to construct a complete image. As the pieces become smaller, resolution is lost' (ibid., p. 31). However, as successively larger parts of the hologram are used for reconstruction the depth of field of the image decreases, i.e. focus becomes narrowed, so that an optimum size for a particular use can be ascertained. These curious properties derive from the fact that 'each point on the hologram receives light from all parts of the subject and therefore contains, in an encoded form, the entire image' (ibid.).

The properties of the hologram are just those demanded by us to account for ordinary perception. I have already made the suggestion that arrival patterns in the brain constitute wave fronts which by virtue of interference effects can serve as instantaneous analogue cross correlators to produce a variety of moiré-type figures. Now, by means of some recording process analogous to that by which holograms are produced, a storage mechanism derived from such arrival patterns and interference effects can be envisioned. This is possible, since reconstructions of images from holograms have many of the attributes of perceptions.

I present these analogies advisedly. Only through them can we at this stage of knowledge of brain mechanisms begin to arrive at the 'possible'. Too long has neurophysiology been restricted to the nerve impulse and its transmissibility at the synapse as the one legitimate function worthy of extensive study. Connectivity and nerve impulse propagation are crucially important in themselves and, as will be seen below, important to the memory problem also. But connectivity and nerve impulse conduction are not enough to handle the richness of behavior and of psychological experience. Nor are they enough to provide a complete understanding of the brain. So, with the reader's indulgence, I will attempt to take the step from the photographic to the neural hologram, before considering more traditional memory mechanisms.

A possible mechanism by which neural holograms are produced suggests itself: Could the conformation of proteins and even longer-range anisotropic orderings of protein structure be altered in one direction during exposure and then later reversed such that, as it were, 'the tape plays backward'? And would this 'drift' in protein memory produce a reverse drift in the synaptically-produced patterns?

L. L. Whyte (1954) has proposed a mechanism which might operate in just this fashion:

A polarization pulse passing through a region of cortical cytoplasm in a given direction may produce a cumulative residual effect by introducing an element of long-range anisotropic ordering into previously disordered protein chains or fibrils, or by increasing an existing element of such order, of such a kind that the region thereafter responds more easily to a repetition of the same stimulus.

Monne has stated that 'memory must be associated with some permanent structural changes of the cytoplasm (cytoplasmic fibrils) of the neurones.' But he considers mainly chemical changes (i.e. the synthesis of new specific proteins) as the basis of memory, whereas the present suggestion relies on the establishment of components of directional ordering in the already-existing fibrillar texture of the neuroplasm.

The rhythmically pulsating cytoplasm may possess a self-moulding property, so that as it pulsates along a particular axis it tends to order its own structure, to work parts into position in relation to the axes of polarization and propagation, with the result that the system repeats the pulsation more easily, with less energy consumption.

This cumulative medium- and long-range ordering of some of the invisible chains throughout a particular volume of cortical cytoplasm is a kind of growth process of a pattern determined not by heredity but by activity, and involving the development not of a differentiated tissue but of an element of ordering in the molecular arrangement of an extended mass of cytoplasm. Here we are concerned with the *differentiation of particular vector directions*, possibly parallel to the cortical surface, in particular cortical layers. The templates of memory are not single localized molecular structures, but extended components of long-range order set at various angles to one another. [However,] the ordering will correspond only to the *statistically dominant pattern of activity*, or simplest overall pattern common to the successive activity patterns. Moreover this tendency to select the dominant pattern will be reinforced by the fact that the simplest overall patterns will be the most stable, since their parts will mutually support one another. The random protein structures may thus act as a structural sieve taking a stable impress at first only of the simplest, most unified, and statistically dominant component in all the patterns of activity of a given general form.

In general [, then,] the development of the modification proceeds from a grossly simplified to a less simplified and more accurate record. This process of the development of a hierarchically organized modification corresponds to Coghill's 'progressive individuation' of behavior patterns during ontogeny, and may hold the clue to the self-coordinating capacity of cortical processes.

This hypothesis, whether valid or not, may provide fresh orientation and assist the design of new experiments. For it implies that in certain regions and layers still to be identified, the functional element in relation to memory processes is not a cell assembly, a neural circuit or net, a synaptic pattern, or any other arrangement of cell surfaces, but an effectively continuous three-dimensional mass of cortical cytoplasm whose *cyto*-organization is irrelevant to its function.

How then can we approach the problem of changes in protein conformation as a basis for memory? Sensitizations akin to the development of immunities have been proposed. And some initial experimental efforts have been directed toward this view (Mihailović and Janković, 1961). Another lead comes from some incidental observations made during the course of experiments carried out for initially different purposes. In my laboratory we have had occasion to cause epileptic seizures in monkeys by implanting aluminium hydroxide cream in their cortex (Pribram, 1951; Kraft *et al.*, 1960; Stamm and Knight, 1963; Stamm and

Pribram, 1960, 1961; Stamm, Pribram, and Obrist, 1958; Stamm and Warren, 1961). Such implantations cause havoc in the learning process. Yet, even a major convulsive episode will leave the immediate performance of a learned task unimpaired in these animals. Only 24 to 48 hours *after* such seizures does performance deteriorate – and this in the absence of further seizures. Further, the deterioration is temporary, lasting only about 48 hours. In short: some process takes this many hours to build up sufficiently to challenge the otherwise dominant neural pattern established by learning. And the challenge is temporary; apparently total recrudescence of the learned pattern is re-established shortly. Organic chemists must have available many macromolecules with similar peculiar characteristics. Are protein conformations subject to such temporary deformations and is the time course of such alterations consonant with that observed in these experiments?

References

KRAFT, M. S., OBRIST, W. D., and PRIBRAM, K. H. (1960), *J. comp. physiol. Psychol.*, vol. 53, p. 17.

LEITH, E. N., and UPATNIEKS, J. (1965), *Sci. Amer.*, vol. 212, p. 24.

MIHAILOVIĆ, L. J., and JANKOVIĆ, D. B. (1961), *Nature*, vol. 192, p. 665.

OSTER, G., and NISHIJIMA, Y. (1963), *Sci. Amer.*, vol. 208, p. 54.

PRIBRAM, K. H. (1951), *Surg. Forum*, vol. 36, p. 315.

SOKOLOV, E. N. (1960), in M. A. B. Brazier (ed.), *The Central Nervous System and Behavior*, Josiah Macey, Jr Foundation, New York.

STAMM, J. S., and KNIGHT, M. (1963), *J. comp. physiol. Psychol.*, vol. 56, p. 254.

STAMM, J. S., and PRIBRAM, K. H. (1960), *J. Neurophysiol.*, vol. 23, p. 552.

STAMM, J. S., and PRIBRAM, K. H. (1961), *J. comp. physiol. Psychol.*, vol. 54, p. 614.

STAMM, J. S., PRIBRAM, K. H., and OBRIST, W. (1958), 'The effect of cortical implants of aluminium hydroxide on remembering and on learning', presented at the *Annual Meeting of the American EEG Society*, 13 June 1958.

STAMM, J. S., and WARREN, A. (1961), *Epilepsia*, vol. 2, p. 229.

WHYTE, L. L. (1954), *Brain*, vol. 77, p. 158.

Part Three Cognition and the Agnosias

Despite the fact that perception and cognition are intricately intertwined I believe that, in the abstract, separation of the concepts can be useful. Loosely, I make the distinction that a perception *is* while a cognition is *meaningful*. William James stated the distinction as between making an existential versus a differential discrimination. According to this distinction, the foregoing papers have dealt with perception, the ones that follow concern cognition. These studies not only make it clear that the distinction in concepts is warranted but also show just how they become so intertwined.

12 S. Brown and E. A. Schäfer

An Investigation into the Functions of the Occipital and Temporal Lobes of the Monkey's Brain

Excerpt from S. Brown and E. A. Schäfer, 'An investigation into the functions of the occipital and temporal lobes of the monkey's brain', *Philos. Trans. Roy. Soc.*, vol. 179 (1888), pp. 310–12.

Experiments on a Fine, Large, Active *Rhæsus* Monkey, ♂

First Operation

Complete removal of the right temporal lobe.

Result. Immediately after recovery from chloroform it was observed that he had left hemiopia. Little, if any, difference of sensibility could be detected on the two sides of the body, nor any muscular paresis. The following day there was still evidence of hemiopia, but it did not persist for more than a day or two.

Second Operation

Five days after the first operation, the wound of which had completely healed, and the animal being in good health and spirits, the remaining (left) temporal lobe was cut away. In both cases the removal was very complete, as was shown on *post-mortem* examination.

Results. These severe operations were recovered from with marvellous rapidity, the animal appearing perfectly well even so early as the day after the establishment of the second lesion. A remarkable change is, however, manifested in the disposition of the monkey. Prior to the operations he was very wild and even fierce, assaulting any person who teased or tried to handle him. Now he voluntarily approaches all persons indifferently, allows himself to be handled, or even to be teased or slapped, without making any attempt at retaliation or endeavouring to escape. His memory and intelligence seem deficient. He gives evidence of hearing, seeing, and of the possession of his senses generally, but it is clear that he no longer clearly understands the meaning of the sounds, sights, and other impressions that reach him. Every object with which he comes in contact, even those with which he was previously most familiar, appears strange and is investigated with curiosity.

Everything he endeavours to feel, taste, and smell, and to carefully examine from every point of view. This is the case not only with inanimate objects, but also with persons and with his fellow monkeys. And even after having examined an object in this way with the utmost care and deliberation, he will, on again coming across the same object accidentally even a few minutes afterwards, go through exactly the same process, as if he had entirely forgotten his previous experiments. His food is devoured greedily, the head being dipped into the dish, instead of the food being conveyed to the mouth by the hands in the way usual with monkeys. He appears no longer to discriminate between the different kinds of food; e.g. he no longer picks out the currants from a dish of food, but devours everything just as it happens to come. He still, however, possesses the sense of taste, for when given a raisin which has been partly filled with quinine he shows evident signs of distaste, and refuses to eat the fruit.

It is also clear that he still both sees and hears. The field of vision appeared at first somewhat limited, and he also seemed to see somewhat indistinctly, making, for example, one or two unsuccessful attempts to pick up a currant from the floor before finally succeeding. This condition, however, soon passed off. He reacts to all kinds of noises, even slight ones, such as the rustling of a piece of paper, but shows no consequent evidence of alarm or agitation, although his attention is evidently attracted by sounds. Thus he was observed to follow with his head the sound of footsteps passing along the corridor just outside his room, directing his attention to them as long as one could oneself distinctly hear them.

This peculiar mental condition was observed for some weeks, becoming gradually less noticeable. A week after the second operation it is noted that he appears brighter in disposition, and is again commencing to display signs of tyrannizing proclivities towards his mate, for which he had been remarkable previously. About this time a strange monkey, wild and savage, was put into the common cage. Our monkey immediately began to investigate the newcomer in the way described, but his attentions were repulsed, and a fight resulted, in which he was being considerably worsted. The animals were, however, separated and tied up away from one another, but our monkey soon managed to free himself, and at once proceeded, without any signs of fear or suspicion, again to investigate the stranger, having apparently already entirely forgotten the result of his former investigation.

Two weeks after the second operation it is noted that this

monkey continues to 'investigate' objects, but with diminishing frequency and thoroughness. He is either rapidly regaining some of his former experience and memory, or forming altogether new ones. He now takes his food up with his hands, and also pays a more natural attention to his fellows than before. All his senses are acute.

Five weeks after the operation his curiosity has sensibly diminished, and he is slowly regaining his former mercurial temperament, continuing, however, tame.

This monkey was kept for nearly eight months after the operation. Long before the expiration of that time he had regained full possession of his mental faculties, and became one of the brightest and most intelligent animals that we had experience of, domineering over all the other monkeys which were kept in the same cage with him. He was shown to and tested before the Physiological and Neurological Societies, and was also seen privately by several eminent neurologists. With regard to this monkey there was no difference of opinion expressed, but it was universally admitted that all his senses, including that of hearing, were perfectly acute. Indeed, it was eventually impossible to detect any abnormality of the cerebral functions.

The animal eventually died of dysentery, after a short illness.

Autopsy

With the exception of the large intestine, which is ulcerated and inflamed, all the organs appear healthy. In the brain the whole of the temporal lobe is completely removed upon both sides; the lesion extending quite up to the Sylvian fissure on the outer surface, and reaching to the inner edge of the hemisphere on the under surface. On the right side the lesion does not quite reach the parieto-occipital fissure on the external surface, but on the left side the removal extends quite up to this fissure. A very small piece of the antero-inferior edge of the lobe remains on the left side, but this is undermined and cut off from the medullary centre. No trace of the superior temporal gyrus is left on either side, except a part of the grey matter bounding the Sylvian fissure below, and this grey matter is devoid of its corresponding medullary centre. The brain is shown from each side and from below in Figure 1a, b, and c, and in vertical sections through the anterior, middle, and posterior parts of the lesion in Figure 1, d, e, and f.

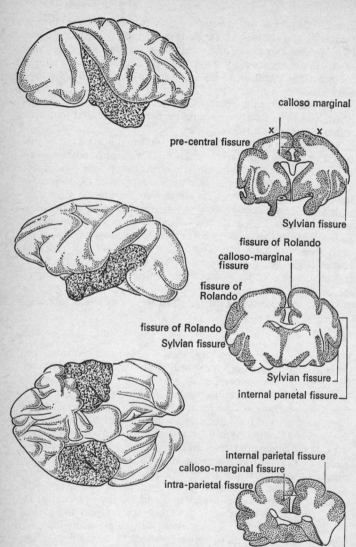

calloso marginal

pre-central fissure

Sylvian fissure

fissure of Rolando
calloso-marginal fissure

fissure of Rolando

fissure of Rolando
Sylvian fissure

Sylvian fissure
internal parietal fissure

internal parietal fissure
calloso-marginal fissure
intra-parietal fissure

Sylvian fissure (at junction with parallel)

Figure 1.

Remarks

This is the most extensive bilateral lesion of the whole temporal region which we have performed. What is most remarkable about it is the *immediate loss* and *ultimate recovery* of the intellectual faculty. On localization of functions the experiment throws no direct light; what evidence there is being entirely negative.

13 K. H. Pribram

Toward a Science of Neuropsychology (Method and Data)

Excerpt from K. H. Pribram, 'Toward a science of neuropsychology (method and data)', in R. A. Patton (ed.), *Current Trends in Psychology and the Behavioral Sciences*, University of Pittsburgh Press, 1954, pp. 118–42.

Thalamocortical systems may be classified according to whether the thalamic component receives its major afferents from within or from outside the thalamus. The term 'intrinsic' has been applied by Rose and Woolsey (17) to those thalamic nuclei which do not receive their major afferents from outside the thalamus. Thalamocortical systems receiving extrathalamic afferents are of two types: those receiving spinal and mesencephalic afferents, and those receiving diencephalic fibers. The former (often called the 'primary projection systems') are hereinafter called 'extrinsic', following Rose and Woolsey; the latter are most usefully considered under the heading 'rhinencephalic' (11). Two examples of current investigation of the intrinsic systems and one example of those of the rhinencephalic systems will be presented.

Figure 1 presents the surgical manipulations of the neural variable in these experiments. Represented are the reconstructions of the cerebral hemispheres of 40 monkeys. The lesions were made, in most instances, on the basis of criteria other than those defining the thalamocortical relationship, a consideration which need not enter this presentation. All diagrams are made by transferring to standard brain outlines the actual reconstructions from serial sections of the lesioned hemispheres.

In order to decide upon a relevant dependent variable, approximately 30 different behaviors were observed and quantified. Those behaviors which were affected by some lesions and not by others were then chosen for further investigation. Our first example of such behaviour is the visual choice reaction or visual discrimination task.

Figure 2 gives the individual animal's pre- and postoperative scores in a visual choice reaction in which painted patterns were used as cues. Figure 3 summarizes these results. Scores were classified into deficit and no-deficit on the basis of whether an animal took longer to relearn the task postoperatively than to learn it preoperatively. As can be seen, there is no overlap in scores between the group with no-deficit and that with deficit; in fact, the latter group contains 12 of 15 animals which *never* relearned the task even though 1,000 trials were given postoperatively (preoperative mean for learning was approximately 375).

Figure 4 groups the lesions of the animals with deficit and those without deficit. A shows the summed area of all of the lesions which produced deficit; B the sum of the area of all of the lesions which failed to produce a deficit in visual discrimination performance. C represents the intersect of the area shown in A with the total area *not* shown (not checker-boarded) in B. This may be considered an approximate minimal locus implicated in visual choice behavior in the 40 lesioned animals. This locus approximates that of one of the posterior intrinsic systems and will be referred to as the 'inferotemporal' sector.

Having established a selective relationship between a lesion in one of the intrinsic systems and a restricted portion of the behavioral spectrum, we proceed to investigate the environmental conditions upon which this relationship is dependent. For instance, we have called the task a visual choice reaction. Is performance of other visual discriminations affected by this lesion? So far, experiments have shown performance of a variety of visual object, color, and brightness discriminations to be altered (5, 6). What would happen if in place of the visual discriminanda, their logical analogues in somesthesis were substituted? Would the same, or a different, cortical area be implicated?

Figure 5 shows the results of an experiment where the visual choice reaction was compared with a task in which vision was excluded and a solution of the problem depended on *handling* the cues. Two intrinsic systems were surgically invaded – the inferotemporal and the occipitoparietal. As can be seen, lesions of the occipitoparietal sector fail to interfere with visual choices but affect those based on somesthesis, where as the lesions involving the inferotemporal sector interfered selectively with the visual (8).

If it can be stated that the decrement in performance is restricted to the visual choice reaction, and other experiments on taste (1), conditioned avoidance (15), and delayed response (2, 6, 9, 10, 14) support this contention, we are faced with a second cerebral 'visual' system. Thus, in addition to the extrinsic (geniculo-striate) system, there is at least one intrinsic system which functions selectively within this modality. It becomes important, therefore, to distinguish between the functions of the extrinsic and intrinsic visual systems. For example, resections

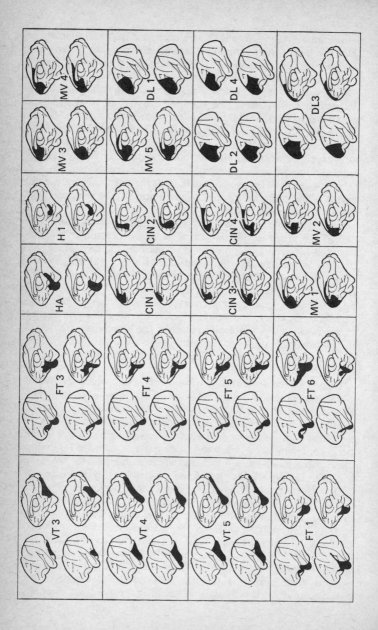

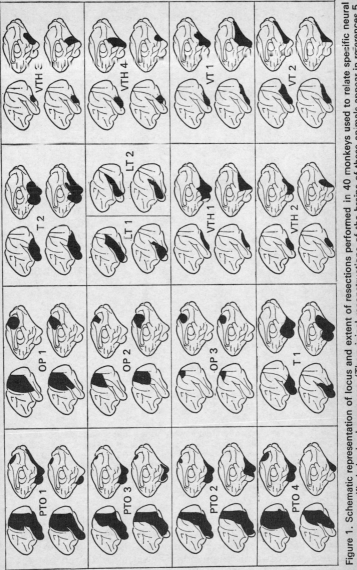

Figure 1. Schematic representation of locus and extent of resections performed in 40 monkeys used to relate specific neural systems to specific behavioral processes. (The original reconstructions of the brains of these animals appear in references 5, 6, 8, 9, 10, 14)

within the former, that is, of the striate cortex, lead to field defects; those of the latter, the inferotemporal cortex, do not. Other studies which specify such differences have been completed or are in progress and will be reported elsewhere (3, 19).

Simultaneous Visual Choice Reaction

Operates without deficit			Operates with deficit		
	Pre	Post		Pre	Post
O P 1	200	0	P T O 1	120	272
O P 2	220	0	P T O 2	325	F
O P 3	380	0	P T O 3	180	F
L T 1	390	190	P T O 4	120	450
L T 2	300	150	T 1	940	F
H 1	210	220	T 2	330	F
H A	350	240	V T H 1	320	F
F T 1	580	50	V T H 2	370	F
F T 3	50	0	V T H 3	280	F
F T 4	205	0	V T H 4	440	F
F T 5	300	200	V T 1	240	F
F T 6	250	100	V T 2	200	F
D L 1	160	140	V T 3	200	890
D L 2	540	150	V T 4	410	F
D L 3	300	240	V T 5	210	F
D L 4	120	100			
M V 1	110	0			
M V 2	150	10	Non-operate controls		
M V 3	290	130	C 1	790	80
M V 4	230	10	C 2	230	20
M V 5	280	120	C 3	750	20
C I N 1	120	80	C 4	440	0
C I N 2	400	60			
C I N 3	115	74			
C I N 4	240	140			

Figure 2. Pre- and postoperative scores on a simultaneous visual choice reaction of the animals whose brains are diagrammed in Figure 1 indicating the number of trials taken to reach a criterion of 90 per cent on 100 consecutive trials. Deficit is defined as a larger number of trials taken in the 'retention' test than in original learning. (The misplacement of the score H 1 does not change the over-all results as given in the text and in the following figures)

Today, I wish to limit myself to one other aspect of the relationship of inferotemporal lesions to visual choice behavior (12). Figure 6 describes an experiment in which animals were taught to choose one of two discriminanda (an ashtray and a tobacco tin) presented simultaneously. The animals were then tested in situations in which these identical cues were presented successively, and the performance of inferotemporal operates was compared with that of control operate and non-operate control groups. Here, as in the experiments of Riopelle and Ades (16), and of Mishkin (5), inferotemporal operates have progressively greater difficulty in a series of tasks graded in 'distinctiveness' as measured by the difficulty of the task for the control groups. In this

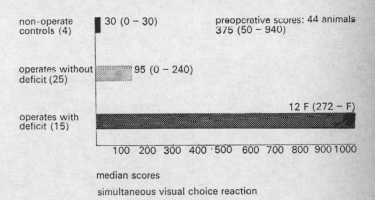

non-operate controls (4)   30 (0 – 30)   preoperative scores: 44 animals 375 (50 – 940)

operates without deficit (25)   95 (0 – 240)

operates with deficit (15)   12 F (272 – F)

100   200   300   400 · 500   600   700   800   900 1000

median scores

simultaneous visual choice reaction

Figure 3. Bar graph of median scores of the groups delineated in Figure 2. The number of animals per group is indicated below group name; the range from which median scores are taken appears in parentheses next to the median

instance, however, 'distinctiveness' is not dependent on the physical dimensions of the cue, but rather on the situation in which these cues are imbedded. Thus, no selective relationship between the visual discrimination impairment and either of these two classes of environmental variables (cue dimension, situation) is established. I believe this lack of a simple relationship between the physical dimensions of cues and the performance of monkeys with inferotemporal lesions will differentiate these results from those obtained when the extrinsic (geniculo-striate) visual system is invaded. Thus, the distinction between such concepts as 'agnosia' (which might account for the results of the 'situational' experiment) and 'acuity loss' (which might account for the results found on varying the physical dimensions of the discriminanda), which have been traditionally employed to explain the disparate visual choice reaction:

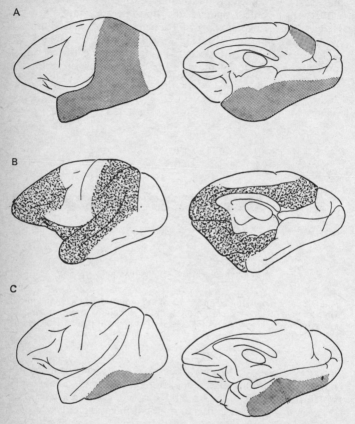

Figure 4. The upper diagram A represents the sum of the areas of resection of all of the animals grouped as showing a deficit in Figures 2 and 3. The middle diagram B represents the sum of the areas of resection of all of the animals grouped as showing no-deficit in Figures 2 and 3. The lower diagram C represents the intersect of the area shown by dots in the upper diagram and the area not coarse-tinted in the middle diagram. This intersect represents the area invariably implicated in visual choice behavior in these experiments

Further Behavioral Analysis of the PTO Cortex

	P48	P46	P49	T44	T45
Visual 10 (0-70)	0	0	0	(500)	(500)
Somatosensory 60 (0-100)	460	120	350	70	50
New somatosensory	(1000)	(1000)	(1000)	320	260

Figure 5. Comparison of retention scores of inferotemporal T and occipitoparietal P operates on a visual and somesthetic task in which logically analogous cues (+ vs. o) were used. The mean and range of the preoperative retention scores appear under the title of the task. The scores on the 'new somatosensory' task indicate original postoperative learning of a length discrimination. Parentheses indicate failure to reach criterion in the number of trials given (8)

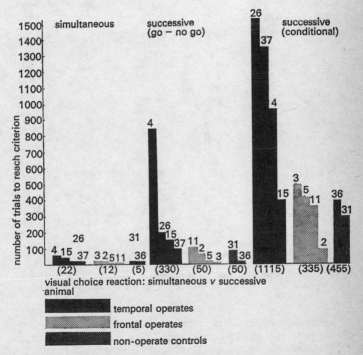

Figure 6. Comparison of learning scores of three groups of animals (inferotemporal operates, anterofrontal operates, and non-operate controls) in a simultaneous and two types of successive tasks in which the same cues were used. The increment of impairment of the inferotemporal group, as compared with controls, appears roughly proportional to the increasing difficulty of the task for controls (13)

effects of lesions in the extrinsic and intrinsic systems, may be revised in more precise terms allowing interdisciplinary translation.

Classical Delayed Reaction

Operates without deficit			Operates with deficit		
	Pre	Post		Pre	Post
PTO 1	680	270	DL 1	290	F
PTO 4	1020	540	DL 2	210	F
T 2	670	120	DL 3	590	F
VTH 1	100	0	DL 4	240	F
VTH 2	60	0	MV 2	610	960
VTH 3	560	0	MV 3	430	750
VT 1	290	20			
VT 2	130	0			
VT 3	740	330	PTO 3	530	630
LT 1	140	0	T 1	60	90
LT 2	140	0			
H 1	350	50			
HA	170	140			
FT 3	200	100			
FT 4	300	0			
FT 5	750	300			
FT 6	1250	400			
CIN 1	820	360			
CIN 2	600	150	Non-operate controls		
CIN 3	215	150	C 1	10	110
CIN 4	345	180	C 2	590	0
MV 1	630	60	C 3	230	250
MV 4	590	240	C 4	440	330
MV 5	380	230			

Figure 7. Pre- and postoperative scores on delayed reaction of animals whose brains are diagrammed in Figure 1, indicating the number of trials taken to reach a criterion of 90 per cent on 100 consecutive trials. Deficit is defined as a larger number of trials taken in the 'retention' test than in original learning

A *second* example of this approach to the functions of the intrinsic systems is presented in Figure 7 which shows the scores in the delayed reaction made by the animals with the lesions presented in Figure 1. Figure 8 summarizes these data on the basis of animals with and without deficits defined in the same way as in the case of visual choice reaction. Figure 9 shows in A the sum of the area of the lesions of the animals with deficit and in B the sum of the area of the lesions of the animals without deficit; C shows the intersect of area A and the area *not* included in B. This area corresponds roughly to another intrinsic system, the antero-frontal sector. We are, thus, ready to investigate another of the intrinsic cerebral systems.

The delayed reaction may be manipulated in a manner similar to that which we used in the visual choice reaction. Figures 10 and 11 present the results of such manipulations (7). A shows the

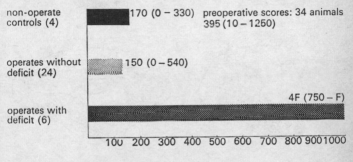

non-operate controls (4) · 170 (0 – 330) · preoperative scores: 34 animals 395 (10 – 1250)

operates without deficit (24) · 150 (0 – 540)

operates with deficit (6) · 4F (750 – F)

100 200 300 400 500 600 700 800 900 1000

median scores

classical delayed reaction

Figure 8. Bar graph of median scores of the groups delineated in Figure 7. The number of animals per group is indicated below the group name; the range from which median scores are taken appears in parentheses next to the median

difference in performance between animals with anterofrontal resections and control operates in the traditional delayed reaction. In this task the animal chooses the cup containing a peanut from one of two identical cups, on the basis of a cue presented some-time prior to opportunity for response. This cue is not present during the delay period or at the time of response. B shows that (i) when the predelay cue is varied from showing a peanut (or object) to the right or to the left of the animal to showing a pea-nut or a bare hand (or two distinct objects), and (ii) when the conditions of response are varied to opportunity for opening or not opening a single centered cup, animals with frontal lesions perform almost as well as their controls. When either the predelay cues or response conditions are varied alone, such dramatic im-provement of frontal operates' performance does not take place. However, as can be seen from Figure 12, manipulations of the

delayed reaction

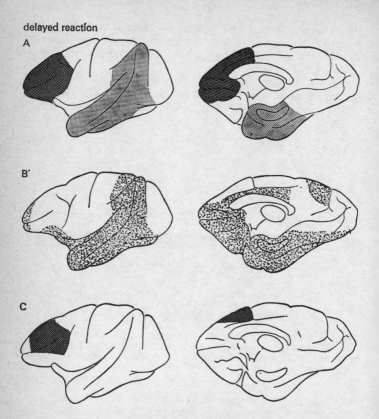

Figure 9. The upper diagram A represents the sum of the areas of resection of all of the animals grouped as showing a deficit in Figure 7 and Figure 8. The middle diagram B represents the sum of the areas of resection of all of the animals grouped as showing no-deficit in Figures 7 and 8. The lower diagram C represents the intersect of the area shown in the upper diagram and that not coarse-tinted in the middle diagram. This intersect represents the area invariably implicated in delayed reaction performance in these experiments. (Note that resections within the lighter shaded area in the upper diagram occasionally result in 'deficit' as defined here. However, note also that a similar 'deficit' appears in the non-operate controls in Figure 7. This finding resolves the discrepancies regarding previously described occasional occurrence of deficit on delayed reaction following posterior cortical resections (2, 4). For the purposes of a 'localization' procedure, the delayed alternation task appears to be more reliably retained. Nevertheless, as demonstrated here, the results of delayed reaction experiments may still be useful)

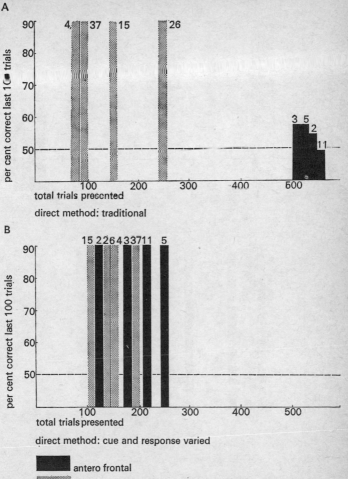

Figure 10. Bar graph comparing the performance of anterofrontal and control (inferotemporal) operates on two types of delayed reaction. Each bar represents the performance of one animal (designated by the number above the bar). Note the successful performance of anterofrontal operates (comparable with that of controls) when the method of presentation of predelay cues and opportunity for response are both changed from a simultaneous, right–left situation (A) to a successive, go–no go situation (B) (7)

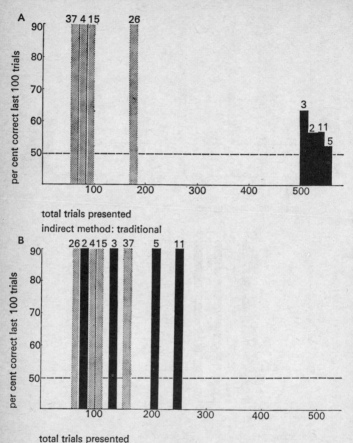

total trials presented

indirect method: traditional

total trials presented

indirect method: cue and response varied

Figure 11. Same as Figure 10 except that the indirect method of cueing was used. Results are comparable to those obtained when peanuts are used (direct method) (7)

predelay cue are markedly more effective than manipulations of the response conditions. In these experiments when the predelay cue was changed from a spatial to a non-spatial one, frontal operates' performance improved. This might have been the result of changes in the spatial aspect of the discriminans. On the other

278

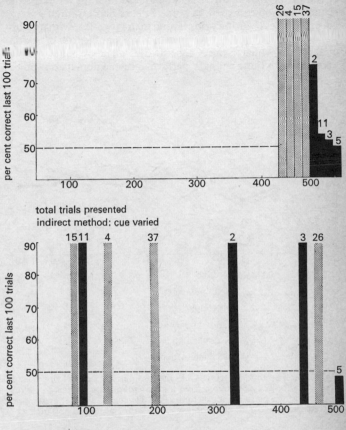

Figure 12. Bar graph comparing the performance of anterofrontal and control (inferotemporal) operates on further variations of the delayed reaction task. A represents performance when cues are presented in right–left positions as in the classical method but opportunity for response is go–no go as in the successive method. B represents performance when cues are presented successively but opportunity for response is unchanged from that used in the classical method (go right–go left) (7)

hand, the relevant change might be the fact that for monkeys the peanuts and objects used as predelay cues had acquired greater 'distinctiveness' during prior testing than is possible with a right–left choice. Comparing performance on another task, spatial alternation, which is also consistently failed by anterofrontal operates, with these animals' performance in a non-spatial object

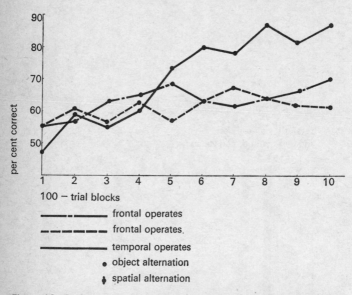

per cent correct

100 − trial blocks

————·—————— frontal operates

—————————— frontal operates.

—————————— temporal operates

● object alternation

♦ spatial alternation

Figure 13. Performance curves of anterofrontal and control operates on spatial and object alternation. Note that anterofrontal operates are equally impaired in the performance of both tasks. On spatial alternation temporal operates achieved a 90 per cent level of performance within 250 trials (12)

alternation, should answer the question of whether spatiality or 'acquired distinctiveness' of cues is the relevant variable accounting for the improved performance of the above tasks. Figure 13 compares performance in 1,000 trials of anterofrontal operates and control operates in spatial and object alternation (13). As can be seen, frontal operates *are* impaired in their performance of both tasks. Thus, spatiality *per se* cannot be the relevant predelay cue dimension responsible for anterofrontal operates' failure in delayed-response type tasks. Rather, the result of this experiment suggests the hypothesis that the remarkably high level of per-

K. H. Pribram

formance achieved by frontal operates on certain variations of delayed response are due to the 'distinctiveness' which the predelay cues had acquired during prior training. Conversely, performance decrement, when present in such animals, must be considered a function of the distinctiveness of the predelay cue. Thus, frontal operates' impairment on classical delayed response is a function, not only of the delay, but also of the distinctiveness of the predelay cue.

Dave 1 dominant, self-assured, feared

Zeke 2 aggressive, attacker

Riva 3 aggressive, active

Herhy 4 placid, unaggressive

Larry 8 submissive, cowering, frequently attacked

Shorty 7 submissive to others, aggressive towards Larry

Arnie 6 noisy, eager

Benny 5 alert, active food getter

hierarchy before any operation

Figure 14. Dominance hierarchy of a colony of eight preadolescent male rhesus monkeys before any surgical intervention (18)

The impairment in choice behavior which follows lesions of both intrinsic systems discussed is, therefore, a function of distinctiveness of cues. The effects of resection of the posterior (inferotemporal) system and the anterior (anterofrontal) are *distinguished* in terms of other relevant variables: The posterior system has been related to discrimination behavior which is modality specific; the anterior system to discriminations made in the presence of a temporal gap between cue presentation and response.

Zeke 1 dominant, aggressive

Riva 2 daring, competes with Zeke

Herby 3

Benny 4

Dave 8 completely submissive, fearful

Larry 7 dominates and attacks Dave

Shorty 6

Arnie 5

hierarchy after Dave's operation

Figure 15. Same as Figure 14 after bilateral amygdalectomy had been performed on Dave. Note his drop to the bottom of the hierarchy

Riva 1 dominant, not threatened by others

Herby 2

Benny 3

Arnie 4

Dave 8 cringer, avoids interaction

Zeke 7 submissive to others, intermittently aggressive towards Dave

Larry 6

Shorty 5

hierarchy after Zeke's operation

Figure 16. Same as Figures 14 and 15 except that both Dave and Zeke have received bilateral amygdalectomies

At this point I should like to turn from the intrinsic systems. Since one of the functions of this symposium is to discuss the relation of all of the behavioral sciences, the following experiment is apropos. In this instance, the surgical manipulation involved a portion of the second rhinencephalic system (18), the amygdaloid

Figure 17. Final social hierarchy after Dave, Zeke, and Riva have all had bilateral amygdalectomies. Minimal differences in extent and locus of the resections do not correlate with differences in the behavioral results. As noted in the text, Herby's nonaggressive 'personality' in the #2 position of the hierarchy seems the most likely explanation of the disparate effects of similar lesions (18)

complex of the cerebral hemisphere. The environmental manipulation concerned a social group of eight preadolescent male macaques. A dominance ranking of each animal with respect to other animals in the group (during feeding) was obtained prior to surgery. Figure 14 demonstrates this preoperative hierarchy. Figures 15, 16, and 17 show the effect on this hierarchy of bilateral amygdalectomy of the three most dominant animals (one animal operated on at a time). Although all lesions are of comparable extent, there are differences among the operates in direction and degree of change in social behavior. Thus, Dave drops from the #1 position to become #8; Zeke, who became the dominant animal after Dave's demise, was also sent downward in the hierarchy by the resection. Riva, Zeke's successor, however, met with no such fate. On the basis of this and subsequent experiments in which relevant variables were manipulated separately, it appears that the amount of aggressive behavior displayed by the #2 animal toward the operate during the immediate postoperative period may be critical in determining the effect of amygdalectomy. Thus, as in the case of the intrinsic systems, complete description of the effects of brain lesions *must* include specification of the environmental variables which determine the changes in behavior.

Summary

As indicated in the title of this presentation, I have discussed method and data (relations between dependent and independent variables) which may lead toward a science of neuropsychology. Conspicuously undeveloped are the laws (relationships to a dependent variable of classes of interrelated independent variables) which form the substance of any science. I feel, perhaps erroneously, that there is, as yet, an insufficient scope of data to allow the formulation of general laws. However, some of the terms which must be included in any rigorous formulation are being uncovered.

As an example, some cerebral systems have been surgically manipulated on the basis of neuroanatomical and neurophysiological data and some relationships to behavior have been described. The cortex of these systems has previously been referred to as 'associative' on the basis of presumed anatomical connections, physiological 'silence', and 'clinical' observation. The experiments described offer one method of delineating more precisely the role of these systems in behavior. The inferotemporal sector has been selectively related to performance of visual choice reactions. Resections of this sector result in impairment of visual choice reactions, the impairment being proportional to the distinctiveness of the discrimination as defined by the difficulty of the task for control animals. The dimension of 'distinctiveness' is related not only to the physical parameters of the cue, but also to some 'non-cue' (situational) variables determining the response.

A second example concerned the relationship of the anterofrontal sector to choice behavior dependent on cues not present at the time of response. Experiments have been reviewed which show that this relationship is insufficiently described by the parameter of temporal contiguity between pre- and postdelay contingencies, and that 'distinctiveness' of the predelay cue is as important a variable as 'time'. Thus, the effects of lesions of both intrinsic systems discussed are a function of the distinctiveness of the cues upon which the choice behavior is dependent. The effects of lesions of the posterior and anterior systems may be distinguished, however, by other relevant variables: the posterior lesion has an effect which is modality specific; the anterior lesion is effective only when choice is dependent on cues temporally remote from the response.

The third example concerned one of the rhinencephalic systems and showed that specification and manipulation of environmental variables is as important in understanding the relation between brain and social–emotional behavior as in understanding such a relationship to choice behavior. The example showed that comparable lesions of the amygdaloid complex resulted in diverse effects on the dominance of a #1 animal in a social hierarchy depending on the amount of aggressive interaction with the #2 animal during the immediate postoperative period.

Accumulation of data according to the approach presented here should make possible, in the future, a systematization of relationships between neurological and behavioral data which will constitute a science of neuropsychology. Though the development of this science is dependent on the development of neurology and psychology, the reductive sibling may be expected to add impetus to the growth of its less hybrid sister sciences. At present, data gathering, guided by hypotheses, fills our time and capacity. It is my hope that the results of these endeavors may stimulate others to join in this approach, for, only when data sufficient in range and scope are available, will the formulations which constitute a science be possible. Our particular science, neuropsychology, has a special role to fill at this time: the largest gap in our conceptualizations lies between the behavioral and the physiological sciences – a gap paralleling that which existed between the physiological and physical sciences a century ago. A common framework for the physical and physiological sciences resulted from experiments such as the synthesis of urea – from neuropsychological experiments we may expect the emergence of a common framework relating physiological and behavioral science.

Cognition and the Agnosias

References

1. M. H. BAGSHAW, and K. H. PRIBRAM, 'Cortical organization in gustation (macaca mulatta)', *J. Neurophysiol.*, vol. 16 (1953), pp. 499–508.
2. J. S. BLUM, K. L. CHOW, and K. H. PRIBRAM, 'A behavioral analysis of the organization of the parieto-temporal-preoccipital cortex', *J. Comp. Neurol.*, vol. 93 (1950), pp. 53–100.
3. R. GUNTER, 'The effect of resection of the striate cortex and of the inferotemporal cortex on a visual brightness discrimination', (in press).
4. K. S. LASHLEY, 'The mechanism of vision: XVIII. Effects of destroying the visual "associative areas" of the monkey', *Genet. Psychol. Monogr.*, vol. 37 (1948), pp. 107–66.
5. M. MISHKIN, 'Visual discrimination performance following ablations of the temporal lobe: II. Ventral surfaces vs hippocampus', *J. Comp. Physiol. Psychol.*, vol. 47 (1954), pp. 187–93.
6. M. MISHKIN and K. H. PRIBRAM, 'Visual discrimination performance following partial ablations of the temporal lobe: I. Ventral vs lateral', *J. Comp. Physiol. Psychol.*, vol. 47 (1954), pp. 14–20.
7. M. MISHKIN and K. H. PRIBRAM, 'Analysis of the effects of frontal lesions in monkey: II. Variations of delayed response', *J. Comp. Physiol. Psychol.*, vol. 49 (1956), pp. 36–40.
8. HELEN PRIBRAM and J. BARRY, 'Further behavioral analysis of the parieto-temporo-preoccipital cortex', *J. Neurophysiol.*, vol. 19 (1956), pp. 99–106.
9. K. H. PRIBRAM and M. H. BAGSHAW, 'Further analysis of the temporal lobe syndrome utilizing fronto-temporal ablations', *J. Comp. Neurol.*, vol. 99 (1953), pp. 347–75.
10. K. H. PRIBRAM and J. F. FULTON, 'An experimental critique of the effects of anterior cingulate ablations in monkey', *Brain*, vol. 77 (1954), pp. 34–44.
11. K. H. PRIBRAM and L. KRUGER, 'Functions of the olfactory brain', *Ann. N.Y. Acad. Sci.*, vol. 58 (1954), pp. 109–38.
12. K. H. PRIBRAM and M. MISHKIN, 'Simultaneous and successive visual discrimination by monkeys with inferotemporal lesions', *J. Comp. Physiol. Psychol.*, vol. 48 (1955), pp. 198–202.
13. K. H. PRIBRAM and M. MISHKIN, 'Analysis of the effects of frontal lesions in monkey: III. Object alternation', *J. Comp. Physiol. Psychol.*, vol. 49 (1956), pp. 41–5.
14. K. H. PRIBRAM, M. MISHKIN, H. E. ROSVOLD, and S. J. KAPLAN, 'Effects on delayed-response performance of lesions of dorsolateral and ventromedial frontal cortex of baboons', *J. Comp. Physiol. Psychol.*, vol. 45 (1952), pp. 565–75.
15. K. H. PRIBRAM and L. WEISKRANTZ, 'A comparison of the effects of medial and lateral cerebral resections on conditioned-avoidance behaviour in monkeys', *J. Comp. Physiol. Psychol.*, vol. 50 (1957), pp. 74–80.
16. A. J. RIOPELLE and H. W. ADES, 'Discrimination learning following deep temporal lesions', *Amer. Psychologist*, vol. 6 (1951), p. 261 (abstract).
17. J. E. ROSE and C. N. WOOLSEY, 'Organization of the mammalian thalamus and its relationships to the cerebral cortex', *EEG Clin. Neurophysiol.*, vol. 1 (1949), pp. 391–404.

18. H. E. ROSVOLD, A. F. MIRSKY and K. H. PRIBRAM, 'Influence of amygdalectomy on social interaction in a monkey group', *J. Comp. Physiol. Psychol.*, vol. 47 (1954), pp. 173–8.
19. W. WILSON and M. MISHKIN, 'Comparison of the effects of inferotemporal and lateral occipital lesions on visually guided behavior in monkeys' *J. Comp. Physiol. Psychol.*, vol. 52 (1959), pp. 10–17.

14 K. H. Pribram

On the Neurology of Thinking

Excerpt from K. H. Pribram, 'On the neurology of thinking', *Behavioral Science*, vol. 4 (1959), pp. 268-87.

Delineations of Problems

On the basis of comparative neuroanatomical and electrophysiological data the forebrain can be divided into two major portions: a dorsolateroposterior and an anteromediobasal. In primates each of these major portions contains intrinsic sectors: posterior intrinsic sectors (the classical sensory association areas, Pribram, 1954; Pribram, 1958b), and a frontal intrinsic sector (the classical frontal association area, Pribram, 1958a). Neurobehavioral experiments performed during the past twenty-five years have shown these intrinsic sectors to be especially related to problem solving processes (Harlow, 1953; Pribram, 1954). The aim of this, and of the following section, is to specify in detail this relationship.

An experiment

Procedure. A modified Wisconsin General Testing Apparatus (Harlow, 1942) is used to test twelve rhesus monkeys on a complex problem. The monkeys are divided into three groups, two operated and one control, each containing four animals. The animals in one operated group had received bilateral cortical resections in the posterior intrinsic cortex and those in the other operated group, bilateral cortical resections in the frontal intrinsic cortex some two and a half years prior to the onset of the experiment (Figure 1); those in the control group are unoperated. In the testing situation these animals are initially confronted with two junk objects placed over two holes (on a board containing twelve holes in all) with a peanut under one of the objects. An opaque screen is lowered between the monkey and the objects as soon as the monkey has displaced one of the objects from its hole (a trial). When the screen is lowered, separating the monkey from the twelve hole board, the objects are moved (according to a random number table) to two different holes on the board. The screen is then raised and the animal again confronted with the problem. The peanut remains under the same object until the

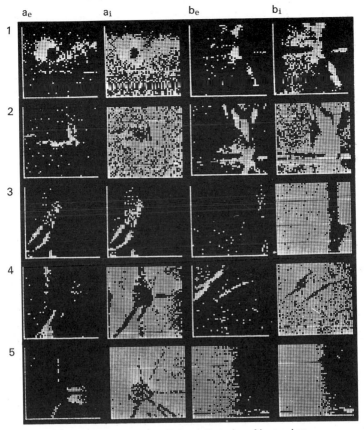

Plate 1 Columns a_e1 through b_e5 show, 'in order of increasing complexity', ten of the receptive fields studied with this method. In column a_e, 1 through 5, the excitory regions of five receptive fields are displayed by showing points where activity was greater than the mean background plus three standard deviations. In column a_i, 1 through 5, the inhibitory regions of the same five receptive fields are displayed as dark areas by showing all points with one or more counts. The same considerations apply to columns b_e and b_i, 1 through 5. (See page 13.)

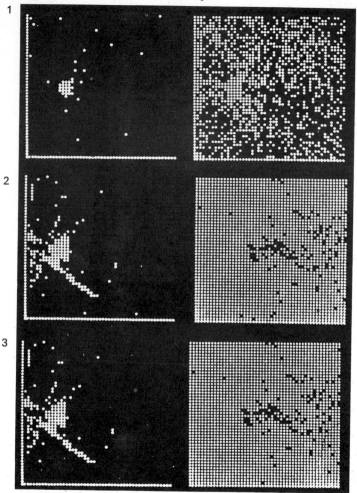

Plate 2 These records show a dark-adaption experiment. In d_e1 and d_i1 the excitory areas and the inhibitory areas, respectively, of an optic-nerve fiber were mapped in the light-adapted eye. In d_e2 and d_i2 the receptive field was mapped after thirty minutes of complete darkness. Finally, in d_e3 and d_i3 the field was mapped again after sixty minutes of darkness. As already noted by Barlow *et al.* (4), the size of the center increases during dark adaptation. Also, d_e2 and d_e3 give an idea of the remarkable repeatability of these mappings. (See page 13.)

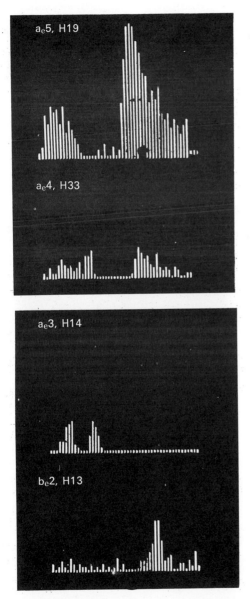

Plate 3 Single horizontal scans at H19, H33, H14, and H13 are shown for units a_e5, a_e4, a_e3, and b_e2, respectively (see Plate 1). (See page 13.)

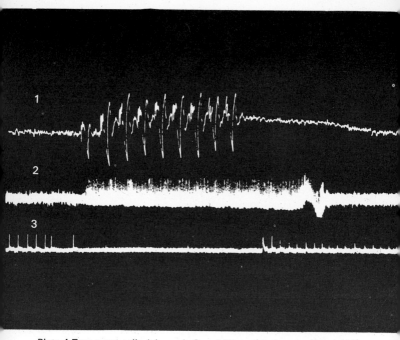

Plate 4 Two nerve cells (channels 2 and 3) recorded extracellularly (tip separation of the two microelectrodes > 100 μ) in the cerebral cortex of the cat during the occurrence of paroxysmal epileptiform discharge and slow potential shift (channel 1). One cell (channel 2) was clearly excited while the immediately adjacent one (channel 3) showed inhibition of spontaneous discharge (see reference 41). (See page 63.)

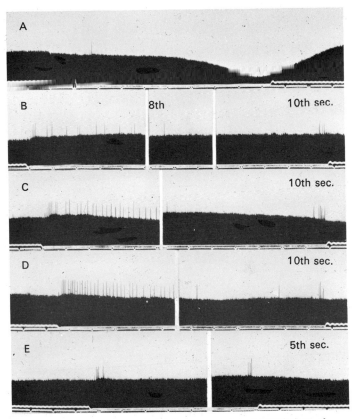

Plate 5 Response, adaption, and fatigue to a series of stimulations of
increasing strength applied by the mechanical stimulator to the most
sensitive spot in the corneal field of a fairly large fiber. 'Few fiber
preparation' of a lateral long ciliary nerve. Duration of stimulation shown
by upper signal; time in 0·2 sec. by lower signal. A, contact; B, 1 gm.
for 10 secs., last response in the 8th sec.; C, 4 gm. for 10 secs., last
response in the 9th sec.; D, 8 gm. adaption still incomplete; E, 1 gm.
for 5 secs., adaption almost at once. (See page 95.)

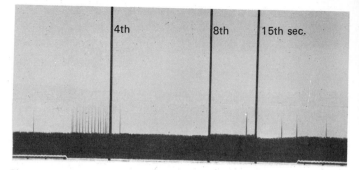

4th | 8th | 15th sec.

Plate 6 Spontaneous activity in a fiber with corneal distribution, and inhibition of this by 4 gm. stimulation applied with the mechanical stimulator to the central region of the fiber's terminal. Inhibition was complete from the end of the 3rd to the middle of the 8th sec., and the control rate of spontaneous discharge was reestablished only in the 12th sec. Few fiber preparation of a lateral long ciliary nerve. Duration of stimulation shown by upper signal; time in 0·2 sec. by lower signal. (See page 95.)

Plate 7 (*Top*) A histological section of the cat spinal cord (lumbar region).
(*Middle*) Cross section of the dorsal quadrant. The dotted region is the substantia gelatinosa.
(*Bottom*) Main components of the cutaneous afferent system in the upper dorsal horn. The large-diameter cutaneous peripheral fibers are represented by thick lines running from the dorsal root and terminating in the region of the substantia gelatinosa; one of these, as shown, sends a branch toward the brain in the dorsal column. The finer peripheral fibers are represented by dashed lines running directly into the substantia gelatinosa. The large cells, on which cutaneous afferent nerves terminate, are shown as large black spheres with their dendrites extending into the substantia gelatinosa and their axons projecting deeper into the dorsal horn. The open circles represent the cells of the substantia gelatinosa. The axons (not shown) of these cells connect them to one another and also run in the Lissauer tract (LT) to distant parts of the substantia gelatinosa. [From Wall (37).] (See page 146.)

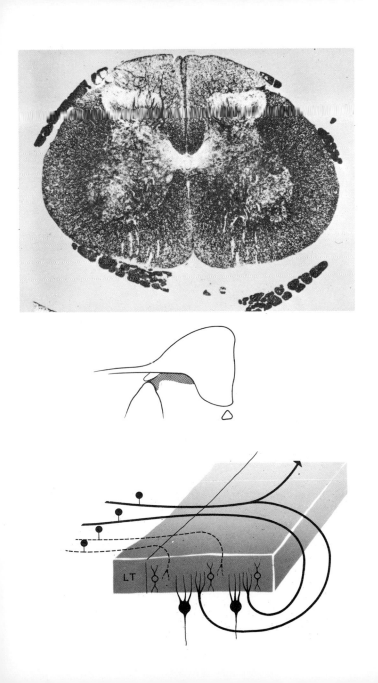

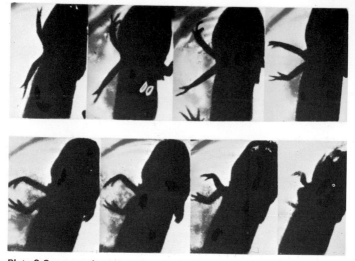

Plate 8 Sequence from a motion picture of a salamander with a pair of limbs of opposite symmetry at left shoulder, performing exact mirror-image movements. (See page 497.)

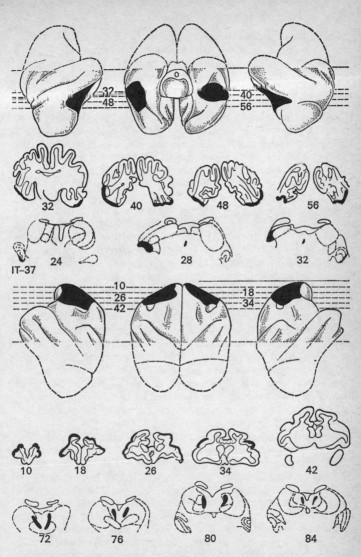

Figure 1. Representative reconstructions and cross sections through cortex and thalamus showing extent of the lesions in the posterior (upper figure) and frontal (lower figure) intrinsic systems. Cortical lesions and resulting thalamic degeneration are shown in black

animal finds the peanut five consecutive times (criterion). After a monkey reaches criterion performance, the peanut is shifted to the second object and testing continues (discrimination reversal). After an animal again reaches criterion performance a third object is added (Figure 2). Each of the three objects in turn becomes the positive cue; testing proceeds as before – the screen separates the animal from the twelve hole board, the objects are placed randomly over three out of the twelve holes (with a peanut concealed under one of the objects), the screen is raised, the animal allowed to pick an object (one response per trial), the screen is lowered and the objects moved to different holes. The testing continues in this fashion until the animal reaches criterion performance with each of the objects positive, in turn. Then a fourth object is added and the entire procedure repeated. As the animal progresses the number of objects is increased serially through a total of twelve (Figure 3). The testing procedure is the same for all animals throughout the experiment; however, the order of the introduction of objects is balanced – the order being the same for only one monkey in each group.

Analysis of the problem posed by this experiment indicates that solution is facilitated when a monkey attains two strategies: (1) during search, moving, on successive trials, each of the objects until the peanut is found; (2) after search, selecting, on successive trials, the object under which the peanut had been found on the preceding trial. During a portion of the experiment, searching is restricted for animals with posterior intrinsic sector ablations; and selection of the object under which the peanut had been found on the previous trial is impaired by frontal intrinsic sector ablations. The effects of the posterior intrinsic sector lesions will be dealt with first.

Figure 4 graphs the averages of the total number of repetitive errors made by each of the groups in each situation in the multiple object experiment. Comparison of Figure 4 with Figure 5, representing the repetitive errors made by each group in each situation during search, illustrates that the deficit of the frontally operated group is not associated with search (a result that is discussed below); however, the peak and general shape of the error curves describing the performance of the control and posteriorly operated groups are similar whether total repetitive errors (Figure 4) or search errors (Figure 5) are plotted. In spite of the increasing complexity of the succeeding situations, the curves appear little different from those previously reported to describe the formation of a discrimination in complex situations (Bush and Mosteller,

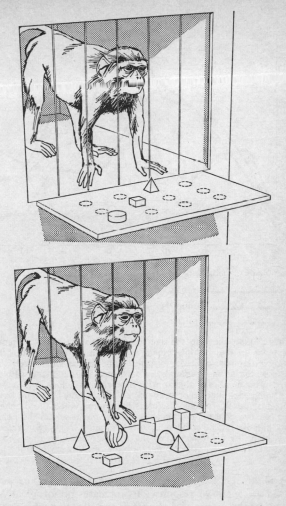

Figures 2 and 3. Diagram of the multiple object problem showing examples of the three and the seven object situations. Food wells are indicated by dashed circles, each of which is assigned a number. The placement of each object over a food well was shifted from trial to trial according to a random number table. A record was kept of the object moved by the monkey on each trial, only one move being allowed per trial. Trials were separated by lowering an opaque screen to hide the objects from the monkey, as they were repositioned

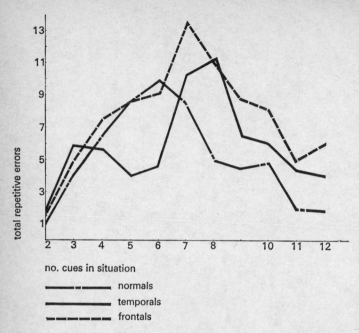

no. cues in situation

— — — — normals

————————— temporals

— — — — — frontals

Figure 4. Graph showing the average of the total number of repetitive errors made in the multiple object experiment by each of the groups (controls = normals; posterior intrinsic sector lesions = temporals; frontal intrinsic sector lesions = frontals) in each of the situations. A situation is defined by the number of objects in the problem and includes successions of trials. During each succession the peanut is consistently placed under one of the objects (cues). The succession is terminated when the monkey has moved, on five consecutive trials, the object under which the peanut is placed (criterion). (See also the legends to Figures 2, 3 and 8.) A repetitive error is made by a monkey when he moves more than once, during a succession of trials, an object *other* than the one under which the peanut is placed

1951; Skinner, 1938). Though one might, *a priori*, expect the number of repetitive responses to increase monotonically as a function of the number of objects in the situation, this does not happen. Rather, during one or another phase of the discrimination, the number of such responses increases to a peak and then declines to some asymptotic level (Bush and Mosteller, 1951; Skinner, 1938). Analysis of the data of the present experiment has shown that these peaks or 'humps' can be attributed to the performance of the control and posteriorly operated groups during

292

the initial trials given in any particular (e.g. 2, 3, 4 ⋯ cue) situation, i.e. when the monkey encounters a *novel* object. The period during which the novel and familiar objects are confused is reflected in the 'hump' (Figure 6). The importance of experience as a determinant of the discriminability of objects has been emphasized by Lawrence (1949, 1950). His formulation of the

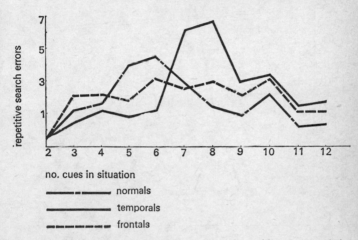

Figure 5. Graph of the average of the number of repetitive errors made in the multiple object experiment by each of the groups during search (see legend to Figure 4). Search trials are those anteceding the first 'correct' response in a succession of trials, i.e. those anteceding the movement of the object (cue) under which a peanut has been placed. Note the difference between the location of the 'hump' in the graph of the normal controls and in that of the posteriorly lesioned group (temporals)

'acquired distinctiveness' of cues is applicable here. In a progressively more complex situation, sufficient familiarity with *all* of the objects must be acquired before a novel object is sufficiently distinctive to be readily differentiated.

But there is a difference between the control and the posteriorly operated groups as to when the confusion between novel and familiar objects occurs. The peak in errors for the posteriorly operated group lags behind that for the controls – a result which forced attention because of the paradoxically 'better performance' of the posteriorly operated group throughout the five and six cue situations (in an experiment which was originally undertaken to demonstrate a relation between number of objects in the situation and the discrimination 'deficit' previously shown by this group).

These paradoxical results are accounted for by a formal treatment based on mathematical learning theory: on successive trials the monkeys had to 'learn' which of the objects now covered the

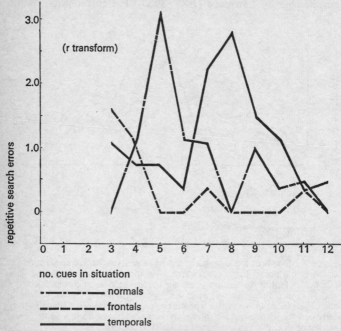

Figure 6. Graph of the average of the number of repetitive errors made in the multiple object experiment during those search trials in each situation when the additional, i.e. the novel, cue is first added. Note that the peaks in errors shown in Figure 5 are accounted for by the monkeys' confusion between novel and familiar objects as graphed here

peanut and which objects did not. At the same time they had to 'unlearn', i.e. extinguish, what they had previously learned – under which object the peanut had been and under which objects it had not been. Both neural and formal models have been invoked to explain the results obtained in such complex discrimination situations. Skinner (1938) postulated a process of neural induction to account for the peak in errors, much as Sherrington had postulated 'successive spinal induction' to account for the augmentation of a crossed extension reflex by precurrent antagonistic reflexes (such as the flexion reflex). Several of Skinner's pupils (Estes, 1950; Green, 1958) have developed formal models. These models are based on the idea that both 'learning' (or 'conditioning') and 'unlearning' (or 'extinction') involve antagonistic response classes – that in both conditioning and ex-

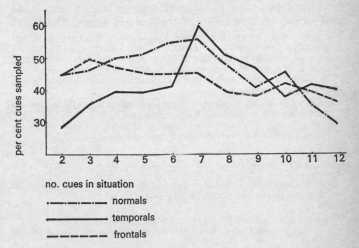

no. cues in situation

.—.—.—.— normals

——————— temporals

— — — — — frontals

Figure 7. Graph of the average of the per cent of the total number of objects (cues) that are sampled by each of the groups in each of the situations (see legend to Figure 4). To sample, a monkey had to move an object until the content or lack of content of the food well was clearly visible to the experimenter. As was predicted (see test), during the first half of the experiment the curve representing the sampling ratio of the posteriorly lesioned group differs significantly from the others at the 0·024 level [according to the non-parametric Mann–Whitney U procedure, (Mann and Whitney, 1947)]

tinction there occurs a transfer of response probabilities between response classes. This conception is, of course, similar to Sherrington's 'this reflex or that reflex but not the two together'. The resulting equations that constitute the model contain a constant which is defined as the probability of sampling a particular stimulus element (Green, 1958), i.e. object, in the discrimination experiment presented here. This constant is further defined (Estes, 1950) as the ratio between the number of stimulus elements sampled and the total number of such elements that could possibly be sampled. This definition of the constant postulates that it is dependent for its determination upon both environmental and organismic factors. According to the model the rapidity of increase in errors in a discrimination series depends on this sampling ratio – the fewer objects sampled, the more delayed the peak in recorded errors. The paradox that for a portion of the experiment the posteriorly lesioned group performs better than the control group stems from the relative delay in the peak of the recorded errors of the operated group.[1] The model

1. The actual model used to interpret the data analysed here was developed by Green (1958) and is patterned after a model of discrimination of learning proposed by Bush and Mosteller (1951). The Green model takes its roots from a parallel model originated by Estes (1955). The general form of the model is derived from Estes' equations describing the conditioning and extinction processes:

$\bar{p}_n(S - I) = 1 - (1 - \bar{p}_0)(1 - \phi_1)^{\pi n}$ for conditioning to those elements which constitute occasions for reinforcement.

$\bar{p}_n(S' - I) = \bar{p}_0(1 - \phi_2)^{\pi n}$ for extinction to those elements which are never occasions for reinforcement

and

$$\bar{p}_n(I) = \frac{\pi \phi_1}{\pi \phi_1 + \pi \phi_2} - \left[\frac{\pi \phi_1}{\pi \phi_1 + \pi \phi_2} - \bar{p}_n\right] \times (1 - \pi \phi_1 - \pi \phi_2)^n$$

for the changes associated with intercept elements, i.e. those present on both reinforced and unreinforced occasions.

where

$\bar{p}_0$ is the initial probability of response (operant level).

π is the relative frequency of reinforced trials in the discrimination series.

ϕ_1 and ϕ_2 are sampling ratios for reinforced and non-reinforced stimulus sets, respectively.

n denotes the number of trials.

It is assumed that the above equations are weighted directly as a function of the proportion of elements within the intercept and non-intercept subsets, such that

$$\bar{p}_n(S') = k'\bar{p}_n(S' - I) + (1 - k')\bar{p}_n(I).$$

In these experiments, then,

S' is the set of unreinforced stimulus elements (objects under which no peanut is located) and

I includes among the subset of elements common to both reinforced and unreinforced trials those objects which 'recently' have had a peanut under them.

k' is the proportion of stimulus elements not common to both reinforced and unreinforced trials.

$\bar{p}_n(S')$ is the mean probability of response on non-reinforced trials (probability of error responses) on the nth trial.

In the present experiment only the objects with no peanuts under them are considered since only one object at a time had a peanut under it. Thus the set of reinforced objects reduces to one, and the sampling ratio associated with it ϕ_1 is maximized with respect to the sampling ratio associated with the unreinforced sets, ϕ_2.

predicts, therefore, that this operated group has sampled fewer objects during the early portions of the experiment. This prediction is tested as shown in Figure 7.

The prediction is confirmed. The posterior intrinsic sector is thus established as one of the organismic variables that determine the constant of the model. As postulated by the model, the ratio of objects sampled turns out to be more basic than the number of objects in the situation, *per se*.

Mechanisms of invariance

Monkeys with posterior intrinsic sector lesions show a lag in attaining the strategy to sample extensively; is this impairment correlated with other deficiencies in differentiation that follow such lesions? These deficiencies differ in some respects from those produced by lesions of the extrinsic systems, but the differences are subtle and have repeatedly eluded precise specification (Pribram and Mishkin, 1956). The available data may therefore be briefly reviewed in a renewed attempt at such specification. (1) As already noted, drastic bilateral removal of an *extrinsic* sector severely limits differentiative behavior in the modality and only in modality served by that sector. The limitation affects practically all differentiations in the mode: e.g. a monkey whose occipital lobes have been removed reacts only to the grossest changes in the environment that affect the visual receptors – changes that can be ascribed to variations in total luminous flux (Klüver, 1942). Comparably, drastic bilateral removal of a posterior *intrinsic* sector restricts differentiative behavior within the mode served by that sector, and only within that mode, but the limitation is not as severe as that produced by drastic removal of the extrinsic sector serving that mode (Chow and Hutt, 1953; Pribram, 1954). (2) Under some conditions, differentiation is unimpaired after drastic resection of the posterior *intrinsic* sector: e.g. after such a removal, a monkey can catch a flying gnat in midair and can pull in a peanut which is beyond reach but attached to an available fine silk thread (0000 surgical). In these situations as in situations that necessitate the opening of a single box or depressing of a single lever, the operated animal is indistinguishable from an unoperated control animal (Pribram, 1958b). (3) Under other conditions, such as those in the experiment described above, differentiation is impaired after posterior *intrinsic* sector ablations. These conditions have in common the requirement that two or more separate responses be systematically related to the differences between the environmental events that determine the stimulus; i.e. alternatives are available to the organism, alternatives that are specified by environmentally determined stimuli. Such stimuli, for convenience, will hereafter be referred to as 'input' variables. Examples of the problems where impairment is found (in the visual mode) are: brightness, color, form, pattern, size, and flicker discriminations (Mishkin, 1954; Mishkin and Hall, 1955; Mishkin and Pribram, 1954); successive and simultaneous discriminations (Pribram and Mishkin, 1956); successions of discriminations ('learning set') (Chow, 1954; Riopelle, Alper, Strong, and Ades, 1953); oddity discriminations (Harlow, Davis, Settlage, and Meyer, 1952); and matching from sample (Harlow *et al.*, 1952). Though the operated animals may perform 'normally' on particular problems within a problem group, decrement is found on other more 'difficult' problems in that group. Difficulty of problem is independently defined by the number of trials taken by naïve unoperated animals to learn the problem. In most instances problem difficulty has also been related to differences between the physical dimensions of the objects, e.g. size discrimination (Mishkin and Hall, 1955), and to other determinants of the alternatives in the situation, e.g. situational differences (Pribram and Mishkin, 1956), sampling in the multiple object problem.

These then are the data. Extensive bilateral ablations of both extrinsic and posterior intrinsic sector resections impair differentiative behavior but differences between the impairments exist. Attempts to portray these differences are familiar. Neurologists have spoken of 'defective sensibility' and of 'agnosia' (Freud, 1953; Head, 1920), the latter often conceived as a disorder of memory. In so far as this distinction assumes an associationistic model of the functions of the intrinsic sectors, it gains little support from neurological or neuropsychological evidence (Pribram, 1958b). An alternate view can be proposed. Psychologists have spoken of 'existential discriminations' and 'differential discriminations' (James, 1950), or of 'sensibility' and 'intelligibility' (Miller, Heise and Lichten, 1951), distinctions that are made on the basis of whether the organism's actions are determined by 'simple presence or absence' of input variables or by 'some more complex relationship' between these variables, such as the number of 'contextual alternatives' in the situation (Miller, 1951). The results of the multiple object experiment warrant an attempt to pursue this conceptualization of the distinction by proposing a formal model of the interaction between the functions of the intrinsic sectors in differentiative behavior.

The defect in differentiative behavior that results from lesions of the extrinsic and posterior intrinsic sectors of the forebrain can be characterized by stating the variety of transformations of descriptions of the input under which behavior remains invariant. Following extensive bilateral resections of the extrinsic sectors, behavior remains invariant under a great variety of transformations of the input. For instance, for these preparations, even brightness and size of luminant are multiplicatively interchangeable quantities (Klüver, 1942), whereas differentiative behavior by organisms with intact extrinsic sectors is invariant under much more restricted ranges of transformations of the input – e.g. differentiation in the case of contrast and contour (Mach, 1897), texture and acuity (Gibson, 1950); continuous (orthogonal) projective in the case of position, distance, form and rigid motion (Gibson, 1950, ch. 8; Gibson and Gibson, 1956).

The effects of lesions of the posterior intrinsic sectors can also be usefully characterized in this way. Differentiative behavior which remains invariant under still fewer transformations of the input is interfered with by such lesions. In the extreme, unique responses, i.e. 'absolute' differentiations, would be most affected.

Unique responses can occur only when both an 'absolute' unit and an 'absolute' reference point have been fixed. As indicated in the discussion of the results of the multiple object experiment, mathematical learning theory provides an approach to the specification of these units and their referents. The fact that this mathematical device has proved so powerful a tool in the analysis of some completely unexpected effects of posterior intrinsic sector lesions lends support to its usefulness in the development of the model.

Partitioning

By what neural mechanism could the posterior intrinsic sectors effect a restriction of the systems of transformations of the input under which differentiative behavior remains invariant? On the basis of neurological and neurobehavioral data, the suggestion has been forwarded that the intrinsic sectors operate, via efferents, on the events occurring in the extrinsic mechanisms (Pribram, 1958b). These efferents can be conceived to partition the afferent activity that results in the events in the extrinsic sectors, events initiated by and corresponding to inputs. Partitioning determines the extent of the range of possibilities to which an element or a set of elements can be assigned. Partitioning results in patterns of information, information given by the elements of the subsets resulting from the partition (von Neumann and Morgenstern, 1953). The posterior intrinsic sector mechanism is thus conceived to provide both referent and units though *not* the elements to be specified. The effect of continued intrinsic sector activity will, according to this model, result in a sequence of patterns of information (partitions) of increasing complexity, which in turn allow more and more precise specification of particular elements in the set (or subsets) of events occurring in the extrinsic systems. Thus, through continued posterior intrinsic sector activity, more and more information can be conveyed by any given input. As a result, the organism's differentiative behavior remains invariant under a progressively narrower range of systems of transformations of the input – differentiations become more 'absolute'.

The programming of the activities of the posterior intrinsic sectors remains in question. Some things are clear, however. The advantage of this model is that the program is not composed solely by the events upon which the program operates. In this respect the model is in accord with neural and neurobehavioral facts (Pribram, 1958b). Other models, whether associationistic or matchmismatch (Bruner, 1957), demand the *storage* of an ever-increasing number of 'bits' of information. The evidence is overwhelmingly against the presence in the intrinsic systems of such minutely specific engrams (Lashley, 1950). In the model here presented, engrams consist of encoded programs; these operate on the neural events that are initiated by the input, transforming them into other neural events which can lead to an ever increasingly finer, i.e. appropriate, differential response (Gibson and Gibson, 1955; Werner, 1940). In this formulation the posterior intrinsic sectors are conceived as programming mechanisms that function to partition events initiated by the input, not as the loci of association of such events, nor as the loci of storage of an ever increasing number of minutely specific engrams.

References

BRUNER, J. S. (1957), 'On perceptual readiness', *Psychol. Rev.*, vol. 64, pp. 123–52.

BUSH, R. R., and MOSTELLER, F. (1951), 'A model for stimulus generalization and discrimination', *Psychol. Rev.*, vol. 58, pp. 413–23.

CHOW, K. L. (1954), 'Effects of temporal neocortical ablation on visual discrimination learning sets in monkeys', *J. comp. physiol. Psychol.*, vol. 47, pp. 194–8.

CHOW, K. L., and HUTT, P. J. (1953), 'The association cortex of Macaca mulatta: a review of recent contributions to its anatomy and functions', *Brain*, vol. 76, pp. 625–77.

ESTES, W. K. (1950), 'Toward a statistical theory of learning', *Psychol. Rev.*, vol. 57, pp. 94–107.

ESTES, W. K. (1955), 'Theory of elementary predictive behavior: an exercise in the behavioral interpretation of a mathematical model', *Mathematical Models of Human Behavior, Proceedings of a Symposium* Dunlap and Associates, Inc., Stamford.

FREUD, S. (1953), *On Aphasia*, International Universities Press, New York.

GIBSON, J. J. (1950), *The Perception of the Visual World*, Houghton Mifflin Co., New York, pp. 110–14, 152–4.

GIBSON, J. J., and GIBSON, ELEANOR J. (1955), 'Perceptual learning: differentiation or enrichment', *Psychol. Rev.*, vol. 62, pp. 32–41.

GIBSON, J. J., and GIBSON, ELEANOR J. (1956), *Continuous Perspective Transformations and the Perception of Rigid Motion*, Research Report under Office of Naval Research Contract and Cornell University on the Visual Perception of Motion and Space, September 1956.

GREEN, E. J. A. (1958), 'A simplified model for stimulus discrimination', *Psychol. Rev.*, vol. 65, pp. 56–63.

HARLOW, H. F. (1942), 'Responses by rhesus monkeys to stimuli having multiple sign values', *Studies in Personality*, McGraw-Hill, New York, pp. 105–23.

HARLOW, H. F. (1953), 'Higher function of the nervous system', *Ann. Rev. Psychol.*, vol. 15, pp. 493–514.

HARLOW, H. F., DAVIS, R. T., SETTLAGE, P. H., and MEYER, D. R. (1952), 'Analysis of frontal and posterior association syndromes in brain-damaged monkeys', *J. comp. physiol. Psychol.*, vol. 45, pp. 419–29.

HEAD, H. (1920), *Studies in Neurology*, Oxford Medical Publications, vol. 2, part 4, chap. 5, pp. 577–608.

JAMES, W. (1965), *Principles of Psychology*, Dover, vol. 1, pp. 489–90, 177–9.

KERR, D. I. B., and HAGBARTH, K. E. (1955), 'An investigation of olfactory centrifugal fiber system', *J. Neurophysiol.*, vol. 18, pp. 362–74.

KLÜVER, H. (1942), 'Functional significance of the geniculostriate system', *Biological Symposia*, Jaques Cattell Press, Lancaster, pp. 253–300.

LASHLEY, K. S. (1950), 'In search of the engram', *Physiological Mechanisms in Animal Behavior*, Academic Press, New York, pp. 454–82.

LAWRENCE, D. H. (1949), 'Acquired distinctiveness of cues: 1. Transfer between discriminations on the basis of familiarity with the stimulus', *J. exp. Psychol.*, vol. 39, pp. 776–84.

LAWRENCE, D. H. (1950), 'Acquired distinctiveness of cues: 2. Selective association in a constant stimulus situation', *J. exp. Psychol.*, vol. 40, pp. 175–88.

MACH, E. (1897), *Contributions to the Analysis of Sensations* (trans. C. M. Williams), Open Court, Chicago.

MANN, H. B., and WHITNEY, D. R. (1947), 'On a test of whether one of two random variables is stochastically larger than the other', *Ann. Math. Statist.*, vol. 18, pp. 50–60.

MILLER, G. (1951), *Language and Communication*, McGraw-Hill, New York, pp. 223–48.

Cognition and the Agnosias

MILLER, G. A., HEISE, G. A., and LICHTEN, W. (1951), 'The intelligibility of speech as a function of the context of the test materials', *J. exp. Psychol.*, vol. 41, pp. 329–35.

MISHKIN, M. (1954), 'Visual discrimination performance following ablations of the temporal lobe: 2. Ventral surface *vs* hippocampus', *J. comp. physiol. Psychol.*, vol. 47, pp. 187–93.

MISHKIN, M. and HALL, MARTHA (1955), 'Discriminations along a size continuum following ablation of the inferior temporal convexity in monkeys', *J. comp. physiol. Psychol.*, vol. 48, pp. 97–101.

MISHKIN, M., and PRIBRAM, K. H. (1954), 'Visual discrimination performance following partial ablation of the temporal lobe: 1. Ventral vs lateral', *J. comp. physiol. Psychol.*, vol. 47, pp. 14–27.

NEUMANN, J. VON, and MORGENSTERN, O. (1953), *Theory of Games and Economic Behavior*, Princeton University Press, pp. 19, 20, 24–8, 39–41, 60–73.

PRIBRAM, K. H. (1954), 'Toward a science of neuropsychology (method and data)', *Current Trends in Psychology and the Behavioral Sciences*, University of Pittsburgh Press, pp. 115–42.

PRIBRAM, K. H. (1958a), 'Comparative neurology and the evolution of behavior', *Behavior and Evolution*, Yale University Press, pp. 140–64.

PRIBRAM, K. H. (1958b), 'Neocortical function in behavior', *Symposium on Interdisciplinary Research in Behavioral, Biological and Biochemical Sciences*, University of Wisconsin Press, pp. 151–72.

PRIBRAM, K. H., and MISHKIN, M. (1956), 'Analysis of the effects of frontal lesions in monkey: III. Object alternation', *J. comp. physiol. Psychol.*, vol. 49, pp. 41–5.

RIOPELLE, A. J., ALPER, R. G., STRONG, P. N., and ADES, H. W. (1953), 'Multiple discrimination and patterned string performance of normal and temporal-lobectomized monkeys', *J. comp. physiol. Psychol.*, vol. 46, pp. 145–9.

SKINNER, B. F. (1938), *The Behavior of Organisms: An Experimental Analysis*, Appleton-Century-Crofts, New York.

WERNER, H. (1940), 'Musical "micro-scales" and "micro-melodies"', *J. Psychol.*, vol. 10, pp. 149–56.

15 B. Milner

Psychological Defects Produced by Temporal Lobe Excision

B. Milner, 'Psychological defects produced by temporal lobe excision', in H. C. Solomon, S. Cobb, and W. Penfield (eds.), *The Brain and Human Behavior*, Williams & Wilkins, 1958, pp. 244–57.

Although experimental ablation studies in monkeys have failed to reveal any significant or consistent behavioral change after unilateral temporal lobectomy (in contrast to the marked deficits (10) which follow a bilateral lesion), in man the manifest non-equivalence of the two hemispheres, at least with respect to language, and the greater range and sensitivity of behavioral measures available encourage the search for clues to human temporal lobe function through a study of unilateral lesions. In fact we find that unilateral epileptogenic lesions of the temporal lobe dating from birth or early life are accompanied by certain cognitive defects which vary in kind depending on whether the lesion is in the dominant (left)[1] or non-dominant (right) temporal lobe. In such cases when unilateral partial temporal lobectomy is carried out for the relief of seizures, these characteristic defects persist and may even be accentuated, despite the fact that over-all intellectual efficiency is apt to increase if the patient is no longer having seizures. These specific defects form the main topic of the present paper.

During the last five years over a hundred patients with temporal lobe seizures have been subjected to formal psychological testing immediately before unilateral operation and again about 18 days later, at the time of the patient's discharge from hospital. Wherever possible, long-range follow-up studies have also been carried out, but these unfortunately have not been very numerous as yet. Twenty-two control cases consisting of patients with atrophic epileptogenic lesions of frontal or parietal cortex have been similarly studied before and after brain operation, in order to determine how far the deficits found are specific to the temporal lobe. All the patients in the series have been operated upon either by Dr Wilder Penfield or by Dr Theodore Rasmussen. In the course of the investigation the test battery has gradually changed

1. For the purpose of this study cases of right hemisphere speech representation are excluded.

and expanded, and we do not have complete data for all patients on all tests.

Temporal lobe seizures are notoriously difficult to control by anti-convulsant medication. In such cases unilateral partial temporal lobectomy constitutes a reasonably successful method of treatment. It is usually followed by upper quadrantic homonymous hemianopsia but by no other neurological deficit. As Pen-

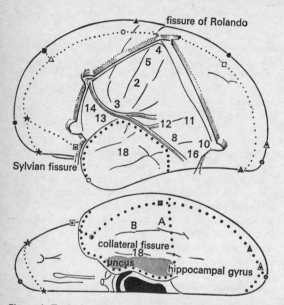

Figure 1. Typical partial temporal lobectomy. The light shading indicates abnormality of the hippocampal zone

field and Baldwin (14) have pointed out, the abnormal sclerotic area of cortex which must be removed usually lies deep to the surface in the most inferior and mesial portion of the temporal lobe, adjacent to the midbrain. It is believed that in most cases this sclerosis is produced by herniation through the incisura of the tentorium and compression of the arteries of supply at the time of birth (3), although seizures may not occur until much later. At operation the surgeon typically finds objective evidence of atrophy in the region of the uncus and anterior portion of the first temporal convolution and also in the hippocampus and hippocampal gyrus, and it is unusual to obtain lasting relief from seizures if these structures are spared. A typical removal is shown in Figure 1: the light shading indicates abnormality of the hippocampal zone which was therefore excised together with the overlying cortex, the heavy dotted line showing the total extent of excision. The fact that abnormality deep to the surface is typically found and that the excisions include both temporal neocortex and allocortex may well have an important bearing on the deficits seen.

Table 1

Preoperative Mean I.Q. Ratings

Group	N	Full scale	Verbal	Performance
Left temporal	15	108·5 (86–129)	107·2 (87–122)	107·3 (87–133)
Right temporal	15	103 (87–127)	107·1 (94–143)	97·6 (78–117)

Results

General intelligence

These patients with focal cortical epilepsy constitute a young group (the average age is 26 years, with a range from 14 to 45), and they are not intellectually retarded. During the last two years, in addition to more specialized tests, the Wechsler Intelligence Scale has been administered to all patients, Form I before operation and Form II after operation. Table 1 shows the mean intelligence ratings before operation for 30 consecutive temporal lobe cases, 15 left-sided and 15 right-sided, all with speech representation in the left hemisphere. The mean Full-Scale, Verbal, and Performance I.Q. ratings all fall within the normal range, and there is no significant difference between the two groups on these various measures. There is, however, a significant difference ($t = 2·57$, $P < 0·05$) between the Verbal and Performance I.Q. ratings for the right temporal group, with the Performance Quotient (based on non-verbal tests) averaging 9 points lower than the Verbal. A relative inefficiency on non-verbal tests has been reported by various workers for miscellaneous lesions of the right hemisphere (1, 9, 11, 16, 20): our observations extend these findings to the right temporal lobe specifically, thus corroborating Hebb's findings in a single case of right temporal lobectomy (6).

After operation the patients were re-tested with Form II of the Wechsler scale which is a slightly harder test, yielding ratings lower rather than higher than Form I in a normal population (4). Thus practice effects can safely be ignored. Table 2 summarizes the findings three weeks after unilateral temporal lobectomy. There is no significant change in Full-Scale, Verbal, or Performance I.Q. ratings for the right temporal group. There were, however, some marked individual changes, a few patients improving

Table 2

Mean Fall in I.Q. Rating 3 Weeks after Unilateral Partial Temporal Lobectomy

Group	N	Full scale	Verbal	Performance
Left temporal	15	10·3	16·6	2·3
Right temporal	15	1·5	2·5˙	1·4

by as much as 11 points in Full-Scale I.Q. rating and others showing a corresponding deterioration. The left temporal lobe group all showed some postoperative dysphasia due to the effects of cerebral edema upon neighbouring speech areas although of course no primary speech area had been destroyed. This dysphasia is a transient phenomenon, usually developing from one to three days after operation and beginning to clear by about the tenth postoperative day. Marked individual differences in the severity and duration of the dysphasia are found, and these are reflected in varying degrees of impairment on verbal tests three weeks after operation. Thus we see in Table 2 that the left temporal lobe group shows a pronounced postoperative deficit in Verbal I.Q. rating, and hence some deficit also in Full-Scale I.Q. rating, changes which are significant beyond the 0·001 level of probability. There is, however, no impairment on performance tests even during this dysphasic period. Furthermore when these patients return for follow-up study a year or more later, we find that the I.Q. rating has returned at least to the preoperative level, provided they are no longer having seizures. Thus we can conclude that no lasting impairment of general intelligence follows unilateral anterior temporal lobectomy in either hemisphere.

Specific defects

Against this background of general intellectual competence certain specific deficits stand out: verbal for the left temporal lobe group, perceptual for the right. These deficits, which differentiate between right and left temporal lobe cases even before operation, will now be described.

a. Verbal recall and the left temporal lobe. Although before operation the patients with left temporal lobe lesions showed no consistent impairment on verbal intelligence tests and no dysphasia, it was possible to demonstrate a specific deficit in verbal learning and retention at this time. As a result of this specific deficit the Wechsler memory quotient fell far below the I.Q. level for the left temporal lobe group, whereas no difference was found for the

Table 3
Comparison of Mean Intelligence and Memory Quotients (Before and Three Weeks After Operation) for Left Temporal, Right Temporal and Frontal Lobe Cases

Group	N	Preoperative means (Form I)			Postoperative means (Form II)		
		I.Q.	M.Q.	I.Q.– M.Q.	I.Q.	M.Q.	I.Q. M.Q.
Left temporal	9	106·6	91·2	15·4	95·1	77·4	17·7
Right temporal	12	102·5	102·2	0·3	102·8	107·8	−5·0
Frontal	9	101·6	94·8	6·8	93·0	92·6	0·4

right temporal lobe cases. Patients with frontal lobe lesions are intermediate between the two temporal lobe groups and do show some relative memory impairment before operation, but the deficit is both different in kind and less severe than that shown by patients with left temporal lobe lesions. Table 3 gives the mean intelligence and memory quotients for three groups of patients before and after brain operation. Analysis of variance yielded *F*-values significant beyond the 0·001 level, and subsequent *t*-tests showed the three groups to differ significantly one from another both before and after operation, the left temporal lobe patients consistently showing the largest discrepancy between intelligence and memory quotients. The intergroup differences remain the same after operation, but Form II of the memory scale appears to be a somewhat easier test than Form I.

The Wechsler memory quotient is based on a heterogeneous sample of subtests, not all of which show impairment in the left temporal lobe group. There is, for example, no impairment in the recall of geometrical drawings. Moreover, although the patients with left temporal lobe lesions tend to do poorly on all verbal memory tests, the defect shows up most clearly and characteristically when they are asked to recall simple prose passages (stories a mere paragraph in length) which have been read to them some time before. Such measures of delayed recall do not contribute to the conventional memory quotient, yet they provide our most valuable localizing sign. It is our current practice to read the patient the two stories of the Logical Memory subtest of the memory scale, obtaining immediate reproductions of each in the

Table 4

Delayed Recall of Stories (Preoperative)

| Group | N | Per cent recall | |
		mean	range
Left temporal	15	13	6–21
Others	29	25	8–42

usual manner, and then about one and a half hours later and without any previous warning we ask the patient to tell us the stories once more. Under these conditions the left temporal lobe group makes very low scores, as can be seen from Table 4 which gives the percentage of material recalled after an interval by the left temporal group as compared with a mixed group of frontal, parietal and right temporal lobe cases. The left temporal lobe patients remember only half as much of the stories as do patients with lesions in other areas, a difference which is significant well beyond the 0·001 level of probability. It is of interest that the patients with frontal lobe lesions showed no impairment on this particular memory task.

All this is before operation, the effect of a focal epileptogenic lesion of the dominant temporal lobe. After operation these patients show the transient dysphasia noted above, at which time scores on all verbal tests, and not merely on verbal memory tests, are seriously impaired. But even after the dysphasia has cleared, the verbal memory difficulty persists, and there is now a detectable impairment even in the initial comprehension of stories. This is illustrated in Table 5, which gives average scores for four patients tested before left anterior temporal lobectomy and again in follow-up study from one to three years later, at which time they were free of seizures and had achieved a mean I.Q. level slightly higher than before operation. All four patients show a residual postoperative impairment in the immediate recall of stories. Quantitatively this falling-off is significant ($P < 0.02$), and there are corresponding qualitative changes also, the postoperative versions being more fragmentary and losing the distinctive pattern of the original story. It appears that only a very limited amount of verbal material can be assimilated in one sequence although any specific sentence or question taken in isolation is readily understood. This is a defect of which a patient

Table 5

Specific Postoperative Impairment of Story Reproduction 1–3 Years after Partial Left Temporal Lobectomy (Means for 4 Cases)

		Before operation	Follow-up
Wechsler I.Q.		104	110
Story recall	Immediate	30	20
(per cent)	Delayed	13·8	9·2

of good intelligence is well aware. A student will report that he cannot follow lectures; a stenographer that she cannot keep up with her dictation; a bank clerk that he cannot handle the rapid give-and-take of conversation in the business world. Such individuals are apt to be less successful in their work than their intelligence and high motivation would lead one to predict. It is interesting that Meyer and Yates (12), working with similar case material in England, have also emphasized the severe learning difficulty of patients undergoing partial temporal lobectomy in the dominant hemisphere. However, they regard this primarily as a postoperative phenomenon, whereas the results of the present study show that there are marked verbal recall deficits present even before operation. These differences in emphasis probably reflect differences in the measures used.

b. *Pictorial comprehension and the right temporal lobe.* Patients with epileptogenic lesions of the right, non-dominant, temporal lobe have none of these verbal difficulties, but they show a clear, specific and reliable impairment on a pictorial test, the McGill Picture Anomaly Series. In this test the subject is shown a number of sketchily drawn scenes and has to point to what is most incongruous in each. A relatively easy item from this test is shown in Figure 2. In this instance the picture on the wall of the monkey's cage is immediately recognized as inappropriate by most normal subjects, and also by patients with lesions of frontal, parietal, or left temporal cortex. However, a patient with a right temporal lobe lesion might have difficulty identifying the various parts of the drawing and so might, for example, point to the

Figure 2. Representative item from the McGill Picture Anomalies test

woman's head in the foreground as 'unidentifiable' and therefore 'wrong'. The error scores for the various groups on this test are shown diagrammatically in Figure 3, different forms of the test being used before and after operation to eliminate practice effects. The right temporal lobe patients make significantly more errors ($P < 0.01$), both before and after operation, than other brain injured subjects, who do not differ significantly from normal control subjects (a regrettably small group). It is particularly noteworthy that the patients with parietal lobe lesions made excellent scores. This pictorial test, whatever it measures, is not to be confused with tests such as Kohs Blocks which are primarily dependent upon spatial ability and are known to be peculiarly sensitive to parietal lobe injury (2, 8).

The Picture Anomalies test was originally intended as a power test only, time of response not being recorded; but it became increasingly clear that the right temporal lobe patients were abnormally slow and hesitant, and not merely inaccurate, in their responses, and therefore time scores for the whole test are now unobtrusively recorded. The results to date are shown in Figure 4. The right temporal lobe group is slower than either the left tem-

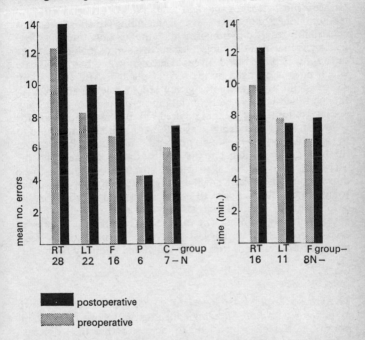

postoperative

preoperative

Figure 3. Picture Anomalies test: error scores for right temporal (RT), left temporal (LT), frontal (F) and parietal lobe (P) cases before and after operation, and for normal control subjects (C) tested twice

Figure 4. Picture Anomalies test: time scores, showing significant post-operative slowing for the right temporal lobe group only

poral lobe or the frontal lobe groups even before operation, and after operation a significant further slowing occurs. Thus on this test we find a defect specific to the minor temporal lobe, and one which is heightened by removal of the epileptogenic area.

c. Auditory discrimination – preliminary observations. The original test battery did not include any auditory tasks, but during the past year the Seashore tests of musical ability have been administered to all patients before and after operation. Despite the small number of cases, we already have some evidence of auditory deficits after unilateral temporal lobe excisions, the evidence so far being most clear for the right temporal lobe group. Unilateral temporal lobectomy, not necessarily including Heschl's gyrus, has consistently resulted in impairment on the Seashore tonal memory test, a test in which the subject listens to a simple melody of three or four notes played twice in rapid succession and has to indicate which note is changed at the second playing. After operation, scores of the right temporal group fall sharply on this test although other auditory tests, including simple pitch and intensity discrimination, may be unimpaired. In two patients seen for follow-up study this deficit was still present though not quite to the same degree. So far we do not see so consistent a deficit from the left temporal lobe, but the numbers are too small and the excision size too variable to permit any final conclusion to be drawn from this. Meanwhile it appears that right temporal lobectomy is in itself sufficient to cause a lasting deficit in the discrimination of tonal patterns. The fact that this deficit only appears after operation, whereas the visual difficulty is present even before operation, suggests that different parts of the temporal cortex are implicated in the visual and auditory tasks.

General v. specific defects and the nociferous effects of epileptogenic cortex

The data so far presented have emphasized specific defects shown by patients with long-standing epileptogenic lesions of one temporal lobe, defects which tend to increase rather than decrease when the epileptogenic area is excised. Apart from these specific defects, most patients show normal intellectual functioning both before and after operation. However there are marked individual differences in this respect, differences which may well be related to differences in degree of electrographic abnormality and seizure frequently before operation, though this has still to be demonstrated. Certainly some patients with unusually active electrographic foci before operation show general intellectual impairment which we attribute to widespread interference with cortical functioning rather than to the temporal lobe lesions specifically (7, p. 282). Unlike the specific defects, this more general intellectual inefficiency is apt to disappear after removal of the epileptogenic area. The following case is chosen to illustrate this point.

Case M. L. This 22-year-old man presented a lifelong history of major and minor seizures, the latter occurring as often as 16 times a day. The attacks were ushered in by a warm, empty sensation in the umbilicus, followed by grunting, chewing and automatic behavior for which there was subsequent amnesia. Repeated electroencephalographic studies showed a very clean right temporal focus which was extraordinarily active, with sharp waves and slow wave sequence present continuously. On December 16, 1953, Dr Penfield carried out a right temporal lobectomy, finding marked abnormality beginning in the first temporal convolution deep anteriorly and extending into the uncus and hippocampus and along the inferior surface of the temporal lobe. The removal extended roughly 4 cm. along the first temporal convolution and 5·5 cm. along the inferior surface, including the anterior portion of the hippocampal gyrus. Since this operation failed to stop the patient's attacks, three weeks later Dr William Feindel extended the removal to include a further 1½ cm. of the hippocampus and adjacent inferior temporal cortex together with the insula. The patient has had no further seizures, and his family considers that his memory has improved greatly and that he is far less irritable than before.

Psychological findings. Preoperative psychological examination on December 12, 1953, showed the characteristic right temporal lobe deficits. The Performance I.Q. rating was only 84, as compared with a Verbal I.Q. rating of 95, and he made poor time and error scores on the Picture Anomalies test. But in addition to these specific and expected deficits he showed abnormal variability on other tests, giving careless answers to simple questions, failing easy items on the mental arithmetic test only to succeed a moment later on more difficult ones, and showing a very restricted attention span. There was marked impairment on short term memory tests, resulting in a memory quotient of only 79, 10 points lower than the I.Q. rating. When tested for delayed recall of stories and drawings, further distortions and omissions occurred. We took these deficits as indicative of widespread interference with intellectual functioning due to the extremely active discharging lesion in the right temporal lobe, and hoped that improvement would follow surgical treatment. This in fact occurred. Fifteen days after the second operation the I.Q. level had risen from 89 to 99, the improvement being most marked on verbal tests. There was also a remarkable all-round improvement on short tests of memory and attention so that the memory quotient rose from 79 to 101, the most marked rise in the whole right temporal lobe group. Yet at the same time there was the typical further slowing on the Picture Anomalies test and also a falling off to chance scores on auditory discrimination tests, from which there has been little improvement to the present time.

This case has been selected to show the non-specific deficits which may result from an extremely active epileptogenic lesion in one temporal lobe. Removal of the epileptogenic focus in such a case may increase all round intellectual efficiency, as shown for example by an appreciable rise in I.Q. rating, but will at the same time tend to aggravate the deficits specific to the area removed. This same principle of course could have been illustrated equally well by a left temporal lobe lesion, but the specific deficits would have been different.

The memory defect in bilateral hippocampal lesions

So far we have been considering only the effects of lesions strictly lateralized to one temporal lobe, cases in which the opposite temporal lobe is, we believe, functioning normally. In such cases only minor deficits are seen: a specifically verbal difficulty from the left temporal lobe, a perceptual difficulty from the right. But in two instances in our temporal lobe series, unilateral partial temporal lobectomy in the dominant hemisphere was followed by a major impairment; a grave, persistent and totally unexpected loss of recent memory, fortunately unaccompanied by other changes of intellect or personality (15). In one instance the temporal lobe removal had been carried out in two stages, separated by a five-year period, and the memory loss followed the second operation only, at which time the uncus, hippocampus, and hippocampal gyrus alone were excised. Interestingly enough, although the patient had been aphasic for a time after the first operation, the second operation caused no language disturbance. The memory loss seen in these two cases appeared to be qualitatively quite distinct from the verbal learning difficulty normally seen in unilateral lesions of the dominant temporal lobe since it affected all postoperative events and not merely verbal material. We believe this distinction to be of fundamental importance.

Both these amnesic patients have continued to earn their living, one as a glove cutter, the other as a draughtsman; and their professional skills are well maintained. There is no defect of attention, concentration, or reasoning ability and no aphasia. Both patients show some retrograde amnesia for a period before the operation (four years in the first patient, three months in the second), but their memory for events before the period of retrograde amnesia is apparently normal. They show a very gross impairment of memory for all events subsequent to operation, and they are unable to recall test material after a lapse of five minutes or less if their attention has been diverted to another topic in the meantime. The retention difficulty is not specific to any one kind of material, but is quite general, affecting stories,

drawings, and numbers, and cutting across any distinction between verbal and perceptual material or between one sense
modality and another.

To account for the severe memory loss in these two patients we
have assumed that, in addition to the known epileptogenic lesion
of the left hippocampal region, there was a second and preoperatively unsuspected destructive lesion of the opposite (right)
hippocampal zone at the time of birth, so that when the surgeon
removed the left hippocampal area, the patient was functionally
deprived of that zone on both sides. And in fact both patients
now show continuing electrographic abnormality in the unoperated temporal lobe. This view then attributes a key role to
the hippocampal zone (hippocampus and hippocampal gyrus) in
the retention and subsequent recall of current experience. A
similar view was advanced by Glees and Griffith in 1952 (5) to
account for memory loss seen in one patient with bilateral destruction of hippocampus and hippocampal gyrus by vascular accident.
Strong and direct support for this interpretation comes from Dr
William Scoville who in 1954 (17) reported a grave loss of recent
memory as a sequel to bilateral medial temporal lobe resection in
one psychotic patient and one patient with intractable seizures.
These operations had been radical ones, undertaken only when
more conservative forms of treatment had failed. The removals
extended posteriorly along the mesial aspect of the temporal
lobes for a distance of about 8 cm. from the temporal tips, and
the excisions were made by bisecting the tips of the temporal
lobes and removing bilaterally the inferior portions of each temporal lobe which lay mesial to the inferior horn of the ventricle.
These ablations must then have included the major portion of the
hippocampus and hippocampal gyrus bilaterally, as well as uncus
and amygdala,[2] but of course spared the lateral neocortex. Dr
Scoville has very generously allowed us to study these patients,
and they present exactly the same type of memory disturbance as
our two cases had shown (18). Interestingly, I think, they do not
have any perceptual difficulty or any disturbance of initial comprehension. The impairment is specifically one of retention.

Conclusions

What do these findings as a whole tell us of the normal function
of the temporal lobes? The data on unilateral lesions show that

2. In his experience, bilateral removals limited to the uncal and
amygdaloid regions cause no memory loss.

the left temporal lobe contributes to the rapid understanding and subsequent retention of verbally expressed ideas. Deprived of this area a man is not dysphasic, but he remains an inefficient listener and a poor reader since he can assimilate less verbal information in one sequence than formerly and forgets this little abnormally quickly. The right, minor, temporal lobe, on the other hand, appears to be more critically involved in perceptual than in verbal skills.[3] When the right temporal lobe is removed, pictures and representational drawings lose some of their former distinctiveness, and the separate parts are less easily identified although there is never anything approaching a true visual agnosia. It seems that the right temporal lobe facilitates rapid visual identification, and that in this way it enters into the comprehension of pictorially expressed ideas.

These data on unilateral lesions have underlined the differences in function between the two temporal lobes, differences which relate to the functional asymmetry of the two hemispheres, the left being primarily concerned with verbal, the right with nonverbal skills. But it is clear that there must still be a considerable overlap of function between the two temporal lobes, the extent of which can only be revealed by bilateral lesions (19). We have no experience of bilateral lesions of the temporal neocortex, but the discovery of generalized memory loss, apparently independent of type of material or sense modality, after bilateral destruction of the hippocampus and hippocampal gyrus suggests that this hippocampal zone plays an essential part in the consolidation of the effects of current experience so that they endure beyond the moment of primary attention.

Summary

Formal psychological testing before and after unilateral partial temporal lobectomy in over 100 cases of temporal lobe epilepsy has yielded the following results:

1. Intelligence as measured by the Wechsler–Bellevue I.Q. rating is not permanently affected by these operations although

---

3. Dr Sean Mullan's observations, reported by Dr Penfield (13) at these meetings, provide further evidence of the importance of the minor temporal lobe for perceptual functions. He finds that visual illusions of changes in the appearance of objects, whether occurring during epileptic discharge or as a result of cortical stimulation, arise almost invariably from the non-dominant rather than the dominant temporal lobe.

there is a deficit on verbal subtests in the left temporal group during the period of postoperative dysphasia.

2. Long-standing epileptogenic lesions of the temporal lobe are associated with defects on certain specialized tests, these defects varying in kind depending on whether the lesion is in the dominant or non-dominant hemisphere.

3. Unilateral epileptogenic lesions of the dominant (left) temporal lobe are accompanied by difficulties in verbal recall although recall of non-verbal material is normal.

4. Unilateral epileptogenic lesions of the non-dominant (right) temporal lobe are accompanied by impairment in the comprehension of pictures although verbal skills are intact.

5. When unilateral partial temporal lobectomy is carried out for the relief of seizures, these specific deficits persist and in fact tend to be accentuated. This is true even in those cases which show a postoperative increase in I.Q. rating and complete cessation of seizures.

6. In contrast to the relatively mild deficits which accompany unilateral lesions, bilateral damage to the hippocampal zone causes profound and generalized loss of recent memory, unaccompanied by other intellectual changes.

7. These findings suggest that (a) the left temporal lobe contributes to the understanding and retention of verbally expressed ideas; (b) the right temporal lobe aids in rapid visual identification; (c) the hippocampus and hippocampal gyrus (either separately or together) play a crucial role in the retention of new experience.

References

1. A. L. ANDERSON, 'The effect of laterality localization of brain lesions on the Wechsler-Bellevue subtests', *J. clin. Psychol.*, vol. 7 (1949), pp. 149–53.
2. M. CRITCHLEY, *The Parietal Lobes*, Edward Arnold Ltd, London, 1953.
3. K. M. EARLE, M. BALDWIN, and W. PENFIELD, 'Incisural sclerosis and temporal lobe seizures produced by hippocampal herniation at birth', *Arch. Neurol. Psychiat.*, vol. 69 (1953), pp. 27–42.
4. R. GERBOTH, 'A study of the two forms of the Wechsler–Bellevue Intelligence Scale', *J. consult. Psychol.*, vol. 14 (1950), pp. 365–70.
5. P. GLEES and H. B. GRIFFITH, 'Bilateral destruction of the hippocampus (cornu Ammonis) in a case of dementia', *Monatsschr. Psychiat. u. Neurol.*, vol. 123 (1952), pp. 193–204.
6. D. O. HEBB, 'Intelligence in man after large removals of cerebral tissue; defects following right temporal lobectomy', *J. gen. Psychol.*, vol. 21 (1939), pp. 73–87.

Cognition and the Agnosias

7. D. O. HEBB, *The Organization of Behavior: a Neuropsychological Theory*, Wiley, New York, 1949.
8. H. HECAEN, W. PENFIELD, C. BERTRAND, and R. MALMO, 'The syndrome of apractognosia due to lesions of the minor cerebral hemisphere', *Arch. Neurol. Psychiat.*, vol. 75 (1956), pp. 400–54.
9. A. B. HEILBRUNN, JR, 'Psychological test performance as a function of lateral localization of cerebral lesions', *J. comp. physiol. Psychol.*, vol. 49 (1956), pp. 10–14.
10. H. KLUVER and P. C. BUCY, 'Preliminary analysis of functions of the temporal lobe in monkeys', *Arch. Neurol. Psychiat.*, vol. 42 (1939), pp. 979–1000.
11. J. McFIE and M. F. PIERCY, 'Intellectual impairment with localized cerebral lesions', *Brain*, vol. 75 (1952), pp. 292–311.
12. V. MEYER and A. J. YATES, 'Intellectual changes following temporal lobectomy for psychomotor epilepsy', *J. Neurol. Neurosurg. Psychiat.*, vol. 18 (1955), pp. 44–52.
13. W. PENFIELD, 'Functional localization in temporal and deep Sylvian areas', *Res. Publ. Assn. Res. nerv. ment. Dis.*, 1957.
14. W. PENFIELD and M. BALDWIN, 'Temporal lobe seizures and the technique of sub-total temporal lobectomy', *Ann. Surg.*, vol. 136 (1952), pp. 625–34.
15. W. PENFIELD and B. MILNER, 'The memory deficit produced by bilateral lesions in the hippocampal zone', *Arch. Neurol. Psychiat.*, vol. 79 (1958), pp. 475–97.
16. R. M. REITAN, 'Certain differential effects of left and right cerebral lesions in human adults', *J. comp. physiol. Psychol.*, vol. 48 (1955), pp. 474–7.
17. W. B. SCOVILLE, 'The limbic lobe in man', *J. Neurosurg.*, vol. 11 (1954), pp. 64–6.
18. W. B. SCOVILLE and B. MILNER, 'Loss of recent memory after bilateral hippocampal lesions', *J. Neurol. Neurosurg. Psychiat.*, vol. 20 (1957), pp. 11–21.
19. H. TERZIAN and G. DALLE ORE, 'Syndrome of Kluver and Bucy produced in man by bilateral removal of the temporal lobes', *Neurology*, vol. 5 (1955), pp. 373–80.
20. T. WEISENBERG, and K. McBRIDE, *Aphasia: A Clinical and Psychological Study*, Commonwealth Fund, New York, 1936.

16 B. Milner

Laterality Effects in Audition

Excerpt from B. Milner, 'Laterality effects in audition', in V. B. Mountcastle (ed.), *Interhemispheric Relations and Cerebral Dominance*, Johns Hopkins Press, 1962, pp. 180–81.

[...]

Visual Functions of the Right Temporal Lobe

We have found no deficits on any verbal task after right temporal lobectomy when that hemisphere is nondominant for speech, but we do find that right temporal-lobe injury is associated with impaired performance on a variety of visual, nonverbal tasks. Patients with epileptogenic lesions of the right temporal lobe are slow and inaccurate in detecting incongruities in sketchy, cartoon-like drawings (Milner, 1958); they also show a deficit in the recognition of overlapping nonsense figures and groups of dots tachistoscopically presented, although they can readily perceive objects to which a name can be attached (Kimura, 1960). Patients with left temporal-lobe lesions do not have these perceptual difficulties. Further evidence of the importance of the right temporal lobe for visual perception comes from Lansdell (1961), who studied a group of patients approximately three and one-half years after unilateral temporal lobectomy. Using Mooney's Closure Faces test (Mooney, 1956, 1957), he found that the group with right temporal-lobe lesions made significantly lower scores than those with left.

Turning to the domain of visual memory, we now have ample evidence of visual memory defect after right temporal lobectomy, but not after left temporal lobectomy of comparable extent. We find this for face recognition, using a one-trial procedure (Milner, 1960); for learning to recognize nonsense figures over a series of recurring presentations (Kimura, 1960); and for the delayed recall of geometric figures, even though these may have been accurately reproduced at the time of the original presentation (Milner, 1960). Thus the method of testing is unimportant, whether it be by recognition, rate of learning, or recall; what is important is the visual, nonverbal nature of the stimuli presented.

The evidence for impairment of visual perception and visual learning after right temporal-lobe injury in man accords well with the results of animal work, where bilateral lesions of the convexity of the temporal cortex cause profound impairment in visual discrimination learning (Chow, 1951; Mishkin and Pribram, 1954). For a deficit to occur in the monkey, a bilateral lesion is required, unless the task be very difficult. The fact that in man visual impairment follows unilateral temporal lobectomy on the right side, but not on the left, suggests that the development of language representation in the left hemisphere has disturbed the functional equivalence of the two temporal lobes for visually guided behavior, with the right now playing a proportionately greater role.

[. . .]

References

CHOW, K. L. (1951), 'Effects of partial extirpations of the posterior association cortex on visually mediated behavior in monkeys', *Comp. Psychol. Monogr.*, vol. 20, no. 3 (whole no. 105).

KIMURA, D. (1960), *Visual and Auditory Perception after Temporal-Lobe Damage*, Unpublished doctoral thesis, McGill University.

LANSDELL, H. C. (1961), *Two Selective Deficits Found to be Lateralized in Temporal Neurosurgery Patients*, Paper read at 32nd Ann. Meeting of Eastern Psychol. Ass., Philadelphia.

MILNER, B. (1958), 'Psychological defects produced by temporal lobe excision', *Publ. Ass. Res. Nerv. Ment. Dis.*, vol. 36, pp. 244–57.

MILNER, B. (1960), *Impairment of Visual Recognition and Recall after Right Temporal Lobectomy in Man*, Paper read at the First Ann. Meeting of Psychonomic Soc., Chicago.

MISHKIN, M., and PRIBRAM, K. H. (1954), 'Visual discrimination performance following partial ablations of the temporal lobe: 1. Ventral *vs* lateral', *J. Comp. Physiol. Psychol.*, vol. 47, pp. 14–20.

MOONEY, C. M. (1956), 'Closure with negative after-images under flickering light', *Canad. J. Physiol.*, vol. 10, pp. 191–9.

MOONEY, C. M. (1957), 'Closure as affected by configural clarity and contextual consistency', *Canad. J. Psychol.*, vol. 11, pp. 80–8.

17 R. Hernández-Peón, H. Scherrer and M. Velasco

Central Influences on Afferent Conduction in the Somatic and Visual Pathways

R. Hernández- Peón, H. Scherrer and M. Velasco, 'Central influences on afferent conduction in the somatic and visual pathways', *Acta Neurol. Latinoamer.*, vol. 2 (1956), pp. 8–22.

Recent studies have demonstrated that activation of sensorimotor cortex or of the brain stem reticular formation, depresses afferent transmission at the first synapse of two groups of somatic afferent fibers, viz., lumbar afferents relaying in the spinal cord (9), and trigeminal afferents relaying in the medulla (10). This inhibitory influence upon afferent conduction in the cord, has been shown to be of a tonic nature, and to proceed from supra-spinal structures, since a high spinal transection enhances cord afferent potentials, both in the ventral (9) and the dorsal columns (22). Furthermore, this inhibitory mechanism appears to be sensitive to central anesthetics, since a similar augmentation of spinal afferent responses was observed during nembutal or chloralose anesthesia (9).

These studies, which provide for the first time, definite experimental evidence for central mechanisms controling synaptic afferent transmission, raise immediately several questions. Are the first sensory medullary relays of dorsal column afferents similarly influenced by these central mechanisms as the other two first sensory synapses of the somatic paths? During wakefulness, is there also a tonic inhibitory influence upon bulbar somatic relays? And, if this influence exists, what supra-spinal structures are essential for this tonic action? The great sensitiveness of the brain stem reticular formation to anesthetics (6, 1) and the fact that integrity of this region is necessary for wakefulness (23, 5) strongly suggest that the tonic inhibitory influence upon afferent transmission may also be dependent upon functional integrity of the reticular system.

The disclosure of mechanisms regulating transmission between the first and second neurons of the somatic pathway, leads logically to wonder about central influences acting upon thalamic conduction in afferent paths. King, Naquet, and Magoun (20) have investigated this problem at the ventro-postero-lateral nucleus of the thalamus, particularly in relation with the interaction of two afferent volleys. Since in the visual pathway, the pre-synaptic fibers of the thalamic relay are grouped together in a tract easily available for monitoring the incoming sensory impulses, and in order to extend these studies to other sensory pathways, it was decided to investigate the problem of central control of sensory thalamic relays in the visual pathway.

The experiments described below were designed to obtain further information concerning central mechanisms that regulate central afferent transmission.

Material and Methods

Twenty-two cats were used for the present study. The operative procedure was performed under ether anesthesia. At the completion of the operation, procaine was locally applied to surgical wounds and pressure points, the anesthesia was discontinued and the animal was immobilized with curare and maintained with artificial respiration. A small trephine opening was made in the convexity of the skull for the insertion of concentric electrodes in the brain stem. In some cats, a wider exposure of the cortex was accomplished for purposes of cortical stimulation. The subcortical electrodes were oriented with the Horsley–Clark stereotaxic instrument and ball silver cortical electrodes were held in place with a Grass cortical electrode holder.

In eight cats, records were obtained from the gracilis nucleus. In them, the medulla oblongata and the upper segments of the cervical cord were exposed and either bipolar (concentric) or fine monopolar electrodes were used for recording from the surface and various depths of the gracilis nucleus. The stimulating bipolar electrode was planted on the corresponding dorsal column about 16 to 20 millimeters below the site of the recording electrode.

In five cats, records from the sensory trigeminal nucleus were taken with bipolar concentric electrodes horizontally oriented with the stereotaxic instrument after adequate exposure of the medulla. A branch of the infraorbital nerve of the same side was carefully dissected free for stimulation in a pool of mineral oil made with the skin flap. Brain stem lesions were made by electrocoagulation between two electrodes bared 3 mm. at the tip.

In nine cats recordings were taken from the optic tract and from the lateral geniculate body with bipolar concentric electrodes stereotaxically oriented. Photic stimulation was applied with two General Radio Strobotax and Strobolux units. Flashes of constant intensity and duration (15 to 30 microseconds) were applied at a rate of 1 sec. or less. Photic stimulation was accomplished in the dark.

Stimulation and recording. The infraorbital nerve and the dorsal column were stimulated with rectangular pulses at regular intervals

(1 sec.) by synchronization with the sweep of the oscilloscope. Unless otherwise stated, the intensity of this test shock was submaximal. Short bursts of repetitive square pulses with a pulse duration of 1 msec. and a frequency of 50–100/sec. were used as conditioning stimulation during 0·25 to 3 seconds. The intensity used varied from 2·5 to 6 volts. A condenser-coupled amplifier and a cathode-ray oscilloscope were used for recording. In some cases, the cortical electrical activity was monitored with an electroencephalograph. At the completion of the experiment, the brain was fixed in formalin and the sites of recording, stimulation, and lesion, were subsequently determined from serial thionin-stained sections.

Results

Afferent evoked potentials in the gracilis nucleus

In records from the gracilis nucleus, either from the surface or from deeper layers, the potential evoked by an afferent volley from the dorsal column typically consists of several components (Figure 1): a primary positive spike approximately 0·4 msecs.

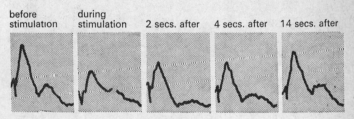

before stimulation   during stimulation   2 secs. after   4 secs. after   14 secs. after

200μV

1   5   10
-msec.

Figure 1. Recordings obtained from the gracilis nucleus to a single shock applied to the corresponding dorsal column. As a result of stimulating the mesencephalic reticular formation, a depression is observed both in the secondary and tertiary waves of the evoked potential, whereas the positive spike following the stimulus artifact remained unchanged

after the stimulus represents the arrival of the afferent volley from the dorsal column fibers. This first component is followed by a negative deflection with a latency of 1·2 msec. and a duration of about 3 msec. The secondary wave is the result of post-synaptic activity of gracilis nucleus neurons. Sometimes, this wave exhibited two peaks, as described by Therman (27); the second peak, as interpreted by the same author, probably corresponds to the relayed response of Hursh (17). Usually a third potential, either positive or negative, of variable amplitude and duration, appeared 6 to 12 msec. after the stimulus. This late component represents activity of the neighboring bulbar reticular formation, and in accord with this interpretation, it increased in amplitude as the electrode reached deeper levels of the nucleus, being maximal when the electrode tip contacted the reticular formation.

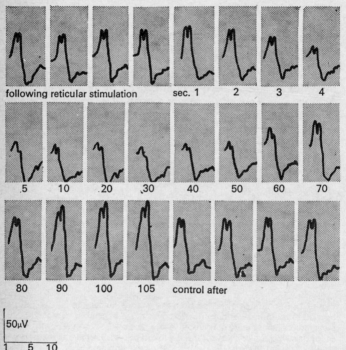

control before

following reticular stimulation   sec. 1   2   3   4

.5   10   .20   .30   40   50   60   70

80   90   100   105   control after

50μV

1   5   10
msec.

Figure 2. Evoked potentials from the gracilis nucleus (upward bi-peaked deflection) to an afferent volley from the dorsal column. The downward deflection represents the reticular potential. After the control series were taken, a short burst of stimuli (100/sec. for a period of 0·25 sec.) was applied to the mesencephalic reticular formation. The time sequence of the effect (depression, overshooting, and recovery) is shown after the end of the stimulation

R. Hernández-Peón, H. Scherrer and M. Velasco

Effects of brain-stem stimulation on gracilis nucleus potential

When the brain stem tegmentum was stimulated, either at the mesencephalic or at the pontine level, a depression was observed both in the secondary nuclear wave, as well as in the late reticular potential, whereas the pre-synaptic spike always remained unchanged. The time sequence of this blocking effect was, nevertheless, different for both components of the evoked potential: the

50μV

0   5   10
msec.

before reticular stimulation   after reticular stimulation   3 secs.
                               1 sec.

5 secs.   18 secs.   90 secs.

Figure 3. Dissociation effect of mesencephalic reticular stimulation upon the gracilis nucleus response (early bi-peaked potential) and the bulbar reticular potential (late rise)

reticular potential was usually immediately depressed; however, a lag from 1 to 3 seconds often elapsed between the onset of the stimulus and the commencement of the depression of the secondary wave, as shown in Figure 2. The nuclear depression was often long lasting. In the experiment illustrated in Figure 2, 70 seconds elapsed before complete recovery occurred. In favorable cases, a progressive diminution of the secondary wave was observed for several seconds. The maximal depression in the above-mentioned experiment occurred 30 seconds after the end of the stimulus. An overshooting of the secondary wave sometimes followed the depression, especially when the latter was maximal. Complete dissociation of the depressor effect in both

325

nuclear and reticular potentials was usually observed. The nuclear response could remain depressed at a time when the reticular component had recovered (Figure 3). In cases when extremely short bursts were applied, there was no detectable change in the reticular component, even though a marked de-

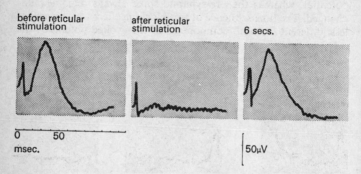

before reticular stimulation

after reticular stimulation

6 secs.

0   50
msec.

50μV

Figure 4. Same experiment as that of Figure 3 (recording from gracilis nucleus), but at a slower sweep speed. Between the upper and middle records the mesencephalic reticular formation was repeatedly stimulated several times in order to produce exhaustion of nuclear inhibition. The middle and lower records were taken one and six seconds respectively after the end of a 3-second period of stimulation of the mesencephalic reticular formation

pression was observed in the nuclear response (Figure 2). When the reticular formation was overactivated by several consecutive stimulations, the depressor effect upon the nuclear potential was no longer observable. This exhaustion lasted usually for several minutes for the depressor effect to be elicitable again. However, during this exhaustive period, the reticular potential could still be abolished by reticular stimulation, as shown in Figure 4.

Interaction at the bulbar level between reticular and dorsal column volleys

Since dissociation of the depressor effect in both the nuclear and reticular components of the evoked potential recorded at the gracilis nucleus, revealed two different mechanisms, further evidence was sought to clarify the nature of these phenomena. If an occlusion effect due to convergence of pathways is responsible for the blocking effect, a blocking interaction would be obtained by appropriate timing of a descending volley from higher portions of the reticular formation and the ascending afferent volley from the dorsal columns. Indeed, when the latter is preceded 25 to 30 msec. by a single shock applied to the pontine reticular formation, a maximal depression was observed in the bulbar reticular poten-tial, whereas the nuclear response remained unaffected.

Effects of cortical stimulation on gracilis nucleus potential

Since it has been shown that activation of sensorimotor cortex depresses afferent synaptic transmission at the spinal (9) and tri-geminal relays (10), the influence of this cortical area upon afferent transmission at the gracilis nucleus was also tested in these experiments. When a short burst of repetitive stimuli was applied to the sensorimotor cortex, depression of the secondary wave from the gracilis nucleus and abolition of the accompanying reticular potential were observed, which outlasted the stimulus for several seconds (Figure 5).

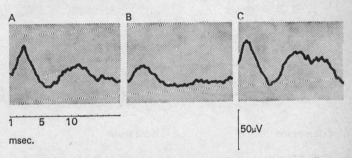

Figure 5. Evoked potentials recorded from gracilis nucleus to an afferent volley from the dorsal column. B and C were 8 and 15 seconds respectively after stimulating the posterior sigmoid gyrus for 3 seconds (100/sec.)

Effects of brain-stem lesions upon afferent transmission in trigeminal nucleus

Before the lesion was made, the potential evoked in the spinal fifth sensory nucleus by an afferent volley from the infraorbital nerve was recorded under two intensities of stimulation, i.e. liminal intensity near threshold values which evoked the smallest distinctive response, and maximal intensity, above which the amplitude of the trigeminal potential could not be increased. Figure 6 illustrates a typical experiment. After destruction of the midbrain tegmentum, which transformed the cortical electrical

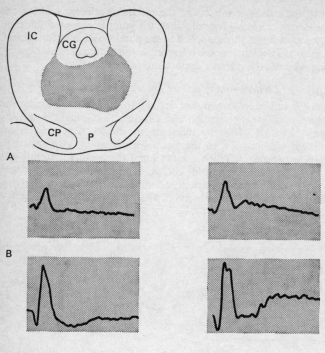

A

B

before lesion   after lesion

```
 1    5    10
 msec.
```

Figure 6. Effect of destroying the mesencephalic tegmentum (stippled area) on the evoked potential recorded from the spinal fifth sensory nucleus to an afferent volley from the infraorbital nerve. A. Liminal intensity of infraorbital stimulation. B. Maximal intensity of infraorbital stimulation

activity from a low voltage and fast frequency pattern to the classical spindling pattern of sleep, the secondary wave of the trigeminal potential elicited with the same liminal intensity used before the lesion, was remarkably enhanced, while the presynaptic spike was unchanged. The response to maximal intensity did not increase further in amplitude although the peak appeared to be slightly wider in duration. Very often, a late wave following

328

the nuclear trigeminal response appeared after the lesion, both with liminal and maximal intensities of stimulation. This long latency probably represents activity of the adjacent bulbar reticular formation. Since this wave appeared with liminal intensities after the lesion and was not present with maximal intensities before the lesion, it can hardly be related to the number of trigeminal units activated, and it may better be ascribed to enhanced excitability of the corresponding reticular neurones.

Effects of brain stem stimulation upon photically evoked potentials in optic tract, lateral geniculate body, and visual cortex

Potentials evoked by single flashes of light were usually multi-peaked, similar to those described by Bartley and Bishop (2) and Noell (26). The first wave of these potentials had a latency of 12 to 15 msec. Very often, three distinct waves appeared, but sometimes four or five waves were present. When the mesencephalic tegmentum was repetitively stimulated (100/sec.) a definite depression of the lateral geniculate potential was observed, and this depression was usually more marked for the late waves. The optic tract response presented two types of modifications by stimulating the brain stem; more often, as shown in Figure 7, a late-on wave was potentiated without apparent modification of the early-on waves; however, in some cases, depression of the optic tract potential was observed, particularly in the late induced activity. When potentiation appeared, it followed a different time sequence than the concomitant lateral geniculate depression. The potentiating effects usually lasted longer than the depressor effects (more than one minute after 2 or 3 seconds of reticular stimulation).

If brain stem activation depresses afferent conduction at the lateral geniculate as the foregoing experiments appear to demonstrate, it is logical to expect a diminution of the arriving sensory impulses to the visual cortical receiving area. Indeed, when the brain-stem tegmentum was stimulated, the photic potential recorded from the visual cortex of the convexity (lateral gyrus) was greatly reduced. In one case, the visual cortex was stimulated to test a possible cortical influence on lateral geniculate transmission. A remarkable reduction of the geniculate potential was observed, which outlasted the stimulation for more than 10 seconds.

329

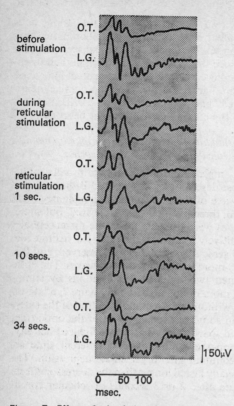

before
stimulation

during
reticular
stimulation

reticular
stimulation
1 sec.

10 secs.

34 secs.

O.T.

L.G.

O.T.

L.G.

O.T.

L.G.

O.T.

L.G.

O.T.

L.G.

]150μV

0   50 100
msec.

Figure 7. Effect of stimulating the mesencephalic reticular formation for 2 seconds (100/sec.) upon photically evoked potentials simultaneously recorded from the optic tract (O.T.) and lateral geniculate body (L.G.)

Effects of barbiturates on afferent conduction in somatic and visual pathways

Nembutal and pentothal yielded effects opposite to those obtained by stimulating the brain-stem tegmentum. Nembutal remarkably enhanced the secondary wave of the trigeminal nucleus potential, and a further enhancement could be observed after the interrupting lesions in the brain-stem reticular formation. The gracilis nucleus potential was similarly increased by a dose of nembutal which greatly depressed the mesencephalic reticular response to the same afferent volley from the dorsal column (Figure 8). It must be noted that the accompanying bulbar reticular potential recorded simultaneously from the gracilis nucleus was not depressed in amplitude, but on the contrary, it was markedly increased in duration. This observation indicates a difference in sensitivity to anesthetics between the mesencephalic and the bulbar reticular formation. Nembutal and pentothal also enhanced the lateral geniculate potential, even when the optic tract response was depressed. The same effect was observed after a lesion involving the brain-stem tegmentum.

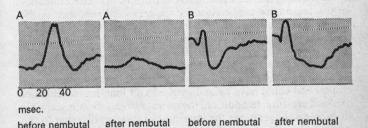

0   20   40

msec.

before nembutal   after nembutal   before nembutal   after nembutal

Figure 8. Potentials recorded : A from the mesencephalic reticular formation, and B from the gracilis nucleus to an afferent volley from the dorsal column. During nembutal anesthesia (30 mg./kg.), while the mesencephalic reticular response is depressed, the gracilis nucleus potential (upward deflection) is enhanced and the bulbar reticular potential (downward deflection) increases in duration

Discussion

The reported experiments demonstrate a blocking influence from the brain-stem reticular formation upon synaptic transmission of the dorsal column afferents at the gracilis nucleus. The synaptic effect is clearly shown by the reduction of the post-synaptic propagated potential, while the pre-synaptic impulses are not prevented from reaching the nucleus. The reduced activation of second-order neurons in the gracilis nucleus indicates lack of depolarization of the post-synaptic membrane, which could be the result of its hyperpolarization (inhibition) resulting from reticular activation, or of interference with the synaptic transmission process. The nature of this blocking effect on post-synaptic neurons appears to be due to a true inhibitory mechanism. Interaction of a descending reticular volley with the ascending dorsal column

volley indicates that an occlusion phenomenon is mainly responsible for the abolition of the reticular potential, whereas this
mechanism does not hold for the observed depression of the
nuclear response. It is obvious also, from the dissociation observed
in the blocking effects upon these two components of the evoked
potential that they correspond to two different mechanisms. The
possibility of backfiring from reticular stimulation – which could
make the second-order neurons refractory to orthodromic stimulation – can be disregarded in those experiments in which a long
lasting depression was observed as a result of an extremely short
stimulation. By the same token, an electrotonic field effect does not
seem a reasonable explanation for the temporal sequence in the
depression of the potential from second order neurons. It might be
argued that general synaptic depression resulting from changes in
blood pressure or from generalized sympathetic activation might
be responsible for the observed depression of the nuclear response.
However, it is highly improbable that stimulation for one quarter
of a second could have caused marked and long-lasting changes
of blood pressure. In addition, the neural systems most susceptible
to depressant agents are the internuncial systems like that in the
reticular formation. It is clear, as illustrated in Figure 2 that the
nuclear response could be maximally depressed with practically
no change of excitability in the neighboring reticular formation.
Therefore, a true inhibition remains as the most probable explanation for the nuclear afferent blockade. In their study of
spinal afferent conduction, Hagbarth and Kerr (9) suggested an
inhibitory mechanism to account for the similar depression that
they obtained by central stimulation. The present experiments
offer additional evidence in support of that interpretation.

The period of exhaustion following overstimulation of the
reticular formation always lasted for several minutes, during
which excitability of the reticular formation itself had already
recovered. In fact, during the exhaustion period, it is possible to
obtain reticular responses to afferent stimuli with the same
features as before reticular stimulation. This observation suggests
interference with the inhibitory mechanism, rather than with the
activation process of reticular neurons. Overshooting following
nuclear depression is probably related to the magnitude of nuclear
inhibition, since it was only readily observable after intense depression, but not after partial blockade of the nuclear potential.
The similar depressor effect observed by stimulating the sensorimotor cortex is probably the result of intense reticular activation
elicited by cortico-reticular projections (10). It may be predicted

that activation of other cortical areas which project to the brain-stem reticular formation (18, 4) will yield the same inhibitory effect on second-order neurons of all afferent somatic pathways. It is not clear from the present experiments whether all sensory modalities transmitted by dorsal column afferents can be influenced at their first relay station, since the unphysiological stimulus applied to the dorsal column prevents discrimination of the various modalities involved. It is classically accepted that the posterior columns carry proprioceptor, as well as cutaneous and pressure sensibilities. Recent evidence (19) suggests that the dorsal columns in the cat may also conduct pain signals. The descending inhibitory influence from the brain-stem reticular formation may constitute a mechanism whereby sensory messages of the above mentioned modalities may be prevented from reaching the level of consciousness. The same may hold true for sensory messages of pain, touch, and temperature conducted in the ventral columns. The present experiments do not provide evidence as to whether all the referred somatic sensory modalities are blocked simultaneously by the activation of this reticular inhibitory mechanism, or as to whether one of them at a time can be selectively blocked without impairment of the others. This interesting question deserves further experimentation. Selective sensory inhibition of the various somatic sensory modalities is not unlikely. In fact, a selective inhibitory influence has been shown in the cochlear nucleus for auditory stimuli to which the animal has become habituated (11, 13).

The findings of Hagbarth and Kerr (9) in the spinal cord, those of Hernández-Peón and Hagbarth (10) in the sensory trigeminal nucleus, and the present results on the gracilis nucleus, substantiate the idea that activation of the brain-stem reticular system blocks transmission of sensory messages in the three known specific somatic pathways as soon as sensory signals relay in the central nervous system.

The inhibitory influence on sensory transmission appears to act tonically during wakefulness, since it can be released by anesthetics as shown by Hagbarth and Kerr (9) in the spinal cord, and by the present experiments in the other somatic sensory relays at the medulla. The action of anesthetics in producing sleep can now be explained by their depressor effect on the brain-stem reticular system (6, 1), a region of the brain which is essential for wakefulness, as it has been abundantly supported by experimental evidence (25). The releasing effect of nembutal on inhibition at sensory relays, may also be accounted for by its depressor action on the reticular substance. Indeed, a lesion of this area of the brain results in a similar enhancement of afferent transmission. Therefore, the present experiments indicate that the brain-stem reticular system is involved in a tonic inhibitory influence for sensory conduction, but they do not tell us whether this inhibitory influence arises at this subcortical level, or whether it comes from higher structures and only passes through this region in its way to sensory relays. A suggestion that sensory inhibition may arise from brain-stem levels is provided by the finding of Lindblom and Ottosson (22) that a dorsal column potential recorded in the spinal cord of a decerebrate preparation is enhanced after high spinal transection. However, more experiments are necessary to elucidate completely this interesting question.

Our observations on the modification of optic tract potentials are in agreement with Granit's finding (8) that electrical stimulation of the reticular substance in the mesencephalic tegmentum may cause potentiation or inhibition of photically induced activity of some ganglion cells in the retina. The changes observed in optic tract potentials following reticular stimulation must be the result of modified activity in the retina, representing thus, centrifugal effects on that structure.

The depressor and enhancing effects observed by Granit (8), and by us, can be accounted for by assuming the existence of two different types of specific centrifugal fibers to the retina: inhibitory and potentiating fibers. This interpretation seems more logical than the alternative explanation of a single type of fiber producing both opposite effects. Although there is no conclusive anatomical evidence to support the first interpretation, Cajal (3) quotes that Dogiel (1895) claimed to have seen in birds two types of centrifugal fibers in the retina, with different modes of termination. Cajal described the termination of centrifugal fibers in the retina, mainly around association amacrine cells connected to ordinary amacrine cells which in turn articulate with ganglion cells, and with arborizations of bipolar cells. He further suggested a possible indirect influence of centrifugal fibers upon the articulation of cones and rods with bipolar cells. From the described anatomical observations, it appears that at least one of the centrifugal effects observed upon the retina, acts at the first sensory synapse. In this respect, the resemblance is evident with the described mechanism influencing afferent conduction at the first synapse of the somatic pathway. It is possible yet, that there might be another centrifugal mechanism acting at the receptor

R. Hernández-Peón, H. Scherrer and M. Velasco

level (or else, at the neuroreceptor junction) in the retina, like those described for proprioceptors (muscle spindles) (21, 16), certain tactile receptors (24) and auditory receptors (7).

In addition to these peripheral effects, the present results indicate a depressor action of the brain-stem reticular formation upon transmission at the lateral geniculate body, since it cannot be explained otherwise, when there is no simultaneous depression of the incoming afferent impulses from the optic tract. The temporal sequence and long-lasting duration of the depression of lateral geniculate neurons after reticular stimulation, as well as the tonic nature of this depressive influence which is released by anesthesia or brain stem lesion, favor the view that this depression represents a true physiological inhibitory process, and is not the result of a post-excitatory refractoriness consecutive to anti-dromic activation produced by our non-physiological electrical stimulation.

The important question arises as to what is the functional role of these central mechanisms influencing afferent transmission at the retina, and at the thalamic relay of the visual pathway.

Recent evidence obtained from the auditory pathway indicates that a similar inhibitory mechanism, which requires functional integrity of the brain-stem reticular system, acts during two physiological situations: 'habituation' and 'attention'. Auditory potentials recorded from the dorsal cochlear nucleus are reduced or abolished during acoustic habituation produced by repeating the same acoustic stimulus (11, 13), and also during attention elicited by visual, olfactory or somatic stimuli (12). More recent experiments (15) indicate that sensory inhibition at the lateral geniculate body is set in action by photic habituation. Indeed, in unanesthetized unrestrained animals, repetition of the same photic stimulus results in diminution of potentials recorded from the lateral geniculate body and visual cortex without reduction of the optic tract potential, and this inhibition is released by nem-butal anesthesia. Other experiments (14) have demonstrated that photic potentials recorded from optic tract, lateral geniculate body, and visual cortex, are reduced or abolished during attentive behavior elicited by an acoustic or olfactory stimulus, and also by electrical stimulation of the mesencephalic reticular formation. It appears that this effect is exerted by inhibitory centrifugal fibers to the retina, and that their functional role, therefore, is to block sensory impulses during attention, preventing them from entering the brain, and from interfering with the neural mechanisms of integration occurring during that psychological situation.

It remains to be determined yet, what is the functional role of the centrifugal potentiating influence upon the retina.

Summary

In curarized cats it has been shown that the brain stem reticular system modifies afferent transmission in the somatic and visual pathways as follows:

1. Electrical stimulation of the mesencephalic or pontine reticular formation, as well as of the sensorimotor cortex depressed or abolished the secondary wave of the evoked potential from the gracilis nucleus representing activity of second order neurons of this nucleus. The pre-synaptic spike was unchanged, however.

2. Overstimulation of the reticular formation causes a period of exhaustion which lasts for several minutes during which sensory synaptic depression is not longer elicitable.

3. A lesion involving exclusively the mesencephalic reticular formation – and which brought about a sleeping pattern of the electrical cortical activity – resulted in an increase of the secondary wave of the potential recorded from the trigeminal sensory nucleus, the pre-synaptic spike remaining unchanged. A similar effect was produced by nembutal anesthesia.

4. Electrical stimulation of the mesencephalic reticular formation and visual cortex depressed photic potentials recorded from the lateral geniculate body. In addition, reticular stimulation yielded either potentiation or depression of the optic tract potential. During nembutal anesthesia the optic tract potential was diminished, and the lateral geniculate potential was enhanced.

It is concluded: (a) That activation of the brain-stem reticular system inhibits sensory transmission at the gracilis nucleus, at the lateral geniculate body and at the retina, similarly to what has been previously shown at the spinal cord and at the spinal fifth sensory nucleus. Potentiation can also be produced at the retina. The observed effects upon the retina are thought to be mediated by centrifugal fibers to that structure. (b) That sensory inhibition upon the first somatic sensory synapses and upon the thalamic visual synapse is acting tonically during wakefulness, and requires functional integrity of the brain-stem reticular system.

References

1. ARDUINI, A. and ARDUINI, M. G.: Effect of drugs and metabolic alterations on brain stem arousal mechanism. *J. Pharmacol. Exp. Therap.*, 1954, 110:76–85.
2. BREMER, D. H. and BISHOP, G. H.: Some features of the optic-nerve discharge in the rabbit and cat. *J. cell. comp. Physiol.*, 1942, 19:79–93.
3. CAJAL, S. R.: *Histologie du système nerveux de l'Homme et des vertébrés.* 1911, Paris, A. Maloine.
4. FRENCH, J. D., HERNÁNDEZ-PEÓN, R. and LIVINGSTON, R. B.: Projections from cortex to cephalic brain stem (reticular formation) in monkey. *J. Neurophysiol.*, 1955, 18:74–95.
5. FRENCH, J. D. and MAGOUN, H. W.: Effects of chronic lesions in central cephalic brain stem of monkeys. *Arch. Neurol. Psychiat.*, 1952, 68:591–604.
6. FRENCH, J. D., VERZEANO, M. and MAGOUN, H. W.: A neural basis for the anesthetic state. *Arch. Neurol. Psychiat.*, 1953, 69:519–29.
7. GALAMBOS, R.: Suppression of auditory nerve activity by stimulation of efferent fibers to the cochlea. *Fed. Proc.*, 1955, 14:53.
8. GRANIT, R.: Centrifugal and antidromic effects on ganglion cells of retina. *J. Neurophysiol.*, 1955, 18:388–411.
9. HAGBARTH, K. E. and KERR, D. I. B.: Central influences on spinal afferent conduction. *J. Neurophysiol.*, 1954, 17:295–307.
10. HERNÁNDEZ-PEÓN, R., and HAGBARTH, K. E.: Interaction between afferent and cortically induced reticular responses. *J. Neurophysiol.*, 1955, 18:44–55.
11. HERNÁNDEZ-PEÓN, R. and SCHERRER, H.: 'Habituation' to acoustic stimuli in cochlear nucleus. *Fed. Proc.*, 1955, 14:71.
12. HERNÁNDEZ-PEÓN, R., SCHERRER, H. and JOUVET, M.: Modification of electrical activity in the cochlear nucleus during 'attention' in unanesthetized cats. *Science*, in press.
13. HERNÁNDEZ-PEÓN, R., JOUVET, M. and SCHERRER, H.: Auditory transmission and neural mechanisms of 'habituation' to acoustic stimuli in the cochlear nucleus, in press.
14. HERNÁNDEZ-PEÓN, R., GUZMAN-FLORES, C., ALCARAZ, M. and FERNANDEZ-GUARDIOLA, A.: Sensory transmission in the visual pathway during 'attention', in press.
15. HERNÁNDEZ-PEÓN, R., GUZMAN-FLORES, C., ALCARAZ, M. and FERNANDEZ-GUARDIOLA, A.: Modification of sensory transmission in the visual pathway by photic habituation, in press.
16. HUNT, C. C.: Muscle stretch receptors; peripheral mechanisms and reflex function. *Cold Spring Harbor Symposia on Quantitative Biology.*, 1952, 17:113–23.
17. HURSH, J. B.: Relay impulses in ascending branches of dorsal root fibers. *J. Neurophysiol.*, 1940, 3:166–74.
18. JASPER, H. H., AJMONE-MARSAN, C. and STOLL, J.: Corticofugal projections to the brain stem. *Arch. Neurol. Psychiat.*, 1952, 67:155–66.
19. KENNARD, M. A.: The course of ascending fibers in the spinal cord of the cat essential to recognition of painful stimuli. *J. comp. Neurol.*, 1954, 100:511–24.

20. KING, E. E., NAQUET, R. and MAGOUN, H. W.: Alterations in somatic afferent transmission through thalamus by central mechanisms and barbiturates, in press.

21. KUFFLER, S. W. and HUNT, C. C.: The mammalian small-nerve fibers: a system for efferent nervous regulation of muscle spindle discharge. *Res. Publ. Ass. nerv. ment. Dis.*, 1952, **30**:24–47.

22. LINDBLOM, U. F. and OTTOSSON, J. O.: Effects of spinal sections on the spinal cord potentials elicited by stimulation of low threshold cutaneous fibers. *Acta physiol. Scand.*, 1953, **29** (Suppl. 106):191–208.

23. LINDSLEY, D. B., SCHREINER, L. H., KNOWLES, W. B. and MAGOUN, H. W.: Behavioral and EEG changes following chronic brain-stem lesions in the cat. *Electroenceph. clin. Neurophysiol.*, 1950, **2**:483–98.

24. LOEWENSTEIN, W. R.: Facilitation in a tactile receptor due to sympathetic stimulation. *Fed. Proc.*, 1955, **14**:94–5.

25. MAGOUN, H. W.: The ascending reticular system and wakefulness. In *Brain Mechanisms and Consciousness.* ed., J. F. Delafresnaye, 1954. Oxford, Blackwell Scientific publ., pp. 1–20.

26. NOELL, W. K.: *Studies on the Electrophysiology and the Metabolism of the Retina*, project no. 21–1201–0004, Report no. 1, Air University U.S.A.F. School of Aviation Medicine, Randolph Field, Texas, 1953.

27. THERMAN, P. O.: Transmission of impulses through the Burdach nucleus. *J. Neurophysiol.*, 1941, **4**:153–66.

18 D. N. Spinelli and K. H. Pribram

Changes in Visual Recovery Functions Produced by
Temporal Lobe Stimulation in Monkeys

D. N. Spinelli and K. H. Pribram, 'Changes in visual recovery functions
produced by temporal lobe stimulation in monkeys', *EEG Clin. Neurophysiol.*, vol. 20 (1966), pp. 44–9.

Introduction

Agnosia, an inability to identify objects due to brain injury, is a
clinical syndrome of central interest to an understanding of
cognitive processes. To advance this interest, an attempt was
made to produce the syndrome in animals and this attempt
proved successful: monkeys with partial ablations of the posterior
'association' cortex have been shown impaired either in visual
(Blum *et al.*, 1950; Mishkin and Pribram, 1954), somesthetic
(Pribram and Barry, 1956; Wilson, 1957), auditory (Mishkin and
Weiskrantz, 1958), or gustatory (Bagshaw and Pribram, 1953)
discriminations depending on the locus of the lesion. In each case,
it was established by the technique of the intersect of sums of
lesions and effects (Pribram, 1954) that the effect of the lesion
was modality specific; i.e. the ablation which disrupted visual
behaviour had no effect on somesthetic, auditory, and taste discrimination; the ablation which disrupted somesthetic behavior
had no effect on visual behavior, etc. Thus the so-called 'association' cortex of monkey turned out to be divisible into areas, each
of which served one or another specific sensory mode.[1]

These impairments were analyzed further and were shown to
involve both an apparent loss of acuity (Mishkin and Hall, 1955;
Pasik *et al.*, 1958a, b) and a difficulty in making the appropriate
response to readily discriminable cues (Pribram and Mishkin,
1955; Ettlinger, 1959a). The suggestion was therefore made that

1. The so-called association cortex of man and monkey which is referred
to here is that part of the cortex which is 'silent' when electrical responses
are evoked elsewhere by peripheral stimulation. For this reason and others,
the primate 'association' areas are thought to be different from the 'association' cortices recently described for the cat in the electrophysiological
literature. These latter electrophysiologically-determined areas appear to be
true multisensory afferent association systems. The primate cortex referred
to here might better be called 'intrinsic' (see Pribram 1960) or 'associated'
areas but for convenience will continue to be labeled 'association', the
quotation marks indicating the apparent impropriety of this appellation.

the difficulty was manifested in searching and selecting, both among alternative cues (Pribram, 1960) and among the distinctive features of a single cue (Butter *et al.*, 1965; Butter, *in preparation*). Experimental results have amply confirmed the hypotheses derived from this suggestion.

The dilemma posed by these neurobehavioral data can be stated briefly. Anatomically, the lesions which produce the effects are limited to association cortex; i.e. they remain clear of the classical projection areas. This is ascertained by the fact that retrograde degeneration in the primary projection nuclei of the thalamus does not occur. Yet the effects of ablation are sensory mode specific. The question thus arises how this modality-specific function is effected. The attempt to attribute the specificity to a restricted input from one or another sensory system meets with difficulties which are as yet not resolved. Lesions of input fibers, whether at the thalamic or cortico-cortical level, fail as a rule to disrupt discrimination. The one exception is the total isolation of the 'association' cortex from ipsi- and contralateral input by ipsilateral sensory nerve section or sensory cortex resection and additional severance of the corpus callosum (Mishkin, 1958; Ettlinger, 1959b).

An alternative and complementary approach to the dilemma of sensory mode specificity of the association areas is that they exert their influence via a corticofugal, efferent pathway which alters the functional activity of the primary sensory system (Pribram, 1958). According to this approach, the effects of the removal or of the stimulation of the visual association cortex, for instance, would be selectively discernible in the primary visual system; the removal or stimulation of the auditory association cortex would be selectively discernible in the primary auditory system, etc. The purpose of the experiments reported here was to take some initial steps to test whether indeed such efferent control by 'association' cortex over primary projection systems can be demonstrated. Specifically, in fully awake monkeys uninterrupted, continuous electrical stimulation was applied via electrodes bilaterally implanted in the visual association area which lies on the inferior surface of the temporal lobe. The effects of such stimulation were assayed by recording responses to flash and to click from other arrays of electrodes implanted in the primary visual and in the primary auditory cortical areas. The effects of the inferotemporal stimulation were compared with those from stimulations of other cortical areas, and with the responses obtained in the pre-stimulated condition. Finally, we tested the

effect of continuous stimulation on the learning of two discrimination tasks.

Method

A transistorized stimulation device was implanted in 5 rhesus
monkeys. This consisted of a transistorized blocking oscillator
powered by 2 nickel–cadmium rechargeable batteries. Leads from
the plus and the minus of the batteries are connected to a plug
that is secured with dental cement to the skull of the animal.
Through these leads the batteries can be recharged when needed.
To the plug are also connected the output of the stimulator, the
center tap of the transformer and the electrodes implanted in the
structures to be stimulated. The stimulator itself is buried in the
cement and delivers bipolar pulses of 1 msec. duration, 2·5 V.
amplitude, the frequency of the pulses being determined by R_1
(10 p/sec. when R_1 is 120,000 Ω) and is activated by connecting
the minus of the battery with the center tap of the transformer.
This is done externally with a male plug which also connects the
output of the stimulator with the appropriate stimulating electrodes. The life of the batteries depends on the desired frequency
and it is of the order of 10 weeks for a frequency rate of 1/sec.

The stimulus parameters used in the experiments were: 9/sec.,
1 msec. duration, 2·5 V. amplitude. In addition, 300 μ nicrome
wire bipolar electrodes with an interelectrode distance of approximately 3 mm. were implanted in the parietal, temporal, and
occipital cortices of these animals.

Recordings were made in unanesthetized, completely awake
monkeys sitting in a restraining chair. Pairs of flashes, of clicks,
and of click-flashes and flash-clicks were presented at the rate of
1/sec. Fifty consecutive responses were recorded on magnetic
tape and, for analysis, accumulated on a Computer for Average
Transients (CAT).

Polaroid photographs were made from a slave scope which was
ganged to the output of the computer. From these photographs
recovery functions were computed, each point on the function
indicating the ratio (expressed as per cent) between the second
and the first response evoked by the pair of flashes. Measurements
were made on the first major deflection recorded.

Experimental monkeys received continuous stimulation in the
inferior temporal cortex; control subjects were given continuous
stimulation in the parietal and precentral regions.

In addition, 3 monkeys were tested in a simple and in a more complex visual discrimination situation. The apparatus used was a special purpose computer (DADTA) (Pribram *et al.*, 1962) designed to randomize over 16 possible positions the cues to be discriminated. Rewards (peanuts) were delivered according to a preset program whenever the correct choice was made by the monkey. Each choice was recorded on tape for easy general purpose computer processing. Each monkey was allowed 50 choices per day until he solved the discrimination problem. Solution of the problem consisted of a performance level of 90 per cent on 100 consecutive choices; i.e. two days.

The first problem consisted of a choice between the numerals 3 and 8. The second required discrimination of the letter M from the set of letters M K H N A.

Results

The results are portrayed in a representative record (Figure 1) and in plots of recovery function (Figures 2 and 3). Figure 2 shows the change in recovery of visual system of one monkey

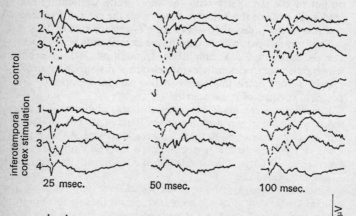

Figure 1. A representative record of the change produced in visual evoked responses by chronic stimulation of the inferotemporal cortex. Upper set of records was taken before stimulation; lower set, during stimulation. All traces were recorded from the visual cortex; in the first column are responses produced by a pair of flashes separated by 25 msec.; flash separation is 50 msec. in the second column and 100 msec. in the third

when pairs of flashes are presented and the inferotemporal cortex is stimulated. Each point on the graph represents the average of 4 electrode placements and therefore of 200 evoked responses. Figure 3 shows the group changes obtained in the experiment. Each point on the graph of the pre stimulation and experimental

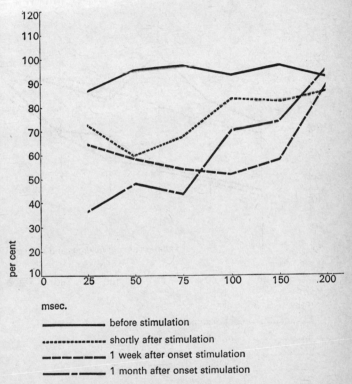

Figure 2. A plot of the recovery functions obtained in one monkey before and during chronic stimulation of the inferotemporal (I.T.) cortex

results represents the average obtained from 20 electrode placements (and therefore 1,000 evoked responses) in 5 monkeys; each point on the graph of the control results represents the average obtained from 8 electrode placements in 2 monkeys and therefore 400 evoked responses. (Two of the monkeys served first as controls and subsequently as experimental subjects.) The extent of the variability is shown by the bars perpendicular to the recovery function.

At 25 msec. the spread of variability among the unstimulated Ss was great. For some monkeys the initial response to the second flash, super-imposed on a large wave, which is continuous with

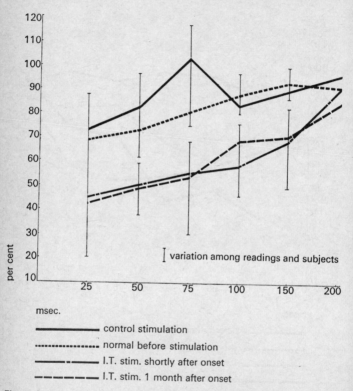

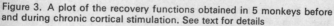

per cent

msec.

——————— control stimulation

················· normal before stimulation

———·——— I.T. stim. shortly after onset

————————— I.T. stim. 1 month after onset

Figure 3. A plot of the recovery functions obtained in 5 monkeys before and during chronic cortical stimulation. See text for details

the initial response evoked by the first flash, was hardly appreciable. Other monkeys, however, showed a clear and measurable separation between the responses evoked by the two flashes – and two of these monkeys showed remarkably good recovery even at this short interval. At 50 msec. there was a clearly discernible second response in all Ss with moderate to excellent recovery. By

100 msec. recovery was almost complete. Extreme variability among Ss at the short intervals (25 msec. or less) has also been reported to be present in man (Schwartz and Shagass, 1964). This *inter*subject variability was in marked contrast to the stability shown by any one subject (unstimulated) on successive runs, even though these were made weeks apart.

Effects of continuous inferotemporal stimulation on the click-evoked recovery functions was also studied in the same monkeys and no reliable changes were observed to take place. On the other hand, in two monkeys the click-evoked response *per se* gradually increased in amplitude over the month of chronic, continuous stimulation. A similar increase in amplitude was observed in visually evoked responses in one of these subjects and in another whose auditory response showed no such change. Click-flash and flash-click interactions did not occur nor did chronic, continuous stimulation influence this non-occurrence.

In summary, the results of this series of experiments show that recovery of responses evoked in the occipital cortex by pairs of flashes is depressed by continuous stimulation of the infero-temporal 'association' cortex. This depression lasts over at least 2 months of continuous stimulation. No such effect was seen on responses evoked in the posterior part of the supratemporal plane by pairs of clicks nor did continuous stimulation of parietal cortex influence visual and auditory recovery functions.

During this period of continuous stimulation both discrimination tasks were learned with alacrity. Comparison with a control group of monkeys shows the stimulated monkeys to be normal in achieving solution on both tasks (Table 1).

Table 1

Trials to Criterion Taken by Control Monkeys and by Monkeys in which the Inferotemporal Cortex was Stimulated

Control monkeys			Stimulated monkeys		
	Trials			Trials	
Subject	3 v. 8	M v. K, H, N, A	Subject	3 v. 8	M v. K, H, N, A
160	280	800	156	50	375
162	180	400	183	200	700
165	280	550	198	199	550
170	350	700			
Average	272	612		183	542

Discussion

The results of this series of experiments demonstrate that the inferotemporal, and not other parts of the posterior 'association' cortex, exerts control on the visual system. Further, this control is not effected on auditory responses.

Another series of experiments performed in our laboratory has pursued the problem of association cortex control over auditory functions (Dewson, Nobel, and Pribram, 1966). These experiments were performed in awake cats who had electrodes implanted in their cochlear nuclei. The insular-temporal area was removed in these subjects. In prior experiments (Dewson, 1964) such removal had resulted in a selective inability to discriminate vowel sounds; pitch and loudness discrimination remained intact. Bilateral removal of insular-temporal cortex was found to speed up response recovery in the cochlear nucleus when the cat was presented with paired clicks. Thus removal of the 'association' cortex produces effects opposite to those found to occur in the present experiment upon continuous stimulation.

In a subsequent experiment this cortical influence on responses in the cochlear nucleus was shown to be mediated via an efferent path synapsing in the inferior colliculus (Nobel and Dewson, 1966). In the present experiments, therefore, the efferent control exerted by the inferotemporal cortex in monkey must not be assumed to influence directly the cells of the occipital cortex – an influence via a tract leading to some subcortical station such as the superior colliculus remains a distinct possibility to be explored experimentally.

The nature of the control on visual function is to produce a delay in the recovery function obtained when records are made of responses in the visual cortex to pairs of flashes. If one is allowed the assumption that the percent recovery obtained with gross (albeit small gross) electrodes reflects accurately the functions of the cell aggregate from which the record is made, a model can be usefully described. This model assumes that recovery functions measure the rate with which nerve cells, after being excited, again become available to stimulation. As the primary visu..l system is continuously functioning, a delay of recovery would mean that some of the cells remain 'occupied' for a longer time and that each new stimulus thus finds fewer cells available. This would, in effect, reduce the redundancy with which the system operates. In another context Lindsley (1961) has suggested that this de-coupling of the functions of cell aggregates is reflected in a de-

D. N. Spinelli and K. H. Pribram

synchronization of their electrical activity and that such desynchronization is evidence of an increased complexity of operation of the system.

There are many experimental results which suggest that under normal circumstances the visual system operates with a considerable reserve redundancy in handling inputs made to it (Attneave, 1954). The proposal has been made (Barlow, 1961) that one of the chief functions of the central visual mechanism is to reduce redundancy. We interpret our results to be in consonance with the hypothesis that ablation results in greater redundancy while both continuous stimulation of the inferotemporal cortex and the normal ordinary activity of this cortex facilitates redundancy reduction. This would be accomplished by the process which keeps some cells in the system 'occupied' for a prolonged time with the result that iterated visual inputs find different populations of cells 'receptive'. Such a process would effectively desynchronize and multiplex the visual channel and thus increase complexity and 'uncertainty' within the system, making the organism more attentive to alternatives.

The excellent discrimination problem-solving ability of the stimulated animals in this study and the marked deficiencies in search and sampling alternatives that follow ablation of the inferotemporal cortex support the formulation presented. According to this model then, pathology of the 'association' cortex – by producing, via efferent pathways, a simplification of the structure of the sensory processing channel – would result in agnosia.

Summary

The effect of continuous stimulation of the inferotemporal portion of the posterior 'association' cortex on potential changes evoked in a primary sensory projection area was studied and changes were found to occur. Further, these changes were found to be restricted to one sensory mode. Lastly, the changes were of such a nature that they permit a model of the action of this system to be suggested.

References

ATTNEAVE, F. (1954), 'Some informational aspects of visual perception', *Psychol. Rev.*, vol. 61, pp. 183–93.

BAGSHAW, M. H., and PRIBRAM, K. H. (1953), 'Cortical organization of gustation (Macaca mulatta)', *J. Neurophysiol.*, vol. 16, pp. 499–508.

Cognition and the Agnosias

BARLOW, H. P. (1961), 'Possible principles underlying the transformations of sensory messages', in W. Rosenblith (ed.), *Sensory Communication*, Wiley, pp. 217–34.

BLUM, J. S., CHOW, K. L., and PRIBRAM, K. H. (1950), 'A behavioral analysis of the organization of the parieto-temporo-preoccipital cortex', *J. comp. Neurol.*, vol. 93, pp. 53–100.

BUTTER, C. M., MISHKIN, M., and ROSVOLD, H. E. (1965), 'Stimulus generalization in monkeys with inferotemporal lesions and lateral occipital lesions', in D. I. Mostofsky (ed.), *Stimulus Generalization*, Stanford University Press, pp. 119–33.

CHOW, K. L. (1964), 'Further studies on selective ablation of associative cortex in relation to visually mediated behavior', *J. comp. physiol. Psychol.*, vol. 45, pp. 109–18.

DEWSON, J. H., III (1964), 'Speech sound discrimination by cats', *Science*, vol. 444, pp. 555–6.

DEWSON, J. H., III, NOBEL, K. W., and PRIBRAM, K. H. (1966), 'Corticofugal influence at cochlear of the cat: some effects of ablation of insular-temporal cortex', *Brain Research*, vol. 2, pp. 151–9.

ETTLINGER, G. (1959a), 'Visual discrimination with a single manipulandum following temporal ablations in the monkey', *Quart. J. exp. Psychol.*, vol. 3, pp. 164–74.

ETTLINGER, G. (1959b), 'Visual discrimination following successive temporal ablations in monkeys', *Brain*, vol. 82, pp. 232–50.

LINDSLEY, D. B. (1961), 'The reticular activating system and perceptual integration', in D. E. Sheer (ed.), *Electrical Stimulation of the Brain*, University of Texas Press, pp. 331–49.

MISHKIN, M. (1958), 'Visual discrimination impairment after cutting cortical connections between the inferotemporal and striate areas in monkeys', *Amer. Psychologist*, vol. 13, p. 414.

MISHKIN, M. and HALL, M. (1955), 'Discriminations along a size continuum following ablation of the inferior temporal convexity in monkeys', *J. comp. physiol. Psychol.*, vol. 48, pp. 97–101.

MISHKIN, M., and PRIBRAM, K. H. (1954), 'Visual discrimination performance following partial ablations of the temporal lobe: 1. Ventral *vs* lateral', *J. comp. physiol. Psychol.*, vol. 47, pp. 14–20.

MISHKIN, M., and WEISKRANTZ, L. (1958), 'Effects of delaying reward on discrimination performance of monkeys with frontal lesions', *J. comp. physiol. Psychol.*, vol. 51, pp. 276–81.

NOBEL, K. W., and DEWSON, J. H., III (1966), 'A corticofugal projection from insular and temporal cortex to the homolateral inferior colliculus in cat', *J. aud. Research.*, vol. 6, pp. 67–75.

PASIK, P., PASIK, T., BATTERSBY, W. S., and BENDER, M. B. (1958a), 'Visual and tactual discrimination by Macaques with serial temporal and parietal lesions', *J. comp. physiol. Psychol.*, vol. 51, pp. 427–36.

PASIK, T., PASIK, P., BATTERSBY, W. S., and BENDER, M. (1958b), 'Target size and visual form discrimination in monkeys with bitemporal lesions', *Fed. Proc.*, vol. 17, p. 481.

PRIBRAM, H. B., and BARRY, J. (1956), 'Further behavioral analysis of the parieto-temporal-preoccipital cortex', *J. Neurophysiol.*, vol. 19, pp. 99–106.

PRIBRAM, K. H. (1954), 'Toward a science of neuropsychology (method and data)', in R. A. Patton (ed.), *Current Trends in Psychology and the Behavioral Sciences*, University of Pittsburgh Press, pp. 115–42.

PRIBRAM, K. H. (1958), 'Neocortical function in behaviour', in H. F. Harlow (ed.), *Biological and Biochemical Bases of Behavior*, University of Wisconsin Press, pp. 151–72.

PRIBRAM, K. H. (1960), 'The intrinsic systems of the forebrain', in J. Field *et al.*, (ed.), *Handbook of Physiology, Sect. 1*, Amer. Physiol Soc., Washington, vol. 2, pp. 1323–44.

PRIBRAM, K. H., GARDNER, K. W., PRESSMAN, G. L., and BAGSHAW, M. (1962), 'An automated discrimination apparatus for discrete trial analysis (DADTA)', *Psychol. Rep.*, vol. 11, pp. 247–50.

PRIBRAM, K. H., and MISHKIN, M. (1955), 'Simultaneous and successive visual discrimination by monkeys with inferotemporal lesions', *J. comp. physiol. Psychol.*, vol. 48, pp. 198–202.

SCHWARTZ, M., and SHAGASS, C. (1964), 'Recovery functions of human somatosensory and visual evoked potentials', *Ann. N.Y. Acad. Sci.*, vol. 112, pp. 510–46.

WILSON, M. (1957), 'Effects of circumscribed cortical lesions upon somesthetic discrimination in the monkey', *J. comp. physiol. Psychol.*, vol. 50, pp. 630–5.

Part Four Motor Function and Action

By what machinery does the organism act on its environment? One of the most exciting moments in the history of brain research occurred when Fritsch and Hitzig, by applying an electrical stimulus to the brain cortex, elicited movement. The following papers show the steady progress in understanding this effect: progress through experiment, controversy and analysis.

19 G. Fritsch and E. Hitzig

On the Electrical Excitability of the Cerebrum

Excerpt from G. Fritsch and E. Hitzig, 'Über die elektrische Erregbarkeit des Grosshirns (On the electrical excitability of the cerebrum)', *Archiv. f. Wissenschaftliche Medizin*, 1870, pp. 300–32. Translated from the German for this edition by D. Harris.

[. . .] The starting point of the present investigations were observations one of us had the opportunity to make on human subjects (1), which concerned the first movements of voluntary muscles produced and observed after direct stimulation of the central organs. It was found quite easy to obtain eye movements by leading constant galvanic currents through the posterior part of the head, movements which in their very nature could only have been provoked by direct stimulation of cerebral centres. Inasmuch as these movements occurred only after galvanization of a certain area of the head, as mentioned above, numerous factors suggested that they were caused by stimulation of the corpora quadrigemina or adjacent parts. However, since similar eye movements occurred after galvanization of the temporal region, after application of certain techniques capable of increasing the excitability, the question arose whether in the latter case loops of current penetrating down to the base caused the eye movements or whether the cerebrum possessed after all – contrary to the generally accepted views – a certain electrical excitability.

After preliminary experiments carried out by one of us on rabbits produced a generally positive result, we chose the following method to settle this point:

In the first experiments the animals (dogs) were not narcotized, but later the skull was trephined under narcosis, on an as far as possible plane area. The whole half of the calvaria, or only the part of it covering the anterior lobe of the brain, was then removed by means of cutting bone with forceps with rounded tips. In most cases the procedure was repeated exactly with the other half of the calvaria after one of the hemispheres had been used up. After we had lost a dog by exsanguination due to a slight injury of the longitudinal sinus we left in all cases a median bony bridge intact, which protected the above vessel. Now a slight incision was made in the hitherto untouched dura mater, and the latter was grasped with forceps and removed up to the edges of the bone. During this procedure the dogs showed signs of great pain by cries and characteristic reflex movements. Later, however, after exposure for some time to the stimulating effect of the open air, the dura mater becomes much more sensitive, a fact that must be taken into account in the arrangement of experiments involving stimulation. On the other hand, injury of the pia mater by mechanical and/or other stimuli, evoked no signs of pain.

The electrical apparatus used for stimulation was arranged as follows: The poles of a battery of ten Daniell cells were led via a commutator to the terminals of a Pohl turnover switch from which the cross had been removed. Wires leading the current of a secondary induction coil ended in the two opposite terminals. Two wires led from the middle pair of terminals to a rheostat included as a shunt, with a resistance of 0–2,100 S.U. The main circuit continued via a du Bois key to two small isolated cylindrical terminals carrying the electrodes in the form of very thin platinum wires ending in small knobs. These platinum wires run through two pieces of cork, the forward of the two pieces being bored so as to obtain two slightly non-parallel channels, as a result of which the distance between the knobs could be easily altered by a small movement of the cork. As a rule, this distance measured 2–3 mm. It was necessary to ensure that the platinum wires moved with only slight mechanical resistance and to provide them with the knobs mentioned above, as otherwise any trembling of the hand or even the respiratory movements of the brain itself could have led to injuries of the soft mass of the central organ.

The battery used by us consisted of tar-paper cells produced by Siemens and Halske, which had – as shown by earlier investigation – less than the full e.m.f. of a Daniell cell and a resistance of 5 S.U. The resistance of the shunt circuit was generally rather low, measuring between 30 and 40 S.U. The current was so weak that touching the tongue with an electrode produced only a slight sensation. Much higher currents and exclusion of the shunt circuit were used only in control experiments. In the much smaller number of experiments in which we used induction currents, the resistance of the shunt circuit naturally depended on the given position of the induction coils. Here too we used for most of the experiments just currents of sufficient strength to cause a slight sensation on the tongue.

Using this method we obtained the following results, presented here as the outcome of a very high number of experiments on the brain of dogs, consistent down to the smallest detail without going into detailed description of each separate experiment. In view of the exact description of the method, and taking into account some factors to be mentioned below, it is in any case so easy to reproduce our experiments that we shall not have to wait very long for their confirmation.

Part of the convexity of the cerebrum in the dog is of motor character (this expression is used in Schiff's sense) and another part of non-motor character.

Generally speaking, the motor part is situated more in the anterior and the non-motor part more in the posterior regions. Electrical stimulation of the motor part can produce combined muscle contractions in the contralateral half of the body.

If very weak currents are used, these muscular contractions can be localized to certain narrowly defined groups of muscles. With stronger currents, stimulation of the same or closely adjacent spots immediately leads to the participation of other muscles, including those of the corresponding half of the body. Using very weak currents, however, the possibility of exciting a well-defined group of muscles is limited to very small spots which may be called centres for the sake of brevity. A very slight shift in the position of the electrode still causes movement in the same extremity, but if initially the stimulus caused extension, for example now, after the change of position flexure or rotation would be evoked. The parts of the cerebral surface lying between the centres were found to produce no response to the method of stimulation used by us if only currents of minimum strength were used. If we increased the distance between the electrodes, however, or if we increased the strength of the applied current, contractions were obtained, but these extended over the whole body in such a manner that it could not be decided even whether they were unilateral or bilateral.

The localization of the centres, discussed in greater detail below, is fairly constant in the dog. Precise establishment of this fact initially caused some difficulties, which could be overcome by first trying to find the spot producing with the smallest effective strength of the current the most marked contraction of the muscle group in question. A pin was then placed in the brain of the still living animal between the two electrodes, and after removal of the brain the various points marked in this manner were compared with the alcohol-fixed preparations from earlier experiments. The high degree of constancy in the position of identical centres appears best of all from the fact that we repeatedly succeeded in finding the desired site in the centre of a single trepanation hole without having to open the skull anywhere else.

After resection of the dura mater the corresponding muscles contracted with the same degree of certainty as if we had uncovered the whole hemisphere. Initially, we encountered somewhat greater difficulties, even when the whole field of operation was uncovered. Although the gyri of the brain are fairly constant, as is well known, their individual development and their relative position still vary appreciably from case to case. It is almost a rule rather than an exception that even the corresponding gyri of the two hemispheres in one and the same animal are different with regard to various parts. Moreover, in some cases the central

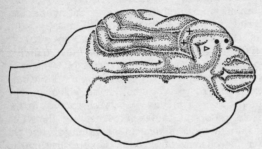

Figure 1.

part of the convexity is better deleloped, and in other cases this applies more to the anterior or the posterior parts (2). If one adds the necessity to spare to a considerable extent the brain membranes and the blurring of the picture by the continuously varying structure of the blood vessels which cover the gyri, it is hardly surprising that initially we encountered certain difficulties.

To facilitate even more reproduction of our experiments, we now present exact data concerning the localization of individual motor centres, following the nomenclature recommended by Owen (3).

The centre for the neck muscles (○ in Figure 1) is situated in the middle of the prefrontal gyrus where the surface of this gyrus begins to fall steeply downwards. The extreme end of the postfrontal gyrus lies near the end of the frontal fissure (● in Figure 1) the centre for the extensor and adductor muscles of the anterior extremity. A little farther back, nearer the coronal fissure (● in Figure 1), lie the centres governing the flexure and rotation of the limb. The centre for the posterior extremity (△ in Figure 1) is also situated in the postfrontal gyrus, but more in the median direction from the centre, and somewhat more dorsally, for the anterior extremity. The facial part $++$ in Figure 1) is innervated from the middle part of the suprasylvian gyrus. The site in question frequently extends over more than 0·5 cm, and extends from the main bend above the sylvian fissure forward and downward.

To this we have to add that we did not always succeed in moving the nuchal muscles from the first of the centres mentioned above. Although we frequently succeeded in causing movements in the back, tail, and abdominal muscles from parts situated between the points enumerated above, we were unable to pinpoint a circumscribed spot from which isolated stimulation of these muscles could be reliably achieved. We found the whole part of the convexity[1] situated behind the facialis centre to be completely refractory, even to currents of disproportionate strength. No muscular contraction could be achieved even if the shunt circuit was excluded, i.e. a current of ten Daniell cells was used.

The character of the contractions produced by stimulation of the motor centres varies depending on the nature of the stimulus. Stimulation by a single metallic closure of the circuit produces only a single quickly transient contraction. If the circuit is not closed in its metallic part but by putting on the electrodes, greater strength of current is required to achieve the same effect. In other words, here too the du Bois Reymond law is valid. All other things being equal, the metallic switch always has a more marked stimulating effect than mere closure of the circuit, but two contractions (the second being for the opening of the circuit) do not arise. Not infrequently, however, the same type of stimulation produced tetanus in the muscle group in question, particularly in the case of the flexor muscles of the toes, although no further stimulation had been applied. If one electrode had exerted its effect, even for a short period, the other electrode would produce a greater effect at the same spot than it would have had before or shortly after.

Although the described facts are fully consistent with our knowledge regarding the properties of the peripheral nerves, we feel obliged, for a reason that will be mentioned below, to call attention to a stimulating factor which does not fit in and which seems highly interesting from the physiological point of view.

1. We deliberately avoid the term lobe, as there are no clear-cut lobes in the dog nor do the formations that might be regarded as lobes fully correspond in their position to human brain lobes; finally, we do not know at all as yet which parts of the canine brain correspond to certain parts of the human brain.

This factor is the constant predominance of the anode. It even seems that with the minimum strength of current only the anode is capable of evoking contractions. To ascertain this point – primarily because knowledge of the fact would greatly facilitate the investigation – we carried out and frequently repeated the following experiments:

1. Keeping the two electrodes at the usual distance from each other, we tried to find the spot from which the minimum current evoked contractions, and to be absolutely certain we closed the circuit several times by means of the metallic switch. We then kept the circuit open and reversed the direction of the current, keeping the electrodes in their place, and closed the circuit again. Now no contraction occurred. If we opened the circuit once more, reversed it, and closed it, the stimulating effect was somewhat more marked than on the first occasions. This procedure could be repeated any number of times. If we now moved away one or the other electrode from its site while the circuit was repeatedly closed, the effect of the stimulation remained the same if it was the cathode that had been removed. The anode, however, could not be moved away any distance from the point of stimulation without producing contractions, or else it produced contractions in a different group of muscles.

2. The anode was placed onto the centre for the extensor muscles and the cathode onto the centre of the flexor muscles for the anterior extremity. Closing of the circuit evoked extension, reversion of polarity (with the circuit still closed) produced flexure, and so on. In other words, it was always the centre corresponding to the anode that proved to be stimulated.

In view of recent physiological investigations it seems rather tempting to relate the above facts to considerations concerning chemical processes participating in the nervous function. However, for the moment we prefer to refrain from doing so. The new facts uncovered in the present investigation are so varied, and their consequences extend in so many directions, that it would be hardly in the interest of the cause to try to follow all the paths requiring thorough further investigation.

To this we have to add that with a slightly prolonged closure of the circuit the greater stimulating effect of reversal of the electrodes also became manifest in the following manner. If we had produced a contraction by putting the anode on a centre and the cathode on a spot known to be indifferent for the current used, and if we continued closure of the circuit for a time, then sometimes opening and subsequent closure of the reversed circuit produced a single contraction: in very rare cases we produced a series of contractions. In other words, after a prolonged action of the anode the substance of the central nervous system reacted for a short time even with a very small current to the cathode, as well. This experiment succeeds only if very weak currents are used, particularly because stronger currents immediately destroy the substance by electrolysis.

If tetanizing induction currents are used for the stimulation, the effects achieved are not so constant in their character. Frequently tonic contractions of the muscle groups in question will occur, the intensity of which subsides only after a considerable time. An initial contraction maximum can often be observed, followed by such considerable relaxation – even if the action of the current lasted only for a second – that one could consider the contraction to be completely gone were it not for a slight movement in the direction of the subsiding contraction occurring at the moment the circuit is opened. The individual features of the experimental animal – its greater or lesser excitability – seem to be in a casual relation to these differences, as well as to some other phenomena that will be mentioned below.

Thus, continuous use of stronger currents causes symptoms of exhaustion: such as the need for stronger currents to achieve the same effects, as well as complete absence of contractions. In these cases sanguineous suffusion of the cortical substance can frequently be observed. In other cases, however, particularly after application of weak currents, a number of phenomena can be observed which must be interpreted in the opposite sense.

It has been reported (4) that opening of a circuit tetanizing the spinal cord of frogs caused subsequent movements in all muscles of the body. This fact seems to have been forgotten, as otherwise the defenders of the view that the spinal cord possessed excitability could have used it as an argument.

Similar facts can be observed after tetanization of the brain substance. Even a stimulation of only a few seconds' duration is followed by after-movements in the dependent musculature. These movements are clearly of tremor character in the facialis region. In the extremities the picture rather resembles clonic convulsions. The above differences depend apparently on the different types of muscle insertions. These local fits of convulsions may reoccur even if the brain is not stimulated any more. In some cases fits of convulsions also occurred after maltreatment of the brain substance by closing of the circuit, but as a rule such fits were not observed after stimulation with these currents. In two of our experimental animals these after-movements developed into well-defined epileptic fits. The fits began in one half of the body, with contractions in the previously stimulated musculature, but later spread to all muscles of the body leading to a complete extensor tetanus. During the fit the pupils were maximally dilated. One of these animals had two and the other three fits. It could be argued that the dogs may have been epileptic before the experiment, but one of them had been with one and the same mistress for six years without ever having suffered from convulsions. The antecedents of the second dog remained unknown.

We shall now try to counter the arguments which could be raised against our experiments.

The first argument, always raised by experts[2] and by the not so expert in relation to experiments with electrical stimulation is based on the assumption that the current may reach more distant parts of the brain. Disregarding the question whether the cortical or the medullar substance of the cerebrum is excitable, this argument is easier to answer than any other. The currents used by us in the experiments in question were very weak, the brain substance has a very high electric resistance, there are no other conducting parts in the vicinity, and finally, the distance between the electrodes was small, so that according to the laws of distribution of currents in nonprismatic conductors the current density could only be minimal even at a very small distance from the point of entry. This alone would be sufficient to counter *a priori* the argument in question. We have, moreover, a whole series of direct further proofs in our favour. If one assumed that the current first of all reached the peripheral nerves, the nerves on the same half of the body would always have been nearer, there would be no reason for the currents to reach exclusively the nerves of the contralateral half of the body. Furthermore, the oculomotor nerves of the same side were much nearer to the source of current than any other nerve in question. The bulbus formation, always balanced in a state of labile equilibrium, would constitute an excellent physiological rheoscope without any preliminary preparation, and would be much more likely to move when touched, even by a very small current, than an anterior extremity let alone a posterior extremity. The whole convexity, however, as far as it can be uncovered, does not contain a single point from which movement of the bulbus can be evoked, even with currents

2. It may be of interest that the great number of doctors to whom our experiments were demonstrated included several specialists highly competent in the field, such as Prof. Nasse (Marburg) and Munk (Berlin).

stronger than those usually employed by us. This argument would settle part of the question which induced one of us to take up the present investigation. Finally, we quote one more fact of considerable physiological and pathological interest. The excitability of the brain decreases rapidly when the animal is bled and is extinguished almost completely prior to the animal's death. Immediately after death the excitability is completely lost, even against the strongest currents, whereas the muscles and nerves still react perfectly. This fact apparently makes it necessary to carry out experiments regarding the excitability of the central nervous system with unimpaired circulation.

The second argument is that even if the current failed to reach the peripheral nerves or the spinal cord to which latter the same counter arguments would apply as to the former, it might reach regions of the brain other than the cerebral hemispheres. If this was the case, demonstration of electrical excitability in other parts of the brain would still represent an important discovery. Even experts in the field still maintain in general that not all parts of the brain are susceptible to direct stimulation. This, however, is not the case, as can be shown with regard to electrical stimulation. The parts which have been at all accepted as being excitable, though only by a few authors, are the posterior part (cauda) of the corpus striatum, the thalamus opticus, the crus cerebri, the corpora quadrigemina, and the pons. Disregarding for the moment the corpus striatum, all other morphologic parts of the brain quoted above are situated so far backward that they are only intersected by frontal sections through the more posterior parts of the brain, which do not react. The only exception is the corpus striatum although the cauda of this formation is also situated in the non-excitable zone.[3] It would therefore be possible that it was just the anterior or middle part of this ganglion – allegedly a non-excitable part – which proved excitable and was the source of our stimulation effects. This latter view seems *a priori* improbable, as despite the unchanged strength of the current the contractions ceased as soon as the electrodes were shifted by a few millimetres. If we were to draw straight lines through the two assumed points of entry and also through a third point situated in the corpus striatum vertically under the line connecting the two points, we would obtain an equilateral triangle the equal sides of which would represent pathways offering the smallest resistance to the current. As the resistance would be necessarily

3. We call 'non-excitable' – without prejudice – all those areas from which we were unable to elicit contractions.

identical in both pathways, all other things being equal, the stimulating effect should be the same, but this was not the case.

Not content with these *a priori* proofs, however convincing these might be, we also made attempts to provide direct evidence. To this purpose we provided Carlsbad-type insect pins with a dense insulating cover by dipping them repeatedly into a solution of guttapercha in chloroform. Only the tip and the head of the pin retained their conducting properties. No trace of contractions was obtained when these pins were stuck into the posterior part of the cerebrum even if the currents used were very much stronger, until the rheophores had penetrated to a depth of several centimetres and touched the crura cerebri. At that moment the animal jumped violently and displayed general muscular convulsions. The results were quite different if the anterior part of the cerebrum was stimulated in the same manner. If we were to assume that current reaching the corpus striatum had provoked the observed contractions after superficial stimulation, one would simply expect intensification of the contractions in step with the penetration of the electrodes. But this was not the case; instead, the convulsions extended to quite different groups of muscles and generally behaved in a different manner, which we are not going to discuss in greater detail at this point. It follows with great certainty that neither the above-mentioned ganglion nor the formations constituting the brain stem took part in the contractions evoked from the convexity.

Another counter-argument that could be raised (as had been the case in all previous successful experiments concerning stimulation of the central nervous system – spinal cord, brain stem) is that the contractions came about on a reflex basis. This argument, too, can be answered by the following convincing proof:

Reflexes could have been elicited via the nerves in the dura mater and the pia mater, as we were protected against stimulation of adjacent nerves in the calvaria by wide uncovering of the brain surface. Besides, the partly freed bulk of the temporal muscles was lying at one edge of the wound. These structures, which presumably retained their excitability, would have immediately indicated even weak current. So far, however, nobody has demonstrated or even assumed the presence of sensory fibres in the cerebrum itself. Moreover, the complete insensitivity of the latter substance does not give the slightest indication of this kind.

As far as the dura mater is concerned, we have said above that it has a certain sensitivity even under physiological con-

4. In agreement with the findings of Longet *et al.* (5).

ditions, a sensitivity which increases rapidly after opening of the skull. For this reason it is advisable to operate very quickly as otherwise the experimental animal, however tightly it may be strapped in, performs violent jumps and makes it very difficult to preserve the brain substance during removal of the dura membrane. Once the dura has been removed up to the edges of the bones, however, one is sufficiently protected against reflexes from the dura nerves. We made sure of this fact in a variety of ways. First of all our stimulation experiments elicited crossed contractions, whereas reflexes always appear on the same side (Pflueger). Secondly, the reflexes ceased after a slight shift in the position of the electrodes, although the distance from the remaining parts of the dura had not been altered. Thirdly, the reflexes ceased even when the electrodes were applied nearer to the dura, provided we did not hit upon motor centres. If the latter condition was observed we did not even obtain contractions when the electrodes were applied very close to the dura but still on the brain substance. If we touched the dura itself, frequently even in the absence of electrical current and always with electrical stimulation, extremely violent and highly characteristic reflex movements could be observed. However, these were completely different from our usual stimulation effects. First of all, these movements always appeared to be purposeful. The head was thrown back, the back muscles contracted, and the animal cried and whimpered, even when narcotized with morphine; the extremities moved only rarely. Quite a different picture was obtained in our stimulation experiments. Here frequently even non-narcotized animals were lying still, indifferently, while we caused movements in an anterior or in a posterior extremity by applying electrical stimuli.

The pia mater cannot be removed in a similar manner by preparation; on the contrary, it has to be dealt with as carefully as possible. Injury to any one of its innumerable abundantly filled blood vessels can cover the whole field of operation with blood, and can cause failure of the whole experiment, when the animal has been sacrificed in vain. This, however, does not invalidate our evidence showing that the pia does not take part in the provocation of our stimulatory effects. In addition to all the arguments already enumerated during the discussion of the dura mater, the following evidence will be more than sufficient. Similarly to Longet et al. (5), we found that the pia mater was insensitive. We excised the pia over a motor centre, sparing the large vessels, without any change in the effect of stimulation. Even if the pia was removed from such a site, the contractions never failed to appear. If we stabbed the brain substance with needles the muscles would still contract if this had been done within a motor area, but under all these conditions no contraction would occur if we went beyond the posterior border of the motor sphere in question. It might be of interest to add that neither morphine nor ether narcosis had any appreciable effect on the success of the experiments.

Finally, the question will arise why so many earlier authors, including some of the most illustrious ones, had come to the opposite conclusion. To this we have only one answer: 'It is the method that brings the results.' Our predecessors could not have uncovered the whole convexity, as otherwise they would have been bound to obtain contractions. The posterior lateral wall of the skullcap in dogs, under which there are no motor parts, is highly suitable because of its formation for the application of the first trepanation hole. The earlier authors presumably started the operation at that spot and failed to proceed further, breaking away more anterior parts of the skullcap, erroneously assuming that the various areas of the brain surface were equivalent. This belief was based on the assumption, discussed in the initial part of this paper [not included in this excerpt] and still generally held, according to which all parts of the cerebral cortex took part in all psychic functions. If the idea of a possible localized character of the psychic functions had arisen at all, the apparent failure of certain parts of the substrate to react to stimulation would have been regarded as an obvious fact, only to be expected, and the authors concerned would not have failed to investigate all parts of that substrate. After all, it can be safely stated that none of the earlier workers assumed that the stimuli used by us were capable of producing psychic conceptions or of bringing about the manifestation of already evoked conceptions in the animal under vivisection. [. . .]

References

1. HITZIG, 'On the galvanic vertigo and a new method of galvanic excitation of the eye muscles', *Berl. Klin. Wochenschrift*, vol. 11 (1870).
2. REICHERT, *Der Bau des Menschl. Gehirns* (The structure of the human brain), Leipzig, 1861, p. 77.
3. OWEN, *On the Anatomy of Vertebrates*, London, 1868, vol. 3, p. 118.
4. R. WAGNER, *Handworterb. d. Physiol.*, vol. 3, p. 15 [Date not known but probably *c*. 1860.]
5. LONGET et al., *Anatomie et Physiologie du Systéme Nerveux de l'Homme et des Animaux Vertébrés* (Anatomy and physiology of the nervous system in man and other vertebrates), Paris 1842, vol. 1.

20 D. Denny-Brown

The Frontal Lobes and their Functions

Excerpts from D. Denny-Brown, 'The frontal lobes and their functions', in A. Feiling (ed.), *Modern Trends in Neurology*, Butterworth, 1951, chapter 2, pp. 13-58.

The large literature on the symptomatology of the frontal lobe has been reviewed many times, notably by Schuster (1902), Feuchtwanger (1923), Goldstein (1923), Baruk (1926), Lhermitte (1929), and Brickner (1936). The evolution of the physiological aspects of the frontal lobe has been reviewed by Bianchi (1922), their relation to intelligence by Lashley (1929), and to equilibrium by Delmas-Marsalet (1936). The last 20 years have brought remarkable changes in two respects. First, advances in neurosurgical technique have made excision of the greater part of the frontal lobe feasible as a radical operation for brain tumour, and have resulted in great improvement in animal experimentation on the brain. Secondly, the remarkable potentialities of the operation of frontal leucotomy (or lobotomy, as it is known in the United States of America), besides presenting challenging problems in psychiatry and neurology, have forced a revaluation of the old evidence, and further consideration of its significance. The subject is a very extensive one, for we are led to reconsideration of what we mean by cerebral 'function'.

Anatomical Data

The frontal lobe is a purely arbitrary anatomical entity. The infolding of the rolandic sulcus, though it contains the line of demarcation between motor and sensory cortex, has been held by some to be the result of expansion of a twin 'sensori-motor' unit of function, with more anatomical homogeneity than the abrupt fissure would suggest. The borders separating the frontal cortex from the insula, and from that portion of the parietal lobe which appears on the mesial aspect of the hemisphere, and to a less extent from the parolfactory area, are a matter of convenience in description. As von Bonin (1948) has remarked, the size of the frontal lobes relative to the remainder of the brain when plotted logarithmically is not greater in man than in the monkeys and anthropoid apes. The extent of the frontal association areas, however, certainly seem greater in man than in the lower primates.

Within the frontal lobe some sulci form conspicuous landmarks. On the lateral surface the pre-central sulcus runs more or

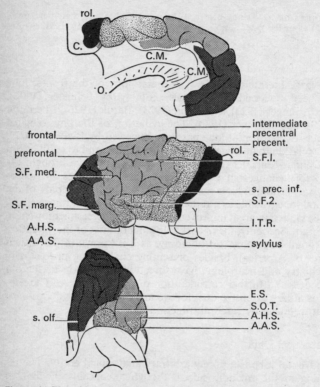

Figure 1. The chief architectural divisions of the human fro ntal cortex according to Campbell (1905). The pre-central cortex is shown in black, the intermediate pre-central cortex by dots, the frontal cortex light-chequered and pre-frontal cortex dark-chequered. The iimbic and opercular cortex is shown unmarked

less parallel with the rolandic fissure, and is in two parts, the superior and inferior pre-central sulci. These may overlap in their middle parts as in Figure 1. From each of these a sulcus runs forward, the superior frontal sulcus (S.F.1 in Figure 1) and inferior frontal sulcus (S.F.2). The horizontal limbs of these may be discontinuous as in S.F.2 in Figure 1. These horizontal sulci divide the lateral aspect of the frontal lobe into superior, middle, and inferior frontal gyri. Some authors refer to these as the first, second, and third frontal convolutions. The inferior frontal gyrus,

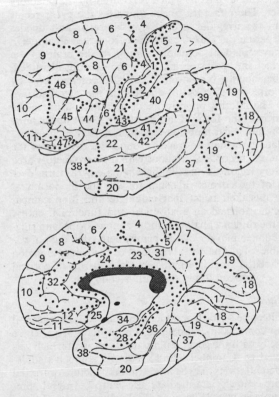

Figure 2. The chief cyto-architectural areas in the human cortex. A simplified version of the chart of Brodmann (1909)

which in the left hemisphere is known as Broca's convolution, is further subdivided by two diverging sulci which radiate upwards from the sylvian (lateral) fissure, and thus form the pars orbitalis, pars triangularis, and pars opercularis. The classical arrangement of these is seen in Figure 2.

On the medial surface of the hemisphere the sulcus cinguli

(callosomarginal fissure, C.M. in Figure 1) separates the inner aspect of the superior frontal gyrus from the cinguli, which follows the general contour of the corpus callosum. The orbital surface of the frontal lobe presents near its inner edge the olfactory sulcus, the caudal part of which is covered by the olfactory bulb and tract. The olfactory sulcus separates the gyrus rectus medially from the irregular orbital gyri laterally, and divides caudally to separate the parolfactory area from the remainder.

We shall have frequent occasion to refer to the brain of the monkey, in which the main sulci and gyri can be readily identified, except that the superior precentral sulcus is represented only by a dimple or horizontal streak (just above 4 on the lateral surface in Figure 4). The inferior pre-central, or arcuate, sulcus, in the monkey brain is in the form of an inverted L, with upper horizontal and lower vertical limbs (enclosing area 8 in Figure 4).

The cingulate gyrus can be traced around the rostrum of the corpus callosum to become continuous with the parolfactory area and the olfactory trigone. Caudally the cingulate gyrus turns over the splenium of the corpus callosum to join the hippocampal gyrus. In the mistaken belief that cingulate and hippocampal cortex and uncus formed an anatomical and functional entity, derived from the rhinencephalon of more simple forms, and ringing the whole inner margin of the hemisphere, this region was called the limbic lobe. The dorsal remnant of the rhinencephalon is, however, not the cingulate gyrus, but a thin rim of cortical tissue which lies between it and the corpus callosum.

Cyto-architecture

The cyto-architecture of the frontal lobe in man exhibits a general plan with most complex and ill-defined subdivisions. We are here concerned chiefly with the general plan, one version of which was carefully plotted by Campbell (1905). From Campbell's study, five major differentiations may be made in the structure of frontal cortex, the pre-central, intermediate pre-central, frontal, prefrontal, and limbic cortex (Figure 1). These differentiations were made chiefly upon criteria of fibre lamination, though cellular structure was also recorded. The numerical system introduced by Brodmann gave a picture which is confusing in its detail, and gives an impression of accuracy which subsequent investigations have failed to confirm. Moreover, there is no certainty that the areas given the same number in different species are homologous. Since the numerals of Brodmann have been widely used as landmarks in the description of experimental and therapeutic procedures, it will be necessary to refer to them frequently. A diagram of their distribution in the human brain is given in Figure 4, and in the monkey brain in Figure 2. A simplified diagram of von Economo's more accurate and verifiable chart for the human brain, with alphabetical lettering, is shown in Figure 3.

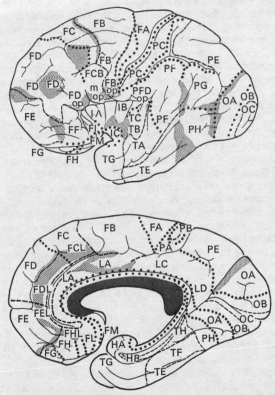

Figure 3. The chief cyto-architectural areas in the human cortex. A simplified version of the chart of von Economo and Koskinas (1925). The shaded areas are transitional

The 'ideal-charts' of Brodmann, and of von Economo and Koskinas (1925), throw special emphasis upon cellular lamination, which certainly gives a clear distinction between the medial parts of the agranular pre-central cortex and intermediate pre-central cortex of Campbell (areas 4 and 6 of Brodmann, areas

F A and F B of von Economo and Koskinas), the cingulate cortex, and the remaining frontal and prefrontal areas. In the frontal and prefrontal region of Campbell, Brodmann identified areas 8, 9, 10, and 11 (Figure 2), to which von Economo's FC, FD, FE, and FG have approximate correspondence in their medial aspect (Figure 3). On the lateral aspect of the frontal lobe, and particularly in the opercular region, considerable difficulty in classification and interpretation arises. Von Economo and Koskinas used a system of combinations of non-committal lettering, such as FDC, FDL, FCB, FDΔ for transitional areas, of which the uncertain boundaries and affiliations are not apparent in the corresponding numbers 8, 32, 44, and 46 of Brodmann. The attempt of Vogt and Vogt (1919), to stretch the numerical areas of Brodamnn into a rigid functional representation had the most disastrous effects, for Foerster (1936) and Fulton (1935) and others began to use the charts of the Vogts for monkey and man as if they represented rigid factual material.

The recent studies of Lashley and Clark (1946), von Bonin and Bailey (1947), and Bailey (1948) have thrown considerable doubt on the constancy of any of the cyto-architectural borders except that between sensory and motor cortex, and of the limits of calcarine cortex. Nevertheless, charting of cyto-architectural differences is necessary if progress is to be made. The chart of von Bonin and Bailey (1947), showing transitions by fusions of colours seems ideal, and we reproduce in Figure 5 a diagram made from it which expresses less adequately the larger transitions in structure in the brain of the monkey. Walker (1940) found that the structure called area 46 by Brodmann, and F D Δ by von Economo could be identified in the macaque brain, and it is now recognized separately by its intense reception from the dorso-medial thalamic nucleus in neuronography. Walker has also a different pattern of numerical subdivision of the other areas, which has much to recommend it, but it has been little used.

From the point of view of the discussion which is to follow, it should be emphasized that all detailed descriptions indicate transitional feature in the opercular region bordering the fissure of Sylvius. Lashley and Clark (1946) find that in the monkey the anterior opercular region often cannot be distinguished from the lateral orbital gyrus, and lateral to area 4 it resembles the postcentral region. Von Bonin and Bailey (1947) state that in the monkey the operculum, below the lower limit of the central sulcus (FCOp and PCOp in Figure 5) is definitely and constantly granular. Von Economo (1929) also mentions the disintegration of the features of FA and FB as they are traced to their lateral limit. It should be clear, therefore, that area 6 (FB) probably does not extend beyond the lateral limit of area 4 in monkey or man, and that the attempt of the Vogts to force the

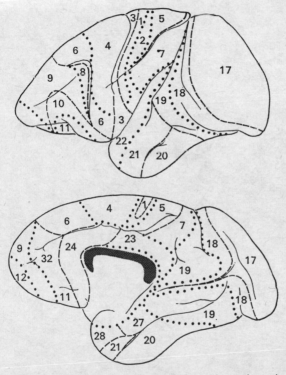

Figure 4. Cortical chart of monkey (*Cercopithecus*) to show the chief areas charted by Brodmann (1906)

complex movements such as chewing and vocalization into area 6 was unfounded. From these recent studies it is also certain that the lateral area charted as area 8 of Brodmann in monkey and man is extremely variable and often difficult to find. There is certainly a narrow transitional granular area in this situation, and in it large pyramidal cells may be numerous or absent in the monkey (Lashley and Clark, 1946).

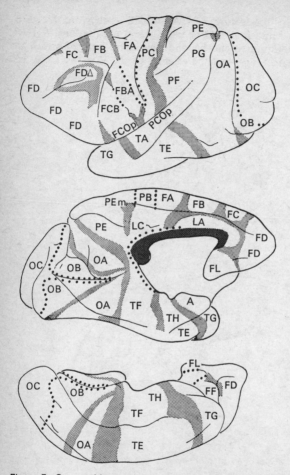

Figure 5. Cyto-architectural areas of monkey (*Macaca mulatta*) prepared from the data given in the coloured chart of von Bonin and Bailey (1947). The transitional areas are here approximately indicated by shading

In general, therefore, the differentiation into granular and agranular cortex can be relied upon if latitude for considerable variation of extent in the same species is allowed for. In evaluating experimental and descriptive data the broad transitions between limbic cortex and the remainder must also be noticed.

Even such transitions as that between areas 4 and 6 are gradual, and when they occur in or near a fissure may be most difficult to establish with exactitude in any given case. When it is realized that undoubted giant cells of Betz are frequently found in the caudal wall of the superior pre-central sulcus in all primates, yet this sulcus is generally pictured in area 6, the fallacy of too complete reliance upon any one diagram is immediately realized. Even the relatively simple brain of *Macaca mulatta* often presents remarkable differences between the two hemispheres and, in all forms, the pre-central sulci vary greatly in development and extent. The remarkable confusion which was introduced by a diagram of the border between areas 6 and 4 in *Cercopithecus* cortex by Vogt and Vogt (1919) will be referred to later. The inability to define with precision the limits of size of the giant cell of Betz and Bevan Lewis has been subjected to cogent criticism by Walshe (1942). Yet, by and large, the transitions from 4 to 6, 6 to 8, 9 to 10, are not difficult to establish in their medial parts. As Lashley and Clark (1946) point out, experimental work planned on the basis of an 'ideal' or 'average' cortical chart suffers from great uncertainty unless rigid histological verification is carried out on each case.

Afferent and efferent tracts

The human frontal lobes, besides giving rise to a considerable part of the pyramidal tract, are the source of several important projections to other parts of the brain. The most prominent is the fronto-pontine tract, which according to Déjerine takes origin in the orbital gyri and the middle frontal convolution in man. Meyer, Beck, and McLardy (1947) were able to trace its origin to area 10. It passes between the head of the caudate nucleus and the putamen, to join the anterior segment of the internal capsule and thence to the pontine nuclei of the brain stem *via* the medial third of the cerebral peduncle. A diffuse system of fibres from the orbital gyri, the superior and middle frontal gyri and the pre-central gyrus mingles with the fronto-pontine tract to reach the red nucleus and its capsule. Area 8 gives rise to cortico-tegmental fibres. Cortico-nigral fibres take origin from the rolandic region, the first frontal gyrus and the opercular region of the pre-central and post-central gyrus. Von Economo and Koskinas (1925) point to the great development of the large pyramidal cells of the fifth and of the third (c) layers (layer *iva* of von Bonin) in the regions from which the cortico-spinal, cortico-bulbat, and cortico-nigral tracts arise, and of the fifth and sixth layers in the areas of origin of the cortico-pontine tract. Walshe (1942) has recently presented a case for regarding all cells of the fifth layer as having motor function, regardless of the area in which they occur, but we shall later return to the question of what is meant by 'motor function'. The cortico-thalamic fibres also form an important outlet, reciprocal with thalamo-cortical fibres, from the caudal parts of the middle and inferior frontal gyri, and from the medial surface, particularly the gyrus cinguli.

In the monkey, further details of degeneration of efferent pathways from the prefrontal areas 9 and 10 of Brodmann to the medial and ventral thalamic nuclei, and to the tegmentum of the mid-brain, have been demonstrated (Levin, 1936), and from area 9 to the lateral thalamic nucleus. Mettler (1947) found Marchi degeneration in the reticular thalamic nuclei, and subcallosal fasciculus (destined for the caudate nucleus) in addition. From area 8 fibres also entered the pallidum. Area 6 was found to have extremely widespread projections to the dorsal reticular and lateral nuclei of the thalamus, the basal ganglia, posterior hypothalamus, the tegmentum of the mid-brain and medulla, the pons, inferior olive, and pyramid. The forward medial part of area 4 has similar projections. Ablation of the caudal part of area 4 led to degeneration in the pyramid, the lateral nucleus of the thalamus, substantia nigra and medullary tegmentum. Each of these areas gave rise to degeneration of association and callosal fibres.

The fibres entering the frontal lobe have been recently reviewed by Walker (1944) and Clark (1948). They include the important projections from the nucleus ventralis lateralis of the thalamus to areas 6 and 4. Areas 6 and 4 receive extensive connexions from both the same and the opposite hemisphere, including not only the post-central cortex, but also areas 21 and 22 (Mettler, 1935–6). Clark and Boggon (1933) first showed that the frontal cortex receives an important thalamic projection from the dorso-medial nucleus to area 8 and diffusely forward of this. Meyer, Beck, and McLardy (1947) have shown a topographic correspondence between the different parts of the dorso-medial nucleus and the frontal cortex in man where it is distributed to the areas 11, 47, 45, 46, 8, 9, and 10 of Brodmann's chart. The nucleus antero-medialis projects, in part, to the cingulate gyrus (Walker). These two thalamic nuclei are essentially relay stations from the hypothalamus. In addition the centre median and diffuse reticular thalamic system project to the frontal lobe, as to the remainder of the hemisphere (Jasper, 1949). The existence of a projection to the frontal lobe from the striatum, red nucleus, and sub-cortical structures other than the thalamus, is now considered questionable.

Physiological neuronography

The above summary of the afferent and efferent connexions of the frontal lobe is based on the methods of Marchi degeneration and retrograde degeneration. The newer method of 'physiological neuronography' introduced by Dusser de Barenne and McCulloch (1938) in charting effects transmitted through one synapse by recording strychnine spikes has been enormously productive. The results of the method have been summarized by McCulloch (1944a and b, 1948), though much has been added since that time. A strip of cortex lying in the region of the superior pre-central gyrus, referred to as area 4s, together with strips in the region of areas 8 (eye-field) and 24 (cingulate), were found to cause strychnine spikes in the caudate nucleus. Area 6 'projected' to the putamen and the external segment of the globus pallidus, and the caudal part of area 4 to the putamen. Stimulation of areas 4s, 8 and 24 (and also of areas 2 and 19 in the parietal and occipital lobes) were found to suppress the motor response to stimulation of any other part of the cortex, and its after-discharge, and McCulloch named these areas 'suppressor areas'. Part of the suppressor effects is abolished by destruction of the caudate nucleus in the monkey, and the mechanism of the remaining suppressor activity, if not all, is presumed to be due to excitation of the reticular inhibitory mechanism in the medulla to which these areas project. By the same method of neuronography the caudate nucleus was shown to project to the ventrolateral nuclei in the thalamus and thus influence the thalamic projection system to the motor cortex. There is some evidence (McCulloch, 1948) that suppressive effects may be even further generalized by connexions with the reticular nuclei of the thalamus. The suppressor bands each correspond to part of a cyto-architectonic area. By means of physiological neuronography it has also been demonstrated that the frontal lobe can directly influence the hypothalamus (Ward and McCulloch, 1947). Area 6 was found to project into the lateral hypothalamus, and the lateral aspects of the frontal lobe (areas 8, 45, 46) into the medial nuclei of the hypothalamus. The orbital surface was found to project into the paraventricular and periventricular systems.

Physiological neuronography has also charted an extensive inter-areal system of communications within the hemisphere. Areas 6 and 4 both give to, and receive generously from, the post-central cortex. Area 6, FC, has peculiarities in its reception from the auditory cortex in the temporal lobe, from the extreme post-parietal region (area 7, PE) and from a small region just rostral to area 8 (area 46) (Ward, Penden, and Sugar, 1946). The motor cortex receives a projection from the upper wall of the

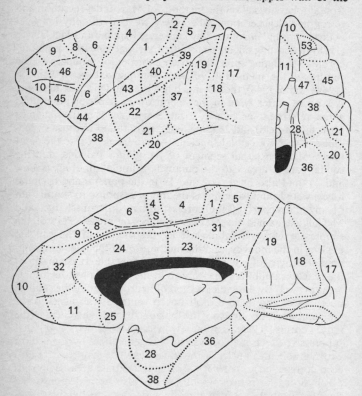

Figure 6. Areas in macaque cortex verified either by neuronography or by histology. Prepared from the chart of McCulloch (1944b)

sylvian fissure, according to these authors. In earlier studies Bailey and his associates (1943) showed the interaction of the prefrontal areas with the occipital lobe, and communications with the superior temporal gyrus.

The numbering of areas used by the neuronographers is shown in Figure 6. Area 46 'fires', that is distributes impulses to, the remainder of the frontal pole in the monkey. Areas 32 and 31 receive impulses from all the suppressor areas, but have not been found to activate any. They, like the caudate nucleus and putamen, are a sort of 'clearing house' for suppressive activity. Areas 9 and 10 do not fire other areas. Area 8 is the only suppressor area to give rise to callosal fibres and fires the contralateral area 18.

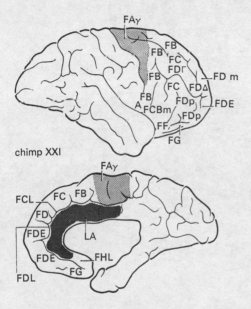

chimp XXI

chimp XXI

Figure 7. Cyto-architectural areas in the frontal cortex of the chimpanzee

Areas 43, 44, 45, 47 and 53 have totally different reactions. Area 43 fires 44 and 22, 45 fires 44 and 40, 47 fires 38, and 53 fires 37. Area 47 receives from 38 and 53 from 22. Any part of the limbic area fires any other part, and areas 6 and 31 (McCulloch, 1944a; Ward, Penden, and Sugar, 1946). Physiological neuronography has in fact justified differentiation of strips of cortex in the general regions of these numbered areas. It is of particular interest that the whole opercular region in the monkey appears by this method to be part of a sylvian (?auditory) area (McCulloch, 1944b) and not related to areas 6 or 4.

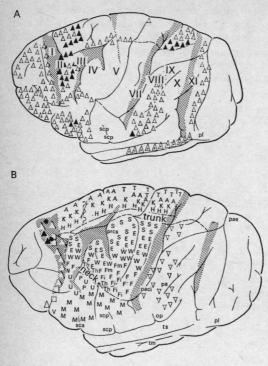

A

B

Neck	Thumb	Pinna
Toes	Elbow	Upper face
Ankle	Wrist	Mouth
Knee	Fm digitus minimus	Vocalization
Hip	F digiti 3 and 4	
Shoulder	Fi digitus indicis	

legend for B

△ oculi contralateral   ◻ oculi contra with pupillary dilat.

▲ oculi ipsilateral   ● lacrimation

▽ arm by faciliation

Figure 8. (A) The commissural and suppressor areas in the chimpanzee cortex. Shading indicates suppressor areas. △ = origin of restricted symmetrical disturbances. ▲ = origin of symmetrical and also more widespread contralateral disturbances. ◬ = origin of symmetrical dis-

The charting of the interrelationship between the two hemi-spheres by the same method by Bailey, Garol, and McCulloch (1941) revealed a striking pattern, which is clearer in the chimpan-zee brain (Figure 8A). All the symmetrical disturbances trans-mitted from one frontal lobe to the other were abolished by section of the corpus callosum. The pattern revealed by these studies suggested a reorientation of anatomical subdivisions of the cortex in vertical compartments, which Bailey and his col-leagues have numbered with the Roman numerals I to XI. It will be observed in this figure that the outer aspect of the frontal and prefrontal lobes have a rich connexion with the opposite hemi-spheres, particularly along the border of the suppressor band, zone I, which identifies area 8. The corresponding cyto-archi-tectural map is shown in Figure 7. The intermediate pre-central area of Campbell (zone II) also possesses a widespread radiation to the contralateral hemisphere (zone II). The suppressor band 4s forms zone III. The broad band of pre-central cortex, including the whole pre-central gyrus (zone IV) has no contralateral radia-tion except for a few points along face–arm and arm–leg borders.

In the more simple organization of the cat brain the projection of the dorsomedial nucleus of the thalamus is to the frontal pole and medial orbital cortex, the gyrus proreus (Rose and Woolsey, 1948) and is here well forward of the small inhibitory strip which is thus identified as area 8 (Garol, 1942). None of the true frontal area is activated by antidromic volleys in the pyramidal tract (Woolsey and Chang, 1948) though these reach areas 6 and 4, and the whole lateral surface of the parietal lobe in the monkey.

It would be convenient if this wealth of diverse information regarding the anatomical connexions of the frontal cortex could be systematized into some general anatomical grouping. The most simple classification appears to be on the basis of primary thalamic radiation – rolandic (areas 4 and 6), sylvian (areas 43, 44, 45), limbic and orbito-temporal region (areas 24, 25, 38), and frontal proper (areas 8, 9, 10, 11, 46). The numbering given is in terms of the chart given by McCulloch (1944a and b) shown in Figure 6. It must again be emphasized that the borders of the areas are only approximate.

---

turbance which persisted after section of the corpus callosum. (B) Chart of results of facilitation of motor responses forward and backward from points on the pre-central gyrus. Movement was elicited on the pre-central gyrus by bipolar electrodes, stimulus frequency 30 per second, and the electrodes were then moved rapidly forwards or backwards, avoiding the shaded areas, each of which produced suppression

Electrically Excitable Areas

Area 4 (FA)

The responses obtained from area 4 (FA) are in general well known. For the benefit of those who have no personal experience of the phenomenon, it should be emphasized that the nature of the response obtained depends greatly upon the depth of anaesthesia and the nature of the stimulus. A cortical stimulus can only be defined by its effect. The strength of stimulation which just produces recognizable movement in the fingers of the opposite hand from application to the appropriate 'hand' area is the threshold stimulus for that area in that experiment. With increasing strength of stimulus, threshold points for leg (usually ankle), foot, and face appear in variable order, and the movement of the hand from the hand area becomes elicitable over a wider area and also has other movements added to it. A strength of stimulus which will elicit a great variety of movements from different points will now elicit few movements singly. The complexity of the overlapping areas from which particular movements can then be elicited is well exemplified by the charts of Brown and Sherrington (1911). The conventional map of the excitable area represents the order of primary movement in various complexes (Leyton and Sherrington, 1917). The movements are strictly unilateral, with two exceptions. Stimulation in the region of the superior pre-central sulcus induces at times flexion of the ipsilateral upper limb or an extension of the ipsilateral lower limb, or both, in addition to movement in the contralateral limb. Though fragments of this ipsilateral movement can be produced with a stigmatic monopolar electrode, it can be more regularly obtained by strong bipolar stimulation. It persists as long as a small number of the large pyramidal cells of the most forward part of area 4 remains intact, and is abolished by their excision (Denny-Brown and Botterell, 1948). The ipsilateral component remains after contralateral spinal hemisection high in the cervical region (Hering, 1899). The other bilateral response is in the lower facial and lingual musculature. Many movements of the tongue persist after section of the hypoglossal nerve on the contralateral side (Walker and Green, 1938).

Boynton and Hines (1933) found the most effective frequency of stimulation of the cortex to lie between 60 and 90 cycles a second. Higher or lower frequencies required a higher voltage of stimulus. The exact form of stimulus is not important, but a regular sine-wave current is preferable to the irregular output of a faradic coil with mechanical interrupter. The advantages claimed for special types of wave and frequency appear to the writer to be only those which are derived from working with a stimulus just above threshold. Other regions of the cortex respond more adequately to low frequencies (3–10 per second). The optimal frequency for any given effect probably depends, as in spinal reflexes, upon the relative proportions of inhibition and excitation and their after-effects that are present. A galvanic stimulus through bipolar electrodes has been used by Foerster, and others, especially in stimulation of area 6. It is claimed that its effect is less liable to spread with high voltages, but electrolytic damage is likely to occur. It is therefore extremely doubtful whether the claims made for production of more discrete movements, or more ipsilateral movements, can be dependent upon the rate or form of the stimulus. The depth of anaesthesia is the most important single factor. Lastly, it should be observed that the timing and duration of successive stimuli greatly affect the response, resulting in either facilitation, exhaustion, or deviation of response as described by Leyton and Sherrington, Dusser de Barenne and others.

Since the discovery of cortical excitability by Fritsch and Hitzig, its meaning has been subject to debate. Though the predictions of Hughlings Jackson regarding localization of control of movement by the pre-central cortex were convincingly mapped by physiologists, Jackson protested from the first against the detailed identification of cortically stimulated movement with the mechanism of voluntary control of muscles. He immediately perceived discrepancies in the recovery of movement after damage to the motor cortex, yet many still appear to regard willed movement and cortical excitability as synonymous.

It was clear from the careful ablation experiments of Leyton and Sherrington (1917) that the return of movement in the hand of the chimpanzee after ablation of the corresponding hand area was not to be found in immediately neighbouring cortex. On re-exploration, electrical excitation of the original and neighbouring areas could no longer give rise to the recovered movements. More ample excision of the pre-central gyrus of the same, or of the opposite side, failed to reproduce the paralysis. Indeed, after excision of the second hand area, the formerly paralysed limb was used even better than before. Fulton and his collaborators maintained that some movement was again lost in limbs recovered from excision of area 4 in the monkey, if area 6 on the same side were then ablated. In the light of subsequent studies it appears likely that, owing to the erroneous charts of the line of separation between areas 6 and 4 on which their studies were based, the second ablation had removed a residual forward strip of area 4 (called by Hines (1937) area 4s). Fulton and Keller (1932) found some renewed weakness in the lower limb when the ipsilateral pre-central cortex was removed subsequent to recovery from contralateral ablation, and Bucy and Fulton (1933), finding that ipsilateral movements could be produced by stimulation in the region of the pre-central sulcus, attributed to this region the ability to 'take over' the motor functions of the previously paralysed limb. Denny-Brown and Botterell (1948) found that when movements of the hemiplegic limbs had recovered, stimulation of ipsilateral cortex usually failed to give its response in them. These investigators failed also to observe renewed paralysis after ipsilateral ablation, finding instead a greater use of the recovering limbs, provided 'pyramidal shock' had passed. The description of a 'second motor cortex' in the sylvian fissure (Sugar, Chusid, and French, 1948) naturally raised the question whether such a cortex could function vicariously for the pre-central area after excision of the latter. We have not found any evidence of such vicarious function, nor does excision of this area alone induce paralysis.

Area 6 (FB)

Reference to Figures 2, 3, and 4 indicates area 6 (or von Economo's equivalent area FB) as a narrow strip of cortex running from the cingulate sulcus to the sylvian fissure. Electrical stimulation of this area is ineffective in moderate strengths with stigmatic unipolar electrodes. Stronger stimulation with such electrodes commonly results in electrical artefact or 'spread' of excitation to distant points. This led such observers as Leyton and Sherrington, for example, to report the region of area 6 unresponsive to physiological limits of excitation. Others, using bipolar electrodes, have elicited a variety of complex movements from area 6 (Vogt and Vogt, 1919; Bucy, 1934). Foerster (1936) claimed that in man a direct galvanic current was more effective. We have ourselves observed these complex movements in the macaque with regularity, using either a simple faradic or a sinusoidal stimulus with bipolar electrodes.

From the most medial part of area 6 such stimulation induces movements of all four limbs and turning of the head and eyes to the opposite side. The movements of the limbs begin most commonly with an extension of the contralateral upper limb and flexion of the lower, and as the stimulation continues, the opposite movement of flexion of the ipsilateral upper limb and extension of the ipsilateral lower limb are added. The depth of anaesthesia requires to be very light for elicitation of such movements. At a deeper level of anaesthesia only fragments of the complex movement are obtained, commonly only an extension of contralateral elbow, or protraction of the shoulder. With still deeper anaesthesia no movements can be obtained with the strongest stimulus in area 6, though simple movements can still be obtained from area 4. Vogt and Vogt (1919) and Bucy (1934) obtained such movements after a section between areas 4 and 6, and were unable to obtain them after undercutting area 6, but time was not allowed for degeneration following these procedures. We ourselves (Denny-Brown and Botterell, 1948) found that, if area 4 were excised completely more than 14 days before, only the movement of head and eyes could be obtained from area 6, and then only in its most forward part where it bordered area 8. The focus of this movement was in area 8, and the movement was not obtainable after ablation of area 8. If a few of the most anterior large pyramidal cells of Betz remained after ablation of the remainder of area 4, the complex limb movement could still be elicited from the part of area 6 bordering this region, and could be abolished by undercutting the strip containing these cells. We therefore feel certain that area 6 is not the direct mechanism of any of the movements mentioned.

If the anaesthesia is kept at such a light level that spontaneous movements and postures begin to occur, it is easily shown that stimulation of area 6 will abolish them. The effect is rapid and such that the animal will be quite limp in 3–5 seconds. All limbs are affected. Continuation of the same stimulus may elicit the movements of head, eyes, and limbs as mentioned above, after a preliminary interval during which the spontaneous attitudes subside. The suppressor effect was still present after total ablation of area 4 in our experiments, that is if no Betz cells remained. No such suppressor effect was obtained from area 4, or from the post-central gyrus. After ablation of area 6, no such effect was obtained from area 9, but it was found along the forward part of area 4 when some small strip of area 6 remained. This suppressor effect was observed by Hines (1937) and attributed by her to area 4s. Tower (1936) described the same response in the cat after section of the medullary pyramid on the same side, and in addition found an area in the cingulate region which had the same effect. She noted the very effective suppression of ether postures, and the less effective suppression of movements under anaesthesia. We ourselves found that it was possible to elicit movements by stimulation of area 4 during the suppression, and that if the level of anaesthesia were such as to allow spasticity from ablation of area 4 to be present, such spasticity was not altered by the stimulus. The relation of this effect to that of the suppressor band 4s of McCulloch and his associates will be discussed later. Our own experiments indicate that it belongs to area 6, though an overlap with the most anterior strip of area 4 is possible. In this connexion it may be noted that globular cells resembling the only large cells in area 6, the scattered globular cells in the deeper part of the fifth layer, can be observed in the most anterior part of area 4 in some specimens, lying superficial to the large pyramids of the fifth layer.

Rhythmical movements of the jaw and tongue, as in mastica-tion, are relatively easily elicited from an area near the most lateral part of the central sulcus, and Vogt and Vogt (1919) placed the area concerned in area 6. Inhibition of respiration was ob-served from stimulation of the frontal operculum by Spencer (1894), and this effect has been more recently studied by Smith (1938) and, in man, by Bucy and Case (1936). Walker and Green (1938) showed that the respiratory responses and the masticatory response of area 6 of Vogt and Vogt persisted after ablation of area 4.

The careful studies of Leyton and Sherrington indicate that even at moderate thresholds of monopolar stimulation the only movements of tongue, jaw, and palate and vocal cords that could be obtained from chimpanzee cortex were from areas well beyond area 4. Indeed, in the chimpanzee a greater part of the elicitable movements of the lips is from an area below the lowest limit of area 4. Walker and Green (1938) found that in the macaque such movements as chewing and swallowing obtained from area 6B of Vogt and Vogt, which borders the sylvian fissure, were not abolished by excision of area 4. They were not obtainable from area 4 if area 6B was excised, though contralateral movements of face, tongue and palate were still obtainable, even from a frag-ment of remaining face area. Section between area 6 and 4 in this area did not change the character of the complex type of response (Walker and Green). Excitation of area 6B near the sylvian fissure was also found to alter respiratory rate and depth. Complete arrest of respiration for 10–15 seconds was the most usual re-sponse, but rarely there was only a diminution of excursion.

Salivation is a common result from stimulation of any part of this most lateral extension of the pre-central gyrus.

All these responses have been obtained from the human cortex. In the older charts of Foerster, the words tongue, jaw, palate, and larynx indicate their location, but give a false impression of topographic discreteness. The maps of Penfield and Boldrey (1937) and Rasmussen and Penfield (1947) show the wide extent of the area for each response obtained, and the ease with which the same responses could be obtained from the post-central cortex. Crude vocalization has the widest representation, extending from the face area to the fissure of Sylvius. Salivation, mastication, and swallowing occupied successively smaller overlapping areas nearer the fissure. Unfortunately, most of the data for the charts of these investigators appear to come from mapping of epileptic cortex, but if outlying points in the human cases can be disregarded as epileptic variants, the distribution followed the precise mapping of Leyton and Sherrington (1917) in the chimpanzee.

The study of unilateral and bilateral ablations of these areas in monkeys by Green and Walker (1938) was particularly instructive. After the unilateral extirpation of area 4c in monkeys, there was a contralateral facial paresis lasting up to 5 weeks, with reduction of lingual movements. The tongue still possessed a considerable range of movement. The remaining innervation from one cortex is therefore bilateral in part. Bilateral ablation of area 4, or area 4c, resulted in great diminution of the range of movement of the lower face, though sucking movements could be obtained by stroking the tongue. Pharyngeal stimulation resulted in protrusion of the tongue but with no movement in its anterior two-thirds. The bite was vigorous, and swallowing not impaired. Some resistance to passive opening of the mouth was encountered.

Unilateral ablation of the opercular cortex, leaving area 4 intact, produced a transient paresis of the contralateral lower facial musculature, lasting about one week. Bilateral ablation of this area, leaving area 4, resulted in some initial paresis of the lips and tongue, but this vanished after 4 weeks. Chewing and swallowing were not affected. Ablation of the post-central cortex did not lead to facial or lingual paralysis, or change an existing defect resulting from an area 4 or 6 lesion. Although section of the opposite hypoglossal nerve only slightly lessens the responses of the tongue to cortical stimulation, simultaneous ablation of areas 4 and 6 on one side and section of the hypoglossal nerve on the same side led to a very severe paralysis of the tongue, which lay motionless on the floor of the mouth. Subsequent stimulation of the remaining cortex showed that a wide range of movement of the tongue could be still elicited. Rasmussen and Penfield (1947) remark on the slight weakness following ablation of one motor face area in man, compared with the wide range of uni-lateral facial movement produced by stimulation of the same cortex. This is another of the discrepancies between the results of electrical stimulation and the effect of ablation.

It is clear, therefore, that electrical stimulation of the area that Vogt and Vogt (1919) labelled as area 6B can induce certain com-plex movements which are not obtained from area 4 and persist after ablation of area 4. We conclude that this opercular region exhibits a special type of motor excitability, with multiple points for rhythmical activity such as deglutition, mastication, vocaliza-tion, salivation, and swallowing. Such activity has much in com-mon with the type of response attributed to area 8, and recent histological investigations (von Bonin and Bailey, 1947) indicate that area 6 does not reach this opercular region.

The true area 6, however, does have an immense potentiality for synthesis of movement, for the studies of Dusser de Barenne and his associates demonstrated that it was possible to carry the excitation of any movement previously set up in area 4 into the corresponding region of area 5 by facilitation. This is well shown in their chart of the chimpanzee cortex (Figure 8B). This is a different matter from the supposition that area 6 contains the ready-made combinations of complex movement.

Area 8

The deviation of the eyes to the opposite side as a result of elec-trical stimulation of an area in the middle frontal convolution was early recognized by Ferrier (1886) and others. Ferrier found that electrical stimulation of the cortex of the monkey could induce deviation of the head and eyes to the opposite side from three different areas, the middle frontal gyrus, the superior temporal gyrus, and the posterior parieto-occipital region. When obtained from the middle frontal convolution, the movement of the eyes was usually preceded by opening of the eyes and dilatation of both pupils. When the movement was obtained from the tem-poral lobe, the opposite ear was raised in addition to the other movement; from the parietal lobe the eyes closed, and the pupils contracted. We have ourselves found pricking and turning of both ears to the opposite side from stimulation of the frontal area. These effects are most easily obtained from the region just anterior to the inferior pre-central gyrus, and less easily from a strip extending medially to the border of the hemisphere. In the medial part of the area the turning of the head to the opposite side is usually first to appear, and may be obtained alone. With stronger stimulation the movements may be obtained from a wider area, including the pre-central gyrus and the prefrontal region, but the lowest threshold corresponds to the medial two-thirds of area 8. Recently the same movement of the head and eyes has been obtained from area 24, but this will be discussed separately.

These movements were examined in detail in the chimpanzee cortex by Leyton and Sherrington (1917) who discuss a number of peculiarities. The movement of the eyes is slow and deliberate, with slow return to the resting posture after the stimulus is withdrawn. Slight upward or downward deviation is often added to the lateral movement, and often the movement of the ipsilateral eye would lag behind the other. Convergence was seldom seen, but occurred as a separate movement, as in fixation, elicited from the same area as lateral movement. Conjugate lateral deviation of the eyes was obtained by stimulation of the pre-central gyrus between the hand and face regions, but was then secondary to lateral movement of the head to the opposite side with opening of the eyes. The deviation of the eyes from the middle frontal gyrus could occur without opening of the eyes, especially in the upper part of the area. Turning of the eyes was also obtained from the occipital region, in the cortex bordering the calcarine area and occipital pole.

Opening of the eyes was closely associated with turning of the eyes by stimulation in the middle frontal gyrus and also in the occipital area for eye movement. Closure of the eyes was seen as an entirely different movement, obtainable from the pre-central gyrus between the points for hand movements and those for movements of lip and nostril. Opening of the eyes was a slow movement co-ordinated with turning or fixation; closure of the eyes was always more vigorous in the opposite eye, and could be restricted to this eye by moderation of stimulus, or even to isolated movement of upper or lower lid. Thus closure of the eyes had all the characteristics of other movements elicited from areas 4.

Vogt and Vogt (1907) and Smith (1936, 1944) attempted to divide the frontal eye field into separate fields for individual movements, but there was great overlap of the different fields. Pupillary dilatation is more easily obtained alone from the medial part of the area, and movement of the ears from the region bordering the inferior pre-central sulcus. Russell (1894) found an upward, downward, or convergent response to frontal cortical stimulation if the opposite recti muscles to produce lateral deviation had been divided. It is clear that the whole area is related to the zone called area 8 in the macaque, but the movements can, under favourable circumstances, be obtained from much further forward. They can no longer be obtained from the lateral region of the frontal cortex when area 8 has been excised. In the chimpanzee, in which the sulci are both more complex and more variable, the frontal eye field is very far forward and corresponds with the area FC of Bailey (1948) (Figure 7). Though its responses identify it as area 8 (Figure 8B), Bailey points out that the cyto-architecture is ill-defined, as in the human. The distribution is consistent with the results of Leyton and Sherrington in the orang-utan, gorilla, and chimpanzee and suggests that a similar pattern will be found in man. In man the electro-stimulable area has not been systematically demarcated. References to the sampled responses in a number of patients observed by Penfield and Boldrey (1937) indicate some points in von Economo's area FC, some in FB and many in FA. Isolated points in the temporal and occipital lobe are also shown. The chart of Foerster (1936) is clearly a transfer of the diagram of Vogt and Vogt (1919) to the human cortex, and the general nature of the responses described indicates that the secondary adversive movement obtained from areas 6 and 4 in the monkey were observed.

Brown (1922) noted that in some experiments under very light anaesthesia, when the head was suspended so that it was free to turn, stimulation of the medial part of area 8 induced turning of head to the opposite side, the eyes remaining fixed in forward gaze. If movement of the head was prevented, the eyes then turned. With deeper anaesthesia the effect was not obtained. Brown argues that this response is identical with the compensatory labyrinthine reflex which causes a movement of the eyes in contrary direction when the head is passively turned. He did not find the same relation between eye and head movement in the occipital region, to which he accordingly relegated the function of primary visual fixation. There is certainly a direct occipito-tectal pathway traced by both degenerative and electrical methods (Crosby and Henderson, 1948). Brown inferred that the frontal eye movements were part of a mechanism which enabled visual fixation to be compensated for movement, but we feel that a better explanation is that the frontal movement is part of a total orientation and not just a visual function.

That some functional relationship exists between the frontal adversive eye field and the labyrinthine mechanism for eye movements has been maintained by many. Bárány, Vogt, and Vogt (1923) found that the eye muscles contracting in the slow component of induced labyrinthine nystagmus could be relaxed by ipsilateral frontal stimulation. Spiegel and Scala (1936) found that labyrinthine nystagmus is modified by frontal lesion. Delmas-Marsalet (1936) found that cocainization of the labyrinth on the same side as a prefrontal lesion greatly increased the nystagmus and forced movements to the opposite side instead of to the ipsilateral side as found by labyrinthine cocainization in the normal animal. This reversal was also obtained in the normal animal by deviating the neck in a plaster cast. Delmas-Marsalet therefore considered that changes in labyrinthine effect are due to the altered neck posture after frontal-lobe lesions, and are not due to direct effect on labyrinthine reflexes. We believe that these effects have only demonstrated an algebraic summation between the relative postural responses obtained from the frontal lobe and labyrinth.

It is of particular significance to our present conception of the functions of the frontal lobe that Sachs (1909) found that excitation of the dorso-medial nucleus of the thalamus causes the slow onset of a state of attention with fixation of the eyes in the midline. Stimulation of the ventral part of the dorso-medial nucleus caused deviation of the head and eyes to the opposite side of the flexion of the opposite forelimb. The movement in question is therefore important in consideration of the function of the whole of this widespread frontothalamic relationship.

The path of conduction of eye movements from the frontal eye fields can be traced to the genu of the internal capsule medial to the cortico-bulbar pathway for movements of the face (Beevor and Horsley, 1890). Denny-Brown and Botterell (1948) found that at a slightly lower level in the macaque the point for movement of the head and eyes on electrical stimulation had left the internal capsule to lie in the region of the subthalamic nucleus. From this point caudally the movement can be obtained from a number of structures, including the field of Forel, capsule of the red nucleus, and central tegmental tract (Ingram, Ranson, and Hannett, 1931). This different course from the cortico-bulbar projection of area 4 explains the infrequent bilateral affection of movement of the head and eyes in the pseudo-bulbar syndrome, and its occurrence as a separate type of supranuclear spastic disorder from frontal lesions (Holmes, 1938). There is no evidence that the globus pallidus is directly concerned in the mechanism, as has been maintained by some. Thus it seems clear that the Marchi degenerations observed by Levin (1936) and others to follow ablation of area 8 and terminating in the substantia nigra and pons are not necessarily concerned with adversive movement of the head and eyes.

Extrapyramidal motor effects

It has been universal experience that stimulation of the region of frontal cortex forward of the area for eye and head movement fails to induce any consistent response. Occasionally a movement of progression will occur in the limbs but fails to occur on repetition of the stimulus. It is only after ablation of areas 4 and 6 or section of the pyramid that one can be sure that any response such as progression is not also a spread of effect to more excitable areas. Though bilateral movement had been obtained from the region of the superior pre-central sulcus in monkeys and shown to persist after section of the medullary pyramid in acute experiments by Hering (1899), the work of Tower first established the widespread nature of excitability remaining after pyramid section. In the cat, Tower (1936) found four 'extrapyramidal motor areas', of which the frontal area was the most elaborate (Figure 9). The parietal area produced often only adversive movements. A lateral ectosylvian area gave a flexion of the contralateral leg, with pronation and extended claws as in readiness to strike, and at times movements of the tail with abrupt acceleration of respiration. A posterior parietal region yielded striking movements of the crossed fore-limb and flexion of the ipsilateral hind-limb, and at times diagonal progression.

The frontal 'extra-pyramidal' field in the cat (Figure 9 a and b) was subdivided into three independent areas which overlapped on the anterior lip of the cruciate sulcus. The 'posterior extra-pyramidal frontal field' was co-extensive with the area of distribution of giant pyramids in the cat (though these were degenerated by pyramid section) and gave a flexion of wrist, ankle, and digits of the crossed limbs with minimal stimulus, extending to flexion of proximal joints with stronger stimulation. The hind-limb was the more affected in the area for leg movement in the intact animal, the fore-limb in its appropriate area. Each ipsilateral extremity extended as the contralateral flexed. Continued stimulation led to a progression, with alternation either between two homologous extremities or two contralateral extremities. Occasionally the alternation was the very deliberate al-

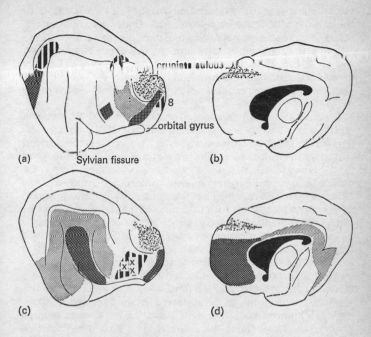

cruciate sulcus

8

orbital gyrus

(a)

Sylvian fissure

(b)

(c)

(d)

Figure 9. Diagram of the brain of the cat. In (a) and (b) various areas
which produced excitatory effects after pyramid section are shown (from
Tower, 1936). Dark shading shows the anterior, lateral (sylvian), and posterior extra-pyramidal motor areas (striking movement, associated with
acceleration of respiration and lashing of the tail). The speckled tint shows
the total area of the 'frontal extra-pyramidal motor area' ('pleasure reaction')
of Tower, surrounding the cruciate sulcus. Light shading shows the area
for licking and chewing movements. The striped areas gave an adversive
movement of head and eyes, and these same areas were found to be suppressor areas by Garol (1942)

In (c) and (d) are plotted the areas found by Tower (1936) to have
inhibitory effect on posture and movement after section of the pyramid.
The total extent of the areas which inhibited posture is shown by speckled
shading. The areas whch inhibited movement and respiration are shown
in light and dark shading. The striped area shows the distribution of a
weaker suppression of movement and respiration found by Smith (1938).
The small crosses show an area which commonly gave acceleration of
respiration

ternation between the two fore-limbs in the 'pleasure reaction' of the cat, the hind-limbs being extended. Under very light anaesthesia these reactions, once initiated, were continued after stimulation, with spontaneous variations. At this depth of anaesthesia the same behaviour could also begin spontaneously. Primary crossed extension of the fore-limb was seldom observed. Progression or pleasure reaction were mutually exclusive, each of the other.

An anterior extra-pyramidal frontal motor field (Figure 9 a and b) was found to occupy the medial half of the pre-cruciate gyrus and extend far forward and laterally into the antero-lateral surface of the frontal lobe. The lowest threshold was just forward of the cruciate sulcus but the effect was obtainable across the coronal and orbital gyri two months after radical removal of the entire pericruciate region. The effect of stimulation was a flexion of the crossed fore-limb with extension of the claws, and protraction at the shoulder, followed at once by flexion of the digits and extension. This is a movement of aggressive striking. It could also occur in the hind-limb. In less active sequence the movement was as if placing the paw on an object, and if some light pressure was brought on the pad of the foot as it was brought down, the movement stopped abruptly and the limb stiffened in extension. If this aggressive type of movement appeared, it could become rhythmical, with humped back, alternately moving tail and accelerated respiration. Throughout the entire field or area the stimulated movement had thus a general pattern with varying *tempo* and aggressiveness.

The median frontal extra-pyramidal motor field of Tower was the most capricious. It was excitable only under very light anaesthesia and lay over the medial extent of the pre-cruciate sulcus. The stereotyped movement obtained from it was a steadily maintained flexion, adduction and supination of the contralateral fore-limb, with extended claws, with or without a similar movement of the hind-limb, and extension of the ipsilateral limb. The trunk was usually flexed to the side of stimulation, and sometimes the head also.

These cortical motor effects obtained by electrical stimulation in the cat after pyramid section were all remarkable in the lightness of anaesthesia required for their presence, and the degree to which the same or similar movements could occur spontaneously at this degree of anaesthesia. They were also remarkable in the slow development of the movement, the adherence to a general pattern throughout a large field, and the independence of the areas concerned. The movements from the ectosylvian and posterior parietal areas yielded variants of those of the anterior frontal region.

The corresponding movements in the monkey after pyramid section have been only briefly described (Hines, 1943). The frontal area was said to include all of areas 6 and 8, and perhaps part of area 9, and extension of these areas on the medial aspect of the hemisphere. The elicited movements varied from 'simple synergies' to 'complex movements involving the total skeletal muscle'. The elaboration of synergies yielded a 'complex reaching and grasping act'. An extensor synergy often had a diagonal variation, sometimes ending in progression. In both cat and monkey the adversive movement of eyes, ears, head, and trunk could be added to any of the above movements if the frontal eye field in area 8 was active at the time of stimulation in its neighbourhood.

In our own experience of stimulation of the frontal lobes in the monkey after recovery from pyramid section we have observed only a movement of progression from stimulation of the general region of areas 8 and 9. There has not as yet been any evidence of separate extra-pyramidal motor patterns of the type described by Tower in the cat. In the monkey, however, the depression of general motor function following section of the medullary pyramid is much more severe than in the cat. It is perhaps significant that the movement from frontal cortex proper is aggressive, and that from the rolandic region is a stereotyped pleasure mannerism peculiar to the cat.

Since there are many reasons for considering the superior pre-central sulcus in primates, including man, as homologous with the cruciate sulcus in cat and dog, it is of interest that the frontal extra-pyramidal areas in the cat should centre on, and overlap in, its anterior lip. It is precisely this region of the pre-central sulcus in the primate (area 4s, forward medial division of area 4) which has been the source of greatest difficulty in physiological and cytological definition. The work of Tower in the cat showed clearly that the extra-pyramidal areas in that animal have separately excitable projections in the underlying white matter, and can be identified by stimulation in the internal capsule after pyramid section. Their individuality is lost at subthalamic level, where only a stereotyped pattern of diagonal movement is usually obtained. Destruction of the caudate nucleus was without effect. The extra-pyramidal somatic motor effects are evidently diffuse and are probably identical with emotional display. Their meaning will perhaps be more clear after consideration of other effects to be discussed below.

Suppression

In their early experiments upon stimulation of the region of the cruciate sulcus in the dog under morphine, Bubnoff and Heidenhain (1881) found that if the anaesthesia was such as to lead to a state of maintained slight contraction in the skeletal musculature, weak stimulation of the cortex could, under some circumstances, relax that postural activity. Brown and Sherrington (1912) analysed the responses of antagonistic pairs of muscles to stimulation of the pre-central gyrus in various primates and noted the occurrence of inhibition of pre-current contraction without excitation, as a phenomenon separate from reciprocal innervation. The latter is a common though not invariable accompaniment of excitation of one of a pair of muscles. Purely inhibitory effects were indeed more commonly encountered than pure excitatory responses. Cooper and Denny-Brown (1927) found a very brief latency for this inhibition of preceding postural contraction when a stimulus was applied to the pre-central gyrus, and long delay in the appearance of muscular contraction when such inhibitory effects were prominent. They considered clonic post-stimulative epilepsy to be a rebound effect from such inhibitory-excitatory conflict. In a study of the thresholds of the pre-central gyrus, Tower (1928) found inhibitory effects to have lower thresholds than motor. These inhibitory effects were studied further by Rioch and Rosenblueth (1935) who found that, apart from reciprocal inhibition in association with excitation obtained from area 4, bilateral inhibition of spinal reflexes was obtainable from the remainder of the agranular cortex, even after hemisection of the spinal cord, in cat, dog, and monkey. This bilateral inhibition was effective against cortically induced contraction.

In 1936 Tower reported inhibitory responses to stimulation of the cerebral cortex of the cat following section of the medullary pyramid. Two areas were found to inhibit postural activity under ether anaesthesia, and three additional areas suppressed the movements which occur spontaneously in light anaesthesia. Since this is the only detailed account of these responses in relation to total behaviour, we may consider them in some detail. The two fields of inhibition of 'tonic' contraction together covered the whole agranular frontal cortex of the cat. The posterior field corresponded to the distribution of the giant pyramids (area 4) of the cat, and its stimulation brought relaxation of any tonic activity of either flexors or extensors of the opposite limbs, during light anaesthesia. The effect was of low threshold and developed rapidly, thus preceding any excitatory effect that might also be present. The anterior field for inhibitory action on tone occupied the medial part of the pre-cruciate gyrus and extended forwards and medially a short distance. It overlapped the posterior field in the cruciate sulcus, but in general corresponded with the extent of frontal agranular cortex (area 6). Stimulation of this field yielded relaxation of any tonic activity in all ipsilateral parts. Contralateral effect was less constant, and was more commonly obtained in the region of overlap of the fields near the cruciate sulcus. Since the difference between the two fields was the accentuation of the effect on the ipsilateral or contralateral side, and since the two effects could summate in any one limb from bilateral stimulation, it was considered that possibly only one mechanism was concerned. The possibility of transmission across the corpus callosum from the anterior field was not excluded. These effects are evidently identical, except only in their greater extent, with the inhibition already observed by others. The total area concerned is shown in speckled shading in Figure 9 c and d.

These relaxing effects on either the pseudo-decerebrate posture or the general flexion of light anaesthesia were differentiated sharply by Tower from the effects obtained from three further areas which were 'powerfully effective against movement' (Figure 9 c and d, light and dark shading). These were a frontal field covering the gyrus proreus and the frontal portion of the gyrus fornicatus, a lateral field in the anterior and posterior sylvian gyri, extending a variable distance into the ectosylvian gyrus in different animals, and a field on the tentorial surface of the occipital lobe. These areas had no striking cyto-architectural feature in common except that the internal pyramidal layer was well developed in all. The inhibitory action was effective against a variety of effects deliberately excited or occurring spontaneously. Rhythmical activities such as progression, side-to-side movements of the tail, mastication or respiration were either slowed or abolished, and frequently occurred in more intense or more frequent rebound immediately after the stimulus. The frontal and sylvian fields were the most effective. Anaesthesia had to be kept at a very light level for the demonstration of these activities, but with the increasing restlessness of very light anaesthesia, the effect appeared to be merely one of quieting the animal. Respiration could be quickened by stimulation of these areas in much deeper anaesthesia. In light anaesthesia movements of any vigour, such as running or striking movements of the fore-legs, came to an abrupt halt, and a fixed attitude replaced them. This assumption of an attitude 'eyes front, head raised, back and tail straight, legs extended or semi-flexed' would sometimes be held for perhaps a minute after stimulation. There was little variation in the type of movements controlled from each area, but it was noted that inhibition of respiration was at times obtained from the pre-cruciate gyrus, and that the attitude of fixation of attention was obtained particularly from the frontal and sylvian areas. A quieting effect was more widespread and could at times be obtained from the region surrounding the cruciate sulcus.

Though Tower made a very abrupt distinction between inhibitory effects on 'tone' and those on 'movements', this interpretation appears to us to be unfortunate. 'Tone' in this connotation meant the fixed postures of moderate grades of anaesthesia, and since under these circumstances, the second type of inhibition either did not occur, or was minimal in effect, it cannot be maintained that the second type of inhibition was not effective against such 'tone'. 'Postures which either precede, or are the immediate remainder of, movement may be abolished, but a steady tonic innervation such as the extension of the pseudo-decerebrate state is quite unaffected' (Tower, 1936). We would therefore prefer to regard the difference as a result of the different background of activity. The observations of Tower, however, established the existence of a pattern of suppression, with a mechanism independent of the medullary pyramids, in widespread but distinct regions of the cerebral cortex. Smith (1938) found the same widespread effect on movement throughout the wide area inhibiting respiration, including the bridging area between frontal and sylvian regions shown by speckled shading in Figure 9 c. In this region the inhibitory effects were weaker.

The next important contribution to this subject emerged from the long series of investigations of facilitation in the motor cortex by Dusser de Barenne and McCulloch, which culminated in a study of the suppression of the motor response from area 4 in the macaque by stimulation of neighbouring cortex (Dusser de Barenne and McCulloch, 1938, 1939; Dusser de Barenne, Garol, and McCulloch, 1941). The local application of strychnine to specific small strips of cortex was found to set up a local disturbance in the nature of the appearance of spikes in the electroencephalogram, but in addition had the effect of suppressing the electrical activity of the remainder of the entire hemisphere. This suppressor effect was found to occur from distinct bands passing medio-laterally (Figure 8) in the region of area 8, the function of areas 4 and 6, and approximately the centres of areas 2 and 19, and these were called the suppressor bands 8s, 4s, 2s, and 19s. The suppression of the electroencephalogram usually began 7–12 minutes after the application of strychnine, lasted several minutes, and required about 15 minutes to cross beyond the central fissure. This slow spread closely resembles that of another electro-encephalographic phenomenon called the spreading depression of Leão (1944), which appears to be some form of electrical disturbance as yet not identified with any physiological process. De Barenne and McCulloch, however, showed that their effect was abolished by section of descending tracts and in some part dependent upon the function of the caudate nucleus and thalamus (McCulloch, 1944, 1948). It has also been found that strychninization of these suppressor bands 'fires' the reticular formation on the opposite side of the brain stem, the direct stimulation of which exerts a strong suppression on the motor mechanism. It was found (McCulloch, 1944) that these suppressor effects were particularly powerfully exerted from area 24 in the cingulate cortex, so that the 'suppressor band 24s' became added to the list.

Dusser de Barenne, Garol, and McCulloch (1941) examined the effects of electrical stimulation of chimpanzee cortex under very light Dial anaesthesia. Their previous experience with suppressor bands in the macaque led them to chart facilitations and suppressions separately, leaving long intervals between examination of a region expected to be excitor and one suspected of being inhibitor. Bipolar electrodes and relatively slow rates of stimulus (1–40 a second) were used. Their chart (Figure 8B) is particularly illuminating. Stimulation of bands 4s and 2s, even with three or four times the voltage which elicited a response from adjacent motor foci, failed to elicit movement. Yet it suppressed the motor response from any motor region for many seconds or even minutes, it suppressed the after-discharge from a previous motor stimulation, even of clonic epileptic nature, and it relaxed any postural activity present in the limbs. Stimulation of band 8s induced movements of the eyes, in addition to the inhibitory effects on other movement. Movements of the eyes had been reported from the region of the band 19s by others, but was found further forward in these experiments. It is now known that the cingulate cortex in the region of band 24s also induces deviation of the head and eyes to the opposite side (Smith, 1949) besides a powerful inhibitory effect on all movement. The band 4s was initially identified with the strip area of Hines, which we shall discuss later in relation to spasticity. It appears to us that the suppressor band '4s' in the chimpanzee was well forward of area 4, and von Bonin (von Bonin and Bailey, 1947) now disclaims any structural peculiarity for the suppressor band 4s in the macaque. Denny-Brown and Botterell (1948) have shown that inhibition of posture and movement was still present in the posterior border of area 6, after complete ablation of area 4. Inhibition was, under these circumstances, bilateral and effective against spontaneous chewing, running, standing, and was present in all muscle groups. It was not obtained in this form from the posterior strip of area 4, stimulation of which induced an appropriately localized relaxation and then movement of the extremity combined with continued spontaneous movement or posture in other limbs. We have no doubt that this latter effect is identical with that described as 'extra-pyramidal inhibitory action on tone' by Tower in relation to the cruciate sulcus of the cat after pyramid section and with the suppressor band 4s of McCulloch. The difference between the large areas found by Hines and the narrow suppressor strips of McCulloch appears to us to be only the inverse of the broad bands of motor facilitation shown in Figure 8B, and the more usually represented pre-central motor strip. Inhibitory effects can be facilitated in the same manner as motor, and primary suppression in the cat was shown by Garol (1942) to occupy the same suppressor bands 8s, 2s, 19s, though none has yet been reported in the 4–6 boundary in this animal, which is probably buried in the cruciate sulcus. We may therefore bring this apparently contradictory and unrelated evidence together in the statement that stimulation of any of the whole limbic frontal and sylvian region can under favourable circumstances inhibit spontaneous motor automatisms and replace them with an attitude of 'expectancy'. In certain limited areas, 24s, 8s, 19s, and probably 2s, both motor and inhibitory effect is more intense, the 'expectancy' then passing into a movement of exploration of the opposite visual field, in which the eyes lead the response. This type of response is weakest in the lateral orbital and opercular region where movements of licking and chewing are prominent. In contrast, the inhibitory mechanism of the pre-central region, though total in its effect, can be fractionated in accordance with the facility with which fractional movement can be obtained from the same area.

The total motor response of the frontal and sylvian cortex appears to be aggressive, that of the pre-central cortex a benign self-satisfying motor automatism, or 'pleasure reaction'. In the

strict anatomical sense these and the associated inhibitory phenomena are all 'extra-pyramidal' activities.

The cingulate gyrus

The responsiveness of the cingulate gyrus to stimulation has only
recently been recognized. McCulloch (1944) in the course of
investigation of suppressor areas found that area 24, the portion
of the cingulate gyrus which lies over the genu and anterior third
of the corpus callosum, contained a particularly powerful suppressor band (24s). By physiological neuronography this was
found to project to the caudate nucleus and also the medial
reticular formation of the medulla. An efferent tract can be shown
by the Marchi method to join the internal capsule and pass into
the ventral and medial portion of the cerebral peduncles on as far
as the pons. The area also projects to the caudal part of the
cingulate gyrus and into area 6 (Ward, Penden, and Sugar, 1946).
The only known afferents to the anterior cingulate gyrus are from
the antero-medial nucleus of the thalamus.

Both motor and automatic effects have been obtained by
stimulation of this area, as well as suppression of motor activity
(Ward, 1948). Pupillary dilatation is obtained from the dorsal
part of the area, as from the medial extension of area 8 nearby.
Pilo-erection follows stimulation of the more caudal parts of the
area and marked respiratory slowing and arrest may be obtained
from the more rostral parts of the area including the pre-callosal
portion. Slowing of the heart and a marked fall (occasional rise)
in blood pressure are also obtained. Stimulation of the more
caudal parts of area 24, which lies under the medial extension of
area 4, elicits turning of the head and eyes to the opposite side.
After prolonged stimulation, bilateral associated movements of
the limbs and trunk occur. Under light anaesthesia stimulation
of the rostral cingulate region induces vocalization and complex
facial movements (Smith, 1949). Changes in pulse, blood pressure
and respiration have also been observed from stimulation of the
rostral cingulate gyrus in man (Pool and Ransohoff, 1949). Interruption of speech and voluntary activity from stimulation of the
margin of the hemisphere overlying this area in man have been
noted by Penfield and Welch (1949).

The orbital surface

Arrest of respiration and change in blood pressure (usually a fall)
in response to stimulation of the orbital surface of the frontal lobe
was described by Spencer in 1894. The area concerned was 'just

399

lateral to the olfactory tract in lightly anaesthetized rabbit, cat, dog, or monkey'. Bailey and Sweet (1940) found in addition a decrease in gastric tonus. Others have confirmed these findings, and Sachs and Brendler (1948) have found that section of the vagi or removal of the adrenals had no effect on the respiratory and vasopressor effects. Bailey and Bremer (1938) found increased electrical activity in this area when the central end of the cut vagus was stimulated. Delgado and Livingston (1948) found that mechanical stimulation of the same region had the same effects and in addition observed a rise of limb temperature when a cold pledget was applied to this area. Stimulation of the same region of the orbital part of the frontal lobe in man during lobotomy operations (Livingston, Chapman, and Livingston, 1948) evoked respiratory arrest and moderate rise in blood pressure. All these effects have been obtained from the postero-lateral orbital region (area 47, Figures 2 and 6) of which the affiliations with the sylvian region have already been noted. It also fires the paraventricular nuclei and lateral area of the hypothalamus.

The essential identity of the postero-lateral orbital area and the piriform cortex which bridges the sylvian fissure to the inner aspect of the temporal pole has recently been emphasized by Smith (1949) and Kaada, Pribram, and Epstein (1949). Excitation of the posterior piriform cortex was found to cause powerful contraction of the bladder in the cat (Smith, 1949) as well as respiratory cardiovascular and pilomotor effects. It has only recently been shown that the visceral effects can also be traced medially to the cingulate cortex (Kaada, Pribram, and Epstein, 1949).

The frontal pole

The uniform cyto-architectural structure of the frontal polar cortex with its small cells and thick internal granular layer and its almost exclusive connexion with the dorso-medial nucleus of the thalamus indicate some uniformity in mechanism. Electrical stimulation in primates has not as yet provided any evidence, except for inconstant adversive or inhibitory response. Its connexions with the temporal region, and with the opposite frontal pole, indicate potentiality for extensive facilitatory effects.

General conclusions derived from the results of stimulation

The pattern of responses to electrical stimulation of the frontal lobe has some general correspondence with the cyto-architectural plan. Yet, just as too great insistence on the details of boundary

lines has led to errors in the localization of effects, so the difficulties inherent in the interpretation of the effect of an electrical
stimulus have led to very artificial conceptions of function.

The three broad divisions of cortical structure into the agranular pre-central, the anterior limbic area, and the frontal cortex,
are found to have three general categories of response to electrical
stimulation. The agranular pre-central cortex, which includes
areas 4 and 6, FA and FB, presents a low threshold for the effects
of stimulation of a topographically arranged series of foci in a
relatively fixed pattern. The anterior limbic cortex, and its extension into the posterior orbital surface and thence across the
sylvian fissure to the piriform cortex, gives stereotyped responses
in which arrest of respiration and vasomotor effects are prominent. The similar character of these responses from widely
separated parts of this area make it likely that the pilo-erection
and active micturition reported from the piriform cortex and
gastric contraction from the posterior frontal cortex will eventually also be obtained from the other parts. As far as suppression
of postures and respiratory effects are concerned, this excitable
area is in fact very wide indeed. The anterior limbic and piriform
cortex constitute the focal areas of this reactivity. Relative concentrations of adversive movement of head and eyes are found
in the cingulate cortex and area 8, of chewing, licking, and salivation in the opercular region. The attitudinal response of expectancy is widely represented.

Comparative anatomy teaches that the external surface of the
cerebral hemisphere is a later addition to the central nervous
system, the neopallium, which enfolds a corresponding neo-
striatum (caudate nucleus and putamen). In the most simply
organized neocortex, such as that of the alligator (Bailey and
Richter, 1924) electrical stimulation of a point in the rostral neopallium results only in a diagonal progression. From this diagonal
(flexion of fore-limb and opposite hind-limb) 'patterned response'
the charts of excitation from rabbit to man exhibit progressive
modification. Except for the appearance of the rolandic motor
system, the remainder of the cortex shows a gradual evolution in
complexity rather than a development of new systems. The original patterns of response are present in the primate cortex, each
with appended areas the response of which to stimulation, if any,
indicates a greater refinement. An evolution in terms of more discrete topographic representation of more detailed parts has
occurred, however, only in relation to area 4. The more particulate representation of lips, fingers, and toes in this area in higher

forms derives no explanation from the effects of electrical stimulation. The evolution of the remainder of the frontal cortex does not show such topographic differentiation. Slowing or arrest of respiration and rise of blood pressure and probably visceral contraction and pilomotor reactions remain as diffusely represented functions the pseudo-affective accompaniments of which indicate that they can be part and parcel of a general emotional response. The more commonly obtained and more diffusely represented reaction of 'expectancy' or 'orientation' appears to be a more fundamental primary response to which reactions commonly associated with aggression or flight may be added.

The frontal cortex proper, the broad expanse of areas 8, 9, 10, 11, 12, 45, and 46, appears to be an expansion of an area, which in the cat is bordered by respiratory and vasopressor responses around its medial oral and lateral edge, and by movement of eyes and head caudally and medially. Though some relative concentration of separate head and eye movement has occurred, there is not a separate area for each. This projection is independent of the parietal, temporal and occipital projections for the same movement. But the movement, as a movement, is the same from all these areas, just as inhibition of respiration, and of other spontaneous movements can be independently projected from cingulate and piriform cortex. Thus the executive effects of the frontal cortex proper, as those of the limbic lobe, appear to be a general category of expression with accentuation of one or other component in poorly localized foci. Except that the demonstrable foci are more obvious, and that a greater proportion of the relative foci are related to small parts of the body, precisely the same process of evolution can be traced for the pre-central gyrus.

It has been noted that emotional respiratory movement has been stimulated as a bark in the dog or a hiss in the cat from the cortex at the neck of the sylvian fissure. In the neighbouring left frontal operculum (Broca's area), the respiratory automatism of speech can be readily affected by stimulation in man (Rasmussen and Penfield, 1947). The result appears to be an expiratory sound rather than formed speech. So also, stimulation of the medial aspect of the superior frontal convolution has produced a rhythmical interruption of speech in man (Brickner, 1940; Penfield and Welch, 1949). Concomitant change in pulse rate (Penfield) suggests that area 24 is primarily concerned. Speech is not disordered by stimulation of area 4 on the lateral aspect of the hemisphere. It therefore appears that we may make the generalization that the frontal cortex proper has within it certain effects also obtainable from the limbic cortex, but that these are in the frontal cortex adapted to special purposes, so that control of respiration in areas 24, 12 and the piriform cortex has appeared in area 44 adapted to the purpose of speech.

It is clear that the greater part of the cerebral cortex is electrically excitable if conditions favour activity. It is no longer possible to speak of a 'motor area' which is defined as being electrically excitable. It is also doubtful whether one can speak of cortical 'centres' or of 'representation'. Every part and every motor function is represented, and each in numerous areas. It is doubtful whether, for example, a hand area or a foot area means more than a local preponderance of connexion. Definition may be primarily in terms of threshold of stimulation, or in relative discreteness of motor effect, but these in the last analysis refer to relative accessibility to direct stimulus. The explanation of these multiple representations is without doubt in the adequate physiological stimulus to which each is designed to respond.

Ablation Experiments

Inferences as to function derived from ablation experiments involve a totally different approach to the problem of frontal lobe function. The early studies on the effects of frontal lobe ablation were concerned with either prefrontal ablation or ablation of the pre-central and post-central cortex. They have been well summarized by Ferrier (1886). Hitzig, Goltz, Horsley, and Schäfer and Ferrier found that bilaterial ablation of the prefrontal cortex in the dog and monkey, sparing areas 8, 6, and 4, and most of the orbital surface of the frontal lobe, resulted in no defect in skin sensation, special senses or movement. All these observers noted a defect in behaviour of the animal and periodic restlessness after such ablation. Hitzig (1884) ascribed the defect to a 'weakness of memory' such that the dog would seem to forget a piece of meat soon after showing he had perceived its presence. He would fail to search in the habitual place where food was left. Goltz (1884) noted a fixed and stupid expression in the eyes and inability to fix the gaze. The animals were able to perceive and recognize persons and objects and would wince at a threatening gesture, but showed no inclination to flee, and made no sound indicative of fear.

If the region, which on stimulation yielded deviation of the eyes, was included in the ablation on one side, a conjugate deviation of the eyes to the side of the lesion immediately resulted, but lasted only a few days. Ablation of the corresponding area on the opposite side then resulted in a transient conjugate deviation of the eyes in the other direction for a few days. After bilateral lesion in the monkey, Ferrier observed inability to turn the head or eyes in either direction, and some rhythmical oscillation of the head was observed in this period. Yet in a few days the ability to turn head and eyes in any direction without unsteadiness or stiffness was regained. Recovery of motor performance in the cat and dog after bilateral removal of the peri-cruciate region (areas 6 and 4) is well known, but movement is unstable and awkward, and the limbs trip over comparatively slight obstacles. The paw cannot be used to reach forth and seize a piece of food out of reach of the lips, and it cannot steady a bone. The animal cannot walk along a horizontal lattice work or ladder. Yet Goltz (1884) after bilateral extirpation of the frontal lobes forward of the cruciate sulcus in the dog found no weakness of trunk musculature and movements of the head and eyes were recovered. The motor defect was not appreciably greater than from removal of the cruciate region alone. The early work on the pre-central gyrus of the monkey demonstrated that an enduring paralysis of arm or leg or both could be induced by excision of the appropriate parts of the pre-central gyrus, but even in this animal a surprising degree of recovery of function could occur after 4–6 weeks. More recent studies will be considered from the point of view of paralysis and spasticity, the grasp reflex, loss of conjugate deviation of the eyes, autonomic effects, change in behaviour, and impairment of test responses.

Paralysis and spasticity

We have already discussed the evidence for topographic localization of motor functions within area 4, and the confusion that was introduced by the inclusion of the forward field of area 4 as a part of area 6. Fulton and Kennard (1934) found that the experimental ablation of the caudal part of area 4 in the monkey and chimpanzee induced a severe paralysis of the limbs which was most complete in the hand and foot. The paralysis was said to be flaccid. Further ablation of 'area 6' (including what we now recognize as the anterior strip of area 4) brought a spastic rigidity in the affected limbs. If these operations were carried out bilaterally and serially, the ablation of the last 'area 6' induced a complete bilateral paralysis, with the appearance of bilateral grasping responses. Ablation of 'area 6 alone' (including the superior pre-central sulcus) induced spasticity and a grasp reflex in the contralateral limbs. The demonstration of a cortico-reticular projection from area 6 was the basis for the proposition that spasticity was the result of interference with this extra-pyramidal projection. Impairment of skilled movements, forced grasping, spasticity, and vasomotor disturbance was advanced as 'the syndrome of the pre-motor cortex' (Kennard, Viets and Fulton, 1934). The term 'pre-motor cortex' (Fulton, 1935) was used to indicate the erroneous area 6 of Vogt and Vogt (1919) in all this work, and is now meaningless.

Hines (1937) found that the spasticity occurring in the experiments such as those described by Fulton and Kennard was produced when a strip of cortex, which included the superior pre-central sulcus, was alone removed and that such a strip included giant pyramidal cells in the fifth layer. She called this strip 4s and found that lesions of the lateral part of 4s induced increase of reflexes without spasticity, and that spasticity without weakness was caused by damage to the medial part of 4s. She reported no change from ablation of area 6, and a flaccid paralysis for discrete movements of the fingers and toes from area 4. In this period Tower (1935, 1940) described a flaccid paralysis of similar distribution in the cat and monkey resulting from section of the medullary pyramid. Fulton (1949b) now holds that spasticity results from damage to the extra-pyramidal projection of either 4 or 6, and that damage to the cortico-spinal projection of area 4 results in flaccid paralysis. Even if the term spasticity be limited to an extremely rigid hemiplegic attitude associated with clonus and clasp-knife reaction, as in the work of Fulton, Hines, and Tower, the work of Hines seems to negate such a conclusion. The crucial test would be the effect of ablation of areas 4 and 6 after section of the pyramid on the same side. Tower (1935) found only 'a slight but definite rigidity in the affected leg' when this was performed in the cat. There is no published account of the operation in the monkey, but our own experience (Denny-Brown and Twitchell, 1950) revealed only a slight reflex change. There is, therefore, some fundamental fault in the whole approach of the investigators we have cited.

Through this period a somewhat confused argument arose as to whether movements or muscles are represented in the pre-central gyrus. Leyton and Sherrington (1917) noted,

the large variety of partial, though discrete and in themselves perfect, movements of separate portions of the bodily framework, evocable from point-to-point stimulation. . . . They lead to the supposition that

405

from movements of locally restricted parts, e.g. movements of a finger or of a limb joint (movements themselves discrete and individually separable in the motor cortex), the upbuilding of larger combinations . . . is one of the main offices performed by the motor cortex.

As a result of observation of the same phenomenon, and of the persistence of weakness in movements of the hand after ablation of the arm area, Hines (1937) and Tower (1940) propounded the that the function of the pre-central gyrus was the initiation of discrete movements. Hines (1944) later speaks of 'loss of ability to select the desired prime mover. . . . After small discrete removals of the hand-finger area the flexors or the extensors of single digits cannot become prime movers without years of training.' Bucy, in a footnote to the above statement, goes so far as to impute lack of interest in the subject to those who do not acknowledge representation of muscles in the pre-central gyrus. Yet none of these writers appears to have troubled to find out what Jackson and Sherrington meant by 'representation'. Walshe (1943, 1947) has critically reviewed the whole matter. None will deny that by using a just-threshold stimulus it is possible to activate part of a single muscle from the cerebral cortex, or indeed a single motor unit in a single muscle. The same is true of a spinal anterior nerve root. The question is, rather, how does the mechanism use this particulate connexion. There is no evidence that destruction of any cortical area will paralyse one muscle, and affect no others. Nor can the use of one single muscle or one digit as a prime mover be abolished in this way.

Denny-Brown and Botterell (1948) describe the course of recovery of movement following ablation of areas 6 and 4, and parts of area 4, in macaques and one chimpanzee in considerable detail. They point out that spasticity, like movement, has to recover from the spinal shock or reflex depression that follows any cortico-spinal lesion, that this shock is the greater the larger the extent of area 4 excised, and that spasticity never occurred without some impairment of motor function (that is, 'paralysis'). The survival of even a few Betz cells in an area of ablation lessens spinal shock and in so doing alters the outcome. Spasticity is a physiological phenomenon, occurring in a variety of circumstances, including cord lesions, when the reticular formation could not possibly remain part of its mechanism. It can be graded in intensity, and clonus or clasp-knife phenomena are not essential features. The depression of function (that is, flaccid phase) was greatest with total cortico-spinal lesion, and least with such lesions as damaged relatively few giant pyramid cells (4s lesion of

Hines). The distribution of spasticity closely followed the pattern of accentuation of paralysis and disappeared only when function was fully recovered, but within the major arm-leg divisions all joints were affected in some degree. In lesions of the caudal part of area 4, spasticity was greatest in the flexors of the fingers and the plantar flexors of the ankle. It could here be made intense by partial lesions of the posterior strip of area 4. We did not find any spasticity or loss of organization of movements when area 6 alone was excised, if care was taken not to include any Betz cells in the excision. Ablation of area 6 in addition to area 4 in the monkey perhaps adds a greater plasticity to the spasticity, but there was no other change.

We find ourselves in complete disagreement with Fulton (1949b) who states that after removal of the arm area in the chimpanzee 'such simple patterns of response as thumb-finger approximation are never regained'. Perusal of the protocols of ablation experiment 2 of Leyton and Sherrington (1917) give a careful description of its recovery, and we ourselves also observed its return as early as the fifteenth post-operative day (Denny-Brown and Botterell, 1948). We are, however, not convinced that there is any evidence that any movement at any joint is solely mediated by the mechanism of area 4, and would rather put it that this area is of importance in all movements at all joints and of greater importance to the mechanism of movements of the lips, the hands, and of the feet than of other parts. In order to understand the role of area 4 in movement, we must look for the adequate stimulus which excites its activity.

Close study of the movements that recover after ablation of area 4 finds some explanation for all these difficulties. It is apparent from the beginning that they are greatly facilitated by emotion such as excitement or fear, and then can result in useful movements of the fingers and foot at a time when the monkey or ape appears to be unable to use these parts under normal circumstances. In the early stage of recovery, use of the limbs is greatly facilitated by pulling on them. Traction on the forearm induces flexion of the wrist, elbow, and shoulder, and if the fingers are pulled on, the digits flex strongly also. This response to traction occurs at first only under emotional stress, but is soon put to some purpose by the animal. The hand is hooked clumsily over objects and the tension of flexion is used to reinforce a movement such as climbing, righting itself, or pulling food towards itself, and later peeling fruit. Denny-Brown and Twitchell (1950) have observed that in later recovery this movement can be directed by vision, without preliminary traction. At that time the limb is still used only passively if the eyes are covered. When the ablation of area 4 is bilateral, this flexion movement is clearly that described by Bieber and Fulton (1938) as the 'grasp reflex', for it is present only in the uppermost limbs when the animal lies on one side. The response is primarily proprioceptive and is not abolished by denervation of the hand. It can be produced by traction on the shoulder alone. This response is also present in the recovering phase of cortical hemiplegia in man. When well developed in man, it is associated with marked spasticity and can be reproduced by extreme voluntary effort, especially under stress of emotion. It is the slow flexion and adduction at shoulder, flexion of elbow, wrist, and fingers, of early recovery from hemiplegia. The response certainly appears first as a body-righting reflex acting on the body. We have found it present after section of the medullary pyramid in the monkey (Denny-Brown and Twitchell, 1950) and after hemisection of the spinal cord. The body-righting reflex is not released by area 6 lesion, and appears only after an area 4 lesion includes the forward part of that area. It is not abolished by desensitization of the hand. The adequate stimulus is traction. It is entirely different from the grasp reflex in man, as described by Schuster and Pinéas (1926) and further analysed by ourselves (Seyffarth and Denny-Brown, 1948).

The hemiplegic limbs of the monkey after complete ablation of area 4 recover a wide variety of movements after the first month, but an important series of reactions remains completely absent. If the eyes of a normal animal are blindfolded and he is brought to the edge of a table so that some part of the hand or foot touches the edge, the limb is normally raised and the hand or foot gently placed on the upper surface. This is the tactile placing reaction. If performed by visual stimulus, the reaction is the visual placing reaction. If some displacement of the limb is required, in the absence of vision, it is a proprioceptive placing reaction. Rademaker (1931) demonstrated the absence of these reactions in the chronic decorticate dog, in spite of recovery of an astonishing variety of other movements. Bard and his associates (Bard, 1938; Woolsey and Bard, 1936) showed that after ablation of either sensory cortex or area 4, the tactile and proprioceptive reactions were absent, though in time some slight proprioceptive reaction returned. If the opposite area 4 were then removed, the proprioceptive reactions in the original limbs were immediately improved, but the tactile response remained absent. Woolsey and Bard showed that the parietal sensory cortex was essential to a tactile placing reaction in the opposite limb, initiated in that limb. After removal of the post-central cortex of one side, tactile placing in the opposite limb could be initiated by contact from the ipsilateral side (crossed tactile placing), but not from contact with the limb itself.

Seyffarth and Denny-Brown (1948) found that the grasp reflex which is found in frontal lobe lesions in man is primarily a contact response which 'triggers' or 'conditions' a proprioceptive response to traction on the flexors of the fingers or toes. In the monkey after ablation of area 4 lesion this grasp reflex is absent in the contralateral limbs, though it then appears in enhanced form in the ipsilateral limbs. The groping of the limb after a tactile stimulus (instinctive grasp reaction) is also absent in the contralateral limbs (Denny-Brown and Twitchell, 1950). In unpublished work we have found this to be the case following section of the medullary pyramid in the monkey. The grasp reflex, the tactile placing reaction, and the instinctive grasp reaction are all aspects of the same mechanism, an adjustment of the animal to spatial contact. In the fingers the movements of instinctive grasping have great precision and individuality when fully developed. The grasp reflex is the most coarse of these reactions, and reappears if any part of area 4 remains after an incomplete ablation.

We have elsewhere pointed out (Denny-Brown, 1950) that these findings indicate that the adequate stimulus for the motor reactions of area 4 is contact, both light and heavy contact, and that the whole sensorimotor cortex of areas 4, 3, 1, and 2 work as a unit in this regard. We have now found that the visual reactions do not appear to be disturbed by ablation of this area, once the effect of spinal shock has subsided, except that they require a background of intense curiosity, hunger, fear, or rage, for their exhibition. They are then visually conditioned righting reflexes, which in the limbs appear chiefly as the neck reflex and the traction response on the flexors. These use the fingers as a group, but can use adduction and opposition of the thumb if appropriate stretch is provided. In no sense can the area 4 of one side function vicariously for that of the other. Fulton (1949b) maintains that bilateral movements are mediated by the leg area 4, and that some recovered motor function after ablation of one leg area is lost when the other is excised. We have not observed this, though bilateral adductor spasticity then appears owing to loss of the bilateral adductor reflex. If both areas 4 are removed piecemeal in stages, the general motor status of the animal suffers a severe setback after the last part is removed, if this includes face area or the anterior part of area 4. This is in part traceable to a change in status of the proprioceptive righting reactions of the body, which require some balanced effect from area 4 for their efficiency, and in part to a special importance of tactile reactions from the mouth in 'leading' motor behaviour in the monkey.

The reactions of pseudo-bulbar palsy in many are familiar to neurologists, together with the finding that a bilateral capsular or cortical lesion is necessary for their exhibition. The degree to which this phenomenon affects movements of the face, deglutition, and labial and lingual speech is traceable to the bilateral contactual representation of these functions in the cortex. It is important to realize that such disintegration of sensory factors in movement occurs without disorder of sensory perception (Denny-Brown, 1950). The anomalous finding of paralysis in the tongue of the monkey after excision of one opercular area and the ipsilateral hypoglossal nerve by Walker and Green, in spite of persisting contraction from stimulation of the remaining face area, is due to the same absence of sensory component. The paralysis of the distal parts of the limbs induced by their complete deafferentation observed by Mott and Sherrington (1895) is another aspect of the same phenomenon. The function of area 4 is comprehensible only in terms of its adequate stimulus, which is surface contact. This mechanism can be disordered without defect in perception of contact.

The return of the grasp reflex in a recovering limb after a partial lesion is associated with an immediate reduction in spasticity, in spite of continuing increase of briskness of tendon reflexes, and this suppression of maintained stretch response is the outcome of triggering of the stretch reflex by a specific tactile stimulus. In the course of this process there is an unstable stage when both the tendon jerk and grasp reflex are clonic. Clonus, a rhythmical instability of the stretch response, is a sign of its incomplete conditioning by the contact reactions. In this way we observe in the clinic a stage of evolution in the movement mechanism. Under some circumstances, for example after hemisection of the cord, section of the nerves to the palm of the hand at the grasping stage of recovery results in reversion to spasticity of the long flexors (Denny-Brown, Twitchell, and Saenz-Arroyo, 1949). This indicates a tonic effect of intact contact sensation. In a similar fashion a progressing frontal lobe lesion induces first instinctive grasping, then a grasp reflex, then clonus ('frontal tremor'), then spasticity with paralysis (Denny-Brown, 1950). We have therefore come to consider spasticity resulting from area 4 lesions as a release of the proprioceptive factor in movement from its contactual conditioning mechanism. In the monkey and man we have found that a visual stimulus can reinforce a weak instinctive grasp reaction, but the specific response cannot be produced by vision in the absence of general sensation.

Our concern here is more particularly the relation of motor centres in frontal cortex to those in other parts of the cortex, and therefore at this point it may be useful to consider the motor status following decortication in man. For example, Bell and Karnosh (1949) recently reported the condition of a patient 10 years after complete decortication of the right cerebral hemisphere at 35 years of age. The hypothalamus, thalamus, and the greater part of the globus pallidus were left intact. The patient had suffered complete paralysis of the left arm, a marked weakness of the left side of the face, and an almost complete paralysis of the left leg. Ability to move the left thigh had recovered rapidly, and after several months the patient could 'walk with the aid of a cane', presumably using the leg as a prop. He could elevate the left shoulder and upper arm, and after a longer period could grasp feebly with the fingers of the left hand. In this and other patients spastic phenomena were present but were mild in degree. Though the tendon reflexes were increased, ankle clonus and Hoffmann response present, the hemiplegic attitude was minimal, so that the arm swung freely from the shoulder in walking. The arm could be adducted as well as abducted, the elbow extended and flexed. Movements such as isolated opposition of the thumb were entirely absent, as were isolated movements of individual fingers, of ankle or toes. Facial weakness was mild in degree (in other cases it has varied from patient to patient and was almost imperceptible in some). Movements of the upper face were stated to be symmetrical. Sensation concerns us little here, but it may be noted that though the discriminative types of sensation remained greatly impaired in most areas of the contralateral half of the body and limbs, sensation to light touch and discrimination of two points returned in the trigeminal area. Painful stimulation on the rest of the body and limbs could be approximately localized and the position of the limbs could be roughly appreciated. Speech was unaffected (ablation of the right hemisphere), but there was some intellectual retardation and emotional blunting, with jocular facetiousness. The patient was not greatly concerned about serious matters and was inclined to dispose of them with a shrug of the shoulders. He would spend money with poor judgement, but could amuse others with his entertaining stories and was a good poker player. He remained immaculate in his personal cleanliness and appearance.

It is clear from this summary that the motor disability from complete unilateral decortication in man, which is supported by reports of 13 cases of lesser duration of recovery by others, differs considerably from the disorder generally known as capsular hemiplegia. Lesion at the thalamic level has a much greater spasticity and general disability. When the results of small lesions of the pre-central gyrus are compared with the state reported by Bell and Karnosh and others for hemispherectomy, it is obvious that there are differences, though these are slight in degree and subtle in nature. Unfortunately, verified isolated lesions of the pre-central gyrus in man are seldom seen, but reference to such cases as that reported by Walshe (1935) indicates that if the whole of the arm area is excised, ability to flex-adduct the shoulder, flex the elbow, and later the wrist and fingers, is preceded by a resistance to passive extension of those joints of the type generally recognized as spasticity. This indicates that some cortical mechanism for facilitating postural effects is absent after decortication.

We therefore conclude that area 4 (area FA) is an exceedingly important part of the mechanism for movement, and mediates delicate integration of the limbs and mouth with the external environment, but that it by no means represents the sole mechanism in cortical movement. The postural disorders of spasticity which result from damage to area 4 are related to disequilibrium of lower centres, but not in such a way as to suggest that any particular part of area 4 is concerned with posture, rather than movement.

Grasping automatisms

A detailed investigation of 'forced grasping' in man by Seyffarth and Denny-Brown (1948) revealed that it was composed of two different orders of phenomena, the grasp reflex and the instinctive grasp reaction. Neither was compatible with more than slight spasticity or hemiplegia. Both were reactions which could be obtained in states of semicoma in which no sign of awareness of other than grossly painful stimulation remained. Both are commonly exhibited by the 'normal' limbs in hemiplegics, as Schuster and Pinéas (1926) first observed. After a careful investigation of the difficulty in relaxation it was concluded that this was due to inability to avoid further stimulation, and not caused by simple defect in relaxation. In other words the appearance of reflex grasping is always due to the presence of new positive effects, and not to the absence of 'willed relaxation'. It is totally different from 'tonic innervation' in the sense of Wilson and Walshe (1914). After ablation of area 4 in the monkey, these reactions are also prominent in the ipsilateral limbs for a time. Release of instinctive grasping appears therefore to indicate some general effect which can be compensated. The natural status of the organism is certainly one in which all the motor automatisms are in some degree suppressed, and we suspect that some general mechanism with bilateral effect, such as the reticular thalamic system of Jasper (1949), is concerned in such co-ordination.

The statements of Fulton (1949b), Hines (1937, 1943), and Mettler (1948) that the grasp reflex is a phenomenon which is released by ablation of area 6 is not in accord with our findings. In our own experiments, reflex grasping, and an exaggerated form of placing and posturing, appeared in the limbs opposite lesions of areas 8 or 24. It was more transient following lesions of area 8, and lasted several weeks following ablation of the cingulate gyrus. It will be recalled that in earlier work Richter and Hines (1934) found that ablation of area 6 had to be extended to reach the corpus callosum in order to elicit grasping. In our opinion this must have involved area 24. These regions, therefore, appear to play a prominent part in suppressing the contactual reactions of areas 4, but it is probable that some reactions in which they are concerned are balanced against the contactual mechanism.

We have already described our finding that the flexion of the fingers in response to traction on the shoulder following area 4 lesion is a proprioceptive righting reaction, identical with that described by Bieber and Fulton (1938) and present in the thalamic animal. We feel certain that much of the confusion regarding the meaning of forced grasping arises from failure to differentiate this proprioceptive righting reaction from the true grasp reflex. The complete response to simple traction appears to be that which Hines (1943) refers to as 'the complex reaching and grasping act' which is prominent in the early behaviour of the infant macaque. The prominence of this proprioceptive body-righting reflex acting on the body, as we shall call it, in cortical and subcortical hemiplegia in man has been the basis of a number of small signs used by clinicians. The *Zugreaction* of Mayer and Reisch (1928), in which passive flexion of the fingers followed by sudden passive extension leads to an increased resistance in the flexors of the elbow and shoulder, is based upon its presence. It is of interest that the *Zugreaction* can often be demonstrated for a time in the non-paralysed limbs of the hemiplegic. We have described the synergic movement pattern of the opposite limbs which is regularly produced by stimulation of the most anterior part of area 4. This pattern of contralateral extension of elbow and flexion of leg, with ipsilateral opposites, represented in the most primitive 'motor cortex', is assumed to represent the most elementary type of proprioceptive righting reflex to be conditioned by unilateral contactual stimulation. The mechanism appears to have both pyramidal and extra-pyramidal conduction systems, for it is partly released by section of the medullary pyramid, more completely by ablation of area 4 (Denny-Brown and Twitchell, 1950).

The two regions, ablation of which most clearly results in the appearance of true contactual reflex grasping and the instinctive grasp reaction in the monkey, are both suppressor bands (8s and 24s). It is of interest, therefore, that both phenomena are occasionally seen following lesion of the temporal lobe and possibly the posterior parietal lobe where other suppressor areas exist. We shall later refer to other responses which become hyperactive following damage to these areas. It appears that each suppressor band, by its activity over the other areas of the cortex, gives priority to the motor automatisms of its own region while suppressing others, including contactual reactions. We have argued that this is the basis for the appearance of the movements of Huntington's chorea (Denny-Brown, 1950) when the caudate nucleus, the 'clearing house' for suppression, becomes atrophic.

Instinctive sucking, and a simpler tactile-proprioceptive response called the bulldog phenomenon of the jaws, are the counterpart of the manual grasping reactions, and serve the lips and facial area. Instinctive grasping, once elicited, can be facilitated by entrance of the object into the visual field contralateral to the lesion ('forced groping'), but this is a secondary visual effect and is present when a primarily visual stimulus is ineffective. The phenomenon of the 'tonic foot response' is related to athetosis and 'tonic innervation', and both appear to require a subcortical level of disorder of the instinctive reactions.

Plastic rigidity

The soft plastic rigidity which follows the ablation of area 6 closely resembles Parkinsonian rigidity, and this is probably related to the projection of the pallidum, which is atrophic in classical paralysis agitans. Stimulation of the suppressor band 4s, in area 6 of man, has been shown to inhibit the tremor, or the rigidity, or both, in cases of paralysis agitans in man (David and Talairach, 1947; Reid, 1948). It is therefore remarkable that some should claim that ablation of area 6 in man should benefit parkinsonism (Klemme, 1942), a finding which has not yet been documented adequately. Our only experience has been the reverse. It is probable that spasticity from area 4 damage, which has long been known to damp Parkinsonian tremor, has accounted for the favourable reports by others.

Accompanying the enhanced contactual reactions which ensue upon damage to areas 8 or 24 in the monkey is an increase in resistance to passive movement which is neither spasticity nor plastic rigidity, though it has certain resemblance to the latter. In this condition the animal almost constantly grasps or maintains contact with some part of his surroundings. If his hand is pulled loose from its resting posture and touched with the examiner's finger, the finger is grasped. If the examiner now moves the finger in any direction, the whole limb of the monkey is felt to be rigid. If passive movement overcomes the mild, often tremulous rigidity, it softens a little until movement ceases in a new position. In the new position the previous resistance to passive movement is again reasserted. This phenomenon is identical with that which Kleist (1931) has called *Gegenhalten* and appears to be a form of fixed relationship to the surroundings. In patients with frontal lobe lesions it accompanies reflex grasping, and when intense closely resembles the rigidity of catatonic states. The examiner often has the impression that the patient anticipates the passive movement that is resisted. The variability of the phenomenon, compared with the relative constancy of Parkinsonian rigidity, has led many to relate it to 'negativism'. The persistence of attitudes in space which are imposed upon the limb seldom, however, accompanies the phenomenon in the monkey, and catatonic persistence of attitude is not necessarily an accompaniment of the *Gegenhalten* associated with frontal lobe lesion in man.

The mild plastic rigidity which follows lesions of area 6 in the monkey is different from the *Gegenhalten* phenomenon of areas 8 and 24 lesions, but is being studied further in this regard. The rigidity of Parkinsonism in man is also relatively seldom associated with release of tactile automatisms, although the grasp reflex which is sometimes associated with it indicates that this may occur. The common association of Parkinsonism with a number of hyperactive proprioceptive reactions, such as the paradoxical contraction of flexors when extensors are stretched, the reactions of Leri and of Meyer, indicate that Parkinsonian rigidity has a close affinity with the proprioceptive aspects of body-righting reflexes. It is likely that the rigidity of lesions of area 6 belongs to this class of disorder.

Deviation of the eyes and head

Transient deviation of the eyes and head to the side of a lesion of the cerebral hemisphere has been a well-known clinical sign since the memoir of Prevost in 1868. Roux (1899) concluded that deviation of the eyes associated with homonymous hemianopia was due to a lesion either in the occipital lobe or in the optic radiation, while its occurrence without field defect indicated either a lesion in the caudal part of the middle frontal gyrus or the projection from that area through the internal capsule. Roux also noted that though deviation of the eyes in response to command was absent in the latter type, the eyes followed an object moving towards the side contralateral to the lesion. Holmes (1938) gave a full description of the defect in eye movement in frontal lesions. He found that deviation of the head to the side of the lesion resulted in a relative movement of the eyes to the contralateral side, when no voluntary movement was possible, and fixation on a moving object only partially effective. The ocular deviations thus obtained failed to occur if the eyes were closed, and were abolished by momentarily preventing fixation by covering the eyes. The phenomenon was therefore not just a labyrinthine compensatory reaction because the deviation of the eyes was sustained after movement of the head ceased. In two cases with pseudo-bulbar phenomena Holmes (1930, 1931) found a spasm of fixation. The patient was then unable to look at a given object unless fixation of an object already attracting his attention was abolished by momentarily covering the eyes. These patients had a staring expression owing to retraction of the eyelids, and appeared unable to blink voluntarily, though a corneal reflex was still present. They seemed to be fully aware of the presence of the object to which they were unable to transfer their fixation. Movement of the eyes in any direction could be readily obtained by movement of the object on which the eyes were fixed, or by movement of the head. The exact location of the lesion in these cases was not known. Foerster (1936) has stated that he did not observe alterations in eye movement following frontal ablations unless the caudal part of the middle frontal gyrus was included. The head was not deviated in such patients, but Foerster notes that the patient failed to make spontaneous glances to the side opposite the lesion. Janischewsky (1909) described a patient with pseudo-bulbar and Parkinsonian signs who exhibited both uninhibited visual fixation and reflex grasping. Though Fox and Couch (1934) have recorded slightly defective pursuit movements of the eyes in patients with ablation of the prefrontal lobes, pronounced defect in conjugate movement has been seldom mentioned in accounts of lobectomy of the frontal lobe in man.

Absence of deviation of the eyes or the head to the side opposite frontal lobe ablation has been more constantly reported in animals. Hitzig, Ferrier, and Bianchi related it to damage to the frontal centre for eye movements, and Ferrier (1886) found that if this centre were spared, no observable defect in deviation of the eyes or head occurred. The defect was always transient, lasting 3–4 days, and removal of the other frontal lobe resulted in lack of deviation to the other side for a further brief period. Ferrier describes one experiment in which paralysis of lateral movement of the eyes following removal of the immediately pre-central area in a monkey had disappeared, and was revived for 3 days by further ablation of the prefrontal region. During this last period rapid oscillations of the head were seen, and the animal was unable to turn to the opposite side except by turning the whole body. At the end of 3 days there was no defect either in motion or sensation. In spite of complete restoration of function Ferrier found extensive degeneration of the fronto-pontine tract 3 months later. Hughlings Jackson (1894) insisted that recovery did not mean that identical function was taken over by some other structure, and he reported Russell's finding that the ocular deviation reappeared under light anaesthesia. Bianchi (1895) made frontal ablations in dogs and monkeys 'two or three millimetres in front of the excitable areas of the arm, face and jaw'. Following unilateral extirpations, in dogs as well as monkeys (cynocephalus) he noted concavity of the trunk to the side of the lesion and the animal would frequently turn round, rotating to the side of the lesion. This is the *mouvement de manège*. These symptoms lasted for about 3 weeks during which the arm opposite the lesion in the monkey was often not used for delicate movements, such as grooming, unless the other arm were immobilized. One monkey showed 'hyperaesthesia' of the opposite ear and face. In all cases, both dogs and monkeys, there was no persistent 'oculomotor disturbance' (deviation of the eyes) and the animal would walk or run without collision with obstacles. If the attention of the animal with such a lesion on the left side was attracted to some point straight in front of him, and a piece of sugar on a thread gradually brought into the field from the right side, the animal saw it only when the sugar was nearly in a line with the visual axis, and he then seized it 'with a rapid and precise movement of the left hand'. This disorder of perception was constantly present for 2–3 weeks, and then disappeared. Ferrier and Turner (1898) also observed 'hemiopia' following this operation in the monkey. Ferrier and Turner also found that ablation of the left angular gyrus, which alone caused a transient hemianopia, was followed by right hemianopia for at least 3 weeks if the left frontal lobe had been excised as well. The animal then turned to the right only in response to sounds. Bilateral extirpation of angular gyri and frontal lobes led to complete 'blindness' for 5 days after the second operation. Care was taken to avoid injury to the optic radiations in these ablations.

Bianchi (1895) described the gradual recovery of visual recognition in the central parts of the visual field after destruction of superior and middle frontal gyri in the monkey, with persisting defect in the periphery for many weeks. When the opposite frontal gyri were damaged in the same region, the defect appeared in the field contralateral to the new lesion. The reflexes were then exaggerated on both sides and the slightest touch produced generalized spasms. After a week the 'hyperaesthesia' diminished and the monkey showed a great deal of aimless activity. There was a loss of usual interests. Sudden stimuli caused 'a quite unusual feeling of terror'. Any object such as plaster or sugar was taken and swallowed automatically. Though the disordered sensibility disappeared, vision in the periphery of the visual field remained slightly defective, and the condition remained unchanged in other respects for 5 months of subsequent survival. It is remarkable that the lesions responsible for this degree of change were superficial and confined to the lateral surface of each frontal lobe (Figure 10, A and B). In two other monkey (cynocephalus) experiments reported in detail by Bianchi, the whole frontal lobe was extirpated on both sides through a line running a few millimetres in front of the inferior pre-central sulcus (Figure 10C). The same visual symptoms and hyperaesthesia occurred. Reflex excitability was exaggerated, and every noise caused a startle response. The animal 'looks at everything but without fixing herself to anything. Her senses are excited but not attracted'. Incoordination of the limbs was not evident, but the gait was altered, the body looked arched. Another animal 'walks badly, swaying, with head and body bent'. This second animal, after 3 weeks of stupor, became restless, and walked aimlessly about, always in the same direction. The sole emotion was fear, though the 'sexual instinct' was present. Asocial behaviour, avid appetite, and complete lack of discrimination of things eaten continued for 3 months before the animal was killed and necropsy was performed.

The excellent reports of Bianchi are mentioned in some detail because they appear to have considerable bearing on the broader aspects of frontal lobe function. It should be immediately clear that 'frontal lobe blindness', as it has been called, is not directly related to the difficulty in movement of the head and eyes, and was a relative phenomenon which 'only a searching examination

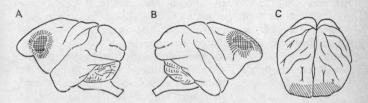

Figure 10. Tracings of the drawings of Bianchi (1895) showing in (A) and (B) the extent of the lesions in his second monkey, and in (C) the extent of lobectomy in his third monkey

will reveal' (Bianchi). It is indeed different from a true hemianopia, for, as we ourselves have found, only after preliminary fixation of vision on a given object is it difficult to get the eyes to turn to the affected field. If preliminary attention is unfixed the animal will turn head or eyes or both to examine a new object in the affected field, but a larger, more rapidly moving stimulus was necessary on the affected side. Blinking to a threat required a larger stimulus, but still occurred. If limb or face is touched on the affected side, the animal reacts violently by prehension with lips or hand, turning head and eyes to do so (Denny-Brown and Twitchell, unpublished observations). If the new stimulus is visual, it is the hand on the side of the lesion that rises to grasp it, possibly because the hand on the side stimulated is already firmly grasping some support, as part of the overactive contact postural reaction we have mentioned earlier.

Kennard and Ectors (1938) describe deviation of the head and eyes and circling progression to the same side following ablation only of that portion of area 8 which is enclosed within the curve of the arcuate sulcus of the macaque monkey. The cortex was ablated to the depths of the sulcus, but the head of the caudate nucleus was not damaged. The deviation of head and eyes was extreme during the first 2–3 days and then became progressively less until it disappeared after 2–3 weeks. A tendency to circle towards the side of the lesion persisted for several months. The animals were restless, easily excited and hyperactive, but showed no abnormal posture or paresis. Removal of superficial cortical tissue in this area was followed by only a fleeting trace of the syndrome. In addition to the deviation of the eyes and head, it was found that the animal paid no attention to food left on the side of the cage corresponding to the visual field contralateral to the lesion. There was no blinking response to threats in the contralateral half of the visual field. 'This defect disappears gradually, but persists for a time after the disappearance of conjugate deviation. The duration and intensity of the abnormality are both affected by lesions elsewhere in the frontal lobe, for the deficit lasts longer and is more pronounced following frontal lobe extirpation than after ablation of area 8 alone' (Kennard and Ectors). When area 8 was ablated from both sides together, or one shortly after the other, the animal sat motionless with head sunk between the shoulders and gaze fixed forward. The eyes tended to follow a moving object but soon returned to a fixed stare. The animals walked into objects. They would reach for and grasp any object offered, but then do nothing with it. 'They did not seem to know what to do with food. . . . Many times things held in the hand are not recognized.' The animals became more alert after one week, and after a few weeks retained only a 'wooden expression' and fixed gaze, with some purposeless restlessness. It was considered that area 8 was 'a region elaborating complex motor performance for the head as does area 6 for the extremities'. The defect in reaction to objects or the opposite field was considered to be a lack of recognition.

In a later study Kennard (1939) analysed the defect by means of a test-box by which the order of choice of particles of food arranged in a circle in the field of vision, and the hand used to reach for them, was recorded graphically. The disturbance of recognition was equivalent to that of unilateral occipital lobectomy, but the hand on the side of ablation of area 8 was not used, whereas there was no difference in the use of the limbs after occipital lesion. Ablation of area 8 alone was thought to determine the defect, from which complete recovery was made in 4 months. Ablation of areas 9 to 12 (Vogt and Vogt) was not followed by any defect, or renewal of a compensated defect. It was considered that:

the abnormality of behaviour in response to visual and to tactile stimuli seems to be of the same order and resembles that of the apraxic patient. . . . The general behaviour of an animal or of a man with disturbances of this sort . . . would be enough to account for the dullness, the intellectual changes and the general stupidity of behaviour ascribed to disturbances of the frontal lobe (Kennard, 1939).

Richter and Hines (1938) reported a careful study of the amount of spontaneous activity of the macaque monkey after various frontal lesions. Unilateral removal of prefrontal cortex produced only a slight increase in activity; subsequent removal of the other prefrontal cortex produced a great increase. Unilateral and bilateral removals of area 8, or of 10, 11, and 12 had little or no effect on general activity, whereas bilateral removal of area 9 (Brodmann) (area 46 in Figure 6), produced a great increase in activity. The restlessness and circling observed by Kennard and Ectors following isolated removal of area 8 was not seen. Mettler (1944) also was not able to produce it. We ourselves have not been able to obtain deviation of the head and eyes, or circling movement, from subpial ablation restricted to the grey matter within the arcuate sulcus in the macaque. Extension of the lesion forward to include area 46, and part of area 9 has produced only a minimal effect, though some defect in recognition in the opposite visual field was present. A slightly larger lesion, damaging more of area 9 and the medial extent of area 8 appears to us to be necessary to produce the syndrome described by Bianchi, and this was essentially the extent of his lesion. Fulton and Bender (1938) reported transient deviation of gaze (3 hours) and circling movement (6 hours) after ablation of the region of the frontal sulcus in a chimpanzee. All observers are agreed that ablation of the whole frontal area produces the syndrome described by Bianchi, and Kennard and Ectors, with much greater certainty and persistence. Ruch and Shenkin (1943) found a significant increase in activity, lasting over 2 months, following bilateral removal of the postero-lateral orbital surface (area 13 Walker, area FF, Figure 5), but this area is infrequently included in frontal ablations.

Though Foerster described transient deviation of the eyes and head and absence of spontaneous glancing to the opposite side following ablation of the caudal part of the middle frontal convolution in man, phenomena corresponding to forced circling have been seldom described in man. Persistent turning to one side as the patient lies in bed, or slight deviation in line of march are occasionally observed. Failure of recognition of objects has not been described, but the phenomenon appears in man as a difficulty in attracting attention by a visual stimulus in the affected field. The area designated as area 8 by Foerster is caudal to the equivalent area FCB of von Economo (Figure 3). The careful examinations of Leyton and Sherrington (1917) and of Dusser de Barenne and his associates in the chimpanzee (Figure 8 B) show an adversive eye field well forward in this animal, and it is unlikely that the focus for these movements is represented by the points found near the inferior pre-central sulcus by Foerster and by Penfield and Boldrey. The appearance of persistent staring of the eyes with infrequent turning of the eyes to the affected side, with persistent grasping, and a difficulty in initiating progression (Bruns' 'ataxia') is not uncommon in patients with frontal lesions in the white matter deep to the superior frontal gyrus near the junction of its middle and caudal thirds. Unfortunately the usual pathology is cerebral tumour, which is unsuitable for close analysis. In this situation the connexions of areas 8, 9, and 24 (which have similar responses to electrical excitation) converge.

The positive movement of head and eyes resulting from stimulation and its transient disequilibrium following ablation indicates only the importance of such movements to the true function of this region. Despite 'compensatory' reassertion of motor equilibrium by other mechanisms for turning the head and eyes, the fundamental defect remains. Behaviour fails to be appropriately activated by a purely visual stimulus. The more coarse attributes such as high contrast and movement still excite visual fixation on the affected side by direct connexions between occipital cortex and brain stem (Rademaker and Ter Braak, 1948). The visual placing reactions and the ability to react to depth in space appear to be the concern of the pre-occipital and posterior sylvian regions. Some more subtle feature of the visual stimulus, which gives it specific meaning, fails to excite reaction after frontal lesion. When the effect is bilateral, the result is a staring fixity of expression, though behaviour in general is restless. The results of ablation indicate that the fundamental mechanism is diffuse and includes at least areas 9 and 46 in addition to area 8, which can be regarded as a relative focus of effect.

The disequilibrium following unilateral ablation indicates not only a normal antagonism or balance between right and left visual determinants of behaviour, but as between visual, auditory, and tactile fields. Over-responsiveness to contact and auditory stimulation are prominent on the affected side, even with isolated ablation of area 8, in our own experience.

We conclude that the suppressor areas 8s and 24s present a

mechanism for achieving a general balance of behaviour by the interacting suppression of motor effects concurrently induced in other parts of the cortex by other stimuli. The frontal cortex is concerned with the direction of behaviour as a whole by events that are primarily visual.

Autonomic reactions

The earlier investigators took considerable pains to establish the occurrence of visceral effects from stimulation of the frontal cortex, and François-Franck (1887), Schäfer (1901), Bechterev (1908–11), and Bianchi (1922) have provided reviews of the extensive early literature. With the exception of Spencer's (1894) finding of changes in blood pressure and respiration from stimulation of the orbital surface, most were concerned with effects obtained from the sensorimotor cortex surrounding the cruciate sulcus. Pupillary changes, salivation and vasoconstriction are readily obtained by stimulation in widespread foci of the cerebral mantle. Contraction of the urinary bladder, stomach, intestine or of such organs as the gall-bladder have been notoriously difficult to obtain in convincing fashion. From the work of Smith (1938, 1945) and others, recently reviewed by Fulton (1949a and b) it is now clear that stimulation of the limbic and piriform cortex is more particularly productive of responses in all visceral spheres, including vaso-constriction, urination and pilo-motor reactions. Fulton quotes the stimulation by Davey of gastric contraction from areas 6 and 8 on the lateral surface of the frontal lobe, and by Livingston of lacrimation from area 8, by the use of slow rates of stimulus. The striking feature of these responses is their diffuse 'representation'. This is possibly the reason for the absence of disturbance in the same functions from focal cerebral lesions. Urinary incontinence from frontal lesions is an apparent exception but even in this instance it is the lack of restraint which characterizes the effect of frontal lesion, and for this a diffuse destruction which involves a large area of cingulate or piriform region would appear to be necessary. Mettler (1944) did not observe any disturbance of automatic function following ablation of the orbital gyri in the monkey, but Messimy (1939) found periodic autonomic instability such as increased sweating, vasomotor instability, gastro-intestinal and cardiac abnormalities to result from experimental frontal lobe lesions. Fulton (1949a) states that 'clinical indication of participation of the cerebral cortex in the affairs of the autonomic system has also become impressive', but in truth persistent defect in autonomic functions resulting from frontal lesions are singularly unconvincing in the clinic. There are many simpler explanations of oedema and change of limb temperature. The statement that 'when muscles contract they need an increased blood supply, and this vascular adjustment can be made from the same focus of the brain that initiates the somatic movement' (Fulton, 1949a) is physiologically preposterous.

It is certain that visceral functions are integrated with the cortical mechanism in an extremely diffuse fashion, and Pavlov clearly demonstrated how salivation in particular, but probably any other function, can be attached temporarily to a cortical discriminatory process. It is of special interest to the present topic that the conditioned reflex of Pavlov demonstrated the indirect mechanism of linkage of cortical adequate stimulus to visceral effect. By a process of training, the cortical stimulus can substitute for the subcortical stimulus, and by further training become highly differentiated. The entire environment and hence the entire sensorium is involved in the process of differentiation.

Pavlov (1927) did not appear to have concerned himself with the location of the cortico-fugal connexion with salivation. He stated that the actual site of the new nervous connexion 'has not yet been clearly answered'. But he preferred an explanation that 'stimuli which lead to activity of an organ gain direct representation in the cortex independently of the simultaneous excitation of a subcortical area'. His method of presentation of his findings always emphasized the 'analysers' (primary sensory differentiating mechanism) of the cortex. After bilateral frontal ablations, which reproduced the motor phenomena and hyperaesthesia described by Bianchi, Pavlov described recovery of visual and auditory conditioned reflexes, with difficulty in establishing tactile responses except for some places on the extremities. The type of visual stimulus used by Pavlov was not suitable for the demonstration of frontal lobe defect, and the visual stimuli still effective after occipito-temporal ablation were such as to be active at subcortical level. The effect of ablation of the fronto-parietal half of the brain on both sides, sparing the temporal, occipital, and posterior parietal regions was fully described. It was not possible to establish conditioned salivary reflexes except to acid introduced directly into the mouth. In both types of extirpation conditioned inhibition of this subcortical salivary reflex could be readily established to auditory and visual stimuli, and to tactile stimuli in the case of purely frontal extirpation. The explanation for these findings was in terms of 'analysers which had been damaged, and which by themselves, although incapable of any positive activity could yet respond to stimuli by the development and irradiation of an inhibition'. It occurs to us that an alternative explanation could be in terms of ablation of the efferent salivary pathway, leaving the suppressor areas for each sensation intact. The remainder of the ablation experiments reported by Pavlov indicate that the salivary efferent cortical connexion for each analyser is diffuse within the caudal parts of the frontal area.

The chief concentrations of stimulable visceral effects in the cingulate, posterior orbital, and sylvian cortex are relative to wide areas of facilitation. It has yet to be demonstrated that any cytoarchitectural area is essential to any single autonomic function. Visceral disorder from frontal lobe lesion could arise only from defect in the total significance of behaviour, that is a defect in the associated *Gestalt*. If instability of visceral effects and lack of restraint of urination are a more particular feature of frontal lobe symptomatology, this reflects only a lack of differential inhibition, which is a widespread cortical function. The effects would therefore be more consistent with quantitative impairment of a widespread representation of the effector side of a conditioning mechanism.

References

BAILEY, C., and RICHTER, C. P. (1924), *Arch. Neurol. Psychiat.*, *Chicago*, vol. 11, p. 257.

BAILEY, P. (1948), *Res. Publ. Ass. nerv. ment. Dis.*, vol. 27, p. 84.

BAILEY, P., BONIN, G. VON, GAROL, H., and MCCULLOCH, W. S. (1943), *J. Neurophysiol.*, vol. 6, p. 129.

BAILEY, P., and BREMER, F. (1938), *J. Neurophysiol.*, vol. 1, p. 405.

BAILEY, P., GAROL, H. W., and MCCULLOCH, W. S. (1941), *J. Neurophysiol.*, vol. 4, p. 564.

BAILEY, P., and SWEET, W. H. (1940), *J. Neurophysiol.*, vol. 3, p. 276.

BÁRÁNY, R., VOGT, C., and VOGT, O. (1923), *J. Psychol. Neurol.*, *Lpz.*, vol. 30, p. 87.

BARD, P. (1938), *Bull. N.Y. Acad. Med.*, vol. 14, p. 585.

BARUK, H. (1926), *Les Troubles Mentaux dans les Tumeurs Cérébrales*, Doin, Paris.

BECHTEREV, V. M. (1908–11), *Die Funktionen der Nervencentra*, Fischer, Jena.

BEEVOR, C. E., and HORSLEY, V. (1890), *Philos. Trans.*, vol. 181b, pp. 49, 129.

BELL, E., and KARNOSH, L. J. (1949), *J. Neurosurg.*, vol. 6, p. 285.

BIANCHI, L. (1895), *Brain*, vol. 18, p. 497.

BIANCHI, L. (1922), *The Mechanism of the Brain and the Function of the Frontal Lobes*, trans. by J. H. MacDonald, Wood, Edinburgh and New York.

BIEBER, I., and FULTON, J. F. (1938), *Arch. Neurol. Psychiat.*, *Chicago*, vol. 39, p. 433.

425

BONIN, G. VON (1948), *Res. Publ. Ass. nerv. ment. Dis.*, vol. 27, p. 67.

BONIN, G. VON, and BAILEY, P. (1947), *The Neocortex of Macaca Mulatta*, University of Illinois Press.

BOYNTON, E. P., and HINES, M. (1933), *Amer. J. Physiol.*, vol. 106, p. 175.

BRICKNER, R. M. (1936), *The Intellectual Functions of the Frontal Lobes*, Macmillan, New York.

BRICKNER, R. M. (1940), *J. Neurophysiol.*, vol. 3, p. 128.

BRODMANN, K. (1906), *J. Psychol. Neurol., Lpz.*, vol. 6, p. 275.

BRODMANN, K. (1909), *Vergleichende Lokalisationslehre der Grosshirnrinde in ihren Prinzipien dargestellt auf Grund des Zellenbaues*, Barth, Leipzig.

BROWN, T. G. (1922), *Arch. neerl. Physiol.*, vol. 7, p. 571.

BROWN, T. G., and SHERRINGTON, C. S. (1911), *J. Physiol.*, vol. 43, p. 209.

BROWN, T. G., and SHERRINGTON, C. S. (1912), *Proc. Roy. Soc.*, vol. 85b, p. 250.

BRUNS, L. (1892), *Dtsch. med. Wschr.*, vol. 18, p. 138.

BUBNOFF, N., and HEIDENHAIN, R. (1881), *Pflüg. Arch. ges. Physiol.*, vol. 26, p. 137.

BUCY, P. C. (1934), *J. nerv. ment. Dis.*, vol. 79, p. 621.

BUCY, P. C., and CASE, T. C. (1936), *J. nerv. ment. Dis.*, vol. 84, p. 156.

BUCY, P. C., and FULTON, J. F. (1933), *Brain*, vol. 56, p. 318.

CAMPBELL, A. W. (1905), *Histological Studies on the Localisation of Cerebral Function*, Cambridge University Press.

CLARK, W. E. LeGROS (1948), *Lancet*, vol. 1, p. 353.

CLARK, W. E. LeGROS, and BOGGON, R. H. (1933), *Brain*, vol. 56, p. 83.

COOPER, S., and DENNY-BROWN, D. (1927), *Proc. Roy. Soc.*, vol. 102b, p. 222.

CROSBY, E. C., and HENDERSON, J. W. (1948), *J. comp. Neurol.*, vol. 88, p. 53.

DAVID, M., and TALAIRACH, J. (1947), *Rev. Neurol.*, vol. 79, p. 726.

DELGADO, J. M. R., and LIVINGSTON, R. B. (1948), *J. Neurophysiol.*, vol. 11, p. 39.

DELMAS-MARSALET, P. (1936), *Encéphale*, vol. 31, p. 15,

DENNY-BROWN, D. (1950), *J. nerv. ment. Dis.*

DENNY-BROWN, D., and BOTTERELL, E. H. (1948), *Res. Publ. Ass. nerv. ment. Dis.*, vol. 27, p. 235.

DENNY-BROWN, D., and TWITCHELL, T. E. (1950), Unpublished observations.

DENNY-BROWN, D., TWITCHELL, T. E., and SAENZ-ARROYO, L. (1949), *Trans. Amer. neurol. Assoc.*, p. 108.

DUSSER DE BARENNE, J. G., and McCULLOCH, W. S. (1938), *J. Neurophysiol.*, vol. 1, p. 96.

DUSSER DE BARENNE, J. G., and McCULLOCH, W. S. (1939), *Amer. J. Physiol.*, vol. 126, p. 482.

DUSSER DE BARENNE, J. G., GAROL, H. W., and McCULLOCH, W. S. (1941). *J. Neurophysiol.*, vol. 4, pp. 287, 324.

ECONOMO, C. VON (1929), *The Cytoarchitectonics of the Human Cerebral Cortex*, trans. by S. Parker, Oxford University Press.

Economo, E. von, and Koskinas, G. N. (1925), *Die Cytoarchitektonik der Hirnrinde des erwachsenen Menschen*, Springer, Berlin.

Ferrier, D. (1886), *The Functions of the Brain*, 2nd edn, Smith, Elder, London.

Ferrier, D., and Turner, W. A. (1898), *Philos. Trans.*, vol. 190, p. 1.

Feuchtwanger, E. (1923), 'Die Functionen des Stirnhirns', *Monogr. Neurol. Psychiat.*, vol. 38, p. 194.

Foerster, O. (1936), *Handbuch der Neurologie*, vol. 6, ed. by O. Bumke and O. Foerster, Springer, Berlin.

Fox, J. C., and Couch, F. H. (1934), *Res. Publ. Ass. nerv. ment. Dis.*, vol. 13, p. 408.

François-Franck (1887), *Leçons sur les Fonctions Motrices du Cerveau*, Doin, Paris.

Fulton, J. F. (1935), *Brain*, vol. 58, p. 311.

Fulton, J. F. (1949a), *Functional Localisation in the Frontal Lobes and Cerebellum*, Oxford University Press.

Fulton, J. F. (1949b), *Physiology of the Nervous System*, 3rd edn, Oxford University Press.

Fulton, J. F., and Bender, M. B. (1938), *J. Neurophysiol.*, vol. 1, p. 144.

Fulton, J. F., and Keller, A. D. (1932), *The Sign of Babinski: A Study of the Evolution of Cortical Dominance in Primates*, Baillière, Tindall & Cox, London.

Fulton, J. F., and Kennard, M. A. (1934), *Res. Publ. Ass. nerv. ment. Dis.*, vol. 13, p. 158.

Garol, H. W. (1942), *J. Neuropath. exp. Neurol.*, vol. 1, p. 139.

Goldstein, K. (1923), *Med. Klinik*, vol. 19, pp. 965, 1006.

Goltz, F. (1884), *Pflüg. Arch. ges. Physiol.*, vol. 34, p. 450.

Green, H. D., and Walker, A. E. (1938), *J. Neurophysiol.*, vol. 1, p. 262.

Hering, H. E. (1899), *Wien. klin. Wschr.*, vol. 12, p. 831.

Hines, M. (1937), *Bull. Johns Hopk. Hosp.*, vol. 60, p. 313.

Hines, M. (1943), *Biol., Rev.*, vol. 18, p. 1.

Hines, M. (1944), 'Significance of the precentral motor cortex', in *The Precentral Motor Cortex*, ed. by P. C. Bucy, University of Illinois Press, p. 459.

Hitzig, E. (1884), *Arch. Psychiat. Nervenkr.*, vol. 15, p. 271.

Holmes, G. (1930), *Tran. Ophthal. Soc., U.K.*, vol. 50, p. 253.

Holmes, G. (1931), *Proc. Roy. Soc. Med.*, vol. 24, p. 65.

Holmes, G. (1938), *Brit. med. J.*, vol. 2, p. 107.

Ingram, W. R., Ranson, S. W., and Hannett, F. I. (1931), *J. Neurol. Psychopath.*, vol. 12, p. 219.

Jackson, J. H. (1894), *Lancet*, vol. 1, p. 1052.

Janischewsky, A. (1909), *Rev. Neurol.*, vol. 18, p. 823.

Jasper, H. (1949), *EEG clin. Neurophysiol.*, vol. 1, p. 405.

Kaada, B. R., Pribram, K. H., and Epstein, J. A. (1949), *J. Neurophysiol.*, vol. 12, p. 347.

Kennard, M. A. (1939), *Arch. Neurol. Psychiat., Chicago*, vol. 41, p. 1153.

Kennard, M. A., and Ectors, L. (1938), *J. Neurophysiol.*, vol. 1, p. 45.

Kennard, M. A., Viets, H. R., and Fulton, J. F. (1934), *Brain*, vol. 57, p. 69.

Motor Function and Action

KLEIST, K. (1931), *Mschr. Psychiat. Neurol.*, vol. 79, p. 338.

KLEMME, R. W. (1942), *Res. Publ. Ass. nerv. ment. Dis.*, vol. 21, p. 596.

LASHLEY, K. S. (1929), *Brain Mechanisms and Intelligence,* University of Chicago Press.

LASHLEY, K. S., and CLARK, G. (1946), *J. comp. Neurol.*, vol. 85, p. 223.

LEÃO, A. A. P. (1944), *J. Neurophysiol.*, vol. 7, p. 359.

LEVIN, P. M. (1936), *J. comp. Neurol.*, vol. 63, p. 369.

LEYTON, A. S. F., and SHERRINGTON, C. S. (1917), *Quart. J. exp. Physiol.*, vol. 11, p. 135.

LHERMITTE, J. (1929), *Encéphale*, vol. 27, p. 87.

LIVINGSTON, R. B., CHAPMAN, W. P., and LIVINGSTON, K. E. (1948), *Res. Publ. Ass. nerv. ment. Dis.*, vol. 27, p. 421.

McCULLOCH, W. S. (1944a), 'Cortico-cortical connections', in *The Prefrontal Motor Cortex,* ed. by P. C. Bucy, University of Illinois Press, p. 211.

McCULLOCH, W. S. (1944b), *Physiol. Rev.*, vol. 24, p. 390.

McCULLOCH, W. S. (1948), *Res. Publ. Ass. nerv. ment. Dis.*, vol. 27, p. 95.

MAYER, C., and REISCH, O. (1928), *Dtsch. Z. Nervenheilk.*, vol. 102, p. 28.

MESSIMY, R. (1939), *Rev. Neurol.*, vol. 71, p. 1.

METTLER, F. A. (1935–6), *J. comp. Neurol.*, vol. 63, p. 25.

METTLER, F. A. (1944), *J. comp. Neurol.*, vol. 81, p. 105.

METTLER, F. A. (1947), *J. comp. Neurol.*, vol. 86, p. 119.

METTLER, F. A. (1948), *Res. Publ. Ass. nerv. ment. Dis.*, vol. 27, p. 162.

MEYER, A., and BECK, E. (1945), *J. ment. Sci.*, vol. 91, p. 411.

MEYER, A., BECK, E., and McLARDY, T. (1947), *Brain*, vol. 70, p. 18.

MOTT, F. W., and SHERRINGTON, C. S. (1895), *Proc. roy. Soc.*, vol. 57, p. 481.

PAVLOV, I. P. (1927), *Conditioned Reflexes; An Investigation of the Physiological Activity of the Cerebral Cortex,* trans. by G. V. Anrep, Oxford University Press.

PENFIELD, W., and BOLDREY, E. (1937), *Brain*, vol. 60, p. 389.

PENFIELD, W., and WELCH, K. (1949), *Trans. Amer. neurol. Ass.*, p. 184.

POOL, J. L., and RANSOHOFF, J. (1949), *J. Neurophysiol.*, vol. 12, p. 385.

PREVOST, J. L. (1868), *De la Déviation Conjugée des Yeux et de la Rotation de la Tête dans Certains Cas d'Hémiplegie,* Masson, Paris.

RADEMAKER, G. G. J. (1931), *Das Stehen,* Springer, Berlin.

RADEMAKER, G. G. J., and TER BRAAK, J. W. G. (1948), *Brain*, vol. 71, p. 48.

RASMUSSEN, T., and PENFIELD, W. (1947), *Fed. Proc.*, vol. 6, p. 452.

REID, W. L. (1948), *Med. J. Aust.*, vol. 2, p. 481.

RICHTER, C. P., and HINES, M. (1934), *Res. Publ. Ass. nerv. ment. Dis.*, vol. 13, p. 211.

RICHTER, C. P., and HINES, M. (1938), *Brain*, vol. 61, p. 1.

RIOCH, D. McK., and ROSENBLUETH, A. (1935), *Amer. J. Physiol.*, vol. 113, p. 663.

ROSE, J. E., and WOOLSEY, C. N. (1948), *Res. Publ. Ass. nerv. ment. Dis.*, vol. 27, p. 210.

Roux, J. (1899), *Arch. Neurol., Paris*, vol. 8, p. 177.
Ruch, T. C., and Shenkin, H. A. (1943), *J. Neurophysiol,*, vol. 6, p. 349.
Russell, J. S. R. (1894), *J. Physiol.*, vol. 17, pp. 1, 378.
Sachs, E. (1909), *Brain*, vol. 32, p. 177.
Sachs, E., Jr. and Brendler, S. J. (1948), *J. Neurophysiol.*, vol. 7, p. 107.
Schäfer, E. A. (1901), *Text-Book of Physiology*, vol. 2, Young, Pentland, Edinburgh.
Schuster, P. (1902), *Psychische Störungen bei Hirntumoren*, Enke, Stuttgart.
Schuster, P., and Pinéas, H. (1926), *Dtsch. Z. Nervenheilk*, vol. 91, p. 16.
Seyffarth, H., and Denny-Brown, D. (1948), *Brain*, vol. 71, p. 109.
Smith, W. K. (1936), *Anat. Rec.*, vol. 64 (suppl.), p. 45.
Smith, W. K. (1938), *J. Neurophysiol.*, vol. 1, p. 55.
Smith, W. K. (1944), 'The frontal eye fields', in *The Precentral Motor Cortex*, ed. by P. C. Bucy, University of Illinois Press.
Smith, W. K. (1945), *J. Neurophysiol.*, vol. 8, p. 241.
Smith, W. K. (1949), *Trans. Amer. neurol. Ass.*, p. 169.
Spencer, W. G. (1894), *Philos. Trans.*, vol. 185b, p. 609.
Spiegel, E. A., and Scala, N. P. (1936), *Arch. Opthal., Chicago*, vol. 16, p. 967.
Sugar, O., Chusid, J. G., and French, J. D. (1948), *J. Neuropath. exp. Neurol.*, vol. 7, p. 182.
Tower, S. S. (1928), *Bull. Johns Hopk. Hosp.*, vol. 43, p. 237.
Tower, S. S. (1935), *Brain*, vol. 58, p. 238.
Tower, S. S. (1936), *Brain*, vol. 59, p. 408.
Tower, S. S. (1940), *Brain*, vol. 63, p. 36.
Vogt, C., and Vogt, O. (1907), *J. Psychol. Neurol., Lpz.*, vol. 8, suppl., p. 277.
Vogt, C., and Vogt, O. (1919), *J. Psychol. Neurol., Lpz.*, vol. 25, p. 276.
Walker, A. E. (1940), *J. comp. Neurol.*, vol. 73, p. 59.
Walker, A. E. (1944), 'Afferent connections', in *The Precentral Motor Cortex*, ed. by P. C. Bucy, University of Illinois Press, p. 1.
Walker, A. E., and Green, H. D. (1938), *J. Neurophysiol.*, vol. 1, p. 152.
Walshe, F. M. R. (1935), *Brain*, vol. 58, p. 81.
Walshe, F. M. R. (1942), *Brain*, vol. 65, p. 409.
Walshe, F. M. R. (1943), *Brain*, vol. 66, p. 104.
Walshe, F. M. R. (1947), *Brain*, vol. 70, p. 93.
Ward, A. A. (1948), *J. Neurophysiol.*, vol. 11, p. 13.
Ward, A. A., Penden, J. K., and Sugar, O. (1946), *J. Neurophysiol.*, vol. 9, p. 453.
Ward, A. A., and McCulloch, W. S. (1947), *J. Neurophysiol.*, vol. 10, p. 309.
Wilson, S. A. K., and Walshe, F. M. R. (1914), *Brain*, vol. 37, p. 199.
Woolsey, C. N., and Bard, P. (1936), *Amer. J. Physiol.*, vol. 116, p. 165.
Woolsey, C. N., and Chang, H. (1948), *Res. Publ. Ass. nerv. ment. Dis.*, vol. 27, p. 146.

21 F. M. R. Walshe

On the Role of the Pyramidal System in Willed Movements

Excerpt from F. M. R. Walshe, *Critical Studies in Neurology*, Williams & Wilkins Co., 1948, chapter 5, pp. 207–16.

In dealing with theoretical considerations concerned with the physiology of the nervous system, one is exceptionally liable to be misled by preconceived or introspectively evolved notions. . . . Symmetry and the desire for classification are apt to be mistaken for physiological principles and we tend to drift into the error of supposing that conceptions that are clear cut, easily comprehensible and 'reasonable,' acquire by that very fact an increased probability of being accurate expositions of the physiological processes they profess to explain . . . physiological necessity is apt to defy our preconceived notions of reasonableness and to escape any classification which is more respectful of logic than of fact. *Wilfred Trotter, J. f. Psychol. u. Neurol.*, vol. 20 (1913), p. 123.

That before a gathering of physicians I should propose to deal with the physiology of the pyramidal system may seem to call for some apology from me, yet, though what I shall have to say may well be of less importance than this meeting deserves, the choice itself can, I submit, be justified.

It is in the tradition of clinical neurology that it should maintain the closest association with the physiological study of the nervous system, and many are the noteworthy contributions to this science that clinical observation has made, Yet, there is a special justification for considering the role of the pyramidal system in willed movements, namely, that the human subject provides better opportunities for this study than does the animal in the experimental laboratory.

This may seem a surprising view, so modestly have we come to think of the clinical method in our time, but I am fortified in my belief by the following circumstance. When, recently, I began to put my ideas upon this subject in order, I ventured to mention my proposal to Sir Charles Sherrington, who replied to me: 'You choose a hard question, and one which the bedside is far better placed to solve than is the laboratory, I think. The pyramidal system is such a human feature.' Thereupon he elaborated this theme with that insight into neural function we have come to regard as peculiarly the gift of this great physiologist.

There remains yet another advantage in the choice of the human subject and the clinical method, namely, that any study of disorders of willed movement from pyramidal lesion demands from the patient a degree of co-operation that no animal affords.[1]

These considerations, therefore, and others as good that could be adduced, are my apology for my subject today. It remains to ask how the problem is to be tackled. As clinicians we turn naturally to the observed phenomena of normal movement, and then to those of hemiplegia as the classic expression of pyramidal deficit: embracing in our survey hemiplegias of every degree of severity, hemiplegia with and without associated changes in muscle tone, hemiplegias from cortical and from subcortical lesions; developing hemiplegia and recovering hemiplegia and so on. Again, we shall have to consider the recorded results of animal experiments: of cortical stimulations and ablations, and of sections of the medullary pyramid.

Definition of the Terms 'Pyramidal' and 'Extra-pyramidal' as Applied to Neurone Systems

There can be few terms in neuro-anatomy and neuro-physiology more in need of precise definition. A number of assumptions has grown up around both, the tacit acceptance of which has confused many a physiological exposition. Thus it was long taught that the pyramidal tract arose exclusively from the Betz or giant cells of the precentral convolution, and that the cells so named possessed an anatomical and physiological specificity.[2] Both assumptions are now at last dispelled, and, in their fall, have badly shaken those physiological hypotheses of motor cortical function which depended for a foundation upon their reality. This aspect of the problem of the identity of the pyramidal system has already been discussed by me elsewhere (Walshe, 1942), while Tower (1944) has summarized the latest details of the origin and constitution of the pyramidal tract. It is not necessary, therefore, to cover this

1. For example, Sarah Tower (1940) speaks of 'the limits set upon minuteness of examination by the unco-operative monkey', and again (1944) she notes that the hemiplegic chimpanzee after pyramidal lesions 'is extraordinarily unstable in mood, swinging from unmanageable unco-operativeness to equally unmanageable co-operativeness'.

2. It is interesting to note that as long ago as 1881, Bevan Lewis, the pioneer of cortical cytoarchitectonics, expressed the view that the 'giant cells' described by Betz did not constitute a specific morphological category, but were merely the largest representatives of a general formation of cells of wider distribution than Betz affirmed (cf. *Brain*, vol. 4, p. 238).

ground anew. What is here referred to as the pyramidal system are those corticospinal fibres which arise from pyramidal cells in the fifth layer of the precentral cortex, and, traversing the medullary pyramid, decussate or remain uncrossed and make up the crossed and uncrossed pyramidal tracts respectively of the spinal cord. It is possible that these fibres in their course from cortex to medullary pyramid give off collaterals which establish anatomical connections and physiological relations with subcortical masses of grey matter. If this is so, then the pyramidal system below the medullary pyramid has a more restricted constitution than it has at higher levels.

It might follow from this that variations in range of function are involved: the higher part of the pyramidal system which contains fibres in addition to those which are corticospinal having a wider physiological role than that subserved by the latter fibres which constitute the medullary pyramid and the pyramidal tracts of the cord. To mention these possibilities is to indicate the incompleteness of our knowledge, not only of the physiology but even of the anatomy of the pyramidal system.

The term 'extrapyramidal' though of comparatively modern origin has also had its vicissitudes, its referents being so often changed that it is now necessary to define it upon each occasion of use. In his classic paper on progressive lenticular degeneration, Kinnier Wilson used the term in connection with both afferent and efferent pathways including a cerebello-rubro-thalamo-cortical and a lenticulo-rubro-spinal path within the category of extrapyramidal pathways. In the early years of the century, Rothman appears to have used it for paths efferent from the cerebral cortex other than the pyramidal, but later, the term became restricted to certain subcortical efferent systems, namely, the basal ganglia and their projection paths. Its renewed extension to refer to pathways arising in, and efferent from, the precentral regions of the cortex is a more recent development. *In the present paper the term 'extrapyramidal' refers to efferent cortical neurone systems other than the pyramidal, and also to all subcortical efferent neurone systems that subserve movement.*

Some General Principles of Study

Before we plunge *in medias res* and proceed to consider the relevant clinical and experimental data, let us for a few moments dwell upon some general principles that should govern our approach to the problem before us.

Whether of clinical or experimental origin our data are in large part the results of lesions of the nervous system, and it is essential to appreciate at the outset that the determination of normal function from the study of the symptoms of lesions is a very complex affair. The failure to grasp this underlies the many unsatisfactory hypotheses of nervous function that obtain currency. If, for example, tremor ensues upon a focal and destroying lesion of some part of the brain, we may not conclude that the function of the part destroyed was to inhibit tremor. It might be thought that no one would propose so naïve a hypothesis, but it is precisely this idea that was invoked by Ramsay Hunt (1917) to account for the tremor of the Parkinsonian syndrome. Nor was he in any way unique in his point of view, for speculations of this order abound in neurological literature in respect of many encephalic structures and their functions.

Many of us can recall those analyses of cerebellar ataxy that were current in the early years of this century, which proposed, on the one hand, that the atonia and asthenia of cerebellar ataxy were due to loss of a normal tonic or sthenic action of the cerebellum upon neuromuscular activity, while, on the other hand, the overshooting of the mark by the hand and arm of the ataxic subject when he stretched out to grasp some object, the so-called dysmetria, was attributed to the loss of a normal 'braking' action of the cerebellum upon the same neuromuscular activity.

Nothing, indeed, could be easier than this facile *ad hoc* creation of a fresh function to explain each manifestation of disordered movement revealed by each different clinical test, but it is not physiology.

The inadequacy of the kind of symptom interpretation we have been discussing may perhaps be most clearly illustrated by a mechanical analogy, as apt in its way as an analogy can be. In the transmission system of a motor car, two toothed and bevelled wheels engage at right angles. If, as may happen, a tooth or cog on one of these wheels breaks off, at the point in each revolution at which the gap left by the lost cog meets the other wheel, there is a jar and a noise. We might therefore argue that since loss of a cog is followed by a noise, it was the 'normal function' of that cog to prevent or 'inhibit' the noise. The cog may then be said to have a dual function: it transmits force and it inhibits noise – and our analogy is well-nigh perfect. Thus, baldly stated, the proposition is manifestly absurd, yet it typifies a line of thought to which the literature of neurology is no stranger.

It is clear, then, that such movements as we may observe after some component of the motor taxis of the organism is out of action, are the resultant, the sum, of the combined activity of the components that remain intact. For example, cerebellar ataxy is the disorder of willed movement which ensues upon a falling out of the cerebellar component and it expresses the activity of what is left of the neural mechanism – it is the product of the attempt at compensation for the lost component. This notion implies, in turn, that the intact mechanisms are themselves modified in their activity under these abnormal circumstances, and thus a fresh complicating factor is introduced in the attempt to infer the nature of cerebellar function from the observation of what is called, somewhat misleadingly, cerebellar ataxy.

It is this same order of complexity that must invest the attempt to deduce pyramidal functions from the observation of such willed movements as remain after pyramidal activity has been lost. It is many years since von Monakow (1917) emphasized the difficulty of 'localizing function' from the study of the symptoms of lesions, and recently, Lashley (1937) has made it clear that this involves the use of intellectual processes somewhat more involved than those commonly thought sufficient to the task.

My second general point is this, that we shall do well to consider something of the circumstances in which the pyramidal system has evolved. I do not intend to embark upon an erudite phylogenetic or evolutionary study, but I believe that we may hope to get a lead as to the essential quality of pyramidal function by considering the place this system occupies in the human brain as evolved.

Seeking for some way out of that state of muddled suspense that is the first stage of thought upon any unresolved problem, I turned, as I have always turned, to C. S. Sherrington's *Integrative Action of the Nervous System* (Yale University Press), to find, as I have often found, what seems to me the point of view essential to the right approach.

In the illuminating ninth chapter of that magnificent book, entitled 'The physiological position and dominance of the brain', there lie implicit, when not indeed explicit, the clues to the solution of many current problems of neurophysiology.

There we have presented to us a conception of the nervous system in which the entire edifice is reared upon two neurones, the afferent root cell and the efferent root cell. The two form the pillars of the fundamental reflex arc, and on the junction between them are superposed, mediately or immediately, all the other neural arcs, even those of the cerebral cortex itself.

It is the receptor neurone which is the driving force, and in particular the distance receptors that are the great 'initiators of reaction'. It is round the central endings of their afferent pathways that the cerebral cortex has been elaborated, and it is characteristic of the distance receptors that they tend to treat the musculature as a whole, and to engage it in long sequences of movement that are anticipatory of, and lead up to, later and consummatory events. In this task, the distance receptors have extensive internuncial paths, paths common to arcs that have arisen indirectly from receptors of various kinds. *The pyramidal tract is, on the efferent side, the principal path of this order, reaching its greatest importance in man.*

Thus we come to the idea of the pyramidal system as the path by way of which the receptors, in particular the distance receptors, can activate and direct movement. It is this notion of directing of movement that seems to me so essential to an appreciation of the role of the pyramidal system, and I cannot do better than to quote what Sherrington says in this matter, thus:

The series of actions of which the distance receptors initiate the earlier steps form series much longer than those initiated by the non-projicient. Their stages, moreover, continue to be guided by the projicient organs for a longer period between initiation and consummation. Thus in a positive phototropic reaction the eye continues to be the starting place of the excitation, and in many cases guides change in the direction not only of the eyeball but of the whole animal in locomotion. ... The mere length of their steps and the vicissitudes of relation between bodies in motion reacting on one another at a distance conspire to give to these precurrent reflexes a multiformity and a complexity unparalleled by the reflexes from the non-projicient receptors.

Later, he says: 'Locomotive progression and distance receptivity are two phenomena so fundamentally correlated that the physiology of neither can be comprehended without recognition of the correlation of the two'.

Very recently the same theme has been taken up by Adrian (1947) in his Hughlings Jackson lecture, where he observes that 'purposive acts, therefore, must be moulded like the movements of walking, by the controlling afferent patterns which are set up as the act progresses'.

The words I wish especially to draw attention to here are the final ones, 'set up as the act progresses'.

Bartlett, also, in his recent Oliver–Sharpey Lectures on the measurement of human skill (1947) emphasizes the same point, saying:

graded action, however simple it may be, has at least one of the fundamental marks of skill – an effector response is not merely set off by a receptor function but is guided and determined by it. The receptor functions that are important in the case of skilled behaviour ... are always of that kind which claims to register something that is going on in the outside world. So they come to be particularly identified with the operations of the special senses, and especially of those distance receptors which are the basis of tremendous development of the central nervous system. Skill, then, whether bodily or mental, has from the beginning this character of being in touch with demands which come from the outside world.

The pyramidal system is the one through which this guidance is exercised, not in any capacity of initiator but in that of an internuncial path.

Germane to this view of pyramidal function are the many experiments that have shown how the cutting off of afferent impulses from the receptors profoundly reduces the spontaneous activity of the animal. Mettler (1935) and his co-workers found that the decorticated dog seemed unable to initiate movement or to cease a movement once initiated, and they conclude that this initiating function is mediated by the pyramidal system. Bard and Rioch (1937) found the same lack of spontaneity in the decorticate cat, a lack in direct proportion to the loss of afferent pathways to the cortex. Other examples could be cited from the abundant literature on the subject.

We may therefore conclude that receptor activity, including both distance reception and proprioception, is so essentially correlated with pyramidal function that the physiology of the latter cannot be comprehended apart from the recognition of this correlation.

In all these circumstances it is, I submit, a fair criticism of much modern thought upon the excitable motor cortex and the pyramidal tract, based upon methods of stimulation, ablation and section, that it has considered both in so complete an isolation from the rest of the nervous system, that the essential importance of the sensory side of that system has been forgotten. Further, this abstraction of the part from the whole tends also to obscure the significance of the part abstracted, and in this instance has led directly to the attribution to the pyramidal system of functions which, as an internuncial system, it could not fulfil. Thus, Tower endows the pyramidal tract with 'full responsibility' for the discrete control of movements, and holds that in virtue of its 'discriminating qualities' it affords the cerebral cortex the latter's effectiveness as 'an agent of choice'. Surely, to take this view is to put the cart before the horse.

It is essential, therefore, to stress the importance of the idea of the receptor system as initiating and directing willed movements, in contrast to the widespread assumption that we may usefully contemplate the physiology of movement as starting *ab initio* from a mechanically conceived 'keyboard' in the motor cortex. This point of view derives from a still earlier assumption, namely, that we may regard the highly artificial phenomena ensuing upon electrical stimulation of the cortex as reproducing the normal activity of the brain in initiating and directing willed movements, or at least as not differing from this in a degree or manner calling upon us for any intellectual exegesis. The willed movement, the 'precurrent' reaction as it so commonly is at its start, is not characteristically predetermined in form, duration or complexity, for it is moulded throughout its course by impulses deriving from the visual, extero-receptors and proprio-receptors. It is thus profoundly unlike the motor response to electrical stimulation of the cortex.

It would seem, therefore, that we may look upon the pyramidal *system as an internuncial, a common, pathway by which the sensory system initiates and continuously directs, in willed movements, the activities of the nervous motor mechanisms.* This sensory afflux is a condition of willed movement, and unless we consider both in association we cannot hope to see the purpose of either.

Having criticized some modern thinking upon pyramidal functions for considering these without due regard for what has been left out of the abstraction, it would ill become me to fall into the same error. This I should be doing were I to make no reference to the psychological considerations involved in the use of the term 'willed' as applied to movement, and developed my argument as though willed movements were simply and immediately responses to sensory stimuli. An 'educated skill', to use Bartlett's apt expression, is a psychophysical process or event, and between the impact of sensory impulses upon the cerebral sensory mechanisms and the motor reactions lie processes of choice, selection, judgement, and timing, which, while they have their concomitant physiological processes, belong also to the realm of the mind. There is motor behaviour, too, that, while its performance demands sensory direction, is initiated by no discoverable present sensory stimulus, but derives from mental processes.

It is not a part of this attempted formulation of an hypothesis of pyramidal function that I should even enter this complex and difficult field of discourse. Let it suffice that we recognize that in the definition just given of the role of the pyramidal system there has been omitted from explicit consideration the psychological aspects of what is involved in the term 'willed' as applied to movements; that but a fraction of the total problem of movement is being considered, and that we recognize that willed movement is not simply a response to sensory stimuli.

In the light of Sherrington's conception of the pyramidal system, we may now see it in its due relation to the sensory side of the nervous system. We can no longer continue to regard it as something enjoying a most unphysiological autonomy within the nervous system, nor as possessing 'discriminating' functions which are the properties of synaptic fields but not of conductors.

References

ADRIAN, E. D. (1947), *Brain*, vol. 70, p. 1.
BARD, P., and RIOCH, D. M. (1937), *Bull. Johns Hopk. Hosp.*, vol. 60, p. 73.
BARTLETT, F. C. (1947), *Brit. Med. J.*, vol. 1, p. 835.
LASHLEY, K. S. (1937), *Arch. Neurol. Psychiat.*, vol. 38, p. 371.
METTLER, F. A., METTLER, C. C., and CULLER, E. A. (1935), *Arch. Neurol. Psychiat.*, vol. 34, p. 1238.
MONAKOW, C. VON (1917), *Ergebn. Physiol.*, p. 206.
RAMSAY HUNT, J. (1917), *Arch. Neurol. Psychiat.*, vol. 35, p. 1399.
TOWER, S. (1940), *Brain*, vol. 63, p. 36.
TOWER, S. (1944), *The Precentral Motor Cortex*, University of Illinois Press, chapter 6.
WALSHE, F. M. R. (1942), *Brain*, vol. 65, p. 409.

22 K. H. Pribram, L. Kruger, F. Robinson and A. J. Berman

The Effects of Precentral Lesions on the Behavior of Monkeys

Excerpt from K. H. Pribram, L. Kruger, F. Robinson and A. J. Berman, 'The effects of precentral lesions in the behavior of monkeys', *Yale J. Biol. Med.*, vol. 28 (1955–6), pp. 428–43.

[. . .] Bucy, in the introduction to the recent monograph on the precentral motor cortex, makes the following statement: 'The editor regards the precentral motor cortex as the principal efferent or effector cerebral cortical mechanism by which the brain expresses its activity through the skeletal musculature' (3). Implicit in this statement is the suggestion that all learned behavior finds expression through efferents leaving the precentral region; that afferents relay signals to the 'primary projection' cortices whence internuncials lead to the 'association areas' which, in turn, play upon the precentral cortical areas. To be validated, this viewpoint must be supported by the following evidence: *anatomical*, showing a preponderance of separation between afferent and efferent tracts in the cerebrum; *electrophysiological*, showing a minimum of overlap between those areas responding (by 'evoked potentials') to peripheral stimulation, and those areas which, when electrically excited, give rise to peripheral responses; *behavioral*, showing that learned behavior is impaired by injury to the more-or-less 'final' common path. This paper deals with some experiments in the last category. The discussion will be concerned, as well, with experiments in the other categories.

Regarding the specific effects of lesions of the precentral cortex on behavior, three conceptions need clarification. The data giving rise to these conceptions are, in brief, as follows: a lesion of the precentral cortex interferes with patterned muscular contraction in some situations but these same or approximately similar patterns may be observed intact in other situations. Thus, an animal may fail to grasp a nail which holds together a box containing a peanut but grasps an equivalently thin wire composing the side of a cage while climbing; a patient may fail to close his fist on a tennis ball when asked to grasp it but will turn a doorknob in order to escape from a ward during a conflagration. Such data have given rise to two conceptions popular in clinical neurology: that the precentral cortex is implicated in 'skilled movement'; that the precentral cortex is implicated in 'voluntary movement'. A third conception emphasizes the lack of effect of precentral lesions on the solution of problems provided some movement is possible. This conception looks, therefore, for an alternate approach to the specification of the relationship of the precentral areas to behavior and characterizes the impairment as an involvement of 'postural mechanisms' (9). In order to estimate the relevance of each of these conceptions, we reinvestigated the effect of precentral lesions on the patterns of response under several conditions. Opening a hasp box to obtain a peanut, discrimination of visually presented patterns, and the delayed reaction were used as quantitative behavioral indices. Neurological examination and observations of the animal's activity in his living quarters and in a relatively free environment provide background material against which the experimental data can be interpreted.

Some questions regarding the nature of the precentral lesions affecting behavior were also asked. Does locus of lesion within the precentral areas make a difference? Is extent of lesion an important factor? Is the decrement in performance of a limb contralateral to a lesion increased when that lesion is made bilateral? Is the effect of lesion dependent on removal of tissue or the result of 'irritative' scar at the borders of the removal? The experiments reported suggest answers to these questions.

Materials and Methods

Nine immature rhesus monkeys were used in these experiments. Eight of these animals received one or another resection of the precentral agranular cortex, the ninth was given multiple implantations of aluminium hydroxide cream over this cortex.

Surgical methods

Under intraperitoneally administered barbiturate anesthesia and using aseptic technique, a frontal osteoplastic craniotomy was performed through a coronal incision. The bone flap was hinged on the temporal muscle, the dural flap based on the sagittal sinus. The frontal cortex was exposed from the arcuate to the intraparietal sulcus, from the midline to the Sylvian fissure. Subpial ablation of the appropriate cortex was carried out through a pial incision and with a 19-gauge needle suction tip. The anterior removals included the posterior bank of the arcuate sulcus; the posterior removals included the anterior bank of the central fissure. All removals extended into the superior bank of the calloso-marginal sulcus. The extensive lesions involved all of these 'buried' areas. Hemostasis was accomplished by temporary packing with cottonoid pledgets and waiting, rather than by cautery. For the 'irritative' lesion, aluminum hydroxide cream was placed in five one-centimeter silver discs and these were distributed over the lateral and medial frontal agranular cortex and the dura closed tightly over them, Interrupted silk closure was routine. Bilateral procedures were carried out in two stages, separated by a 7- to 8-month interval.

Behavioral methods

Experimental subjects were observed in their living cage at least twice a day for 15 minutes and in a large enclosure once a day. They were observed in a relatively free situation; in addition, their reaction to threat and to feeding were noted. Their manipulations of food, of sticks, of the cage and enclosure walls during climbing, and their loco-motion were recorded. Neurological examinations were performed on the animals while they were restrained in a neurological chair. At least two observers compared their findings in most instances.

Quantitative behavioral measures, made in a modified Wisconsin general testing apparatus designed for primates (15), included timing of the opening of a simple latch box. This box, approximately 5 by 8 cm. is closed by a sliding metal lid which is locked by a 2-in. nail inserted through the lid into the side of the box. To open the box (which contains a peanut during the test trials) the monkey has to grasp the nail, pull it out, push the lid back, and take the peanut from the box. These maneuvers have to be performed in the order stated to accomplish the trial. The mean of the time taken in 30 consecutive trials was used as an index of performance. Thirty trials per day were given until stable performance was reached preoperatively; postoperatively, 30 trials per day were given for five days following surgery and then five days each month. Motion pictures were taken both pre- and postoperatively in this situation, and these were studied when shown at regular and slow-motion speed.

Another quantitative behavior measure recorded performance on the classical delayed reaction task. In this situation *two* cups appear before the monkey. Into one of these (*which* one is determined by a random sequence) a peanut is dropped in full view of the animal. Then an opaque screen is lowered, hiding the cups from view for 10 seconds. When the screen is again raised, the animal has to choose between two identical appearing, closed cups. Correct choice depends on the mon-key's remembering which of the two cups had been baited 10 seconds before. The subjects were trained beginning two weeks postoperatively until they reached a performance level of 90 per cent on a hundred consecutive trials. The number of trials required to reach this criterion was compared with the mean of the number of trials taken by 35 un-operated monkeys tested in the same manner.

Visual discrimination was also tested. This task utilized the same boxes as those used in the delayed reaction, but in this instance the boxes were closed by covers on one of which a black plus sign was

441

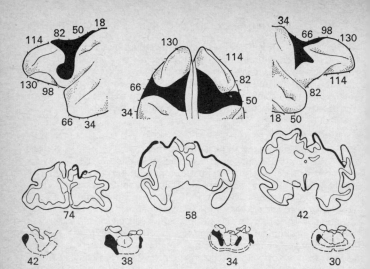

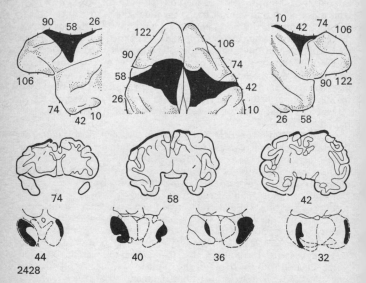

Figure 1. Reconstructions and representative cross-sections through lesion and thalamus of brains of the animals used in this experiment. Black indicates locus and extent of ablation of cortex (top and middle figures in

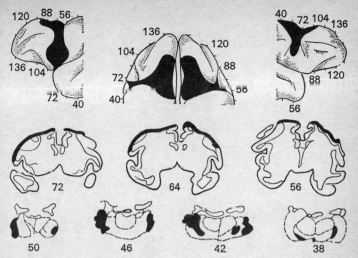

2400

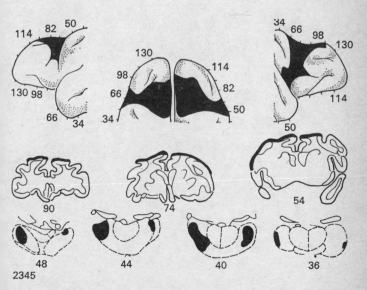

2345

each set. Numbers and locus and extent of retrograde thalamic degeneration (bottom four figures in each set) refer to subject and to the actual cross-section from which diagram was made

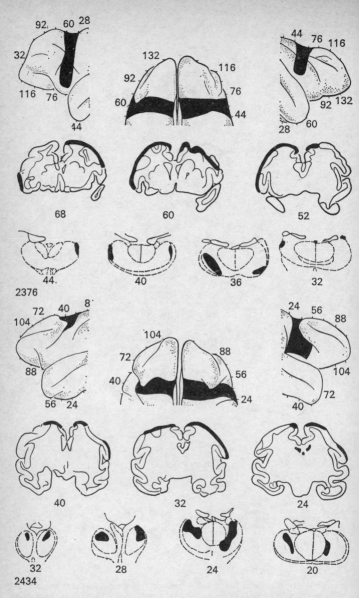

Figure 1—*Continued.*

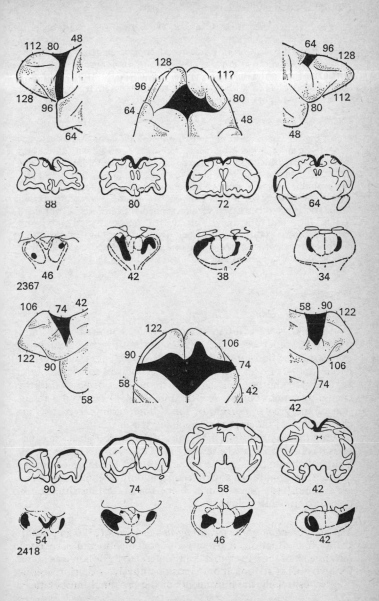

painted, on the other, a black square. The peanut was invariably concealed in the box marked 'plus' but the position of the 'plus' was
varied from box to box in random sequence. Thus, the task for the
monkey was to choose the box marked plus; the numbers of trials taken
by the operated animals to accomplish this in 90 out of 100 consecutive
trials was compared with the mean score taken to teach the same
criterion by 44 unoperated control subjects.

Anatomical methods

Following the completion of the neurological and behavioral examination, all the animals were sacrificed, the brains perfused with saline and
formalin, dehydrated in alcohols, and imbedded in celloidin. In animals
2400 and 2345 the operated region was exposed under ether anesthesia
and excitable points were identified and mapped in cortex and exposed
white matter. Serial sections at 25 micra. were made, every tenth section
saved and every other saved section stained with thionin. From these
sections the extent of lesion was orthogonally reconstructed onto graph
paper; reconstructions and representative cross-sections demonstrating
depth of resection are presented in Figure 1. Retrograde thalamic
degeneration was plotted and is also shown in this figure.

Results

Experiment 1. Unilateral lesions

Five monkeys were tested preoperatively, operated upon, and
retested. Two of these animals (2428 and 2427) received extensive
unilateral resections of the dorsolateral, frontal, agranular cortex;
in one animal (2376), the unilateral resection was restricted to the
posterior; in another animal (2434), to the anterior portion of the
frontal agranular cortex. A fifth animal (2418) received a resection of the greater portion of the frontal agranular cortex, including that of the anterior cingulate gyrus.

A preliminary report of the results of the neurological examinations has been presented elsewhere (1). Observations of the movements of the animals in the home cage and the large enclosure
under 'free' conditions and in feeding and threatening conditions
are summarized; performance in the formal testing situation is
described in detail below.

Subtotal resection of the frontal agranular cortex (2376 and 2434).
In the free situation, a paucity of spontaneous and associated
movements of the extremities contralateral to the lesion was noted
for two weeks to one month postoperatively. Anterior lesions
affected especially the movements of the proximal musculature:

movements about the shoulder and hip were awkward when they were present at all. Posterior lesions, on the other hand, affected movements of the distal musculature: especially flexion of the digits in climbing was impaired. When in a threatening or feeding situation, the affected movements would be present initially but faded as the situation continued. However, these effects were not detected beyond the first postoperative month.

In the latch box test situation these animals showed a decrement in performance only during the first operative week. Whereas their performance with the hand ipsilateral to the lesion continued at the preoperative rate of under 2 seconds to accomplish a trial, performance with the hand contralateral to the lesion took between 6 and 7 seconds during this period. The performance difficulty differed for the two subjects, however. The animal with the posterior resection was clumsy in manipulating the nail and the box cover; the animal with the anterior resection showed clumsiness in bringing the arm to the latch box and occasionally in 'letting go' the nail or box cover preparatory to making the next movement in the sequence. After the first postoperative week, these difficulties were no longer observed and performance time became equal for both extremities.

Extensive resection of the frontal agranular cortex (2428 and 2427). In the free situation a hemiparesis of the limbs contralateral to the lesion was consistently noted during the first postoperative month, i.e. the animals rarely used the affected extremities; when movements did occur, they were gross, clumsy, and of short duration. During the second postoperative month the affected extremities were moved in association with climbing and running movements of the other side; however, when only one extremity was required for the performance of an act, the extremity ipsilateral to the lesion was consistently employed. This preference persisted for three months after which it receded gradually and disappeared, first in the threatening and feeding situations. In these situations the affected extremities were used after the second postoperative week to accomplish prehension of, or escape from, the stimulus object.

In performing the latch box task no effect of the resection was observed when the animal used the arm ipsilateral to the lesion. However, when only the arm contralateral to the lesion was available for the task performance, *no trial was accomplished within six months following surgery*. Only occasionally would the subject make an attempt to dislodge the nail and open the box;

on each occasion the movements were executed in a gross manner precluding accomplishment of the trial. For the most part, the animal just sat quietly or began to play in the testing cage rather than manipulate the latch. As soon as the arm ipsilateral to the resection was released from restraint, however, testing with this extremity proceeded at speeds indistinguishable from those obtained preoperatively. In the seventh to ninth postoperative month, clumsy attempts were made by the animals to open the latch with the affected extremities. Performance scores of 16 to 30 seconds were recorded, but difficulty in maintaining the animal's attempts to perform a series of trials with the affected hand attended each session. Consistent performance with this extremity was thus never re-established in these animals. The grave deficit shown by all animals made it difficult to evaluate any difference between them (differences which might be attributed to the additional resection of the cingulate cortex in one of them).

Aluminum hydroxide cream implantations of the precentral agranular cortex. During the fifth postoperative week, this animal (2398) began to have Jacksonian convulsions in the right side of the face, contralateral to the lesion and spreading quickly to involve the entire right side. Occasionally the seizures would become generalized. Seizures occurred most frequently during the third and fourth postoperative months; at this time, from four to a dozen seizures per day were noted. The feeding and threatening situations almost invariably induced convulsions. As reported for other 'irritative' frontal lesions (13), the monkey soon became 'conditioned' so that when a stick was shown him, the seizure activity would be initiated. Beginning in the fifth postoperative month these generalized seizures became less frequent; instead, an almost continual 3 to 4 per second rhythmic activity of the right arm and hand was present whether or not the arm was engaged in some activity. This 'tremor' persisted but became less noticeable toward the end of the first postoperative year.

As indicated in Table 1 the scores of performance of the latch box task reflect the appearance of the 'tremor' but do not correlate with the onset of Jacksonian convulsions. Time scores taken for the affected extremity are markedly increased after the fifth postoperative month and continue to reflect the awkwardness of performance for the remainder of the time the animal was tested.

Electroencephalographic abnormalities (marked slowing and spike activity) began to appear in the left central scalp leads during the second postoperative month and persisted thereafter,

Table 1
Two-Stage Bilateral Resections of Frontal Agranular Cortex

Animal	Lesion	Pre-2nd op.	1 Week	1 Month	2 Months	3 Months	4 Months	5 Months
2400	Extensive Dorsolateral	L. 1.4 R. 1.4	L. — R. 6.7	L. 11.4 R. 11.0	L. 4.1 R. 3.5	L. 3.2 R. 3.4	L. 2.2 R. 4.7	L. 2.0 R. 2.1
2345	Extensive Dorsolateral	L. 1.9 R. 2.7	L. — R. 4.3	L. — R. 13.5	L. 16.9 R. 4.3	L. 6.9 R. 4.1	L. 5.1 R. 3.3	L. 3.4 R. 3.2
2376	Precentral	L. 1.9 R. 3.9	L. 3.7 R. 5.1	L. 1.7 R. 2.1	L. 1.4 R. 3.4	L. 1.8 R. 2.4	L. 1.7 R. 2.0	
2434	Anterior	L. 2.6 R. 2.1	L. 4.2 R. 2.3	L. 3.2 R. —	L. 2.8 R. 1.9	L. 2.3 R. 2.2	L. 2.3 R. 2.5	
2367	Anterior plus Cingulate	L. 1.4 R. 1.4	L. 4.4 R. 1.6	L. 3·0 R. 2.2	L. 2.0 R. 1.6	L. 1.7 R. 1.7	L. 1.6 R. 1.7	

Right side operated

'Irritative' Unilateral, Left 2398

	1 Month	2 Months	3 Months	4 Months	5 Months	6 Months	7 Months	8 Months	9 Months
	L. 2.1 R. 2.6	2.8	2.0 2.5	1.6 2.4	1.8 4.2	2.1 11.0	1.8 10.0	2.0 22.8	1.8 11.1

Upper: Results of the two-stage bilateral procedure. Numbers indicate the mean of time scores of 150 consecutive trials. Dash indicates that no score was obtained, usually because the subject failed to manipulate the latch box.

Lower: Results of the irritative scarring procedure. Time scores indicated as in upper portion of table.

with gradual decline, for the entire postoperative year. The appearance of the electrical abnormality correlated with the appearance of convulsive episodes, not with change in test performance.

Experiment 2. Bilateral lesions

Seven monkeys served as subjects for this experiment. Four of these (2427, 2428, 2434, 2367) had been used in Experiment 1. Since consistent latch box performance with the affected extremity had not been re-established by monkeys 2427 and 2428, they were used following the second surgical procedure only to study performance of the delayed reaction and visual discrimination tasks. Two other subjects (2400 and 2345), with somewhat more superficial but equally extensive resections of the precentral agranular cortex, were trained in the latch box situation beginning six months after the initial unilateral procedure. When consistent performance of this task was established with both extremities, the second surgical procedure was undertaken. A similar program of testing was pursued with another monkey (2367) with an ablation of the cingulate cortex in addition to an anterior precentral lesion. In this animal the cortex surrounding the central fissure was spared in order to assure the possibility of some performance in the test situation. Subject 2376 with a posterior and subject 2434 with an anterior lesion were used to compare the effects of bilateral subtotal resections. Before the second surgical procedure was undertaken, these animals had re-established consistent latch box performance following the unilateral procedure as described in Experiment 1.

Protocols of the neurological examinations of these animals will be presented elsewhere. Observations of the movements of the animals in the home cage and the large enclosure under 'free' conditions and in feeding and threatening conditions are summarized; performance in formal testing situations is described below.

Subtotal resections of the frontal agranular cortex (2376, 2434, 2367). In the free situation a paucity of movement was observed in the extremities contralateral to the second lesion for one, or at the most two, weeks. When these extremities were used, paresis was noted; e.g. the animal did not suspend itself from the cage wall for as long a period with the affected extremity. After the first week or two no difference between the two sides could be distinguished. However, the animals continued to tire easily when running (in the threatening situation) for about six months after the second operation; no difference between the two sides could be seen. Nor was a difference between the effects of anterior and posterior subtotal resection as marked as that observed after unilateral ablation. Nevertheless, posterior resection affected primarily the movements of the hands and feet as in climbing; anterior resection affected primarily running and hanging from cage walls and ceiling.

Records obtained in the latch box situation appear in Table 1 (2376, 2434, 2367). Note that only during the first postoperative week was performance with the hand contralateral to the second operation defective. Even during this period, the problem was solved within twice the time taken preoperatively. Note also that the posterior subtotal resection and only this one affected performance of the ipsilateral hand as well as that of the contralateral hand. Such exacerbation of a defect which had subsided during the months following the first resection is still more noticeable with extensive resections as will be seen below. All in all, there is remarkably little effect of these lesions on performance of the latch box task; and this finding is not altered when the cingulate cortex is added to the resection.

Extensive resections of the precentral agranular cortex (2400, 2345, 2427, 2428). Both with regard to general observations and test behavior, the effects of extensive precentral resections were more drastic and more lasting. In the free situation, the animals with these resections fell frequently to the side contralateral to the second operation. For a month to six weeks they used the extremities contralateral to the lesion sparingly. Instead of running in the threatening situation, they would 'lope' somewhat awkwardly. They were never observed to jump from wall to wall following the second surgical procedure. Nevertheless, in both the feeding and threatening situations, movements were executed in appropriate sequences to accomplish getting food into the mouth or in fending off a stick. These movements were carried out slowly, however, and the animals tired easily; they could also be caught easily even six months after the second operation.

Performance of the latch box task with the hand contralateral to the lesion could not be obtained at all for a month in one subject, for over six weeks in another. Scores obtained with the hand ipsilateral to the resection also suffered markedly, as can be seen from Table 1. Performance did not return to preoperative levels during the five months of testing but stabilized for one animal during the second month and for the other animal during the fifth postoperative month at slightly longer values than the pre-operative. Performance was thus impaired but not abolished; impairment consisted in awkwardness of movement resulting in longer time scores. The sequence of acts was unimpaired.

The monkeys with extensive bilateral precentral resections performed the delayed reaction and visual discrimination as well as did the unoperated controls. Thirty-five unoperated monkeys tested in the delayed reaction procedure as outlined took a mean of 380 trials to reach criterion. The operated subjects of the present experiments took 210 and 270 trials to reach criterion. Forty-four unoperated monkeys tested in the visual pattern discrimination procedure as outlined took a mean of 375 trials to reach criterion. The operated subject of the present experiment took 150 and 310 trials to reach criterion. Clearly, there is no deficit in learning of the delayed reaction or of the visual pattern discrimination following extensive resection of the precentral agranular cortex.

Discussion

It is clear to us from our experiments that extreme views of the role of the precentral gyrus cannot be maintained. Neither the idea that the 'motor' cortex is 'more concerned with the maintenance of excitability and the regulation of postural reflexes than with the excitation and control of finely integrated adaptive movements'(9), nor the conception that this cortex serves as the sole or even 'principal cerebral efferent or effector mechanism by which the brain expresses its activity' (3), accounts satisfactorily for our observations. Nevertheless, both statements, especially when taken in the context of the discussions from which they were excerpted, have considerable usefulness in pointing out problems that must be faced in any evaluation of the effects of precentral lesions on behavior.

Observations of the movements (such as manipulating food) of the monkeys with extensive precentral resections in the free and the more structured situations cannot all be classified as impairments of postural mechanism. The increased time scores made by these animals in the latch box problem, confirming Lashley's own earlier results, make such an interpretation inadequate. Furthermore, according to Lashley's view 'impulses descending from the precentral gyrus do not initiate the finer adaptive movements through the lower motor neurons, but only "prime" these cells so that they may be excited by impulses from other sources' (9).

K. H. Pribram, L. Kruger, F. Robinson and A. J. Berman

Although Lloyd's work on the pyramidal system of cats (10) does indicate an indirect pyramidal influence on the motoneurons of the ventral horn, the recent work of Bernhard and his co-workers (2) shows that impulses from the motor cortex do indeed directly impinge upon and excite motoneurons *in the monkey*. Lashley's conception was originally derived from experiments on rodents (8), animals which show little motor defect with cortical ablation. Perhaps assigning the motor cortex a predominant role of reflex regulation of postural mechanisms is more easily envisaged in the more primitive mammals, but this view is unlikely to apply to primates.

On the other hand, the evidence that primates with extensive precentral resections learn and perform delayed reaction and visual discrimination tasks without impairment suggests the necessity for a revision of the conception that the precentral pyramidal system need be the principal cerebral efferent mechanism or even the 'internuncial' between cerebral mechanisms involved *in problem-solving behavior* and the organism's effectors. The origin of pyramidal tract fibers in regions other than the precentral cortex, the evidence of efferents from the optic cortex and from the supratemporal auditory cortex (4), the efferents from Ammon's formation (the fornix) as well as the efferents from the anterior frontal (Arnold's bundle) and the temporal cortex (Turck's tract), must be assigned equal importance to precentral efferents when *selective* effects on behavior follow the disruption of each of these systems (14). Nonetheless, one cannot dodge the issue that the selective effects resulting from the resection of the precentral gyrus is particularly devastating to an organism's *effector* mechanisms. Thus, extensive precentral lesions can be seen to interfere with performance of almost any task given to the primate provided the appropriate measure – e.g. time required for the manipulation – is made. However, in an analysis of the meaning of our measurements and observations, we must take into account the things undisturbed as well as those disturbed. When this is done, it becomes obvious that those actions involving discrete movements or 'skills' are the ones most susceptible to disruption by precentral lesions. However, the disruption is limited to the effectors controlled by the portion of precentral cortex involved in the lesion – no general 'forgetting' of the problem solution ensues. Thus, skills are interfered with by precentral lesions, not lost through excision of the locus of the 'habit'. These results are analogous to those following restricted resections of the optic cortex of the occipital lobe. Whereas the latter produces scotomata in the visual field, lesions of the precentral cortex may be said to produce scotomata of action. In vision, no decrement in the retention of learned discriminations follows subtotal occipital resections; in motor activity, no decrement in the retention of problems solution can be determined following precentral resections.

But what of the idea that 'will' as well as skill is affected by the precentral lesions? Experimental resections restricted to the precentral cortex of man (3, 5, 12) suggests that such lesions do *not* interfere with what is commonly called 'voluntary' activity; in fact, the clinical syndrome differs little from that described here for the monkey. It is likely that the more severe disturbance found in man which is characterized as a 'loss of voluntary movement' is due to deep frontal lesions involving the internal capsule. Such lesions disturb not only precentral but a variety of other cerebral mechanisms.

Regarding the effects of different precentral lesions, some reconciliation of divergent views may also be suggested. Woolsey's (18) precise maps of the responses obtained from electrical stimulation of the precentral cortex show that the posterior portions of this area, in and adjacent to the central fisure, are concerned with the control of appendicular musculature, while the anterior portions are more concerned with axial musculature. Our observations show that posterior lesions do, indeed, affect the precision of the animal's hand movements in the latch box more than do anterior lesions. The latter, on the other hand, affect primarily the movements around the shoulder and hip muscles. Former conceptualizations of the difference between the effects of anterior and posterior lesions in terms of 'discrete' *v.* 'coordinated' movements may thus be understood since movements carried out primarily with the distal portions of the extremities *are* more discrete than those involving primarily the larger axial muscle groups. The other differences which are presumed to exist between anterior and posterior lesions have been discussed elsewhere (1). However, coordination is involved whether discrete or more massive movements are or are not concerned – thus, the conceptualization in terms of somatotopy, which has been presented here, is preferred.

The extent of precentral cortex resected is important, as shown by the relatively small and transient effect of subtotal lesions as compared with the greater and more lasting effect of the extensive ablations. However, recourse to a simple notion of 'mass action' is ruled out by the apparent lack of increased decrement in per-

formance of the latch box problem when anterior cingulate ablation is added, either to a subtotal or to a total precentral resection.
Within the precentral agranular isocortex, when a unilateral
lesion is made bilateral, there is an effect on the extremity ipsilateral to the second lesion – so effective 'mass' is distributed
bilaterally within the cortex. Lesions of comparable extent in
other cortical fields studied produce either no observable motor
defects (frontal granular, temporal, striate, peristriate, and limbic
fields) or minimal transitory defects (post-central and parietal
fields). The recent study of Semmes and Chow (16) in which the
effects of lesions of all the cortex except the precentral agranular
were found to be similar to those of precentral motor cortex
ablation – except in the duration of effect – implies a lack of specificity in the function of different cortical areas in motor behavior.
Although other regions of the cortex can be implicated in motor
behavior, this may also be said of total de-afferentation of a limb.
By applying a diversity of appropriate measures, the specificity
of any such deficit may be elucidated. Such techniques used by
Fulton and his co-workers (6) in analysing motor function have
led to the demonstration of defects in posture, the various forms
of tactile and proprioceptive placing, hopping, resistance to
passive limb manipulation, palpable muscle tone, the degree and
form of tendon reflexes, influence of body and head position, the
alterations in stimulation conditions required to elicit grasping,
and other detailed neurological tests related to motor function
which in our experience clearly differentiate the motor defect
following frontal agranular lesions from that seen with any other
cortical lesion.

There have been suggestions (7) that the effects of lesions are
due solely to irritative scars at their borders. Comparison of
aluminum hydroxide cream lesions with those of ablations in the
present experiments suggests that the two types have different
effects – that both these effects might be conceived as a disequilibrium of function, but that a distinction can be made. Resections
impair performance, i.e. in a particular situation, the repertory
of action available to an animal with precentral resection is more
limited than the repertory available to an intact animal. However,
within that repertory, a fairly stable, albeit limited, performance
of tasks results. The animal with aluminum hydroxide cream
implantation, on the other hand, shows impairment in a larger
spectrum of behavior by the pervasiveness of the repetitive muscular contractions which persist whether he is active or inactive,
whether he is performing a task requiring skill or one where only

grosser movements are concerned. Thus, the animal's limitation in a particular task may or may not be as severe as that of the subjects with resection, and often fluctuates to a considerable extent for reasons that have not as yet been determined.

In conclusion: we feel that certain tentative answers can be given to the questions which initiated these experiments and were posed in the introduction. Extent of ablation is an important consideration in evaluating the effect of a precentral lesion. Effects of unilateral ablations are enhanced when the lesion is made bilateral. Effects of ablation cannot be attributed to 'irritative' scarring at the border of such lesions since the effect of 'irritative' lesions *per se* can be distinguished from those of ablation.

Precentral lesions interfere especially with skilled acts; the acts are not lost, however, through excision of the locus of a 'habit': rather, a scotoma of action may be said to result. Thus, the extreme conception that the precentral cortex is the principal efferent system by which the brain expresses its activity is modified in favor of the conception that the precentral cortex modulates a variety of reflex mechanisms basic to action. The numerous anatomical studies on the afferent and efferent relations of the somatic 'sensory' and 'motor' areas of the monkey cerebral cortex have recently been supported by electrophysiological demonstrations of efferents (17) and afferents (11) to both of these regions. The 'unity' of the 'sensorimotor' cortex is further emphasized by the remarkable constancy of proximity of somatic 'sensory' and 'motor' fields and the absence of intercalated 'association' areas in all mammals. Although it is recognized that the preponderance of afferent and efferent fibers differ in the precentral and postcentral regions, we believe that their close anatomical relationship should be emphasized rather than any conceptualization based on analogy with the dorsal and ventral roots of the spinal cord.

Experiments in both monkey and man indicate that resections limited to the precentral cortex do not interfere with behavior of the type usually described as 'willed'. Rather, we think it possible that deep lesions involving the internal capsule are responsible for such grosser changes in behavior by interrupting a variety of cerebral mechanisms. Thus, the clinically derived conception that the precentral motor cortex serves 'skilled action' is corroborated; it is clear, however, that this cortex is not the locus of a 'habit' or of a mechanism basic to any performance of the skill, but rather that precentral lesions result in a scotoma of action

K. H. Pribram, L. Kruger, F. Robinson and A. J. Berman

which interferes with the skill. On the other hand, the clinically derived conception that the precentral cortex is involved in 'willed action' is considerably modified: deep lesions involving not only precentral, but also additional, cerebral mechanisms are thought to be responsible for the grosser defects in behavior which led to this conception.

Summary

Ablation of the precentral agranular cortex was found to interfere especially with skilled acts as measured by time scores in performing a latch box task. Lesions restricted to the posterior portion of this cortex caused a greater defect in digital dexterity than anterior lesions which more markedly affected the more proximal musculature. Total ablation caused the most marked defects. Visual discrimination and delayed response performance were unaffected by precentral ablations. Bilateral ablations exacerbated the effects of unilateral ablation and caused a renewed defect on the side ipsilateral to the second operation. The effects of ablation cannot be attributed to 'irritative' scarring at the border of such lesions since the effects of 'irritative' lesions *per se* can be readily distinguished from those of ablation. It is concluded that the motor defect in precentral ablations is not due to acts lost through excision of the locus of a 'habit', but rather that scotoma of action result.

References

1. A. J. BERMAN, L. KRUGER, and J. F. FULTON, 'Recovery of function following lesions of frontal agranular cortex in the monkey', *Trans. Amer. Neurol. Ass.*, 1954, p. 178.
2. C. G. BERNHARD, E. BOHM, and I. PETERSEN, 'Investigation on the organization of the corticospinal system in monkeys (macaca mulatta)', *Acta Physiol. Scand.*, vol. 29 (1952), p. 79.
3. P. C. BUCY, *The Precentral Motor Cortex*, University of Illinois Press, 1949, pp. 3, 355.
4. D. FERRIER, *The Functions of the Brain*, Smith, Elder and Co., London, 1876, p. 323.
5. O. FOERSTER, 'Symptomatologie der erkrankungen des grosshirns: motorische felder und bahnen', *Handb. Neurol.*, J. Springer, Berlin, 1936.
6. J. F. FULTON, *The Physiology of the Nervous System*, 3rd edn, Oxford University Press, 1949.
7. D. O. HEBB and W. PENFIELD, 'Human behavior after extensive bilateral removal from the frontal lobes', *Arch. Neurol. Psychiat.*, vol. 44 (1940), p. 421.
8. K. S. LASHLEY, 'Studies of cerebral function in learning. The motor areas', *Brain*, vol. 44 (1921), p. 255.

9. K. S. LASHLEY, 'Studies of cerebral function in learning. V. The retention of motor habits after destruction of the so-called motor areas in primates', *Arch. Neurol. Psychiat.* vol. 12 (1924), p. 249.

10. D. P. C. LLOYD, 'The spinal mechanism of the pyramidal system in cats', *J. Neurophysiol.*. vol. 4 (1941), p. 525.

11. L. I. MALIS, K. H. PRIBRAM, and L. KRUGER, 'Action potentials in "motor" cortex evoked by peripheral nerve stimulation', *J. Neurophysiol.*, vol. 16 (1953), p. 161.

12. W. PENFIELD, and T. RASMUSSEN, *The Cerebral Cortex of Man*, Macmillan, New York, 1950, p. 241.

13. K. H. PRIBRAM, 'Some aspects of experimental psychosurgery: the effect of scarring frontal cortex on complex behavior', *Surg. Forum*, vol. 36 (1951), p. 315.

14. K. H. PRIBRAM, 'Toward a science of neuropsychology. Method and data', *Current Trends*, University of Pittsburgh Press, 1954, p. 115.

15. K. H. PRIBRAM, M. MISHKIN, H. E. ROSVOLD, and S. J. KAPLAN, 'Effects on delayed-response performance of lesions of dorsolateral and ventromedial frontal cortex of baboons', *J. Comp. physiol. Psychol.*, vol. 45 (1952), p. 565.

16. J. SEMMES and K. L. CHOW, 'Motor effects of lesions of precentral gyrus and of lesions sparing this area in monkeys', *Arch. Neurol. Psychiat.* (*Chicago*), vol. 73 (1955), p. 546.

17. C. N. WOOLSEY and H. T. CHANG, 'Activation of the cerebral cortex by antidromic volleys in the pyramidal tract', *Res. Publ. Ass. Nerv. Ment. Dis.*, vol. 27 (1948), p. 146.

18. C. N. WOOLSEY, P. H. SETTLAGE, D. R. MEYER, W. SENCER, T. P. HAMUY, and A. M. TRAVIS, 'Patterns of localization in precentral and "supplementary" motor areas and their relation to the concept of a premotor area', *Res. Publ. Ass. Nerv. Ment. Dis.*, vol. 30 (1952), p. 238.

Part Five Conation: The Neural Programming of Behaviour

In the first part of this volume it was found useful to hold the conceptual distinction between perception and cognition. On the behavioural side of the psychological process, also, a distinction can be entertained and found valuable. Here, too, the processes which can be distinguished in abstract form appear to intertwine. As yet, the mechanism of interaction is not nearly as clear as it is in the case of perception and cognition – and this problem remains as one of the most challenging in brain and behaviour research. But a great deal has been done to clarify the issues. Miller, Galanter, and I have devoted a volume (*Plans and the Structure of Behavior*, Holt, 1960) to such clarification and an excerpt from it is included here. One over-riding issue emerges: the neural code cannot be purely spatial; some temporal mechanism must be operative.

23 G. E. Coghill

Growth of the Nerve Cell and the Interpretation of Behaviour

Excerpt from G. E. Coghill, *Anatomy and the Problem of Behaviour*, Cambridge University Press, 1929, Lecture 3, pp. 79–91.

[. . .]

Learning as Development of Behaviour

Our specific data on the subject are drawn from relatively early periods of the life of the animal when behaviour is in a process of perfectly obvious development. But in reality behaviour is always in process of development in animals that can learn by experience. When new turns in behaviour cease to appear in the life of the individual its behaviour ceases to be intelligent.

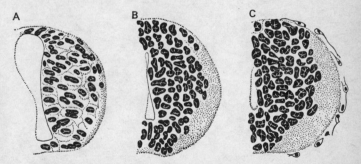

Figure 1. Camera lucida drawings at the same magnification of transverse sections of the spinal cord at the level of the fourth spinal motor root of *Amblystoma punctatum*: A, of the early swimming stage; B, at the time when the fore limb moves only with trunk movement; C, in the early fore-limb reflex stage

Stereotyped behaviour in its most intensive form characterizes those animals in which no special provision is made for the growth of neurones after the nervous system begins to function in determining the behaviour of the individual. In insects, for example, when they emerge from the chrysalis, the functional nervous system is not embedded in a matrix of embryonic nervous tissue as it is in the young of *Amblystoma* and other vertebrates.

Insects, accordingly, learn relatively little from experience, whereas the highest degree of modifiability of behaviour is possessed by those vertebrates whose brain cells have the largest potentiality of growth when the nervous system begins to function as a conducting mechanism. Figures 1 and 2 illustrate

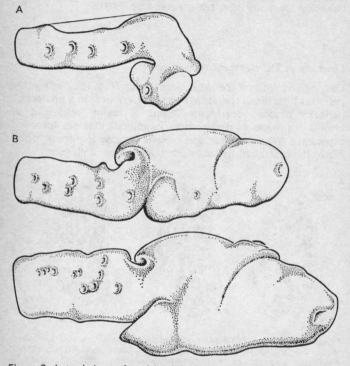

Figure 2. Lateral views of models of the brain of *Amblystoma punctatum* made at a magnification of 200 diameters: A, at the early swimming stage; B, at the age when the limb can move only as the trunk moves; C, at the time when the animal begins to walk. The figures ×40

crudely the growth of the nervous system of *Amblystoma* from the time it begins to swim till it begins to walk. This potentiality of growth in the functional neurone of *Amblystoma* has a very definite and specific relation to the development of behaviour. We infer, therefore, that potentiality of growth is a factor in the development of behaviour of other vertebrates in proportion to the degree or scope of its occurrence; and that it is in the same proportion a factor in the process of learning, provided learning in its broadest sense connotes development of behaviour.

Inadequacy of the Neurone Concept

The neurone theory, as it is usually employed to elucidate the anatomy and physiology of the nervous system, deals with the nerve cell, at least by implication, as a definite and fixed unit of structure and function. It is commonly recognized, of course, that nerve cells increase their dimensions after they begin to function as conductors, as, for example, in the lengthening of the nerves in the limbs with the lengthening of the limbs in growth; and that upon severing the fibres of the peripheral system they will regenerate by processes of growth that are essentially embryonic in nature. But it is not generally recognized that after the nerve cell has assumed a definite and specific role as conductor in a functional mechanism it grows for a relatively long time in strictly embryonic fashion and thereby extends its sphere of action enormously.

Ramón y Cajal, probably more than any other investigator, has emphasized this phase of activity of the neurone, and he has in a very general way applied it in the interpretation of physiological and psychological phenomena (16). All of his discussions of the subject, however, appear to be based upon the hypothesis that the growth which occurs in neurones after the embryonic period, as the latter is ordinarily understood, is activated by exercise or intensified function in those parts of the nervous system in which it occurs. He has made no correlation of particular growth processes in neurones with specific results in behaviour. In fact, adequate data on such correlations have not formerly been available upon which to base hypotheses. On the other hand, our investigations, as presented in the earlier lectures, have revealed certain facts concerning the growth of the neurone and the development of behaviour that enable us to see the growth of the neurone and the development of behaviour in their actual relation to each other under definite and specific conditions.

Nerve cells, like seeds planted by a gardener, spring up and grow according to a definite pattern.[1] This pattern, in the nervous system, is established in its main outlines before nervous function,

1. Kingsbury has used the figure of the germinating seed to elucidate his interpretation of cephalocaudal development of the nervous system (12).

excitation or exercise begins. It is established, also, before vascularization of the nervous system occurs, which Ramón y Cajal holds is an intermediary process between increased nervous function and the growth of neurones under adult conditions. Nervous function or exercise, therefore, cannot be either directly or indirectly the cause of growth and differentiation of the nerve cell. This is confirmed by the growth of nerve cells *in vitro* in normal embryonic fashion (7). Under these artificial conditions their orientation and direction of growth can be determined by extrinsic agencies (10). Under natural conditions, also, the path along which they grow seems to be determined by surrounding conditions. Among these conditions, in early periods, as presented in the last lecture, are metabolic gradients of the organism and localized centres of growth or differentiation of nerve cells themselves. During later periods processes of conduction in established tracts may be one activating factor in directing the line of growth (1, 2); vascularization may be another (16). But, in the nerve cell as in the seed, growth as such must be regarded as the expression of an intrinsic potentiality of the cell.

Furthermore, this potentiality, as shown in the last lecture, is not exhausted when the nerve cell begins to conduct impulses according to its definitive role. After this the cell continues to grow and seek out new realms to conquer. The functional nerve cell is, then, more than a conducting mechanism, whatever may be involved in conduction. It is from the beginning a dynamic system reacting to its environment after the manner of a living organism. Physiological conduction is, so to speak, its accessory or secondary function. If it ever loses its potentiality of growth and differentiation we do not know when or where.[2]

It is not proposed, of course, that nerve cells of higher vertebrates carry over into the later life of the individual the potentiality to grow long fibres within the central nervous system. The lack of evidence for the growth of new conduction paths in the brain of man or other mammals, even by way of regeneration after lesions, is fully recognized. But growth of such magnitude is not in mind when we speak of the potentiality, for example, of the cells of the cerebral cortex to grow after the brain has attained

2. That Purkinje cells enter upon retrogressive development relatively early in the life of the individual has been shown by Ellis for man and by Inukai for the rat (6, 11), These results, however, do not imply that other cells in the cerebellum may not meanwhile continue in a progressive development. An analogy of this is seen in the loss of Rohon–Beard cells or lateral line components of the cranial nerves in certain forms while other components of the nervous system continue in development.

its apparently full growth in mass; nor must growth be so extensive in order to affect behaviour. Growth of the terminals axones and dendrites through microscopic dimensions is sufficient to have profound effect in behaviour. This we have demonstrated in the first lecture in a vertebrate of such primitive form as *Amblystoma*, which, by the growth of terminals of nerve cells over a distance of less than one one-hundredth of a millimetre, transforms itself from an animal that must lie helpless where chance places it into one that can explore its environment in response to impulses from within or stimulation from without.[3] This is for *Amblystoma* a discovery, so to speak, of incalculable significance. It is to all intents and purposes a solution of one of the crucial problems of life. Furthermore, as illustrated in the first lecture, this solution of the problem of transportation by water is applied by *Amblystoma* to the problem of transportation over land.

Psychologists may object to this connotation of problem-solving; but our treatment of the subject is biological. In the biological sense *Amblystoma* is certainly solving its immediate problems of survival by means of the growth of neurones that are already functional conductors. Such an interpretation can scarcely be rejected upon *a priori* grounds by the behaviourist who believes that the mechanism is the individual. It is not our purpose to question this belief. Our purpose, on the other hand, is to determine what is the real nature of the mechanism, and how it works. In so far as our knowledge goes concerning specific relations between the development of the nervous mechanism and the development of behaviour, the conception that a neurone grows during a certain so-called embryonic period, or period of maturation, and then ceases to grow and becomes simply a conductor in a fixed mechanism is erroneous, and wholly inadequate to account for the function of the nervous system as a mechanism of learning.

The Form of the Behaviour Pattern *versus* the Conditioning of Performance

The relation that is found to exist between the structural development of the nervous system and the development of the organism

3. Tracy has shown that the early behaviour pattern of the toadfish is established before the afferent system is functional and that the motor system is subject to endogenous stimulation, in part at least, by carbon dioxide (18). Similar excitation may occur in *Amblystoma*, but masked by a dominating afferent system.

to perform particular acts makes it necessary, in the present state of our knowledge, to distinguish sharply between the process by which the animal determines what acts it can do and the process by which it determines when and to what extent it will do them. That a muscle contracts, and in its contraction produces a particular form of activity, depends largely, if not wholly, upon developmental mechanics to which the value of the act in terms of definitive behaviour can have no immediate causal relation. The neuromuscular structural relations that make the act possible must exist before the act is performed.

A specific example of this may be drawn from the first lecture [not included in this excerpt]. It was there shown that a nervous motor mechanism is established in *Amblystoma* for some time before the animal responds to stimulation, that this mechanism is such as to conduct impulses to the muscles from the head tailward, and that this order of conduction to the muscles gives the resulting movement locomotor value and thereby becomes the basic principle of both aquatic and terrestrial locomotion. The general pattern of the primary nervous mechanism of walking is, therefore, laid down before the animal can in the least respond to its environment. Also, the conversion of the simple flexure into a compound flexure is brought about by the growth of side branches from certain nerve fibres into specific relation with other neurones; but swimming is the end result of this mechanical adjustment, not its cause. So it can be shown, as in the first lecture, that the form of the behaviour pattern in *Amblystoma* develops step by step according to the order of growth in particular parts of the nervous mechanism.

Accordingly, the normal experience of the animal with reference to the outside world appears to have nothing specifically to do with the determination of the form into which the behaviour of the animal is cast. On the other hand, experience has much to do with determining when and to what extent the potentiality of behaviour shall rise into action. This will be discussed presently.

'Gestalt' in Determining the Form of Behaviour

The 'Gestalt' school of psychology stands for total unity as the dominant principle governing mental processes (13). It seems, however, to have been concerned wholly with the processes that condition behaviour, and to have entirely neglected the processes which determine the form of the behaviour pattern. According to

466

'Gestalt', a simple, pure or elementary sensation does not exist as such. There are no such units which combine to form perceptions. The perception is a 'quality upon a ground': a total unity from the first. The apparently particular channels to conscious ness emerge from a general field and exist only in relation to that field. This is equivalent, in the motor phase of the organism, to a totally integrated pattern in which partial patterns become more or less individuated. This principle was demonstrated in the first lecture as operating in the development of the form of the behaviour pattern of *Amblystoma*, and in the second lecture it was demonstrated for the origin of the mechanism which determines the early behaviour forms.

According to our interpretation of the observations presented in the second lecture, there is no hiatus between the preneural and the neural modes of integration. The longitudinally conducting motor path, for example, arises from cells that are under the dominance of a metabolic gradient which determines physiological polarity in the developing conduction path. The specialized conduction path emerges, so to speak, from the organismic gradient. It was demonstrated, also, how the general pattern of conduction paths in the midbrain and forebrain makes its appearance along lines of action of secondary metabolic gradients. Conduction paths do not come into existence, then, as absolutely new and discrete entities. They arise from a general field of organic activity by a process of specialization, emergence, or individuation.

From the facts related in the first lecture it is obvious that there are two processes that are operating simultaneously in the development of behaviour. The one is expansion of the total pattern as a perfectly integrated unit; the other is the individuation of partial systems which eventually acquire more or less discreteness. In *Amblystoma* the total pattern first extends through the trunk and tail. As this pattern enlarges, the parts involved are always perfectly integrated. This totally integrated pattern then extends into the gills, next into the fore limbs and finally into the hind limbs. But as the totally integrated pattern expands through the organism, its parts, one after another, in the same order as they were invaded by the total pattern, begin to acquire a measure of individuality of their own: first the gills, then the fore limbs and finally the hind limbs. This means that local reflexes emerge as, in the language of 'Gestalt', a 'quality upon a ground'; that is to say, they emerge as a special feature within a more diffuse but dominant mechanism of integration of the whole organism.

They cannot be regarded as simply the action of a chain of neurones, excepting as every link of the chain is conceived to be welded into the organism as a whole.

This principle is thoroughly demonstrated for *Amblystoma*, a typical vertebrate, and there is nothing in our knowledge of the development of behaviour to indicate that the principle does not prevail universally in vertebrates, including man. There is no direct evidence for the hypothesis that behaviour, in so far as the form of the pattern is concerned, is simply a combination or co-ordination of reflexes. On the contrary, there is conclusive evidence of a dominant organic unity from the beginning. That evidence appears not only in the manner in which behaviour develops, but particularly in the manner in which the nervous system puts the principle into effect, for, as shown in the first lecture, the nervous system concerns itself first with the maintenance of the integrity of the individual, and only later makes provision for local reflexes.[4]

Growth of Functional Neurones and the Integrity of the Individual

The development of behaviour primarily through the extension of the total pattern, rather than through the projection of pri-

4. Tracy's studies on the development of behaviour in the toadfish (*Opsanus tau*) show that the earliest movements are localized and unco-ordinated (18). These are probably myogenic; for Tracy explicitly holds that reflexes are not the primary components of behaviour. Although the toadfish is a very highly specialized member of the most specialized group of fishes (Teleostei), the writer finds nothing in the development of the toadfish, as described by Tracy, that is fundamentally inconsistent with the development of *Amblystoma*.

The work of Sherrington and his associates has, by their analytical method of study, brought the reflex out into such bold relief that its discreteness, as related to the behaviour pattern as a whole, has come to be overestimated and overemphasized by behaviourists who are not themselves technically familiar with the experimental results in a broad way (17). The synthetic method of Pavlov, also, has been accepted by many as exalting the place of discrete reflex mechanisms in behaviour, whereas the conditioned reflex involves only the afferent side of the arc and evokes nothing new in effector functions (15). The work of Magnus, on the other hand, emphasizes the solidarity of the total mechanism and the inseparable linkage of reflexes with it (14). This dominance of the total pattern over all of its components, virtually as Magnus saw it experimentally, is seen unmistakably in the development of the behaviour of *Amblystoma*. It is also obvious in the development of movements in the human foetus as recorded by M. Minkowski in numerous contributions which cannot be given appropriate treatment here.

468

marily isolated parts to become integrated secondarily, means that the maintenance of the integrity of the individual as a whole is the elementary function of the nervous system. This function is performed in *Amblystoma* through the growth of functional neurones into nascent organo. The same neurones, for example, that integrate the muscles of the trunk, while performing this function, grow into the limb by means of new branches long before the limb has power of movement. In like manner, the tissues of the tongue receive branches from motor neurones that are engaged in integrating the trunk long before the tongue has muscle tissue in it. It is therefore the potentiality of the functional neurone to grow in embryonic fashion that gives to the organism as a whole its ability to subjugate new parts and thereby maintain its unity during the development of behaviour. Such growth of the already conducting neurones accomplishes, then, the primary function of the nervous system: the maintenance of the integrity of the individual while the behaviour pattern expands.

The Mechanism of Individuation

That part of the nervous system of *Amblystoma* which effects and maintains the integrity of the total pattern as it expands, for instance, into the limbs, is small as compared with the remainder of the mechanism of functional conductors in the brain and spinal cord. There is at this time a surplus of neural mechanism over and above that which is actually engaged in executing the immediate behaviour pattern. Some of this nervous surplus can be recognized as involving that part of the motor mechanism which eventually participates in the control of the movements of the limbs, the tongue and the extrinsic muscles of the eyes. It appears, therefore, that the individuation of a partial pattern or local reflex within the total pattern is anticipated in the central nervous system by the growth of a nervous organization with specific reference to that partial pattern long before the latter makes its appearance in behaviour. The details of this process are still to be determined; but its general nature is obvious.

References

1. ARIENS KAPPERS, C. U. (1917), 'Further contributions on neurobiotaxis. IX. An attempt to compare the phenomena of neurobiotaxis with other phenomena of taxis and tropism. The dynamic polarization of the neurone', *Journ. Comp. Neur.*, vol. 27, no. 3.

2. BAKER, R. C. (1927), 'The early development of the ventral part of the neural plate of *Amblystoma*', *Journ. Comp. Neur.*, vol. 44, no. 1.

3. BODINE, J. H., and ORR, P. R. (1925), 'Respiratory metabolism', *Biol. Bull.*, vol. 48, no. 1.

4. BOK, S. T. (1915), 'Die Entwicklung der Hirnnerven und ihrer Zeutralen Bahren. Die Stimulogene Fibrillation', *Folia Neurobiologica*, vol. 9.

5. BOLTON, J. S. (1910, 1911), 'A contribution ot the localization of cerebral function, based on the clinico-pathological study of mental diseases', *Brain*, vol. 33.

6. BOLTON, J. S., and MOYES, J. M. (1912), 'The cyto-architecture of the cerebral cortex of a human foetus of eighteen weeks', *Brain*, vol. 35, part 1.

7. CHILD, C. M. (1915), *Senescence and Rejuvenescence*, Chicago.

8. CHILD, C. M. (1915), *Individuality in Organisms*, Chicago.

9. CHILD, C. M. (1921), *The Origin and Development of the Nervous System from a Physiological Viewpoint*, Chicago.

10. CHILD, C. M. (1924), *Physiological Foundations of Behaviour*, New York.

11. COGHILL, G. E. (1902), 'The cranial nerves of *Amblystoma tigrinum*, *Journ. Comp. Neur.*, vol. 12, no. 2.

12. COGHILL, G. E. (1906), 'Cranial nerves of *Triton taeniatus*', *Journ. Comp. Neur.*, vol. 16, no. 4.

12a. COGHILL, G. E. (1908), 'The development of the swimming movement in amphibian embryos', *Anat. Rec.*, vol. 2, no. 4, p. 148.

12b. COGHILL, G. E. (1909), 'The reaction to tactile stimuli and the development of the swimming movement in embryos of *Diemyctylus torosus*, Eschscholtz', *Journ. Comp. Neur.*, vol. 19, no. 1.

12c. COGHILL, G. E. (1913), 'The primary ventral roots and somatic motor column of *Amblystoma*', *Journ. Comp. Neur.*, vol. 13, no. 2.

13. COGHILL, G. E. (1914), 'Correlated anatomical and physiological studies of the growth of the nervous system of Amphibia. I. The afferent system of the trunk of *Amblystoma*', *Journ. Comp. Neur.*, vol. 24, no. 2.

14. COGHILL, G. E. (1916), 'II. The afferent system of the head of *Amblystoma*', *Journ. Comp. Neur.*, vol. 26, no. 3.

15. COGHILL, G. E. (1924), 'III. The floor plate of *Amblystoma*', *Journ. Comp. Neur.*, vol. 37, no. 1.

16. COGHILL, G. E. (1924), 'IV. Rates of proliferation and differentiation in the central nervous system of *Amblystoma*', *Journ. Comp. Neur.*, vol. 37, no. 1.

17. COGHILL, G. E. (1926), 'V. The growth of the pattern of the motor mechanism of *Amblystoma punctatum*', *Journ. Comp. Neur.*, vol. 40, no. 1.

18. COGHILL, G. E. (1926), 'VI. The mechanism of integration in *Amblystoma punctatum*', *Journ. Comp. Neur.*, vol. 41, no. 1.

19. COGHILL, G. E. (1926), 'VII. The growth of the pattern of the association mechanism of the rhombencephalon and spinal cord of *Amblystoma punctatum*', *Journ. Comp. Neur.*, vol. 42, no. 1.

20. GOGHILL, G. E. (1928), 'VIII. The development of the pattern of differentiation in the cerebrum of *Amblystoma punctatum*', *Journ. Comp. Neur.*, vol. 45, no. 1.

21. DETWILER, S. R. (1923), 'Experiments on the reversal of the spinal cord, in *Amblystoma* embryos, at the level of the anterior limb', *Journ. Exp. Zool.*, vol. 38, no. 2.

22. DETWILER, S. R. (1927), 'Experimental studies on Mauthner's cell in *Amblystoma*', *Journ. Exp. Zool.*, vol. 48, no. 1.

23. ELLIS, R. S. (1919), 'A preliminary quantitative study of the Purkinje cells in normal, subnormal, and senescent human cerebella, with some notes on functional localization', *Journ. Comp. Neur.*, vol. 30, no. 2.

24. FULTON, J. F. (1926), *Muscular Contraction and the Reflex Control of Movement*, Baltimore.

25. HARRISON, R. G. (1910), 'The outgrowth of the nerve fibre as a mode of protoplasmic movement', *Journ. Exp. Zool.*, vol. 9, no. 4.

26. HERRICK, C. J. (1924), *Neurological Foundations of Animal Behaviour*, New York.

27. HERRICK, C. J. (1926), *Brains of Rats and Men: A Survey of the Origin and Biological Significance of the Cerebral Cortex*, Chicago.

28. HERRICK, C. J., and COGHILL, G. E. (1915), 'The development of reflex mechanisms in *Amblystoma*', *Journ. Comp. Neur.*, vol. 25, no. 1.

29. HOOKER, D. (1917), 'The effect of reversal of a portion of the spinal cord at the stage of closed neural folds on the heading of the cord wounds, on the polarity of the elements of the cord and on the behaviour of frog embryos', *Journ. Comp. Neur.* vol. 27, no. 4.

30. INGVAR, S. (1920), 'Reaction of cells to the galvanic current in tissue cultures', *Proc. Amer. Soc. Exp. Biol. and Med.*, vol. 17.

31. INUKAT, T. (1928), 'On the loss of Purkinje cells, with advancing age, from the cerebellar cortex of the albino rat', *Journ. Comp. Neur.*, vol. 45, no. 1.

32. KINGSBURY, B. F. (1926), 'The so-called law of antero-posterior development', *Anat. Rec.*, vol. 33, no. 4.

33. KOFFKA, KURT (1924), *The Growth of the Mind. An Introduction to Child Psychology*. Translated by R. M. Ogden. New York.

34. LANDACRE, F. L. (1921), 'The fate of the neural crest in the head of the urodeles', *Journ. Comp.*, vol. 33, no. 1.

35. LANGWORTHY, O. R. (1927), 'Histological development of cerebral motor areas in young kittens correlated with their physiological reaction to electrical stimulation', *Contr. to Embryol.* no. 104; *Carneg. Inst. Wash. Pub.* no. 380.

36. LASHLEY, K. S. (1920), 'Studies of cerebral function in learning', *Psychobiol.*, vol. 2, no. 1.

37. MAGNUS, R. (1925), 'Animal posture'. Croonian lecture. *Proc. Roy. Soc.* (B), 98 B.

38. MATHEWS, A. P. (1903), 'Electrical polarity in the hydroids', *Amer. Journ. Phys.*, vol. 8, no. 4.

39. PAVLOV, I. P. (1927), *Conditional Reflexes: An Investigation of the Physiological Activity of the Cerebral Cortex*. Translated and edited by G. V. Anrep, Oxford.

40. RAMÓN Y CAJAL, S. (1904), *Textura del Sistema Nervioso del Hombre y de los Vertebrados*, vol. 2, pp. 1150–52, Madrid.

41. SHERRINGTON, C. S. (1906), *The Integrative Function of the Nervous System*, New York.

42. TRACY, H. C. (1926), 'The development of motility and behaviour reactions in the toadfish (*Ospanus tau*)', *Journ. Comp. Neur.*, vol. 40, no. 2.

24 J. Hughlings Jackson

On the Anatomical and Physiological Localisations of
Movements in the Brain

Excerpt from J. Hughlings Jackson, *Clinical and Physiological Researches on the Nervous System*, J. and A. Churchill, 1873, chapter 1, pp. 2–25.

Movements Lost from 'Destroying Lesions'

*1. The order of loss of movements, faculties, etc., is from the special
or voluntary to the general or automatic; illustrated by hemiplegia*

I begin by speaking of destroying lesions, and take the simplest
case – hemiplegia of the common form from lesion of the corpus
striatum. A blood clot which has destroyed part of the corpus
striatum has made an experiment, which reveals to us that movements of the face, tongue, arm, and leg are represented in that
centre. This is the localization of the movements anatomically
stated. Physiologically we say that the patient whose face, tongue,
arm, and leg are paralysed, has lost the most voluntary movements of one side of his body, and it is equally important to keep
in mind that he has not lost the more automatic movements.
The study of cases of hemiplegia shows that from disease of the
corpus striatum those external parts suffer most which, psychologically speaking, are most under the command of the will, and
which, physiologically speaking, have the greater number of
different movements at the greater number of different[1] intervals.
That parts suffer more as they serve in voluntary, and less as they
serve in automatic operations, is, I believe, the law of destroying
lesions of the cerebral nervous centres. It may be illustrated in
the hemiplegic region itself: that limb which has the more
voluntary uses – the arm – suffers more.

I have illustrated by a case of hemiplegia of limited range from
a lesion of moderate gravity. But from lesions of different degrees
of gravity we have hemiplegia of very different ranges, varying
gradually from palsy of the face, tongue, arm, and leg of one side,

1. I shall use (and, after the physiological definition, without any
psychological implication) the words voluntary and automatic. It is not to
be implied that there are abrupt demarcations betwixt the two classes of
movements; on the contrary, there are gradations from the most voluntary
to the most automatic.

to universal powerlessness.[2] Or, physiologically speaking, there are all degrees, from paralysis limited to the most voluntary parts of one side of the body to paralysis of the most automatic parts of the whole body. The movements of the heart and respiration are less frequent, and the temperature is abased (soon after the seizure, of course, is meant). The patient, to put it in the shortest way, *is reduced to a more or less automatic condition*, according to the gravity of the lesion.

It must be added that degrees of hemiplegia are not simple degrees; that is to say, they are not either degrees of more or less loss of power only, nor degrees of more or less range only, but of both. They are Compound Degrees. For example, if there be paralysis not only of the *most* voluntary parts of the body – face, tongue, arm, and leg – but also of those next[3] most voluntary, viz. loss of certain movements of the eyes and head and side of the chest, we find that the most voluntary parts (face, arm, and leg) *are very much paralysed*. In other words, the graver the lesion not only the more are the most voluntary parts paralysed, but the further spread to automatic parts is the paralysis.

From these facts, supplied by cases of destroying lesions of the centre producing *loss* of movements, we may conclude that the physiological order of representation of movements in the corpus striatum is such that action in health spreads from the automatic to the voluntary; or rather (the unit of action of the nervous system being a double unit – a molecule of two atoms) that there is *first* action spreading from the automatic to the voluntary, and then action spreading in the reverse order.[4] The

2. Of course, the term 'hemiplegia' becomes a misnomer when there is universal powerlessness. I shall have more to say of the universal powerlessness which occurs from disease of but one side of the brain when I consider convulsive seizures.

3. Or, in equivalent terms, of those next least automatic.

4. That the Unit of Action of the nervous system is double the Unit of Composition is inferable from the fact that the whole nervous system is double. This conclusion runs physiologically parallel with the psychological law that all mental operations consist, fundamentally regarded, in the double process of tracing relations of likeness and unlikeness. The lower parts of the nervous system are plainly double in function, and it would be marvellous if the higher parts were not so too. The most automatic of the visible movements of the body 'practically' constitute a single series, although we see that they are in duplicate. The two sides of the chest act so nearly together in time and so nearly equally in range that there is 'practically' but one movement. But the very highest movements – those for words – are *apparently* in single order too, but for the very opposite reason. It is because we only consider the *end* of word processes (speech), and neglect altogether the prior automatic reproduction of words. In the double action, of which

spreading of healthy movements is best illustrated by degrees of 'effort', as in lifting weights. There is first fixation of the more automatic parts of the arm, side of chest (and still further in automaticity according to the preconceived degree of heaviness of the object), before the most voluntary part, the hand, grasps the weight and then lifts it. The heavier the weight, not only the more strongly are the most voluntary parts used, but the further does the movement spread to the more automatic parts. This compound spreading of healthy movement corresponds to the compound degrees of hemiplegia.

2. The order applied to the movements and motor impulses of speech (applied to cases of aphasia)

I will try now to show that the physiological order of gross movements applies to the movements of speech. I say *movements* of speech advisedly, as I think the abrupt distinction made in the expressions 'loss of memory for words' and 'ataxic affection of speech' is arbitrary and misleading.

The physiological order applies to the classification of the whole of the phenomena of cases of so-called aphasia: to the positive – the inability to speak; and to the passive – the ability to understand speech. Taking an ordinary case of entire *loss* of speech, we find that the patient has lost the most voluntary form of expression (speech), and has not lost the most automatic (emotional manifestations). We find that pantomime, which, bordering on gesticulation, stands half-way, suffers little. We find that the exception to the statement that the patient is speechless (for he can usually *utter* some one or two words) is frequently the exception proving the rule. He has lost speech altogether, *except the most automatic of all propositions* – '*yes*' and '*no*'. Even these real words are often only of interjectional value; they can often be used only along with emotional manifestations – can be used, that is to say, automatically only. And, curiously, we find occasionally that the patient who can *reply* 'No' correctly may be quite unable to *say* 'No' when told. Another occasional exception proves the same thing: He may *utter* oaths or other

---

the second part is speech, there is first, I suggest, the automatic and un-conscious reproduction of words. Later in this paper (sections 13 and 14) will be given facts which tend to show – (1) that the unit of action of the nervous system is double the unit of composition; (2) that the higher the nervous processes are the more unlike become the two components of the unit of action; (3) that the unlikeness is first in time, one acting before the other; and second in range, one being in stronger action that the other.

ejaculations when excited which he cannot *say* – cannot repeat – when he tries to do so. Occasionally he gets out ejaculations of a less automatic character (less general in the sense of being suitable to fewer occasions). Thus he may say 'Thanks', 'Good-bye', on fit occasions, but not when he tried. In a narrow corner we see the same thing: he may be unable to put out his tongue when he tries, and yet move it well in all automatic operations.

3. The order accords with the hypothesis that the left side of the brain is the leading side for words, and the right the automatic side

But there is a far wider and far more important illustration to be given.

Coining the word 'verbalizing' to include all the modes in which words serve, we see that there are two great divisions or rather extremes of verbalizing: one is the voluntary use of words (speech); the other is the automatic use of words, as in receiving speech of others. Now in the ordinary 'specimen' of loss of speech the former is lost, and the latter is intact. The patient cannot speak at all, but understands all we say – on simple matters, at any rate.

That he cannot write is simply loss of speech in another form. For the physiological reality of speech it matters nothing whether the proposition be uttered aloud or to ourselves; it is enough that certain nervous processes *be excited, and excited in definite order*: if they be strongly excited, there is external speech; if slightly, there is internal speech. So that internal speech and internal reproduction of words are not synonymous: there is a voluntary internal reproduction of words in new and propositional forms (as occurs when we write); and there is an automatic internal reproduction of words in old and acquired forms, or in forms given us, as when we receive and understand words in propositions spoken to us.

4. The order applied to mental symptoms

This physiological order will, I think, be of great use in the investigation of mental diseases proper. It seems to me to apply, at any rate, to some comparatively simple mental symptoms which occur in a general physician's practice. After some epileptic or epileptiform seizures, the patient becomes strange or outrageous, and acts queerly or violently. My speculation is, that in these cases he is reduced by the fit to a more automatic mental condition. Thus I have recorded the case of a man (the *Lancet*,

18 March 1871) who walked eight miles in a state like that of somnambulism. He was subject to fits, beginning by a subjective sensation of a disagreeable smell, and depending on (as, I suppose, *petit mal* always does) changes in the region of the anterior cerebral artery. Now, just as after a fit of unilateral convulsion a patient is often reduced to a more automatic condition, so far as his *physical* state goes – he is paralysed on one side, – so I suppose this patient was reduced to a more automatic condition, so far as his mental state was concerned.[5]

Possibly it will be objected by some readers that I speak in one article of several things which are very different. The reply is, that the same principle is displayed in each of them. That a hemiplegic patient's arm suffers more than his leg; that an aphasic patient cannot put out his tongue when he tries, although he moves it well in swallowing; that he cannot speak, and yet is able to understand all that we say; that a patient in *petit mal* loses consciousness and behaves strangely and outrageously, – these are evidently facts of different kinds, but they are all facts of the same order. In each instance there is Reduction to a More Automatic Condition.

Movements Developed by 'Discharging Lesions' of Convolutions

I pass now to speak of symptoms resulting from 'discharging lesions' of the brain. The movements in chorea, as well as those in convulsion, are the result of abnormal discharges; but I shall speak in this paper only of convulsions ordinarily so called. Here, again, it may be objected that I consider still another topic; but I think it will be seen that the facts to be pointed out illustrate the same principle as do the symptoms already spoken of as resulting from 'destroying lesions'.

5. In cases of slow deterioration of brain, the disposition 'alters'; I fear it is that the natural disposition has its way, and that our more animal, our more instinctive habits and desires are no longer subordinated. There is reduction to a more automatic condition; there is dissolution, using this word as the corresponding opposite of evolution. The weaker the mind the more do the more automatic desires have their own way. In a few cases of intracranial haemorrhage the patient becomes violent and swears; resembles the 'drunken man', whose 'natural disposition comes out'; the condition expressed by the proverb 'in vino veritas' is equivalent to a Reduction to a More Automatic Condition in which the natural impulses have freer play.

(*Lancet*, 1 February 1873)

5. *The nature of the morbid discharge in convulsion*

The nervous discharge in a convulsion differs from the discharge which occurs in a healthy movement in that it is sudden, excessive, and of short duration. The discharge being of the grey matter of processes for *movements*, there is caused by it a development of movements in the related and connected external regions. But the development of the movements is so abrupt, and the number of movements developed at once is so great, that the visible result is apparently a mere heedless struggle of muscles, in which at first glance it seems unlikely that we shall trace any kind of order. If we take for first investigation cases of *general* convulsions (such as are sometimes called 'idiopathic epilepsy'), we shall, I believe, make little out. The paroxysms are too sudden, too quickly universal, and of too short duration for precise investigation. But if we take simple cases we shall, I think, accomplish a great deal. Most unquestionably the simplest cases of convulsion are those in which the spasm begins deliberately on one side of the body and affects that side only, or affects it more than the other. Such fits are often very limited in range, and then the patient is not unconscious, and can describe the seizure. As they begin deliberately, and as they may last many minutes, we are able, if we are present at a paroxysm, to note the place of onset and the order of spreading of the spasm. But even these simple convulsions represent the healthy movements contained in the region discharged only in outline and, so to speak, in caricature. For besides the facts already mentioned (that the discharge is sudden, excessive, and soon over) the discharge is of a *limited part of the brain* – of a part picked out, as it were, somewhat at random, by disease. The presumption is that there are no more isolated discharges of parts of the brain – an *excessive* discharge of a small part – *in health* than there are movements of single muscles in health. (Movements of single muscles, except perhaps in the face, are, Duchenne insists, only producible artificially – that is, by galvanism.)

6. *Convulsion beginning unilaterally, the mobile counterpart of hemiplegia*

These seizures I used to call unilateral convulsions, but since the spasm (although it affects one side first and most) may *become* universal, it is more correct to call them 'convulsions beginning unilaterally'. Indeed, as is well known to careful clinical observers, they occur in all degrees, from twitching of a finger to universal convulsion. It is important to bear this in mind, especially as the same patient may have fits of several degrees; unless we do, we may erroneously suppose that he has several *varieties* of convulsions. Convulsions beginning unilaterally depend on disease of the same *cerebral* region as does hemiplegia of the common form, but hemiplegia depends on 'destroying lesion' of the corpus striatum, the convulsion on a 'discharging lesion' of the convolutions near to this body – convolutions in the region of the middle cerebral artery. We have, indeed, not only 'a corpus striatum paralysis', but a 'corpus striatum convulsion'. To prove that the convulsion is one of the mobile counterparts of hemiplegia, we find both in the same case. After a severe fit which has begun in the hand, we occasionally find hemiplegia like that which is so often produced by a clot in the corpus striatum, like it in degree and in range, but unlike it in being transitory. When the convulsion is partial, the palsy left by it is partial too. Thus I have recorded the case of a patient who had paralysis limited to the arm after a convulsion of that limb dependent on tumour in the hinder part of the first (superior) frontal convolution.[6] (There was a tumour in each lobe of the cerebellum as well.) There can, in short, be no doubt that these convulsions are the mobile counterparts of hemiplegia.

7. *The convolutions near the corpus striatum re-represent the movements represented in that centre*

When in such cases we do discover disease of the brain, we do find it in the region of the corpus striatum, but occasionally no local morbid change is found in any part of the brain. Nevertheless, the very fact that the convulsion has been one-sided or has begun on one side, warrants the inference that there *is* in such cases also a local lesion, although we are unable to detect it. The lesion – when a lesion is discovered – involves more or less of convolutions which are near to, and, I suppose, *discharge through* the corpus striatum. I suppose that these convolutions represent over again, but in new and more complex combinations, the very same movements which are represented in the corpus striatum. They are, I believe, the corpus striatum 'raised to a higher power'. *Discharge* [7] of the grey matter of these convolutions *develops*

---

6. See *Medical Mirror*, September 1869.

7. It is supposed that in the part which is occasionally discharged the grey matter is highly unstable. This, indeed, seems to me to be a truism; the difficulty is to discover the *pathological process* by which that instability results. In the cases I shall mention later on it has been *associated with*

the same groups of movements which are *lost* when the corpus striatum is *destroyed*.

8. The most voluntary or most special movements first and most affected by the discharge of convolutions

But there are several varieties of convulsions beginning unilaterally. They may be classified according to the places of onset of the spasm. There is nothing more important than to note where a convulsion begins, for the inference is, that the first motor symptom is the sign of the beginning of the central discharge.

There are three parts where fits of this group mostly begin – (1) in the hand; (2) in the face, or tongue, or both; (3) in the foot. In other words, they usually begin in those parts of one side of the body which have the most voluntary uses. The order of frequency in which parts suffer illustrates the same law. I mean, that fits beginning in the hand are commonest; next in frequency are those which begin in the face or tongue, and rarest are those which begin in the foot. The law is seen in details. When the fit begins in the hand, the index-finger[8] and thumb are usually the digits first seized; when in the face, the side of the cheek is first in spasm; when in the foot, almost invariably the great-toe.

9. Leading movements; compound order of spreading of spasm

In each of these varieties there must be some difference in the situation of the grey matter exploded. In one part the movements

---

tumour; the tumour does not discharge, but in some way it leads to changes involving instability of grey matter. My speculation is that, speaking in chemical language, the highly unstable grey matter of disease remains of the same Constitution as the comparatively stable grey matter of health, but that it is of a different Composition; and a further speculation is that the phosphorus ingredient is replaced by its congener nitrogen – that the nervous matter is more nitrogenized, and therefore more explosive. If this be so, we see that although the nutrition of grey matter is carried on abnormally, in cases of convulsion, chorea, etc., we cannot say without much qualification that its nutrition is *defective*. The supposed therapeutical value in nervous affections of the other member of the group of triads (arsenic) is significant.

8. Perhaps it may be well here to mention again that the word 'voluntary' is used for a part like the hand, which has the greater number of different movements and the greater number of different intervals of movements, and that the word 'automatic' is used for a part like the chest, which has the greater number of nearly similar movements and the greater number of nearly equal intervals. The hand is a more 'voluntary' part than either the cheek (or articulatory organs altogether) or the leg. Indeed, the hand is the mōst important part of the body from any point of view. Hence the significance of the fact that in disease of the highest centres it usually suffers first and most.

of the hand have the leading representation, in another part those of the cheek and tongue, and in a third those of the foot. I say *leading* representation because spasm of the hand, etc., is only the *beginning* of the seizure. I had under my care a patient whose fits always *began* in his left thumb. [Case recorded *Med. Times and Gazette*, 30 November 1872.] We found, after death, a tubercle the size of a hazel-nut in the hinder part of his third right frontal convolution. Now in this case the most that one could say was, that in the convolution or region first discharged there lay processes for movements in which the thumb had *the leading part*. For although the spasm *began* in that digit, it went up the arm, and at length probably all over the body.

Besides, since the movements of the thumb and fingers could scarcely be developed for any useful purpose without fixation of the wrist (and of parts further and further in automaticity according to the force required), we should *a priori*, be sure that the centre discharged, although it might represent movements in which the thumb had the leading part, must represent also certain other movements of the forearm, upper arm, etc., which serve subordinately. These remarks have partly anticipated the next topic – the march of the spasm.

10. The order in which movements are developed by discharge of convolutions. The march of spasm

After noting the part in which the fit begins, we have to observe how the spasm spreads (the 'march of the fit'), and this for two purposes. We have not only to learn *how much* of the body is ultimately involved by the spasm, but also to note the *order* in which the several parts involved are affected. For example, we have not only to report of a case that the spasm 'affected the whole of one side of the body', but also that 'the spasm began in the hand, spread *up* the arm, next took the face, and then passed *down* the leg'. We have to note not only the range of a fit, but the *order* of development of movements one after another in that range. Or, speaking now of the nerve-centres, we have to study convulsion not only to learn what particular movements are represented in a nervous centre (anatomical localisation), but also to learn the particular order in which those movements are therein represented (physiological localisation).

As already remarked, the movements first developed in a fit probably represent those which take the lead; those next developed are, we may suppose, the subordinately associated movements. Let me illustrate by a healthy movement. When we grasp strongly, although the flexors take the lead the extensors must be in subordinate, and yet in associated action, or the grasp would not be vigorous; and the more strongly the hand is used, the farther up the arm does the movement spread: The observation therefore, of the order of development of spasm will enable us, it is reasonable to hope, to determine the association of leading with subordinate movements. For example, if a fit begins in the thumb and index-finger, there will probably[9] be developed as the spasm spreads that series of movements which in health serves subordinately when the thumb and index-finger are used. Of course we can only make very rough observations, as in a convulsion a great number of movements are developed all at once.

It is to be observed that, just as degrees of hemiplegia are compound degrees, so the order of development of spasm is a compound order. For example, when the fit begins in the hand, the spasm does not leave the hand when it involves the rest of the arm. Two things occur: the spasm of the hand becomes more powerful, and the spasm spreads up the arm. This compound order – as are degrees of hemiplegia (see section 2 – is roughly in accordance with the order of development of movements in increasing strains, as in lifting things of different weight in what is technically called 'effort'). It is important to note this compound order, especially when we consider that it implies that increasing discharge of a centre has not only the effect of intensifying movement, but also the effect of increasing the range of movement. It has an important bearing on the method of mental operations. For brevity and clearness, we shall, however, in what follows, speak of the spreading of spasm as if it were simple.

11. The same muscles represented in different order in several places

To show, further, the importance of noting sequence as well as range, I would mention that there are two varieties of fits, in each of which, so far as I can learn, the same muscles are involved, but in each they are involved in a different order. The range is the same; the sequence is different. Thus one man's fits begin in his hand, go up his arm and down his leg; another man's begin in his foot, go up his leg and down his arm. But, though the same muscles are in action in each of the two fits, the fact that parts of both limbs are involved in different order and probably in very different degrees, renders the inference irresistible that the two

9. In the case mentioned we had no opportunity of noting the march of the spasm.

fits depend on discharge of two different centres. For the nervous centres do not represent muscles, but very complex movements in each of which many muscles serve. In each of the two centres discharged the *very same muscles* are represented in two different orders of movements. In one there are represented movements in which the arm leads and the leg is subordinate; in the other, movements in which the leg leads and the arm is subordinate. The very same notes are made up into two different tunes; in chemical metaphor, the fits are isomeric.[10]

My impression is, that the face is differently affected according as the spasm *begins* there and then goes to the arm, or comes there after the arm has been first seized. In the former case the spasm, I believe, begins in the mouth (both sides of the lips, or in the cheek near the angle of the mouth), and spreads all over the face. When the spasm begins in the hand, I believe the orbicularis palpebrarum is the part of the face first in spasm. If the order be as I suppose, the muscles of the face will be represented in movements of different orders, and therefore in several parts of the nervous system.

Thus, then, the three fits may be looked upon as experimental stimulations, each of some different part in the region of the corpus striatum, and as showing us (i) what movements have the leading representation in each part; (ii) the movements which are sequent and subordinate to those having the leading representation. It is freely granted that no definite results have as yet been obtained on the second point. Very few cases have been carefully observed, very few autopsies indeed have been obtained on cases which *have been* observed carefully; and, lastly, as I shall point out very prominently later on, there are complications which impede our attempt to draw exact conclusions. It is for the very reason that so little has been done that I urge the careful investigation of these seizures.

12. Movements of the two sides of the body represented in each side of the brain (Lancet 15 February 1873)

We have now to consider the method of representation of movements on the largest scale. Just as there are from *destroying lesions* of different gravities in the region of the corpus striatum

10. I have recently had two patients under my care whose fits begin in the foot. When the spasm does get to the arm in these cases, it begins in the fingers and goes up the limb; but even in these cases the centre discharged must be a different one from that discharged when the fit begins first of all in the hand.

ranges of paralysis from weakness of the face, arm, and leg of *one* side to universal powerlessness, so from *discharging lesions* in this region there are all ranges of spreading of spasm from the most local to universal convulsion. Let us consider a severe convulsive paroxysm. The spasm begins, we will suppose, in the right hand, affects the *right* side (the face, arm, and leg), then *both* sides of the trunk, and next the face and limbs of the *left* side. What I wish to draw attention to prominently is, that from destroying or discharging lesions of but *one* side of the brain there results paralysis or convulsion of *both* sides of the body. This seems to me to warrant the inference that movements of the *two* sides of the body are represented in each side of the brain. Some years ago Dr Broadbent put forth the hypothesis that the bilaterally-*acting* muscles of the two sides are equally represented in each side of the brain. That this is so I have proved by observations on cases of convulsion; and, as above stated, I believe that the muscles of the *limbs* of both sides – the muscles of those parts, that is to say, which can act independently of their fellows – are represented in each side of the brain.[11]

I must consider both the *universal powerlessness* from a

11. My colleague, Dr Gowers, has kindly drawn my attention to the following remarks by Sir Charles Bell: – 'It is a fact familiar to pathologists that, where debility arises from affection of the brain, the influence is greatest on those muscles which are, in their natural condition, most under the command of the will. We may perceive this in the progressive stages of debility of the drunkard, when successively the muscles of the tongue, the eyes, the face, the limbs, become unmanageable; and, under the same circumstances, the muscles which have a double office – as those of the chest lose their voluntary motions and retain their involuntary motions; the force of the arms is gone long before the action of breathing is affected.' (*Nervous System*, 3rd ed, p. 165.) – With regard to one point in the above, it is interesting to observe that in some cases of hemiplegia the two sides of the patient's chest move equally in quiet breathing, whilst in voluntary breathing there is less expansion of the paralysed side. As to another point, we have to account for the *increase* of power (the excitement) in the drunkard who has lost *voluntary* power. I believe it to be a fact of the same order as the increased excitability of a nerve after its division, and of the same order as the increased reflex excitability of the lower segment of the cord when cut off from the brain. (The last-mentioned fact has been used by Dr Thompson Dickson to illustrate his views on epilepsy, the paroxysm of which, he believes, results from a loss of control.) I believe that the outrageous and violent conduct which occasionally occurs in an epileptic patient who *has lost consciousness* is a fact of the same order – that after *sudden* loss of voluntary power there is an increase of *automatic* action. In hysteria there is loss of voluntary power, and yet there is often excitement. The contradiction disappears if we can establish that the excitement is of lower and more automatic processes from lack of inhibition by the higher and more voluntary.

destroying lesion of one side of the brain, and the *universal spasm* from a *discharging* lesion of one side of the brain. (We shall, for verbal convenience, suppose, throughout these remarks, that the left is the side of the brain damaged.) I begin with universal powerlessness. I believe this to be really two-sided paralysis. (That the right side should be paralysed presents no difficulty, of course.) Universal powerlessness is the result of a grave[12] lesion. Now this grave lesion is usually a bulky clot, and thus it may be said that the palsy of the left side of the body results because the clot on the left side of the brain squeezes the opposite side of the brain; or again, that, as the patient is deeply insensible, the left side of the body only *appears* to be paralysed. I confess that I have no satisfactory proof that the left side of the body has been palsied from a haemorrhage limited to the left side of the brain in a patient who was conscious at the time I examined him. I have, however, only to show that the left side is *weak*, not that it is as much palsied as the right. For whilst wishing to prove that movements of the left side of the body *are* represented in the left side of the brain, I wish also to prove that they are *less* represented therein than are the movements of the right side. It is only to be expected that the left side will suffer for a short time. There is an order of recovery in cases of hemiplegia, and I suppose in all other palsies; it is that the more automatic movements are re-gained first. Thus, in hemiplegia (right side, we suppose), the leg recovers before the arm, and if there be at the outset a further degree of paralysis – viz. lateral deviation of the eyes and head – these deviations are usually transitory. It is then only reasonable to suppose, when there is yet a further degree of paralysis – namely, of limbs of the left[13] side, that this will pass off first of all.

12. The word gravity is used as inclusive of two factors, *quantity* of nerve-tissue destroyed and *suddenness* of destruction. Suddenness is a most important factor; hence a difference betwixt cerebral embolism and cerebral thrombosis; betwixt the symptoms of cerebral haemorrhage and cerebral tumour; betwixt bleeding an animal to death slowly and suddenly (in the latter there are convulsions). It *seems* to make a difference even in the *kind* of symptoms, for as Prévost says of the lateral deviation I have so often mentioned in this paper, 'C'est surtout dans les attaques *brusques* que s'observe cette déviation.' Of a large clot we have to observe that it destroys, that it destroys suddenly, and that it squeezes widely and suddenly.

13. Here it may be well to advert to a difficulty, a very superficial one, in the use of the words voluntary and automatic; one which would equally attend the use of the words special and general, independent and dependent. Perhaps the best words would be, varied and similar. Those movements of the left side of the body which are supposed to be represented in the same (the left) side of the brain (and from *sudden* lack of which there results transitory left-sided palsy) are called automatic. It seems contradictory to

But there is proof that fibres pass from the left corpus striatum down into the left side of the cord, as well as into the right side; there are 'direct' as well as 'decussating' fibres. That there is a 'decussating paralysis' from lesion of the left corpus striatum no one doubts; but the existence of direct fibres, I think, supports the inference that there is also a transient 'direct paralysis' from extensive lesion of that centre. After old lesions of the left corpus striatum there is Wallerian wasting of nerve-fibres, traceable from the seat of disease not only down into the *right* side of the cord, but also into the left. This splitting of the bundle of wasted fibres on entering the cord is, I think, demonstrative evidence that *both* sides of the body are represented in the *left* corpus striatum. Does it not show that movements of the *left* face, arm, and leg, are represented in the *left* corpus striatum by the *non-crossing* fibres, as well as that movements of the *right* face, arm, and leg, are therein represented by the *crossing* fibres? It may, however, be urged that these non-crossing fibres are solely for the bilaterally acting muscles ('muscles of the trunk'). But if now we consider the phenomena of a severe convulsion, and find that from a discharging lesion of the left side of the brain the muscles of the face, arm and leg of the left side are convulsed (after those of the right side), it is, I think, most reasonable to conclude that the non-crossing fibres are for the movements of the muscles of the left face, arm, and leg, although perhaps chiefly for those of the left side of the trunk.

13. Nature of duality of brain – the two halves not mere duplicates (see section 3 on leading and automatic sides of brain)

From these facts we may conclude that the movements of both sides of the body – those of the limbs as well as those of the trunk – are represented in each side of the brain. The inference is that the units of the nervous system are double units, as the whole nervous system itself is double. In chemical metaphor, the unit of action is a molecule of two atoms. But it is not meant that the double unit is a mere duplicate. For again, referring to the *whole nervous system*, we see that *its* highest halves are not *mere* duplicates. Saying nothing of right-handedness, of the fact that disease

---

call movements of the *limbs* automatic. The speculation is that those movements of the left side which are represented in the left side of the brain are automatic, or subordinate to those of the right side of the body, which also are represented in that left side to the brain. Put otherwise, the muscles of the limbs of the left side are, in the right side of the brain, represented in movements from the voluntary to the automatic, and in movements from the automatic to the voluntary in the left side of the brain.

of but *one*[14] hemisphere can make a man speechless, and of the statement of Gratiolet that the left frontal and right sphenoidal and occipital convolutions are developed earlier than their fellows, there is the striking fact that the convolutions of the two hemispheres are not symmetrical. These differences in form imply differences in function.[15] This is the more significant when we find that the asymmetry becomes greater the higher we go up in the animal kingdom, not only from lower to higher animals, but from the lower to the higher races of men. According to Dr Todd, there is greater asymmetry in the convolutions of intellectual men. We see, then, that the higher in the scale of intellectual life the less of a duplicate are the two halves of the highest and most important divisions of the nervous system. It is reasonable to suppose, then, that the two elements of the units which enter into the composition of the highest centres are not mere duplicates.

14. *Movements of the two sides of body represented in different order in each side of brain* (?)

Whilst insisting that movements of the two sides of the body are represented in the left side of the brain, it has been pointed out that they are not equally represented; the movements of the left side are *less* represented in the left side of the brain, for they suffer less from a destroying lesion (and, as I have said, it may be urged that they do not suffer at all), and they suffer less in convulsion.

14. The fact of most significance is, not that disease of the *left* hemisphere mostly makes a man speechless, but that disease of but *one* hemisphere can make him speechless. I have suggested that one hemisphere is for the automatic, and the other for the voluntary and automatic, use of words. It is well known that speechless patients may sing; on this point, and on the singing of imbecile children, I have remarked in the *Mirror* of this journal, 17 February, 1866, and again in a subsequent *Mirror*, where I quote Dr Langdon Down. There is in this month's number of the *Edinburgh Medical Journal* a valuable paper by Dr Ireland, in which he says that in mere taste for music idiots are not much behind other children. Music is probably one of the most *automatic* of higher mental operations; hence the significance of the existence of musical faculty in those who have little higher mental faculty. It is a fact of the same order as many stated in the text. Spencer (*Psychology*, vol. ii., p. 471) says (when speaking of inherited experiences) that faculties, *as of music*, which scarcely exist in some inferior human races, become *congenital* in superior ones.

15. It is possible that the asymmetry may be such that whilst the third left frontal convolution is, so to say, the 'yellow spot' of speech, some other convolution on the right is the chief seat of word-processes. I think this is probable because in one seizure dependent on disease of the third *right* frontal convolution, the discharge was *first* on the muscles of the thumb, and not on the parts for the exteriorization of speech.

The fit which begins in the right side, and passes at length to the left, affects that second side less, and for a shorter time, and, I believe, the parts of this side are affected more contemporaneously. But besides this difference in *quantity* of representation, there are other differences. The left side suffers *later* than the other. This difference is quite as important as any. It is as necessary to know that in certain centres movements of different parts are represented in different order as it is to note that they are represented in different degrees.

We have, then, two things to bear in mind – (i) that movements of the right and left limbs are represented in the left side of the brain; and (ii) that the right are represented more than the left, and so represented that they are developed at a different time. Are there other differences? Other facts supplied by the Wallerian wasting, already spoken of, warrant us in seeking further differences. For descending wasting occupies different tracts of the cord. The fibres wasted in the right side of the cord (crossing fibres) are those of the posterior part of the lateral column, those in the left side (direct fibres) are in the anterior column near the middle line (as before stated, the lesion is supposed to be of the left corpus striatum). These facts justify the inference that the two sides of the body are not represented in each half of the brain in the same way. To suppose otherwise would be to hold that the two different parts of the cord had the same function. We have already spoken of difference of quantity of representation (the left side being less represented). Will not the difference we are now in search of be one of *order* of representation? We find that, speaking generally, the order of representation in the right side is from the voluntary to the automatic movements.[16] Is the order on the left side from the automatic to the voluntary? It will be observed that it is not supposed that the two different strands of fibres in the cord represent *muscles* on the two sides of the body; but that each strand represents the corresponding muscles of the two sides of the body, but made up into movements of different degrees and orders. Thus, to put it roughly, the speculation is, that on the right side the order is from the limbs to the trunk, on the left from the trunk to the limbs.

I have, I regret to say, no useful observations of the order of spreading of spasm on the *left* side. As I think it very important

16. Strictly this is the order of the *loss* of movements from breaking up of nervous processes. The representation of movements in the healthy organ will be in the reverse order.

to make observations thereon, I will write down certain questions. 1. Does the spasm of the left side begin in the leg? 2. Does it go *down* or *up* these limbs? 3. Does it affect the extensors more than the flexors, or *vice versa*? 4. Is the spasm more tonic than on the other side? (The fit is supposed to begin in the right hand.)

Of course, since our object is to learn the plan of representation of movements, we must also study healthy movements, taking the simplest of these. I have several times spoken of 'effort', using the word in its technical sense. In lifting objects of increasing heaviness with the right hand we bring into play movements spreading from the most voluntary to the most automatic. At a certain stage the left limbs are engaged; the left arm is lifted away from the side, the forearm is more or less extended, and the hand is open; the leg is held off the ground somewhat stiffly from the hip. I think it probable that the spreading of spasm to the left side will conform roughly to the spreading of movement in effort to the left side. We shall be assisted in investigating the order of representation of movements by considering the play of the limbs in walking. Thus, when the right leg comes forward, the right arm goes backwards and left forwards. Probably, however, these movements have their representation in the cerebellum; but somewhere the order, as well as the degree, of these movements will be represented.

15. Certain correlations of movement – lateral movements of eyes and movements of tactual organs represented in the cerebrum

Both in hemiplegia and in convulsions beginning unilaterally we note certain associations, e.g. affection of the orbicularis palpebrarum along with affection of the limbs. Donders' researches give an explanation of this association. The most important, however, is the association of affection of *certain* movements of the eyes with affection of those of our limbs. Significantly (and in accordance with the principle spoken of throughout this paper) the movements of the eyeball which are first affected are the *lateral*. We can overcome a prism of from 20° to 30° with its base placed outwards, and one of 6° to 8° with its base placed inwards; but few persons can overcome more than a prism of 1° or 2° with its base turned upwards or downwards. There is then greater variety or independence in the lateral movements of the eye. (The internal rectus is the strongest of the ocular muscles.) In association with this greater independence of the lateral movements we may note that the sensibility of the retina diminishes less rapidly outwards than upwards and downwards. That the movements of our chief tactual organs should have close and direct associations in the *highest* nervous centres with certain movements of the eyes is what one would expect if, as Spencer says (*Psychology*, part 24, p. 385), 'tactual impressions are those into which all other impressions have to be translated before their meanings can be known'. I suppose visual impressions and ocular movements may be said to 'stand for' tactual impressions and movements in the sense that the strong excitation of the nervous processes of the former leads to *faint* excitation of those of the latter (movements of the hands, etc.). The study of cases of hemiplegia and convulsion shows us, not only that there is an association, but the *order* in which eye movements and limb movements are associated. Of course a coarse lesion of a nervous centre, or a sudden discharge of one, is not a very neat experiment. In hemiplegia the parts suffer in degree, I believe, in the following order: arm, leg, side of face and tongue, orbicularis palpebrarum, lateral movements of eyes, lateral movements of head. The difficulty obviously is that several systems are damaged all at a blow – the movements of lifting, by which we have ideas of weight, the eye to hand movements of writing, the movements of speech, etc.

I have observed cases of hemiplegia complicated with hemiopia. I have as yet had no autopsy on a case of this kind; but I think it important to draw attention to the association because I think it is a very significant one, especially as there has been a very persistent and a very unusual amount of loss of sensation in the hemiplegic region; and in one case under my care the power of estimating weights is very much affected. I believe the lesion to be in the thalamus opticus. It is very significant that a *lateral* loss of vision occurs with hemiplegia. In these cases the patient cannot *see* to the paralysed side; his condition is the sensory analogue of that of the hemiplegic patient who, having lateral deviation of the eyes, cannot *look* to the paralysed side. Since the sensori-motor processes which form the anatomical substrata of our ideas of objects are [highly special arrangements representing] retinal impressions and ocular movements, the study of deviations of the eyes and corresponding limitations of the fields of vision has an important bearing on mental physiology.

18. Certain movements of the eyes for estimation of distance represented in the cerebellum along with locomotor movements

There are other conjugate deviations of the eyes besides lateral. Thus in lesions of the right middle peduncle of the cerebellum the right eye is turned upwards and outward, the left downwards and inwards. Just as there is an association of lateral movements of the eyes with movements of our tactual organs for ideas of objects, so we may suppose that there will be associations of ocular movements of convergence and divergence (the former especially downwards, the latter especially upwards) with those movements of the spine, legs, and arms in locomotion, represented in the cerebellum, for ideas of distance; hence the importance of studying particular ocular deviations in association with accompanying disorder of movement. That the two sets of ocular movements are to a large extent separately represented seems clear from the researches of Adamük. He finds that the anterior tubercles of the corpora quadrigemina rule the side-to-side movements of the two eyes, whilst irritation of the posterior part of either the right or left eminence produces strong convergence, lowering of the visual lines, and contraction of the pupil. The cerebrum contains processes of eye movements and tactual movements for seeing objects; the cerebellum, we may suppose, contains processes of the eye movements and locomotor movements for estimation of distance. The association of ocular deviations with circus movement, rotation, and rolling, is well known, and is obviously very significant with regard to what has just been discussed.

25 P. Weiss

Central versus Peripheral Factors in the Development of Coordination

P. Weiss, 'Central versus peripheral factors in the development of co-ordination', in P. Bard (ed.), *Patterns of Organization in the Central Nervous System*, Williams and Wilkins Co., 1952, chapter 1, pp. 3–23.

Introduction

The central nervous system develops its coordination systems essentially independently of peripheral control, yet the peripheral organs, receptors, and effectors, put themselves in the proper response relations with the centers by a peculiar mechanism perhaps best described in figurative terms as 'tuning in'. This principle and the experimental facts underlying it have been known for nearly thirty years. Since my first report of the phenomenon of 'homologous response' in 1922, much additional evidence has been brought to light (16, 19–22, 25–8, 33) and been summarized periodically (18, 24, 31, 36, 39). Even though the story has been told before, its lessons do not seem to have been fully understood, hence it bears repeating. Since it opens rather unsuspected vistas, it is not surprising to find that conventional neurological concepts contain no terms in which to relate it adequately. We must accept it, for the time being, in and on its own terms, much as physics accepted a wave theory of light long before recognizing its electromagnetic basis.

What is Coordination?

For the purpose of our discussion let us define coordination as the 'orderly activation of functional units'. 'Coordination' is the principle according to which from among a large number of units, e.g. muscles, certain fixed combinations are activated in definite associations and sequences; in contradistinction to the 'unco-ordinated' operation of merely random selections. Coordination refers to the orderly relation of parts. Such order may or may not be of immediate biological utility. The fact that, in the normal body, coordination usually makes sense when viewed from the standpoint of the biological needs of the organism, naturally suggests that biological utility is a prime factor in determining

491

coordination. This is an illusion, for, as we shall demonstrate below, the basic patterns of coordination develop and persist even in cases in which their effects are utterly contrary to the interests of the individual.

The Hierarchical Order of Neural Functions

It is fairly well recognized now that the functions of the nervous system are hierarchically organized. Thus the most elementary units, the individual neurons, operate in groupings which have some degree of autonomy and stability, and these groupings, in turn, form part of more comprehensive activities which again have their own characteristics, and so on up in an ascending order of magnitudes. The very title of this conference implies recognition of this principle. We speak of functional systems of higher or lower orders, of dominance and subordination, of integrative and analytic functions, and so on. Since more comprehensive functions operate through the activation of functional systems of lower order and more restricted scope, which themselves are composed of functional subunits of still lower order, integration, and analysis proceed in steps (15). The gist of this hierarchical principle is represented in Figure 1, in which a few representative levels have been singled out. Any given level operates through the selective activation and combination of unit functions of the next lower level, each characterized by a high degree of stability, integrity, and individuality.

Since coordination exists at all levels, disturbance of coordination at any one level need not imply disturbance or disruption of coordination at the others. Disregard of this fact accounts for much of the confusion in past discussions of functional regulation, re-integration, re-education, compensation, etc. In order to avoid vagueness, we shall confine ourselves here to one specific type of coordination, namely that at the lowest level of our diagram, referring to the regular sequential order in which muscles are activated in the movement of a given member. This limitation permits us to pose the problem of coordination in simple, concrete, and precise form.

A Standard Model of Coordination

Specifically, we choose the movements of the forelimb, and among the several types of movement of which it is capable, the one exhibited in forward locomotion. Our sample object will be a

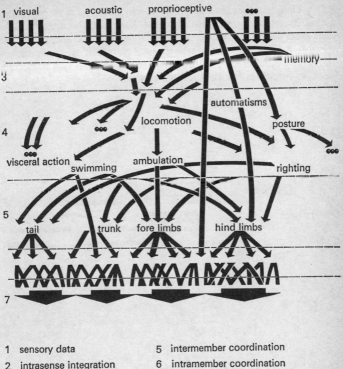

1 visual   acoustic   proprioceptive

memory

automatisms

locomotion   posture

visceral action   swimming ambulation   righting

tail   trunk fore limbs   hind limbs

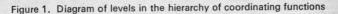

1 sensory data	5 intermember coordination
2 intrasense integration	6 intramember coordination
3 intersense integration	7 muscle contraction
4 visceral activity	

Figure 1. Diagram of levels in the hierarchy of coordinating functions

tailed amphibian, for this animal of great tolerance for experimental manipulation has held a key position in most of our tests. We further restrict our discussion to four representative muscles of the forelimb, concentrating, moreover, on the timing of their contractions only and disregarding relative strength. The selected muscles are an abductor (B) and adductor (D) of the shoulder, and a flexor (F) and extensor (E) of the elbow. Their operation in the cycle of ambulation is indicated in Figure 2. The lower strip shows characteristic phases of the movement, and the upper strip gives the approximate time-score in which the four muscles are found in action, hence also the time-score for the motor nerve cells innervating the respective muscles. As one can see, there is a roughly cyclic activity, with the excitatory condition sweeping (in the sense of the arrows in the insert) from F to B to E to D and back to F and on for another cycle or more.

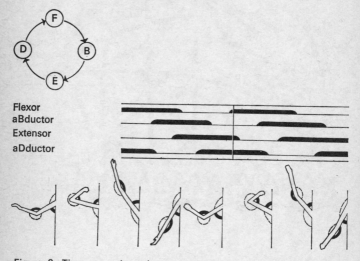

Figure 2. Time score (myochronogram) of four representative forelimb muscles during forward locomotion (simplified from Weiss [31])

In terms of this diagram, the problem of coordination resolves itself into the question as to why the motor neurons leading to the appropriate muscles are actuated in precisely the sequence in which they are, and how the central nervous system knows – if indeed it does – that this is the sequence required to produce successful forward locomotion. If we visualize the motor neurons as the strings of a piano, what is it that strikes the keyboard in such well ordered groupings and sequences that peripheral harmony results instead of dissonance? Let us examine what answers have been and are currently being given to this question as explicit contentions or merely tacit assumptions. The diagram shown in Figure 3, will help to crystallize the issue. The right side shows our four muscles attached to their ganglion cells, which lie interspersed with many other ganglion cells whose connections have been omitted in the picture. The arrows, F to B to E to D to F indicate the sweep necessary for forward motion.

It is commonly assumed that the pathway of this sweep is mapped out by a corresponding pattern of anatomical connections. Opinions diverge only as to the origin of such patterns. One school of thought assumes them to arise as stereotyped in-

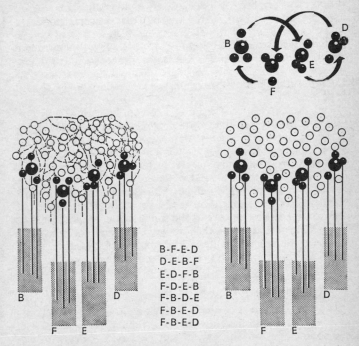

B-F-E-D	
D-E-B-F	
E-D-F-B	
F-D-E-B	
F-B-D-E	
F-B-E-D	
F-B-E-D	

Figure 3. Diagram of hypothetical development by 'trial-and-error' of a coordinated sequence F B E D in a neuronal network (from Weiss [36])

herited patterns. Processes of embryonic morphogenesis, so aptly predesigned that they will necessarily yield an anatomical network of the proper functional order would mould the central patterns prior to, and without the aid of, actual functional control. Another school would ascribe the functional order not to a pre-established anatomical order but to a progressive ordering process under the direct control of function, either by systematic input–output relations, as in the Gestalt theory, or by a trial-and-error procedure. This school starts from a situation such as in the left half of the diagram (Figure 3), which represents a neuron pool of initially equivalent elements abundantly inter-connected and capable of being activated in varying combinations. By discarding the unsuccessful ones, while reinforcing and improving those that have happened to turn out the desired peripheral effect, orderly associations would gradually be carved out from an initially unordered matrix. This concept is illustrated in the center panel of the diagram, in which successive sample trials are represented from top to bottom, leading to the gradual emergence and fixation of FBED as the only consistently success-ful combination. In this concept, functional success with its adaptive value rules supreme in the determination of central patterns.

Both these concepts of the origin of coordination – (i) by pre-arranged, rigidly determined, and precisely stereotyped micro-connections, or (ii) by gradual elimination of all but the successful and adequate associations – are theoretically possible. Yet, when put to a rigorous experimental test such as I will report presently, both were found to be invalid while in their place a wholly un-expected third concept emerged. The crucial test consisted of abolishing at the same time the supposedly critical order of central connections as well as the functional appropriateness of the peripheral organs and their activity. Anatomical connections thus being randomized and the criterion of usefulness eliminated, coordination nevertheless persisted essentially unimpaired.

The Principle of Myotypic Response

The basic experiment consists of breaking into the assumed cir-cuit, FBEDF, and inserting into it at random an extra muscle, the contractions of which will be of no service, or even of dis-service, to the body. In practice, this is done by transplanting a supernumerary muscle into the region of the limb plexus and in-nervating it by some arbitrary branch from that plexus. Instead of grafting a single muscle, one can graft a set or, most con-veniently, a whole limb (for illustrations of the anatomy of the innervation of such cases, see 16, 26, 44). All muscles of the transplant are supplied by the nerve branch put at their disposal. The choice of nerve as well as its subsequent regeneration being quite accidental, it is wholly unpredictable with what sort of motor cells a given transplanted muscle will find itself connected in its new condition. Moreover these muscles or limbs are attached in such abnormal positions that their movements are either useless to the animals or even a decided hindrance. Deprived thus of the criteria of pre-appointed connections and functional evaluation, how and when will the central nervous system call such muscles into action? The experiments, repeated in hundreds of cases, in dozens of different varieties, have given an unequivocal answer. The muscles respond as if they were

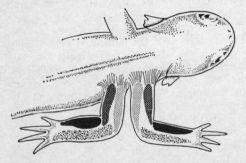

Figure 4. Diagram to show the mirror-image arrangement of muscles in a normal right limb and a supernumerary left limb transplanted near-by. Muscles of identical names are indicated by identical shading

called up by their names, for each always contracts simultaneously with, and with the same strength as, the muscle of the same name in the normal limb innervated from the common plexus. This phenomenon has been called 'homologous', or better, 'myotypic' response. Since each and every supernumerary muscle contracts with its counterpart, a supernumerary limb of the same symmetry as the host limb duplicates all movements of the latter, while a transplant of opposite symmetry (e.g. a right limb close to a left limb) mirrors all movements of its normal mate in appearance, hence counteracts them in effect. This is best realized by a glance at Figure 4, and the frames taken from a film strip shown in Plate 8, central inset. Absurd though this function is, it is never abandoned or rectified.

It must be emphasized that in these cases, the central nervous system has produced no new neurons to take care of the additional muscle load; the nerve fibers assigned to the transplants were definitely old nerve fibers switched to new and unpredictable destinations. It must also be stressed that any possible intervention of sensory control in the establishment of these peculiar muscle relations can be discounted because myotypic response appears just the same even if the whole region has previously been radically deafferented. For further details, the reader is referred to earlier publications.

The Meaning of Myotypic Response

Let us now examine the implications of this remarkable phenomenon. Evidently what counts in the engagement of a particular muscle, hence the key to coordinated timing, is neither a prearranged pattern of connections nor the utility of the response, but some personal characteristic of the individual muscle symbolized by its name. In other words, while we normally associate with the name of a muscle characteristics of shape, attachment, histological structure, and perhaps mechanical action, we now realize that we must include in this list some subtle and discriminatory specificity, presumably of molecular order, through which each muscle establishes and regulates its own individual relations with the nervous system. If you took five different urodele muscles, transplanted them one after another into the same abnormal and functionally irrelevant position, and gave them the same nerve fibers for innervation, they would still contract at different times, each according to its name, each at the appropriate time when we know that particular name to be up in the central time-score of coordination. The supernumerary muscle thus signals that a call for its kind is broadcast in the corresponding spinal segment, and by its proper response, also reveals that its own motoneurons have understood and selectively reacted to the specific call.

In order to appreciate just what this specific relation signifies, let us return to the diagram of Figure 3, augmented by the addition of a supernumerary test muscle, B (Figure 5). Let us assume that B gets some of its innervation from, among others, former D neurons. According to our observations, supernumerary muscle B and regular B always contract in unison. This means that the ganglion cells innervating both muscles are excited simultaneously. The ganglion cells of the supernumerary muscle thus have lost their old and have acquired new associations, and since their new order is ruled by the specific character of the new muscle at their end, the nature of which they could not have known beforehand, it is clear that the muscle must have informed its ganglion cells of its 'name'. Since this occurs even if no sensory units are present, the 'information' evidently arrives as a retro-

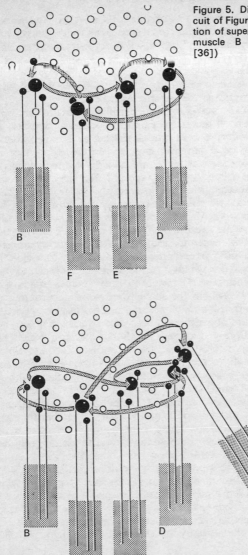

Figure 5. Diagram of circuit of Figure 3 with addition of supernumerary test muscle B (from Weiss [36])

grade influence over the motor fibers themselves. The muscle imparts its specific quality to the motoneurons by a process which I have called 'modulation' and which bears formal resemblance to the specific moulding of antibodies by antigens. Instances of retrograde effects of the periphery on the state of central neurons are being uncovered in increasing numbers (42, 45) though none of them is as specific as the one discussed here.

But 'modulation' solves only the peripheral part of the problem. The enigma of central coordination remains. Suppose all the motoneurons have been modulated by, and in accordance with, their respective terminal muscles, to the effect that all ganglion cells of identical 'tune' are now bound to respond in unison; to just what do they respond? We understand why synonymous muscles, wherever located and however attached, contract together, but this contains no hint as to why they are called on to respond at all in a particular sequence for a particular act. If we look at the sweep FBEDF of the left half of Figure 5, we realize that in order to accommodate the supernumerary muscle B (right half of the figure), we would have to divide the sweep in F in such a way that it can take in both B foci and then have both branches converge again on E. If we drew this type of pathway not for one but for some twenty-odd supernumerary muscles, as in a transplanted limb, and not for just one conveniently clustered trio of ganglion cells as shown in the diagram, but for all the randomly dispersed ganglion cells with which the transplant happens to be connected, a confusion of lines would result that would startlingly contrast with the simplicity and monotony of the response. It would be wholly in keeping with current habits of thought to interpret such a profusion of arrows as a complex network of newly formed morphological connections among ganglion cells, although it would hardly seem credible that the centers should contrive all that minute reorganization for no better purpose than to cause useless duplicate limbs to engage in absurd waste motions. Yet the habitual tendency is strong to keep ascribing the order FBEDF to some inherited order of neuronal connections for the 'normal' muscles, and merely add some subsidiary relief mechanism by which the centers would manage to hitch any duplicate muscle to the center of its corresponding namesake. Even this compromise position is, however, made untenable by the following experiments.

The Inherited Central Action Repertory

Suppose instead of transplanting supernumerary test muscles, we remove the original set of muscles entirely and replace it by another similar set but with random connections and in abnormal anatomical relation to the body; suppose, for instance, we replace a left limb by a right limb. The experiment has been done with the expected results: Each muscle of the transplant contracts at precisely the time that the muscle of the same name would have contracted in the original normal limb if the latter were still present. A right limb in the place of a left one thus walks backwards whenever the animal tries to walk forward. In other words, the centers keep right on calling up muscles in the sequence FBEDF, and the ganglion cells connected with the muscles F, B, E, and D, and appropriately modulated by them, respond to their call. Centrally, everything goes on as in a normal animal; only the peripheral result turns out to be functionally incongruous. Since in these cases, none of the ganglion cells had normal peripheral relations, it is no longer possible to relate the altered relations to an original pre-existing pattern of inherited connections. Whatever primordial connections may have existed, must have been superseded in the rearrangement. Yet the action score FBEDF continued unimpaired in an invariant sequence. This makes it impossible to refer the stable pattern FBEDF to a stable concatenation of neurons.

Alternative hypotheses are a matter of speculation. One could assume, for instance, that the sequence FBEDF represented a succession of different excitatory states in a common neuropil, each state connected with a particular biochemical process alerting the corresponding neuron set, vaguely comparable to the orderly succession of specific enzymatic steps in a metabolic reaction chain. Coordinated sequences might thus be conceived of as preformed in chains of reactions rather than in chains of neurons. In terms of the conventional multiple-switch picture of central conduction, these biochemical events would be the coordinating agents that set the switches.

At any rate, it is clear from the experiments that coordination is essentially an intracentral affair and that the function of modulation is not to create coordination, but merely to engage each individual muscle in the proper response relations with the intracentral action systems. That central coordination develops quite autonomously, is dramatically illustrated by animals whose forelimb buds had been reversed during their developmental phase. The movements of such limbs appear from the very first coordinated, but reversed, hence counteract the normal hind limbs in a continual struggle throughout life. All that would have been necessary to make these limbs useful to the bearers would have been for the centers to discharge the normal retreat sequence in the forelimb centers with the advance sequence in the hindlimb centers. The fact that this has never occurred shows the rigidity, yet orderliness, muscle for muscle, in the development of the central repertory of coordination patterns. Each animal develops a definite but limited number of such, and the periphery just executes and steers them but plays no role in their determination. For similar conclusions derived from wholly different lines of evidence, see von Holst (3) and Tinbergen (14).

The central coordination patterns develop bilaterally. That is, each half of the spinal cord controls its ipsilateral musculature while dealing with the opposite musculature through the mediation of the coordinative mechanisms of the other half of the cord. Moreover, the coordinative mechanisms are localized segmentally within areas corresponding to the peripheral innervation sites. A limb innervated from trunk segments, for instance, remains functionless, indicating that trunk segments do not produce discharges of the proper design to activate motor cells modulated by limb muscles (2). Further evidence along this line has recently been produced in my laboratory by the transplantation in embryonic stages of a portion of trunk spinal cord in the place of the future hindlimb segments (4). The transplanted cord piece develops in continuity with the rest of the cord and without microscopically visible deficiencies. It innervates the hind limbs, yet is unable to move them, while forelimb segments transplanted into the same region produce good coordinated movements. There is thus an intrinsic difference between various levels of the cord in their coordinative ability, differences which are not effaced by exposure to the appropriate peripheral areas.

This regional mosaic character of coordinative mechanisms is, however, in sharp contrast to the conspicuous lack of a finer mosaic condition within each district. A given cord segment can stand considerable diminution and experimental disarrangement and still produce typical coordinative sequences (25). When hindlimb segments of the cord are excised and replaced by others in dorso-ventral inversion or antero-posterior reversal, the limbs innervated by such disharmonious centers still display fairly typical coordination (Holtzer, unpublished observations). We may conclude, therefore, that within each circumscribed coordination system some degree of equipotentiality may prevail, much as that established by Lashley (6) for circumscribed brain areas, although functional circumscription need not mean morphological delineation.

For further details, I can only refer to the earlier more extensive publications. Here I have to content myself merely with illustrating in simple fashion the main features of the phenomenon of myotypic response and their implications. On the terminological side, considering that the ganglion cells modulated by their muscles respond as if they were 'tuned' to a corresponding action of the central excitatory system, I still like to refer to the principle involved as having 'resonance' character. The term never has been meant to be more than a descriptive simile.

Proprioceptive Specificity

The same resonance relation that we have just outlined for the motor system also binds periphery and centers on the sensory side. The evidence comes from animals in which a sensory area had been anatomically displaced and abnormally innervated, yet upon stimulation evoked a central response as if it were still in its normal place with its normal innervation. This can be demonstrated only for those types of reflexes in which a given sensory stimulus evokes a constant and discriminative motor response. One can find out then whether the motor reaction following stimulation of a dislocated area corresponds to the place or rather the type of area from which the reflex had been elicited. In all tests thus far performed in amphibians, the response proved to be determined by type, rather than location.

The first test of this kind was described for the proprioceptive excitation coming from stretched muscles and leading to myotatic reflex contraction of the very same muscles. A supernumerary limb is a convenient device for demonstrating such myotatic reflexes, for whenever the stretch of a given muscle in the normal limb yields an isometric reflex contraction of that muscle, this is accompanied by a simultaneous isotonic contraction of the synonymous muscle in the unstimulated extra limb, which thus signals the type of the response. Similarly, the normal limb serves to identify the type of response the centers give to the stretching of a muscle in the supernumerary limb. Applying this criterion, it was found that the centers always identified correctly the name of a displaced muscle from which an afferent impulse came, for they responded by sending an efferent excitation to the muscles of precisely that name (16, 25, 44).

In conclusion, each muscle modulates, besides its motoneurons, also its sensory neurons in accordance with its own specific character, thus enabling them to establish selective communication with the intracentral apparatus. The nature of the latter is not further clarified by these observations. The only thing that stands out clearly is that the response relations between the intracentral coordinating systems and the peripheral organs are established and maintained by the indicated resonance mechanisms, both in the motor and sensory fields.

Corneal Specificity

The first instance in which a similar response specificity could be proven for an exteroceptive field was the corneal discharge. Mature amphibians possess a lid-closure reflex, the reflexogenous area of which is in some species strictly confined to the cornea of the eye. Touch to the cornea (innervated by trigeminal fibers) produces withdrawal of the bulb (through the abducens nerve). Following the standard design of our experiments, a supernumerary eye was transplanted to the ear capsule (Figure 6).

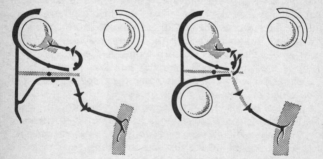

Figure 6. Diagram of corneal reflex from transplanted supernumerary eye (right), compared with normal animal (left). (See text)

Normally, cutaneous stimulation in the ear region produces neck flexion to the opposite side. These same cutaneous fibers, however, after having taken over the innervation of the transplanted cornea, now elicit a lid-closure reflex in the normal ipsilateral eye (5, 33). Evidently these neurons have become so remodulated by their new corneal termination that their central discharge activates

504

the abducens motor center instead of the spinal center of the neck muscles. The strip of skin between the two transplanted eyes when stimulated gives rise to no such reaction and thus accentuates the selectivity of the response from the two corneal areas which it separates.

Cutaneous Specificity

That the skin itself is similarly parcelled into patches of different specificity has recently been shown by Miner (7) who rotated a strip of flank skin in the frog tadpole dorso-ventrally so that the dorsal half came to lie over the belly, and the ventral half over the back, each innervated by sensory fibers of its new locality. In the normal metamorphosed frog, touch to the skin leads to the familiar wiping reflex, which is typically executed with the fore limbs when the stimulus is on the belly and with the hind limbs when the stimulus is on the flank or back. When, after metamorphosis, the transplanted flaps were touched, the motor response proved to depend entirely on whether the stimulated area had originally been belly or back skin; it had no reference to the new location of the skin areas. Touching the original belly skin, now on the back and innervated by sensory fibers of the back region, evoked wiping with the fore legs, while stimuli applied to the original back skin (now on the belly) produced wiping with the hind legs. In each case the responding leg aimed at the site of the origin of the graft rather than at its actual location. Evidently, therefore, gross localization, or what might be called the crude local signs, register centrally not in terms of topographical relations of the sensory units, but in terms of distinct specificities of the emitting areas, a sort of 'submodalities' of the senses. However, just as in the motor field, we may expect to find some degree of equipotentiality within each facet of the peripheral modality mosaic so that finer discrimination and localization within any given sensory submodality might still be mediated by topographic or dynamic relations among the unit discharges of that particular area.

Specificity in the Visual Field

An essentially logical extension of our demonstration of sensory specificity – and perhaps also its most spectacular illustration – is contained in the systematic work of my former student, Sperry, on the visual sense of amphibians after retinal disorientation

505

(9–11). The main features of the experiments are summarized in Figure 7. The top strip shows, from left to right, the retina in profile, the retina in surface view, the optic centers of the midbrain, the spinal cord of the neck region, and the front part of a newt. The dorsal, ventral, lateral and mesial quadrants of the retina are indicated by appropriate letter symbols, and their projection areas on the tectum opticum are similarly labelled. BA is the spinal center for back muscles and BE that for belly muscles.

retina   brain   cord

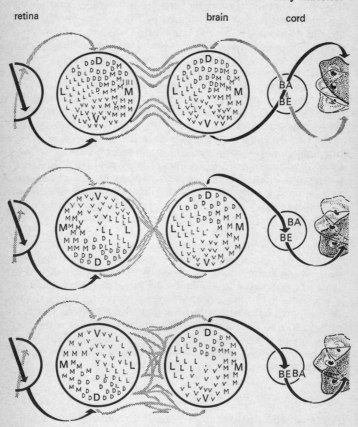

Figure 7. Diagram of motor response to dorsal or ventral images in normal animal (top), after inversion of eyes (middle), and after inversion combined with optic nerve regeneration (bottom). (See text for description)

The solid arrows indicate the chain of events following the appearance of an object above the animal. The image falls on the ventral retina, sets up an excitation which activates the ventral projection area of the brain, which in turn yields spinal activation of the back muscles. As a result, the animal bends dorsal toward the object. Actually, of course, the response is much more complicated, and if the object is moving prey, the animal strikes upward for the catch. Conversely, an object appearing from below, whose image falls on the dorsal retina, evokes the sequence indicated by broken arrows ending up in contraction of the belly muscles and bending downward.

Now, when the eyes are rotated in their sockets by 180° without interruption of the optic nerves, which merely undergo a half-turn twist, the response will be as indicated in the middle strip of the diagram. An object appearing in the upper half of the visual field projects its image on the lower half of the retina, originally the dorsal half and connected with the dorsal projection area, which activates the belly musculature. Consequently, as indicated by the row of solid arrows, the animal strikes downward, obviously missing the prey. Similarly, food offered from below is responded to by turning upward. All visual reactions of such animals are reversed. The reversal in the mesio-lateral direction is particularly striking. In a normal animal, an object moving horizontally produces neck flexion in the same sense, hence optical fixation of the object. In the animal with rotated eyes, however, the neck flexion occurs in the reverse direction. When the object moves to the left, the animal turns to the right; since this entails a further relative movement of the whole visual field to the left and since the animal keeps compensating in the wrong direction, any experimental animal, once it starts moving, goes into a protracted spin.

Just as in the case of the other reactions thus far described, this completely perverted, though consistent, behavior has never undergone any adaptive change of improvement. It thus could serve the same purpose as the inverted limbs of our motor experiments when combined with randomization of nerve connections. In the present case, the experiment consisted of transecting the optic nerves of the rotated eyes and allowing the nerves to regenerate at random, as indicated in the bottom strip of Figure 7. In crossing the gap, the optic fibers, like those of regenerating peripheral nerves, form an irregular tangle and enter the central stump in random distribution. They, therefore, arrive in the brain in a wholly arbitrary constellation, obliterating any orderly topographical representation of the retinal areas in the optic fiber distribution that may have existed in the normal animal. Nevertheless, when these animals were tested again after recuperation of vision, they responded precisely as before the transection of the nerve, that is, in reverse.

As in the case of our previous experiments, the absolute ineptitude of the response rules out any explanation by adaptive learning that might have been advanced for restoration of normal vision after nerve regeneration in unrotated eyes. The conclusion is, as before, that every sensory area – each individual retinal sector in this instance – establishes selective communication with its corresponding brain center irrespective of the detailed pattern of nerve connections. For the retinal projection, this point can be most elegantly demonstrated by correlating localized lesions in the optic tectum with the resulting blind sectors of the retina (11). It was found that a tectal lesion in the area which is the normal projection area of, for instance, the ventral retinal field blinds the animal for images exciting that part of the retina which has the native 'ventral' constitution no matter what its actual position relative to space, body, and brain may be.

In summary, we must concede to the neural elements of the various sectors of the retina distinctive constitutional properties by means of which they can establish selective discharge relations with the normal corresponding brain stations. The validity of this principle has also been shown for the vestibular organ (12).

The experimental results of Sperry have been confirmed and partly extended by Stone (13a), whose moving picture has been widely shown and aroused the interest which these demonstrative results duly deserve. Yet, it would seem that this sudden upsurge of interest only confirms my initial remark that the true meaning of this whole train of experimental facts has not been properly appreciated in the nearly three decades since they were first reported.

Concluding Remarks

This brings us to the end of our brief factual account. Many details have been omitted in order to put the basic principle of the specificity of central-peripheral relations into sharp relief. This principle has been derived from the fact that orderly part-for-part communication between centers and periphery is established and maintained even if the normal order of anatomical connections and the functional appropriateness of the peripheral effects have been abolished. Thus any theories that would ascribe the central-peripheral correspondence either to the geometrical order of the nerve connections or to an assumed primacy of functional success are clearly ruled out. The further fact that central-peripheral communication remained not only orderly but strictly selective according to the constitutional specificities of the intercommunicating parts has plainly revealed the instrumental role of these specificities in the selective ('resonance'-like) linking of centers and periphery, and perhaps also of different central components among one another.

We have deliberately described this principle in neutral phenomenological terms with no reference to possible points of contact with current neurological concepts, for any attempt at translation into conventional physiological vocabulary would at present be gratuitous. That existing theories of conduction and synaptic transmission contain no clue to the described phenomena is amply proven by the fact that they could not have predicted them. Since the reality of the phenomena is undeniable, they will have to find a place in our neurological thinking. Whether they can be accommodated by mere additions to current physiological concepts without resorting to major revisions, is an open question. It is important, however, in this connection to point to certain qualifications of the resonance principle which might justify a conservative attitude.

First, since all our basic observations have been made on amphibians, it is legitimate to ask whether the conclusions can rightly be applied to other vertebrates and man. Second, the question can still be raised whether the selective (resonance) relations play a role in the functional operation of the mature nervous system or are merely developmental factors in establishing the right setting and resetting of the neural machine.

As for the first point, it can be said that the existence of the myotypic response has been shown in supernumerary digits in man (22, 43) and in the twin head muscles of a double-headed cow (unpublished observations). The general principle, therefore, appears to be valid for all vertebrates. However, the period during which it can be tested is definitely restricted in higher forms, and this places increased emphasis on our second point. The test of a resonance relation, it will be recalled, is based primarily on the remodulation of neurons after reconnection with end-organs of different specificity. Already in amphibians, the faculty for remodulation subsides during metamorphosis so that neurons switched to new terminations in the fully mature stage are not remodulated but continue to respond according to their old specificity acquired during premetamorphic life (13, 24). In mammals, remodulation of peripheral neurons has never been obtained in the postnatal period (8); one would have to go back into intrauterine stages in order to perform test experiments comparable to those carried out on larval amphibians.

These facts would seem to encourage the view that we are dealing with a phenomenon of developmental conditioning rather than with one of physiological operation, a view which, if true, would entitle us to keep on treating the latter in the customary sense as devoid of selective mechanisms. As for the modulation of a nerve by its muscle or sense organ, this phenomenon unmistakably belongs in the class of developmental rather than physiological events. The gradual imparting of a specific character from one specialized tissue to another contiguous tissue is a common occurrence in development ('induction'), for which one can even imagine some sort of stereochemical explanation (34, 37). Since modulation, as I have pointed out repeatedly, may proceed from ultimate neurons to penultimate ones, and from there even farther central, this developmental process projects the peripheral specificities into the centers to varying depths.

There is an obvious temptation to let the process continue all the way through the centers and let neuron chains link themselves into permanent circuits by progressive modulation and association of elements of like modulus. Sperry has explicitly taken this view. Intriguing though it may seem for its appeal to orthodoxy, it fails under critical inspection on three counts. First, the scheme would imply rigid delineation of all excitatory pathways from an individual type of sense organ to an individual muscle. But for rare special cases (e.g. myotatic reflex), such point-to-point determinacy does not exist, nor could it be expected in view of the hierarchical plan of neural functions (see Figure 1). Secondly, it is contradicted by the fact that the same muscles are brought into play in various (though limited) combinations, as first stressed in Sherrington's principle of the final common path. Thirdly, even if modulation were able to account for the distribution of excitation at any one moment, it would still leave wholly unexplained the problem of the orderly sequence of changes from moment to moment, as illustrated in our sample sequence FBED. No formula of coordination that does not take into account its four-dimensional order in space and time can be satisfactory.

For these reasons, it would seem to me that merely adding modulation to the known properties of neuronal networks will not be enough. Somewhere in the physico-chemical structure of the nervous system we must look for a patterned activity to represent such standard and invariant time sequences of selective activations as F B E D for advance, F D E B for retreat, etc. I have mentioned above the fanciful idea that these may be engendered by chains of complex chemical reactions whose constituent links would 'unlock' correspondingly tuned neural elements. Though being sheer speculation, it indicates the direction in which we may have to look.

It may be comforting to keep pretending that the resonance phenomena are matters of development and require no major innovations of physiological theory; but I doubt whether it is realistic. Surely, if we were already in possession of a good and valid theory of coordination, the case would be different. Yet, we are not. We are still relying heavily on verbal and purely formal symbols (e.g. 'control', 'integration', etc.) to fill the gaps in our knowledge, and so long as this is the case, there really is no doctrine to which a doctrinary mind need cling. The neurons, to quote Adrian (1) 'have a fairly simple mechanism when we treat them as individuals. Their behavior in the mass may be quite another story, but this is for future work to decide' (p. 93). It would seem that the phenomena I have reported above form an integral part of that 'other story'. The rest is still up to the future.

Discussion

Dr Grayson P. McCouch (Philadelphia, Pa.): I cannot let so important a contribution pass without discussion, although I am at a loss to know how to correlate it with other data. It recalls the early work of the Lapique School on differences in chronaxia between different muscles and the more recent work of Therman suggesting other differences between the properties of flexor and extensor motoneurons. It may well be that if such studies are carried further they will afford a clue to the mechanism of the interesting phenomena that Dr Weiss has described.

Dr Alexander Forbes (Cambridge, Mass.): I have little to add to what Dr McCouch has said except that at first sight, it puzzles one a good deal to see how all this fits in with the picture of the 'all or none' principle of nerve conduction, in accordance with which we look upon the nerve fiber as conducting one and the same type of impulse regardless of how it is stimulated. But Dr Weiss has certainly given us something that we cannot brush aside casually, and we must find a way to explain it, presumably through some property of specificity, such as he suggested, but for the life of me I cannot visualize just how it works. However, I hope that some day somebody can.

Conation: The Neural Programming of Behaviour

Dr Paul Weiss (Chicago, Ill.): I only want to say that I am grateful for the support that I have found in my contention that we have really no clue for this phenomenon in our standard physiological concepts. Some of you may know that most of my scientific activities have been devoted to the analysis of development, and there we are much farther advanced in demonstrating interactions of high specificity. There we find many mechanisms that follow the same pattern of selective activation that I have postulated here for neural interaction, and I see no reason why we should deny the nervous system discriminatory powers that other systems of the organism definitely possess.

President Bard: I think that Dr Weiss's paper provides us with a very basic and fundamental group of facts which will serve as a background for the remaining papers of the morning, all of which are concerned with the activities of spinal mechanisms.

References

1. E. D. ADRIAN, *The Mechanism of Nervous Action; Electrical Studies of the Neurone*, University of Pennsylvania Press, 1932, pp. 103.
2. S. R. DETWILER, *Neuroembryology: An Experimental Study.*
3. E. VON HOLST, 'Vom wesen der ordnung im zentralnervensystem', *Naturwissenschaften*, vol. 25 (1937), pp. 625, 631, 641, 647.
4. H. HOLTZER, 'Differentiation of the regional action systems in the urodele spinal cord', *Anat. Rec.*, vol. 108 (1950), pp. 127–8.
5. J. J. KOLLROS, 'Experimental studies on the development of the corneal reflex in amphibia. III. The influence of the periphery upon the reflex center', *J. exp. Zool.*, vol. 92 (1943), pp. 121–42.
6. K. S. LASHLEY, 'The problem of cerebral organization in vision', *Biol. Symposia*, vol. 7 (1942), pp. 301–22.
7. N. MINER, *Integumental Specification of Sensory Neurons in the Genesis of Cutaneous Local Sign*, Ph.D. thesis, University of Chicago, 1951.
8. R. W. SPERRY, 'The effect of crossing nerves to antagonistic muscles in the hind limb of the rat', *J. comp. Neurol.*, vol. 75 (1941), pp. 1–19.
9. R. W. SPERRY, 'Visuomotor coordination in the newt (Triturus viridescens) after regeneration of the optic nerve', *J. comp. Neurol.*, vol. 79 (1943), pp. 33–55.
10. R. W. SPERRY, 'Effect of 180 degree rotation of the retinal field on visuomotor coordination', *J. exp. Zool.*, vol. 92 (1943), pp. 263–79.
11. R. W. SPERRY, 'Optic nerve regeneration with return of vision in anurans', *J. Neurophysiol.*, vol. 7 (1944), pp. 57–70.
12. R. W. SPERRY, 'Centripetal regeneration of the 8th cranial nerve root with systematic restoration of vestibular reflexes', *Amer. J. Physiol.*, vol. 144 (1945), pp. 735–41.
13. R. W. SPERRY and N. MINER, 'Formation within sensory nucleus V of synaptic associations mediating cutaneous localization', *J. comp. Neurol.*, vol. 90 (1949), pp. 403–24.
13a. L. S. STONE, 'Functional polarization in retinal development and its reestablishment in regenerating retinae of rotated grafted eyes', *Proc. Soc. Exp. Biol., N.Y.*, vol. 57 (1944), pp. 13–14.

14. N. TINBERGEN, 'An objectivistic study of the innate behavior of animals', *Bibl. Biotheoret. ser. D*, vol. 1 (1942), pp. 39–98.

15. N. TINBERGEN, 'The hierarchical organization of nervous mechanisms underlying instinctive behavior', *Symposia Soc. exp. Biol.*, vol. 4 (1950), pp. 305–12.

16. P. WEISS, 'Die Funktion transplantierter Amphibienextremitäten. Aufstellung einer Resonanztheorie der motorischen Nerventätigkeit auf Grund abgestimmter Endorgane', *Arch. Entw. Mech. Org.*, vol. 102 (1924), pp. 635–72.

17. P. WEISS, 'The relations between central and peripheral coordination', *J. comp. Neurol.*, vol. 40 (1926), pp. 241–51.

18. P. WEISS, 'Erregungsspezifität und Erregungsresonanz. Grundzüge einer Theorie der motorischen Nerventätigkeit auf Grund spezifischer Zuordnung ("Abstimmung") zwischen zentraler und peripherer Erregungsform', *Ergebn. Physiol.*, vol. 3 (1928), pp. 1–151.

19. P. WEISS, 'Neue experimentelle Beweise für das Resonanzprinzip der Nerventätigkeit', *Biol. Zbl.*, vol. 50 (1930), pp. 357–72.

20. P. WEISS, 'Das Resonanzprinzip der Nerventätigkeit, dargestellt in Funktions-prüfungen an transplantierten überzähligen Muskeln', *Pflüg. Arch. ges. Physiol.*, vol. 226 (1931), pp. 600–58.

21. P. WEISS, 'Die Nervenversorgung der überzähligen Extremitäten an dem von Verzar und Weiss in Bd. 223 dieser Zeitschrift beschriebenen hypermelen Frosch', *Pflüg. Arch. ges. Physiol.*, vol. 228 (1931), pp. 486–97.

22. P. WEISS, 'Homologous (resonance-like) function in supernumerary fingers in a human case', *Proc. Soc. exp. Biol. N. Y.*, vol. 33 (1935), pp. 426–30.

23. P. WEISS, 'A study of motor coordination and tonus in deafferented limbs of amphibia', *Amer. J. Physiol.*, vol. 115 (1936), pp. 461–75.

24. P. WEISS, 'Selectivity controlling the central-peripheral relations in the nervous system', *Biol. Rev.*, vol. 11 (1936), pp. 494–531.

25. P. WEISS, 'Further experimental investigations on the phenomenon of homologous response in transplanted amphibian limbs. I. Functional observations', *J. comp. Neurol.*, vol. 66 (1937), pp. 181–206.

26. P. WEISS, 'Further experimental investigations on the phenomenon of homologous response in transplanted amphibian limbs. II. Nerve regeneration and the innervation of transplanted limbs', *J. comp. Neurol.*, vol. 66 (1937), pp. 481–535.

27. P. WEISS, 'Further experimental investigations on the phenomenon of homologous response in transplanted amphibian limbs. III. Homologous response in the absence of sensory innervation', *J. comp. Neurol.*, vol. 66 (1937), pp. 537–48.

28. P. WEISS, 'Further experimental investigations on the phenomenon of homologous response in transplanted amphibian limbs. IV. Reverse locomotion after the interchange of right and left limbs', *J. comp. Neurol.*, vol. 67 (1937), pp. 269–315.

29. P. WEISS, 'Autonomous versus reflexogenous activity of the central nervous system', *Proc. Amer. Philos. Soc.*, vol. 84 (1941), pp. 53–64.

30. P. WEISS, 'Does sensory control play a constructive role in the development of motor coordination?' *Schweiz. med. Wschr.*, vol. 71 (1941), pp. 591–5.

31. P. WEISS, 'Self differentiation of the basic patterns of coordination', *J. comp. Psychol. Monogr.*, vol. 17 (1941), pp. 1–96.

Conation: The Neural Programming of Behaviour

32. P. WEISS, 'Nerve patterns: The mechanics of nerve growth', *Growth*, vol. 5 (1941), pp. 163–203.

33. P. WEISS, 'Lid-closure reflex from eyes transplanted to atypical locations in Triturus torosus: Evidence of a peripheral origin of sensory specificity', *J. comp. Neurol.*, vol. 77 (1942), pp. 131–69.

34. P. WEISS, 'The problem of specificity in growth and development', *Yale J. Biol. Med.*, vol. 19 (1947), pp. 235–78.

35. P. WEISS, 'Differential growth', in *Chemistry and Physiology of Growth*, Princeton University Press, 1949, pp. 135–86.

36. P. WEISS, 'Experimental analysis of coordination by the disarrangement of centralperipheral relations', *Symposia Soc. exp. Biol.*, vol. 92 (1950), pp. 92–111.

37. P. WEISS, 'Some perspectives in the field of morphogenesis', *Quart. Rev. Biol.*, vol. 25 (1950), pp. 177–98.

38. P. WEISS, 'The deplantation of fragments of nervous system in amphibians. I. Central reorganization and the formation of nerves', *J. exp. Zool.*, vol. 113 (1950), pp. 397–461.

39. P. WEISS (ed.), *Genetic Neurology: Problems of the Development, Growth and Regeneration of the Nervous System and its Functions*, University of Chicago, 1950.

40. P. WEISS, 'Introduction to genetic neurology', in *Genetic Neurology: Problems of the Development, Growth and Regeneration of the Nervous System and its Functions*, University of Chicago Press, 1950, pp. 1–39.

41. P. WEISS and P. F. BROWN, 'Electromyographic studies on reco-ordination of leg movements in poliomyelitis patients with transposed tendons', *Proc. Soc. exp. Biol.*, *N.Y.*, vol. 48 (1941), pp. 284–7.

42. P. WEISS, M. V. EDDS, JR, and M. CAVANAUGH, 'The effect of terminal connections on the caliber of nerve fibers', *Anat. Rec.*, vol. 92 (1945), pp. 215–33.

43. P. WEISS and T. C. RUCH, 'Further observations on the function of supernumerary fingers in man', *Proc. Soc. exp. Biol. N.Y.*, vol. 34 (1936), pp. 569–70.

44. P. WEISS and F. VERZAR, 'Untersuchungen über das Phänomen der identischen Bewegungsfunktion mehrfacher benachbarter Extremitäten. Zugleich: Direkte Vorführung von Eigenreflexen', *Pflüg. Arch. ges. Physiol.*, vol. 223 (1930), pp. 671–84.

45. J. Z. YOUNG, 'The determination of the characteristics of nerve fibers', *Genetic Neurology: Problems of the Development, Growth and Regeneration of the Nervous System and its Functions*, University of Chicago Press, 1950, pp. 92–104.

26 K. S. Lashley

The Problem of Serial Order in Behavior

K. S. Lashley, 'The problem of serial order in behavior', in L. P. Jeffress (ed.), *Cerebral Mechanisms in Behavior: The Hixon Symposium*, John Wiley, 1951, pp. 112–36.

The previous speakers have approached our common problem by considering the properties of the elementary units of which we believe the cerebral structure to be built up. They have considered the kinds of neural integration or behavior which can be anticipated from those properties. The remaining members of the symposium have in their research been concerned chiefly with the analysis of complex behavior, seeking to derive general principles of neural integration from the infinitely complex products of that integration. Our common meeting ground is the faith to which we all subscribe, I believe, that the phenomena of behavior and of mind are ultimately describable in the concepts of the mathematical and physical sciences. In my discussion here, I have deliberately turned to the opposite extreme from the neuron and have chosen as a topic, one aspect of the most complex type of behavior that I know; the logical and orderly arrangement of thought and action. Our discussion so far has dealt chiefly with the conditions of input and of immediate switching in the nervous mechanism, without explicit consideration of what is already going on within the system.

My principal thesis today will be that the input is never into a quiescent or static system, but always into a system which is already actively excited and organized. In the intact organism, behavior is the result of interaction of this background of excitation with input from any designated stimulus. Only when we can state the general characteristics of this background of excitation, can we understand the effects of a given input.

The unpronounceable Cree Indian word 'kekawewechetushe-kamikowanowow' is analysed by Chamberlain (7) into the verbal root, *tusheka*, 'to remain', and the various particles which modify it as follows: *ke(la)wow*, the first and last syllables, indicating second person plural; *ka*, a prefix of the future tense; *we*, a sort of imperative mode expressing a wish; *weche*, indicating conjunction of subject and object; *mik*, a suffix bringing the verb into

515

agreement with a third person subject and second person object; and *owan*, a suffix indicating that the subject is inanimate and the object animate. A literal translation: 'You will I wish together remain he-you it-man you' or, freely, 'may it remain with you'. This difference in structure between Cree and English illustrates an outstanding characteristic of verbal behavior; the occurrence of predetermined, orderly sequences of action which are unique for each language. In English the adjective precedes, in French it follows the noun which it modifies. In English the movement or action of the subject is expressed as early as possible after the subject; in German the expression of action may be postponed until all qualifying thoughts have been expressed. In a sentence discussing this subject, Pick (20) introduces fifty-five words between the subject and the principal verb. Each Chinese word, and to a lesser extent, each English word, stands as an unchanging unit. In the highly inflective languages, such as Sioux, the form of almost every word in the sentence may be altered, according to some attribute of the subject, as when two objects rather than one or several are discussed.

The study of comparative grammar is not the most direct approach to the physiology of the cerebral cortex, yet Fournié (10) has written, 'Speech is the only window through which the physiologist can view the cerebral life.' Certainly language presents in a most striking form the integrative functions that are characteristic of the cerebral cortex and that reach their highest development in human thought processes. Temporal integration is not found exclusively in language; the coordination of leg movements in insects, the song of birds, the control of trotting and pacing in a gaited horse, the rat running the maze, the architect designing a house, and the carpenter sawing a board present a problem of sequences of action which cannot be explained in terms of successions of external stimuli.

Associate Chain Theories

In spite of the ubiquity of the problem, there have been almost no attempts to develop physiological theories to meet it. In fact, except among a relatively small group of students of aphasia, who have had to face questions of agrammatism, the problem has been largely ignored. It is not even mentioned in recent textbooks on neurophysiology or physiological psychology, nor is there any significant body of experimental studies bearing upon the problem. The spinal animal scarcely exhibits serial activity, so the physiologist may be excused for overlooking the phenomenon. On the other hand, psychologists have been concerned chiefly with the question of whether or not the organizing processes displayed in serial action are conscious, and very little with the organization itself. I have chosen to discuss the problem of temporal integration here, not with the expectation of offering a satisfactory physiological theory to account for it, but because it seems to me to be both the most important and also the most neglected problem of cerebral physiology. Temporally integrated actions do occur even among insects, but they do not reach any degree of complexity until the appearance of the cerebral cortex. They are especially characteristic of human behavior and contribute as much as does any single factor to the superiority of man's intelligence. A clearer formulation of the physiological problems which they raise should be of value, even though a solution of the problems is not yet in sight.

I shall consider first some of the questions raised by the structure of language, then turn to other forms of serial action for indications of the nature of the nervous mechanisms involved.

To the best of my knowledge, the only strictly physiological theory that has been explicitly formulated to account for temporal integration is that which postulates chains of reflexes, in which the performance of each element of the series provides excitation of the next. This conception underlay the 'motor theories' of thinking which were advocated by several psychologists early in this century. Watson (26) sought to identify thought with inaudible movements of the vocal organs, linked together in associative chains. The peripheral chain theory of language was developed in greatest detail by Washburn (25). She distinguished what she called 'successive movement systems' and, although she drew her examples from memorized series of nonsense syllables, her implication was that such series are typical of all language behavior. She defined a movement system as 'a combination of movements so linked together that the stimulus furnished by the actual performance of certain movements is required to bring about other movements'. She described speech as a succession of vocal acts in which the kinesthetic impulses from each movement serve as a unique stimulus for the next in the series (25, pages 11 ff.). Attempts to confirm these peripheral theories by mechanical (Thorsen, 23) or electrical (Max, 19) recording of muscular tensions have given no valid evidence in support of them. It should be noted that, at the time when the theories were proposed, it was generally believed that conduction in the nervous system is always downstream from sense organ to muscle, and that muscular contraction must always follow promptly on stimulation. The existence of reverberatory circuits which could maintain central activity was scarcely suspected.

The introspective psychology which objected to such peripheral theories did not explicitly formulate an alternative neurological theory, but there is implicit in it a view that verbal thought is a simple chain of central processes in which each element serves to arouse the next by direct association. Titchener, for example, maintained that the meaning of a word (or of an auditory image in his system) consists of the chain of associations which it arouses; that it has no meaning until such a sequence has occurred. From this it must be inferred that he was thinking in terms of a simple associative chain, since no other relating process is suggested.

Objections to the Associative Chain Theory

A consideration of the structure of the sentence and of other motor sequences will show, I believe, that such interpretations of temporal organizations are untenable and that there are, behind the overtly expressed sequences, a multiplicity of integrative processes which can only be inferred from the final results of their activity. There is an extensive controversial literature dealing with this inferred integrative activity. Pick (20) devotes almost his entire book, *Die agrammatischen Sprachstörungen*, to reviewing discussions of the subject. Most of this literature deals with the question of whether or not the integrative processes are conscious. Much of this is irrelevant to the present topic, but the advocates of so-called imageless thought did present a great deal of material indicative of the complexity of the problem of thought structure. From this, and other evidence which I shall present, I believe that the production of speech involves the interaction of at least three, possibly four, major neurological systems which are interrelated but somewhat independently variable.

Let us start the analysis of the process with the enunciation of the word. Pronunciation of the word 'right' consists first of retraction and elevation of the tongue, expiration of air, and activation of the vocal cords; second, depression of the tongue and jaw; third, elevation of the tongue to touch the dental ridge, stopping of vocalization, and forceful expiration of air with depression of the tongue and jaw. These movements have no intrinsic order of association. Pronunciation of the word 'tire' involves the same motor elements in reverse order. Such movements occur in all permutations. The order must therefore be imposed upon the motor elements by some organization other than direct associative connections between them. So, for the individual movements in writing or typing the word, finger strokes occur in all sorts of combinations. No single letter invariably follows *g*, and whether *gh*, *ga*, or *gu* is written depends upon a set for a larger unit of action, the word.

Words stand in relation to the sentence as letters do to the word; the words themselves have no intrinsic temporal 'valence'. The word 'right', for example, is noun, adjective, adverb, and verb, and has four spellings and at least ten meanings. In such a sentence as 'The mill-wright on my right thinks it right that some conventional rite should symbolize the right of every man to write as he pleases,' word arrangement is obviously not due to any direct associations of the word 'right' itself with other words, but to meanings which are determined by some broader relations.

It has been found in studies of memorization of nonsense syllables that each syllable in the series has associations, not only with adjacent words in the series, but also with more remote words. The words in the sentence have, of course, associations with more remote words as well as with adjacent ones. However, the combination of such direct associations will not account for grammatical structure. The different positions of the word 'right' in the illustrative sentence are determined by the meanings which the positions in relation to other words denote, but those meanings are given by other associations than those with the words in the spoken sentence. The word can take its position only when the particular one of its ten meanings becomes dominant. This dominance is not inherent in the words themselves.

From such considerations, it is certain that any theory of grammatical form which ascribes it to direct associative linkage of the words of the sentence overlooks the essential structure of speech. The individual items of the temporal series do not in themselves have a temporal 'valence' in their associative connections with other elements. The order is imposed by some other agent.

This is true not only of language, but of all skilled movements or successions of movement. In the gaits of a horse, trotting, pacing, and single footing involve essentially the same pattern of muscular contraction in the individual legs. The gait is imposed by some mechanism in addition to the direct relations of a reciprocal innervation among the sensory-motor centers of the legs. The order in which the fingers of the musician fall on the keys or fingerboard is determined by the signature of the composition; this gives a *set* which is not inherent in the association of the individual movements.

The Determining Tendency

What then determines the order? The answer which seems most in accord with common sense is that the intention to act or the idea to be expressed determines the sequence. There are, however, serious difficulties for this solution. There is not much agreement among psychologists concerning the nature of the idea. The structuralist school, under the leadership of Titchener, held that the idea consists of mental images, often the auditory images of words, and the meanings are nothing but sequences of such images. Describing the role of images in his lecturing, Titchener wrote (24), 'When there is any difficulty in exposition, a point to be argued *pro* and *con* or a conclusion to be brought out from the convergence of several lines of proof, I hear my own voice speaking just ahead of me.' What solution of the lecture problem for the lazy man! He need not think but only listen to his own inner voice; to the chain of associated auditory images. A behaviorist colleague once remarked to me that he had reached a stage where he could arise before an audience, turn his mouth loose, and go to sleep. He believed in the peripheral chain theory of language. (This clearly demonstrates the superiority of behavioristic over introspective psychology. The behaviorist does not even have to listen to his own inner voice.)

Seriously, such positions offer no solution for the problem of temporal integration. Titchener finds his grammar ready made and does not even raise the question of the origin of the succession of images. The chain-reflex theory, while definite, is untenable.

The third view of the nature of the idea was developed by a group known as the 'Würzburg School' (see Boring, 4); exponents of imageless thought. It held that some organization precedes any expression that can be discovered by introspective or objective means. Thought is neither muscular contraction nor image, but can only be inferred as a 'determining tendency'. At most, it is discovered as a vague feeling of pregnancy, of being about to have an idea, a *Bewusstseinslage*. It is not identical with the words which are spoken, for quite frequently no word can be recalled which satisfactorily expresses the thought, and we search a dictionary of synonyms until a word or phase is found which does seem appropriate.

In his discussion of the relation of thought to speech, Pick (20) accepts this point of view, but he asserts further that the set or the idea does not have a temporal order, that all of its elements are cotemporal. Evidence in support of this conclusion comes, for example, from translation of one language into another which has a different sentence structure. I read a German sentence, pronouncing the German words with no thought of their English equivalents. I then give a free translation in English, without remembering a single word of the German text. Somewhere between the reading and free translation, the German sentence is condensed, the word order reversed, and expanded again into the different temporal order of English. According to Epstein (9), the polyglot shifts readily from one language to another, expressing the same thought in either, without literal translation. The readiness with which the form of expression of an idea can be changed, the facility with which different word orders may be utilized to express the same thought, thus is further evidence that the temporal integration is not inherent in the preliminary organization of the idea.

The Schema of Order

The remaining alternative is that the mechanism which determines the serial activation of the motor units is relatively independent, both of the motor units and of the thought structure. Supporting evidence for this may be found in the mistakes of order, the slips, and interferences which occur in writing and speaking. For some time I have kept records of errors in typing. A frequent error is the misplacing or the doubling of a letter. *These* is typed t-h-s-e-s, *look* as l-o-k-k, *ill* as i-i-l. Sometimes the set to repeat may be displaced by several words. The order is dissociated from the idea. Earlier, in preparing this paper, I wrote the phrase, 'maintain central activities'. I typed *min*, omitting the *a*, canceled this out and started again; *ama*. The impulse to insert the *a* now dominated the order. I struck out the *a* and completed the phrase, only to find that I had now also dropped the *a* from *activities*. This example suggests something of the complexity of the forces which are at play in the determination of serial order and the way in which conflicting impulses may distort the order, although the primary determining tendency, the idea, remains the same.

The polyglot, who has become proficient in a secondary language, who thinks in it and even dreams in it, may still tend to use the grammatical structure of his native tongue. If, as in French, that tongue applies gender to inanimate things, the English pronouns referring to them may take the gender of the French equivalents, though the French nouns are not thought. The German postponement of the verb or the Magyar use of the past infinitive may be incorporated in the new language. In such cases, the structuring seems to be dissociated both from the content and from the simple associative connections of the words themselves.

The ease with which a new structure may be imposed on words is illustrated by the quickness with which children learn dog Latin. The form which I learned involved transposing the initial sound of each word to the end of the word and adding a long *a*. Thus – at-thay an-may oes-gay own-day e-thay eet-stray. Some children become very facile at such inversions of words, and restructure new words without hesitation. From such considerations it seems to follow that syntax is not inherent in the words employed or in the idea to be expressed. It is a generalized pattern imposed upon the specific acts as they occur.

'Priming' of Expressive Units

There are indications that, prior to the internal or overt enunciation of the sentence, an aggregate of word units is partially activated or readied. Evidence for this comes also from 'contaminations' of speech and writing. The most frequent typing errors are those of anticipation; the inclusion in the word being typed of some part of a word or word structure which should properly occur later in the sentence. It may be only a letter. Thus I wrote, *wrapid* writing, carrying the *w* from the second word to the first. Not infrequently words are introduced which should occur much later in the sentence, often five or six words in advance.

In oral speech, Spoonerisms illustrate the same kind of contamination. The Spoonerism is most frequently an inversion of subject and object: 'Let us always remember that waste makes haste.' But it may be only a transposition of parts of the words: 'Our queer old dean' for 'our dear old queen'. The frequency with which such contaminations occur is increased by haste, by distraction, by emotional tension, or by uncertainty and conflict as to the best form of expression. In some types of aphasia the tendency to disordered arrangement of words is greatly increased, and, in extreme cases, the attempt to speak results in a word hash with complete loss of grammatical organization. Professor

Spooner, after whom such slips are named, was probably suffering from a mild form of aphasia. In these contaminations, it is as if the aggregate of words were in a state of partial excitation, held in check by the requirements of grammatical structure, but ready to activate the final common path, if the effectiveness of this check is in any way interfered with.

In his *Psychopathology of Everyday Life*, Freud has given numerous examples of similar contaminations of action outside the sphere of language. We do not need to accept his theories of censorship and suppression to account for such slips. They are of the same order as misplacements in typing and represent contaminations of co-existing, determining tendencies to action.

Such contaminations might be ascribed to differences in the relative strength of associative bonds between the elements of the act, and thus not evidence for pre-excitation of the elements or for simultaneous pre-excitation. However, the understanding of speech involves essentially the same problems as the production of speech and definitely demands the postulation of an after-effect or after-discharge of the sensory components for a significant time following stimulation. Thus, in the spoken sentence, 'Rapid righting with his uninjured hand saved from loss the contents of the capsized canoe', the associations which give meaning to righting are not activated for at least 3 to 5 seconds after hearing the word.[1] I shall refer later to other evidence for such long after-discharge of sensory excitations. The fact of continued activation or after-discharge of receptive elements and their integration during this activation justifies the assumption of a similar process during motor organization. The processes of comprehension and production of speech have too much in common to depend on wholly different mechanisms.

Internal and Overt Speech

One other point with respect to the organization of speech: The earlier literature on aphasia emphasized the distinction of internal and overt speech. The aphemia of Broca and the pure motor aphasia of Wernicke and later writers were held to be a loss of the ability to enunciate without loss of ability to think in words and without paralysis of the organs of speech. The brain insult was

1. Dr Lashley ingeniously laid the groundwork for these three paragraphs earlier, when he mentions 'wrapid writing'. The audience all heard, 'Rapid writing with his uninjured hand,' etc. 'Capsized canoe' required a complete and amusing about-face.

assumed to affect only the transition from the thought to the enunciation of the word. We may doubt the existence of instances of such 'pure' defects and question the reliability of the early clinical examinations in view of the more careful analyses that have been made since 1917, but the distinction of internal and overt speech is still valid and the transition still unexplained. Watson interpreted internal speech as inaudible movements of the vocal organs, and Jacobsen (15) and Max (19) have given evidence of changes in muscular tonus during verbal thinking or thought of movement. This is far from proving that the motor discharge is essential for the internal formation of words, however.

I once devised an instrument to record small movements of the tongue. Within the limits of its sensitivity, it showed that in silent thinking the tongue usually drops to the back of the mouth and shows no detectable movement. Verbal problems, such as the correct squaring of three-place numbers, could be carried out with no trace of overt movement. If, however, I urged the subject to hurry or if I slapped his face, his tongue came forward and showed movements corresponding to the syllabification of internal speech or of the computation he was performing. This I interpret as indicating that internal speech may be carried out wholly by processes within the nervous system, with some unessential discharge upon the final common path for vocal movements. Facilitation of the motor path, either by increased emotional tension or by 'voluntary' reinforcement, increases its excitability until the same central circuits whose activity constitutes internal speech are able to excite the overt movements. This aspect of the language function is irrelevant to the problem of syntax or serial order, but is important as illustrating a further point in the dynamics of the cerebrum. Many activities seem to require for their performance both a specific patterning and also a general facilitation, a rise in dynamic level. There are, I think, indications that hemiplegia and motor aphasia are primarily expressions of a low level of facilitation rather than a loss of specific integrative connections which are involved in the use of language or in the patterning of our movements. A monkey, for example, after ablation of the precentral gyrus may seem unable to use the arm at all, but if emotional excitement is raised above a certain level, the arm is freely used. As soon as the excitement dies down, the arm is again hemiplegic. I have seen something of the same sort in a human hemiplegic. The problem of the availability of memories, which was raised earlier in the discussion here, may find a partial solution in such fluctuations in dynamic level. In many of the organic amnesias the pattern of integration seems to be retained but can be reactivated only by an abnormally intense sensory or central reinforcement.

Generality of the Problem of Syntax

I have devoted so much time to discussion of the problem of syntax, not only because language is one of the most important products of human cerebral action, but also because the problems raised by the organization of language seem to me to be characteristic of almost all other cerebral activity. There is a series of hierarchies of organization: the order of vocal movements in pronouncing the word, the order of words in the sentence, the order of sentences in the paragraph, the rational order of paragraphs in a discourse. Not only speech, but all skilled acts seem to involve the same problems of serial ordering, even down to the temporal coordination of muscular contractions in such a movement as reaching and grasping. Analysis of the nervous mechanisms underlying order in the more primitive acts may contribute ultimately to the solution even of the physiology of logic.

It is possible to designate, that is, to point to specific examples of, the phenomena of the syntax of movement that require explanation, although those phenomena cannot be clearly defined. A real definition would be a long step toward solution of the problem. There are at least three sets of events to be accounted for. First, the activation of the expressive elements (the individual words or adaptive acts) which do not contain the temporal relations. Second, the determining tendency, the set, or idea. This masquerades under many names in contemporary psychology, but is, in every case, an inference from the restriction of behavior within definite limits. Third, the syntax of the act, which can be described as an habitual order or mode of relating the expressive elements; a generalized pattern or schema of integration which may be imposed upon a wide range and a wide variety of specific acts. This is the essential problem of serial order; the existence of generalized schemata of action which determine the sequence of specific acts, acts which in themselves or in their associations seem to have no temporal valence.

I shall turn now to other phenomena of movement which may be more readily phrased in physiological terms and which may suggest some of the mechanisms underlying serial order.

Duration and Intensity of Nervous Discharge

A consideration of the control of extent and rate of movement supports the view that sensory factors play a minor part in regulating the intensity and duration of nervous discharge; that a series of movements is not a chain of sensory-motor reactions. The theory of control of movement which was dominant at the turn of the century assumed that, after a movement is initiated, it is continued until stopped by sensations of movement and position, which indicate that the limb has reached the desired position. This theory was opposed by a good bit of indirect evidence, such as that accuracy of movement is increased rather than diminished with speed. I had opportunity to study a patient who had a complete anesthesia for movements of the knee joint, as a result of a gunshot wound of the cord (16). In spite of the anesthesia, he was able to control the extent and speed of movements of flexion and extension of the knee quite as accurately as can a normal person.

The performance of very quick movements also indicates their independence of current control. 'Whip-snapping' movements of the hand can be regulated accurately in extent, yet the entire movement, from initiation to completion, requires less than the reaction time for tactile or kinesthetic stimulation of the arm, which is about one-eighth of a second, even when no discrimination is involved. Such facts force the conclusion that an effector mechanism can be pre-set or primed to discharge at a given intensity or for a given duration, in independence of any sensory controls.

Central Control of Motor Patterns

This independence of sensory controls is true not only of intensity and duration of contraction of a synergic muscle group but is true also of the initiation and timing of contraction of the different muscles in a complex movement. The hand may describe a circular movement involving coordinated contractions of the muscles of the shoulder, elbow, and wrist in about $\frac{1}{10}$ second, and the stopping of movement at a given position, of course, is only a small fraction of that time. The finger strokes of a musician may reach sixteen per second in passages which call for a definite and changing order of successive finger movements. The succession of movements is too quick even for visual reaction time. In rapid sight reading it is impossible to read the individual notes of an arpeggio. The notes must be seen in groups, and it is actually easier to read chords seen simultaneously and to translate them into temporal sequence than to read successive notes in the arpeggio as usually written.

Sensory control of movement seems to be ruled out in such acts. They require the postulation of some central nervous mechanism which fires with predetermined intensity and duration or activates different muscles in predetermined order. This mechanism might be represented by a chain of effector neurons, linked together by internuncials to produce successive delays in firing. In some systems the order of action may be determined by such a leader or pace-setter. Buddenbrock (6) has shown for the stick insect, and Bethe (3) for a number of animals from the centipede to the dog, that removal of one or more legs results in a spontaneous change in the order of stepping. Thus, for the insects, the normal order is alternate stepping of the first pair of legs with right first, left second, right third leg advancing together. With removal of the left first leg, the right first and left second alternate and the order becomes right first, left third, right third stepping together, with left second and right second advancing together, instead of alternately. These investigators were interested in spontaneity of reorganization, rather than in the mechanism of coordination, and did not propose any theory for the latter. They did show, however, that it is necessary to remove the leg completely to get the change in pattern of movement; sensory impulses from a limb stump would prevent it. Such coordination might be explained, perhaps, by a combination of loss of excitability in the centers of the absent limb, by the excitation of the remaining anterior center as a leader or pace-setter, and the spread of alternate waves of inhibition and excitation from the more anterior to the more posterior limb centers. The spontaneous change in coordination shows, however, that the coordination is not due to the action of predetermined anatomic paths but is the result of the current physiological state of the various limb centers.

Such an hypothesis implies also the assumption of a polarization of conduction along the neuraxis, with the order of excitation determined by the spatial arrangement of the centers of the legs. I see no other possibility of accounting for the facts. The examples of circular movement and of finger coordination, involving temporal integration of movements, seem to call for a similar hypothesis. They might be ascribed to an habitual linkage of the movements through a simple chain of internuncials but for two facts. First, such series are usually reversible at any point or can be started from any point. This would require the assumption of a second set of internuncials habituated to conduct in the opposite direction, and this in turn leads to the further assumption of a polarization of conduction. Second, such patterns of coordinated movement may often be transferred directly to other motor systems than the ones practised. In such transfer, as to the left hand for writing, an analysis of the movements shows that there is not a reduplication of the muscular patterns on the two sides, but a reproduction of movements in relation to the space coordinates of the body. Try upside-down mirror writing with the left hand and with eyes closed for evidence of this. The associative linkage is not of specific movements but of directions of movement. An analysis of systems of space coordinates suggests mechanisms which may contribute to production of such series of movements in a spatial pattern.

Space Coordinate Systems

The work of Sherrington, Magnus, and others on postural tonus and reflexes has defined one level of spatial integration rather fully, yet it is doubtful if these studies have revealed the effective neural mechanism. The work has shown that the tonic discharge to every muscle in the postural system is influenced by afferent impulses from every other muscle, toward increased or decreased activity, according to its synergic or antergic action. To these influences are added vestibular and cerebellar effects. Diagrammatically these mutual influences of the muscular system may be represented by separate reflex circuits from each receptor to every muscle, as Sherrington (21, p. 148) has done. But no neuroanatomist would, I am sure, maintain that such separate circuits or paths exist. What the experiments on posture actually show is a correlation of sensory stimulation and of tonic changes in a network of neurons whose interconnections are still undefined. The reactions isolated experimentally have the characteristics of simple directly conducted reflexes, but their combination results in patterns of movement and posture which have definite relations to the axes of the body and to gravity.

This postural system is based on excitations from proprioceptors. The distance receptors impose an additional set of space coordinates upon the postural system, which in turn continually modifies the coordinates of the distance receptors. The dropped cat rights itself, if either the eyes or the vestibular senses are intact, but not in the absence of both. The direction of movement on the retina imposes a directional orientation on the postural system. Conversely, the gravitational system imposes an orientation on the visual field. Upright objects such as trees or the corners of a room appear upright, at no matter what angle the head is inclined. Derangement of the vestibular system can disturb the distance orientation or the orientation of the receptors, as in the apparent swaying of the vertical as a result of the after-images of motion following hours of rocking in a small boat.

There are other, still more generalized systems of space coordinates. We usually keep track of the compass points or of some more definite index of direction by a temporal summation of the turns made in walking, though not always with success. Finally, there is a still more plastic system in which the concepts of spatial relations can be voluntarily reversed, as when one plays blindfold chess alternately from either side of the board.

Explanation of these activities, these complex interactions, in terms of simple isolated interconnections of all of the sensory and motor elements involved seems quite improbable on anatomic grounds and is ruled out by results of our experiments on sectioning of the spinal cord. Ingebritzen (14) studied rats with double hemisection of the cord; one-half of the cord cut at the second, the other at the fifth cervical segment. In the best case only a small strand on the spinocerebellar tract of one side remained intact. These rats were able to balance in walking, oriented to visual stimuli, scratched with the right or left hind foot according to the side of the face stimulated, were able to run mazes correctly, and even learned to rise on the hind feet and push down a lever with the forepaws in opening a box.

The alternative to the isolated-path theory of the space coordinates is that the various impulses which modify postural tonus are poured into a continuous network of neurons, where their summated action results in a sort of polarization of the entire system. I shall consider later the integrative properties of such a net. For the moment I wish to emphasize only the existence of these systems of space coordinates. Their influences pervade the motor system so that every gross movement of limbs or body is made with reference to the space system. The perceptions from the distance receptors, vision, hearing, and touch are also constantly modified and referred to the same space coordinates. The stimulus is *there*, in a definite place; it has definite relation to the position of the body, and it shifts with respect to the sense organ but not with respect to the general orientation, with changes in body posture.

Memories of objects usually give them position in the space system, and even more abstract concepts may have definite spatial reference. Thus, for many people, the cardinal numbers have definite positions on a spiral or other complicated figure. What, if anything, such space characters can contribute to temporal integration is an open question. They provide a possible basis for some serial actions through interaction of postural and timing mechanisms.

Rhythmic Action

The simplest of the timing mechanisms are those controlling rhythmic activity. T. Graham Brown (5) first showed by his studies of deafferented preparations that the rhythmic movements of respiration and progression are independent of peripheral stimulation and are maintained by a central nervous mechanism of reciprocal innervation. He suggested that this mechanism of reciprocal innervation, rather than the simple reflex, is the unit of organization of the whole nervous system. He thus foreshadowed, in a way, the conception of reverberatory circuits which is coming to play so large a part in neurological theory today. Holst (13) has recently shown that the rhythmic movement of the dorsal fin of fishes is a compound of two superimposed rhythms, that of its own innervation and that of the pectoral fins. These two rhythms are centrally maintained.

Musical rhythms seem to be an elaboration of the same sort of thing. The time or beat is started and maintained at some definite rate, say 160 per minute. This rate is then imposed upon various activities. The fingers of the musician fall in multiples of the basic rate. If the leader of a quartet speeds up the time or retards, all the movements of the players change in rate accordingly. Not only the time of initiation but also the rate of movement is affected. The violinist, in a passage requiring the whole bow, will draw the bow from frog to tip at a uniform rate for the required number of beats, whether the tempo is fast or slow. With practised violinists, the rate of movement is extremely accurate and comes out on the beat at the exact tip of the bow.

Superimposed on this primary rhythm is a secondary one of emphasis, giving the character of 3/4, 4/4, 6/4, or other time. The mechanism of these rhythms can be simply conceived as the spread of excitation from some centers organized for reciprocal innervation; as a combination of the principles of Brown and of Holst. There are, however, still more complicated rhythms in all music. That of the melodic line is most uniform. In much music, the melodic progression changes in 2, 4, or some multiple of 4 measures. In improvisation, the performer keeps no count of measures, yet comes out almost invariably in a resolution to the tonic of the key after some multiple of 8 measures. Here a general ized pattern is impressed on the sequence, but it is a simpler pattern than that of grammatical structure. It only requires the recurrence of a pattern at certain rhythmic intervals; a pick-up of a specific pattern after so many timed intervals.

There are, in addition, still less regular rhythms of phrasing and emphasis. Parallels to these can be found in speech. The skilled extemporaneous speaker rounds his phrases and speaks with a definite though not regular rhythm.

The rhythms tend to spread to almost every other concurrent activity. One falls into step with a band, tends to breathe, and even to speak in time with the rhythm. The all pervasiveness of the rhythmic discharge is shown by the great difficulty of learning to maintain two rhythms at once, as in three against four with the two hands. The points to be emphasized here are the widespread effects of a rhythmic discharge indicating the involvement of almost the entire effector system, the concurrent action of different rhythmic systems, and the imposition of the rate upon both the initiation and speed of movement. Consideration of rhythmic activity and of spatial orientation forces the conclusion, I believe, that there exist in the nervous organization elaborate systems of interrelated neurons capable of imposing certain types of integration upon a large number of widely spaced effector elements; in the one case transmitting temporally spaced waves of facilitative excitation to all effector elements; in the other imparting a directional polarization to both receptor and effector elements. These systems are in constant action. They form a sort of substratum upon which other activity is built. They contribute to every perception and to every integrated movement.

Interaction of Temporal and Spatial Systems

Integration ascribed to the spatial distribution of excitations in the nervous system has been much more intensively studied than the temporal aspects of nervous activity. Theories of integration are based almost exclusively upon space properties, time entering only in theories of facilitation, inhibition, and after-discharge. In cerebral functions, however, it is difficult to distinguish between spatial and temporal functions. The eye is the only organ that gives simultaneous information concerning space in any detail. The shape of an object impressed on the skin can scarcely be detected from simultaneous pressure, but the same shape can readily be distinguished by touch when traced on the skin with a moving point or when explored by tactile scanning. The temporal sequence is readily translated into a spatial concept. Even for vision it might be questioned whether simultaneous stimulation gives rise directly to space concepts. The visual object is generally surveyed by eye movements, and its form is a reconstruction from such a series of excitations. Even with tachistoscopic exposures, the after-discharge permits a temporal survey, and, with visual fixation, shifts of attention provide an effective scanning.

Since memory traces are, we believe, in large part static and persist simultaneously, it must be assumed that they are spatially differentiated. Nevertheless, reproductive memory appears almost invariably as a temporal sequence, either as a succession of words or of acts. Even descriptions of visual imagery (the supposed simultaneous reproductive memory in sensory terms) are generally descriptions of sequences, of temporal reconstructions from very fragmentary and questionable visual elements. Spatial and temporal order thus appear to be almost completely interchangeable in cerebral action. The translation from the spatial distribution of memory traces to temporal sequence seems to be a fundamental aspect of the problem of serial order.

I spoke earlier of the probability of a partial activation or priming of aggregates of words before the sentence is actually formulated from them. There is a great deal of evidence for such preliminary facilitation of patterns of action in studies of reaction time and of word association. Reaction time, in general, is reduced by preliminary warning or by instructions which allow the subject to prepare for the specific act required. In controlled association experiments, the subject is instructed to respond to the stimulus word by a word having a certain type of relation to it, such as the opposite or a part of which the stimulus is the whole; black-white, apple-seed. The result is an attitude or set which causes that particular category to dominate the associative reaction. Whether such preliminary reinforcement is to be ascribed to accumulation of excitatory state, as defined by Sherrington (21), or to some other physiological process, the facts of behavior assure that it is a genuine phenomenon and plays a decisive role in determining the character of the response.

Once the existence of such states of partial activation is recognized, their possible role in temporal integration must be considered. There are indications that one neural system may be held in this state of partial excitation while it is scanned by another. Here is an example. A series of four to six numbers is heard: 3–7–2–9–4. This is within the attention or memory span and is almost certainly not remembered in the sense in which one's telephone number is remembered, for memory of it is immediately wiped out by a succeeding series of numbers. While it is retained in this unstable way, subject to retroactive inhibition, the order of the numbers can be reassorted: 3–7–2–9–4, 3–2–7–9–4, 4–9–2–7–3, and the like. It is as if, in this case, a rhythmic alternation can suppress alternate items, or a direction of arousal can be applied to the partially excited system. Another example which illustrates even more clearly the spatial characteristics of many memory traces is the method of comultiplication, used in rapid mental calculation. In attempts to play a melody backward, we have a further illustration. I find that I can do it only by visualizing the music spatially and then reading it backward. I cannot auditorily transform even 'Yankee Doodle' into its inverse without some such process, but it is possible to get a spatial representation of the melody and then to scan the spatial representation. The scanning of a spatial arrangement seems definitely to determine, in such cases, the order of procedure. Two assumptions are implied by this. First, the assumption is that the memory traces are associated, not only with other memory traces, but also with the system of space coordinates. By this I do not mean that the engram has a definite location in the brain; our experiments show conclusively that such is not the case. Rather, when the memory trace is formed it is integrated with directional characters of the space system, which give it position in reference to other associated traces. Second, the assumption is that these space characters of the memory trace can be scanned by some other level of the coordinating system and so transformed into succession.

This is as far as I have been able to go toward a theory of serial order in action. Obviously, it is inadequate. The assumptions concerning spatial representation and temporal representation may even beg the question, since no one can say whether spatial or temporal order is primary. Furthermore, such determining tendencies as the relation of attribute to object, which gives the order of adjective and noun, do not seem to be analysable into any sort of spatial structure or for that matter, into any consistent relationship. I have tried a number of assumptions concerning the selective mechanism of grammatical form (spatial relations, the relative intensity or prominence of different words in the idea, and so on) but I have never been able to make an hypothesis which was consistent with any large number of sentence structures. Nevertheless, the indications which I have cited, that elements of the sentence are readied or partially activated before the order is imposed upon them in expression, suggest that some scanning mechanism must be at play in regulating their temporal sequence. The real problem, however, is the nature of the selective mechanism by which the particular acts are picked out in this scanning process, and to this problem I have no answer.

Such speculations concerning temporal and spatial systems do little more than illustrate a point of view concerning nervous organization which is, I believe, more consistent both with what is known of the histology and elementary physiology of the brain and also with behavior phenomena than are the more widely current theories of simple associative chains of reactions.

Nearly forty years ago Becher (2, p. 243) wrote: 'There is no physiological hypothesis which can explain the origin and relations of temporal forms in mental life, indeed, there is no hypothesis which even foreshadows the possibility of such an explanation.' The situation is little better today, but I do feel that changing conceptions of the fundamental organization of the nervous system offer more hope for a solution of such problems than did the physiological knowledge available when Becher wrote. However, we are still very far from being able to form an explicit explanation of temporal structure.

The Fundamental Mechanism of Integration

Neurological theory has been dominated by the belief that the neurons of the central nervous system are in an inactive or resting state for the greater part of the time; that they are linked in relatively isolated conditioned reflex arcs and that they are activated only when the particular reactions for which they are specifically associated are called out. Such a view is incompatible both with the widespread effects of stimulation which can be demonstrated by changes in tonus and also with recent evidence from electrical recording of nervous activity. It is now practically certain that all the cells of the cerebrospinal axis are being continually bombarded by nerve impulses from various sources and are firing regularly, probably even during sleep. The nervous activity which they in turn elicit depends upon the current physiological state of the neurons with which they are connected. It is probably not far from the truth to say that every nerve cell of the cerebral cortex is involved in thousands of different reactions. The cortex must be regarded as a great network of reverberatory circuits, constantly active. A new stimulus, reaching such a system, does not excite an isolated reflex path but must produce widespread changes in the pattern of excitation throughout a whole system of already interacting neurons.

The facts of cerebral structure support such a view. The cortex is composed chiefly of neurons with short axons. Le Gros Clark (8) has found for the striate area of the monkey that Marchi degeneration extends for only a short distance from a point of injury. In the striate area of the rat, I have never been able to trace degeneration beyond three or four cell diameters from the margin of a lesion, and I believe that this lack of long transcortical fibers is true of other areas as well as of the visual cortex. Visual perception reveals close integration of different parts of the striate areas in spite of the absence of long association fibers. In the visual cortex of the rat there are only 19 neurons for each afferent fiber. To produce the animal's visual acuity, all of the afferent fibers must be firing continually. There are approximately 34,000 cell bodies in the lateral geniculate nucleus of the rat, and the minimum number of visual units necessary to produce the visual acuity of the rat is actually above this figure. (The acuity is determined by direct experimental tests.) These figures should be of interest in relation to the numerical values cited by Dr von Neumann. The number of cells in the visual cortex of the rat is only about 10^6, and in some of my experiments where I have removed the greater part of the visual cortex the capacity for discrimination of visual forms has been retained when no more than 20,000 cells of the visual cortex remain. There is also evidence that no part of the cerebral cortex except the visual areas is essential for visual perception and memory.

Dr Lorente de No: What is the number of afferents in the optic nerve?

Dr Lashley: There are 290,000 afferents in the optic nerve of the rat, and the figure is reduced to 34,000 in the lateral geniculate. The actual numbers are 9,000,000 myoids, 290,000 ganglion cells, and 34,000 cells in the lateral geniculate. That may include cells with short axons also. There are about 125,000 cells in each of the five layers of the cortex. These figures are for one eye and hemisphere.

Dr von Neumann: In the human being the corresponding number is about 125,000,000 for the first, isn't it?

Dr Lashley: I know of no figure for that level.

Dr Lorente de Nó: It hasn't been analysed in any way.

Dr von Neumann: The optic nerve corresponds to the second one?

Dr Lashley: Yes. The axons of the ganglion cells pass through the optic nerves. There is an average of 300 visual cells firing into each central pathway. There are fewer than 5 cells in the receptive layer of the visual cortex of the rat for each afferent fiber of the optic radiation and only 19 cells per afferent fiber in the entire visual cortex. Since the visual acuity of the rat requires that all of the 34,000 cells of the radiation be firing constantly, it seems certain that all of the neurons within the striate areas, the visual cortex, must be firing constantly. There is a good bit of evidence that all of the integrative functions of vision are carried out within the striate areas. In the rat, I have removed, from one or another animal, practically every other part of the isocortex without disturbing visual perception or memory. With monkeys I have removed the supposed visual associative areas without producing any significant loss of visual functions.

These facts lead to the conclusion that the same cells in the visual cortex participate in a great variety of activities. Practically all of the cells of the area must be fired by every visual stimulation, and these same cells must be the ones which retain the visual memories. The conclusion follows that differential responses depend upon the pattern of cells which are excited in combination. The visual cortex is a network of cells of short axon without long interconnections between its parts or with other cortical areas. Its integrative functions are an expression of the properties of such a network.

The same conception must be applied to other cortical areas. There are, of course, long association tracts in the cortex, such as the corpus callosum, the superior longitudinal fasciculus, and the temporo-frontal tracts. Once, 26 years ago, I suggested facetiously that these might be only skeletal structures, since I could find no function for them. No important functions of these tracts have yet been demonstrated. Section of the corpus callosum produces only a slight slowing of reaction time, ipsilateral as well as contralateral (Akelaitis, 1); section of occipito-frontal fibers produces, perhaps, a temporary disturbance of visual attention but no other symptoms. The integrative functions seem to be carried out as well without as with the main associative tracts. The major integrative functions must, therefore, be carried out by the network of cells of short axon. The properties of such networks of cells must be analysed before the mechanisms of the cerebral cortex can be understood. Something can be inferred from the characteristics of excitability of cells and their arrangement in recurrent loops. If, as seems a necessary conclusion from the histology of the striate area, all of the cells of the network are subject to constant excitation and are firing whenever they recover from the refractory state, then mutual interference of circuits will produce complicated patterns throughout the area, patterns which will stabilize in the absence of differential stimulation, as is perhaps indicated by the regularity of the alpha rhythm. Any new afferent impulses reaching the area can only produce a reorganization of the existing pattern. What happens at any particular point in the system, as at an efferent neuron, is the statistical outcome of the interaction of myriads of neurons, not of the transmission of impulses over a restricted path, of which that efferent cell forms a link. It is possible to isolate parts of the system by operative means or by anesthetics and so to get a one-to-one relation of stimulus locus and responding muscles, from which the reflex mechanism has been inferred. As Goldstein (12) has pointed out, however, the parts isolated in the reflex are influenced by a multiplicity of effects in the intact organism of which there is little or no trace in the isolated preparation.

I can best illustrate this conception of nervous action by picturing the brain as the surface of a lake. The prevailing breeze carries small ripples in its direction, the basic polarity of the system. Varying gusts set up crossing systems of waves, which do not destroy the first ripples, but modify their form, a second level in the system of space coordinates. A tossing log with its own period of submersion sends out periodic bursts of ripples, a temporal rhythm. The bow wave of a speeding boat momentarily sweeps over the surface, seems to obliterate the smaller waves yet leaves them unchanged by its passing, the transient effect of a strong stimulus. Wave motion is not an adequate analogy because the medium which conveys the waves is uniform, whereas the nerve cells have their individual characteristics of transmission which at every point may alter the character of the transmitted pattern.

The great number of axon terminations on every nerve cell has not been considered in theories of integration. It implies, of course, that the cell can be fired by impulses from a variety of sources. But it also suggests another possibility, more fruitful for understanding of integrative processes. A nerve impulse arriving over a single axon terminal may not fire the cell but may modify its excitability to impulses from other sources. In an elaborate system of neurons such subthreshold effects might establish a pattern of facilitation which would determine the combination of cells fired by subsequent excitations. The space coordinate system and various types of *set* or priming may be pictured as patterns of subthreshold facilitation pervading the network of neurons which is activated by the more specific external stimulus.

Such a view of the mechanism of nervous action certainly does not simplify the problems nor does it as yet provide any clue to the structuring that constitutes the set or determining tendency, or to the nature of such relations as are implied in the attribute–object, opposites, or other abstract concepts. A few relations seem reducible to spatial terms, part-whole, for example, but even for these there is no clear conception of the neural basis of their space properties. These considerations do not, I believe, contradict fundamentally the basic conceptions that have been formulated by Dr McCulloch. They do, however, indicate a direction of necessary elaboration. The nets active in rhythmic and spatial organization are apparently almost coextensive with the nervous system. The analysis must be extended to the properties of such nets; the way in which they are broken up into reactive patterns in the spread of excitation, to give, for example, directional propagation or its equivalent. I strongly suspect that many phenomena of generalization, both sensory and conceptual, are products, not of simple switching, but of interaction of complex patterns of organization within such systems.

Summary

The problems of the syntax of action are far removed from anything which we can study by direct physiological methods today, yet in attempting to formulate a physiology of the cerebral cortex we cannot ignore them. Serial order is typical of the problems raised by cerebral activity; few, if any, of the problems are simpler or promise easier solution. We can, perhaps, postpone the fatal day when we must face them, by saying that they are too complex for present analysis, but there is danger here of constructing a false picture of those processes that we believe to be simpler. I am coming more and more to the conviction that the rudiments of every human behavioral mechanism will be found far down in the evolutionary scale and also represented even in primitive activities of the nervous system. If there exist, in human cerebral action, processes which seem fundamentally different or inexplicable in terms of our present construct of the elementary physiology of integration, then it is probable that that construct is incomplete or mistaken, even for the levels of behavior to which it is applied.

In spite of its present inadequacy, I feel that the point of view which I have sketched here holds some promise of a better understanding of cerebral integration. Attempts to express cerebral function in terms of the concepts of the reflex arc, or of associated chains of neurons, seem to me doomed to failure because they start with the assumption of a static nervous system. Every bit of evidence available indicates a dynamic, constantly active system, or, rather, a composite of many interacting systems, which I have tried to illustrate at a primitive level by rhythm and the space coordinates. Only when methods of analysis of such systems have been devised will there be progess toward understanding of the physiology of the cerebral cortex.

References

1. A. J. AKELAITIS, 'Studies on the corpus callosum. ii. The higher visual functions in each hononymous field following complete section of the corpus callosum', *Arch. Neurol. Psychiat.*, vol. 45 (1941), pp. 788–96.
2. E. BECHER, *Gehirn und Seele*, Heidelberg, 1911.
3. A. BETHE, 'Plastizität und Zentrenlehre', *Handb. d. norm. u. path. Physiol.*, vol. 15 (1931), pp. 1175–220.
4. E. G. BORING, *A History of Experimental Psychology*, Century Co., New York, 1929.
5. T. G. BROWN, 'On the nature of the fundamental activity of the nervous centers', *J. Physiol.*, vol. 48 (1914), pp. 18–46.
6. W. v. BUDDENBROCK, 'Die Rhythmus der Schreitbewegungen der Stabheuschrecke Dyxippus', *Biol. Centralb.*, vol. 41 (1921), pp. 41–8.
7. A. F. CHAMBERLAIN, 'Indians, North American', *Enc. Brit.*, vol. 14 (1911), pp. 452–82.
8. W. E. LeGros CLARK, 'Observations on the associative fiber system of the visual cortex and the central representation of the retina', *J. Anat. London*, vol. 75 (1941), pp. 225–36.
9. I. EPSTEIN, *La Pensée et la Polyglossie*, Payot et Cie, Paris. (Date not known.)
10. FOURNIÉ, *Essai de Psychologie*, Paris, 1887.

11. G. FRITSCH and E. HITZIG, 'Ueber die elektrische Erregbarkeit des grosshirns', *Arc. f. Anat. u. Physiol.*, 1870, pp. 300–32.

12. K. GOLDSTEIN, *The Organism*, Ginn & Co., Boston, 1939.

13. N. v. HOLST, 'Vom Wesen der Ordnung im Zentralnervensystem', *Die Naturwissenschaften*, vol. 25 (1937), pp. 625–31; 641–7.

14. O. C. INGEBRITZEN, 'Coordinating mechanisms of the spinal cord', *Genet. Psychol. Monogr.*, vol. 13 (1933), pp. 483–555.

15. E. JACOBSEN, 'Electrophysiology of mental activities', *Amer. J. Psychol.*, vol. 44 (1932), pp. 677–94.

16. K. S. LASHLEY, 'The accuracy of movement in the absence of excitation from the moving organ', *Amer. J. Physiol.*, vol. 43 (1917), pp. 169–94.

17. K. S. LASHLEY, 'The mechanism of vision. xvii. Autonomy of the visual cortex', *J. genet. Psychol.*, vol. 60 (1942), pp. 197–221.

18. K. S. LASHLEY, 'The mechanism of vision. xviii. Effects of destroying the visual "associative areas" in the monkey', *Genet. Psychol. Monogr.*, vol. 37 (1948), pp. 107–66.

19. L. W. MAX, 'Experimental study of the motor theory of consciousness. IV', *J. comp. Psychol.*, vol. 24 (1937), pp. 301–44.

20. A. PICK, *Die agrammatischen Sprachstörungen*, Berlin, 1913.

21. C. S. SHERRINGTON, *The Integrative Action of the Nervous System*, Constable, London, 1906.

22. C. S. SHERRINGTON, 'Some functional problems attaching to convergence', *Proc. Roy. Soc.*, B, vol. 105 (1929), pp. 332–62.

23. A. M. THORSEN, 'The relation of tongue movements to internal speech', *J. Exp. Psychol.*, vol. 8 (1925), pp. 1–32.

24. E. B. TITCHENER, *Lectures on the Experimental Psychology of the Thought Processes*, The Macmillan Co., New York, 1909.

25. M. F. WASHBURN, *Movement and Mental Imagery*, Houghton Mifflin, Boston. 1916.

26. J. B. WATSON, 'Is thinking merely the action of the language mechanisms?', *Brit. J. Psychol.*, vol. 11 (1920), pp. 86–104.

27 G. A. Miller, E. Galanter and K. H. Pribram

The Unit of Analysis

G. A. Miller, E. Galanter and K. H. Pribram, *Plans and the Structure of Behavior*, Holt, 1960, chapter 2, pp. 21–39.

Most psychologists take it for granted that a scientific account of the behavior or organisms must begin with the definition of fixed, recognizable, elementary units of behavior – something a psychologist can use as a biologist uses cells, or an astronomer uses stars, or a physicist uses atoms, and so on. Given a simple unit, complicated phenomena are then describable as lawful compounds. That is the essence of the highly successful strategy called 'scientific analysis'.

The elementary unit that modern, experimental psychologists generally select for their analysis of behavior is the *reflex*. 'The isolation of a reflex,' B. F. Skinner tells us, 'is the demonstration of a predictable uniformity in behavior. In some form or other it is an inevitable part of any science of behavior. . . . A reflex is not, of course, a theory. It is a fact. It is an analytical unit, which makes the investigation of behavior possible' (1938, p. 9). Skinner is quite careful to define a reflex as a unit of behavior that will yield orderly data: 'The appearance of smooth curves in dynamic processes marks a unique point in the progressive restriction of a preparation, and it is to this uniquely determined entity that the term reflex may be assigned' (Skinner, 1938, p. 40). This somewhat odd approach to the reflex – in terms of the smoothness of curves – results from Skinner's consistent attempt to define a unit of behavior in terms of behavior itself instead of by reference to concepts drawn from some other branch of science.

Although Skinner's approach absolves the psychologist of certain burdensome responsibilities toward his biological colleagues, the fact remains that the reflex is a concept borrowed originally from physiology and made to seem psychologically substantial largely by the myth of the *reflex arc*: stimulus → receptor → afferent nerve → connective fibers → efferent nerve → effector → response. For many years all those elementary textbooks of psychology that mentioned the nervous system featured the traditional, simplified diagram of the reflex arc in a very prominent position. You may ignore a behaviorist when he tells you that the reflex is a fact, but you can scarcely ignore a physiologist when he draws you a picture of it. You might as well deny the small intestines or sneer at the medulla oblongata as to doubt the reflex arc. Even the most obstinate opponent of physiological explanations in psychology can scarcely forget the bloody tissue from which the reflex – even the reflex-sans-arc – originally grew.

But let us suppose, by a wild and irresponsible flight of fancy, that the physiologists and neurologists suddenly announced that they had been mistaken, that there was no such fact as a reflex arc and that the data on which the theory had been based were actually quite different from what had originally been supposed. What then would psychologists say? Would they persist in talking about reflexes? Has the reflex concept been so tremendously helpful that behaviorists could not afford to give it up, even if its biological basis were demolished?

There is some reason to think that the reflex unit has been vastly overrated and that a good many psychologists would like to get out from under it if they could. The reflex arc may have been helpful in getting psychology started along scientific paths, but the suspicion has been growing in recent years that the reflex idea is too simple, the element too elementary. For the most part, serious students of behavior have had to ignore the problem of units entirely. Or they have had to modify their units so drastically for each new set of data that to speak of them as elementary would be the most unblushing sophistry. After watching psychologists struggle under their burden of conditioning reflexes, Chomsky, the linguist and logician, recently summarized their plight in the following terms:

The notions of 'stimulus', 'response', 'reinforcement' are relatively well defined with respect to the bar-pressing experiments and others similarly restricted. Before we can extend them to real-life behavior, however, certain difficulties must be faced. We must decide, first of all, whether any physical event to which the organism is capable of reacting is to be called a stimulus on a given occasion, or only one to which the organism in fact reacts; and correspondingly, we must decide whether any part of behavior is to be called a response, or only one connected with stimuli in lawful ways. Questions of this sort pose something of a dilemma for the experimental psychologist. If he accepts the broad definitions, characterizing any physical event impinging on the organism as a stimulus and any part of the organism's behavior as a response, he must conclude that behavior has not been demonstrated to be lawful. In the present state of our knowledge, we must attribute an overwhelming influence on actual behavior to ill-defined factors of attention, set, volition, and caprice. If we accept the narrower definitions, then behavior is lawful by definition (if it consists of responses); but this fact is of limited significance, since most of what the animal does will simply not be considered behavior (Chomsky, 1959, p. 30).

Faced with the choice of being either vague or irrelevant, many psychologists have been restive and ill at ease with their borrowed terms. What went wrong? How was the reflex arc conceived originally, and for what purpose? Can we supplant the reflex arc with some theory of the reflex that is more suited to our current knowledge and interests?

Sir Charles Sherrington and Ivan Petrovitch Pavlov are the two men who are probably most responsible for confirming the psychologist's image of man as a bundle of S-R reflexes. Yet one may be permitted to speculate that neither of them would approve of the way their concepts have been extended by psychologists. In his *Integrative Action of the Nervous System* (1906) Sherrington is particularly explicit in his qualifications and warnings about the reflex. Again and again he states that 'the simple reflex is a useful fiction' - useful for the study of the spinal preparation. He expressed considerable doubt that a stretch reflex, of which the knee jerk is the most frequently quoted example, represented his notion of a simple reflex and questioned whether it should be considered a reflex at all. The synapse was invented by Sherrington in order to explain the differences between the observed properties of nerve trunks and the properties that had to be inferred to describe the neural tissue that intervenes between receptor stimulation and effector response. Nerve trunks will transmit signals in either direction. Characteristically, the signals are of an all-or-none type. Reflex action, on the other hand, is unidirectional and the response is characteristically graded according to the intensity of the stimulus. How can these be reconciled? Sherrington resolved the differences by supporting the neuron doctrine: the nervous system is made up of discrete neural units that have the properties of nerve trunks; intercalated between these units are discontinuities which he christened 'synapses', and these have the properties unique to reflexes.

In recent years, graded responses have been shown to be a prepotent characteristic not only of synapses but also of all excitable tissue, for example, of the finer arborizations of the nerve cells. The cerebral cortex, man's claim to phylogenetic eminence, 'still operates largely by means of connections characteristic of primitive neuropil [which is] the most appropriate mechanism for the maintenance of a continuous or steady state, as contrasted to the transmission of information about such states' (Bishop, 1956).

Moreover, additional data have come to light. Today we know that neural and receptor tissues are spontaneously active irrespective of environmental excitation. This spontaneous activity is, of course, altered by environmental events – but the change in spontaneous activity may outlast the direct excitation by hours and even days. Furthermore, we know now that the activity of receptors is controlled by efferents leading to them from the central nervous system. As an example, consider the events that control muscular contraction. (Similar, though not identical, mechanisms have also been described for the various sensory systems.) One third of the 'motor' nerve fibers that go to muscle actually end in spindles that are the stretch-sensitive receptors. Electrical stimulation of these nerve fibers does not result in contraction of muscle; but the number of signals per unit time that are recorded from the 'sensory' nerves coming from the spindles is altered drastically. It is assumed, therefore, that the central nervous mechanism must compare the incoming pattern of signals with the centrally originating 'spindle control' signal pattern in order to determine what contribution the muscular contraction has made to the 'spindle sensing' pattern. The outcome of this comparison, or *test*, constitutes the stimulus (the psychophysicist's *proximal* stimulus) to which the organism is sensitive. The test represents the conditions which have to be met before the response will occur. The test may occur in the receptor itself (e.g. in the retina) or in a more centrally located neuronal aggregate (as is probably the case for muscle stretch).

It is clear from examples such as this that the neural mechanism involved in reflex action cannot be diagrammed as a simple reflex arc or even as a chain of stimulus–response connections. A much more complex kind of monitoring, or testing, is involved in reflex action than the classical reflex arc makes any provision for. The only conditions imposed upon the stimulus by the classical chain of elements are the criteria implicit in the thresholds of each element; if the distal stimulus is strong enough to surmount the thresholds all along the arc, then the response must occur. In a sense, the threshold is a kind of test, too, a condition that must be met, but it is a test of strength only. And it must have encouraged psychologists to believe that the only meaningful measurement of a reflex was its strength (probability, magnitude, or latency).

The threshold, however, is only one of many different ways that the input can be tested. Moreover, the response of the effector depends upon the outcome of the test and is most conveniently conceived as an effort to modify the outcome of the test. The action is initiated by an 'incongruity' between the state of the organism and the state that is being tested for, and the action persists until the incongruity (i.e. the proximal stimulus) is removed. The general pattern of reflex action, therefore, is to test the input energies against some criteria established in the organism, to respond if the result of the test is to show an incongruity, and to continue to respond until the incongruity vanishes, at which time the reflex is terminated. Thus, there is 'feedback' from the result of the action to the testing phase, and we are confronted by a recursive loop. The simplest kind of diagram to represent this conception of reflex action – an alternative to the classical reflex arc – would have to look something like Figure 1.

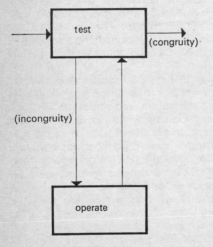

Figure 1. The TOTE unit

The interpretation toward which the argument moves is one that has been called the 'cybernetic hypothesis', namely, that the fundamental building block of the nervous system is the feedback loop (Wiener, 1948; Wisdom, 1951; Sluckin, 1954). The development of a mathematical theory for servomechanisms, wedded to the physiological accounts of homeostatic mechanisms, has stimulated widespread discussion and speculation about devices closely akin to Figure 1. The argument, therefore, moves toward popular ground.

But what good is this alternative interpretation of the reflex? The psychologist was interested in reflexes because he thought they might provide the units he needed to describe behavior. But simple reflexes have been inadequate. And if reflexes based on afferent–efferent arcs would not turn the trick, why should we hope for better things from reflexes based on feedback loops? It is the reflex itself – not merely the reflex arc – that has failed, and repairing the neurological theory underlying it is not likely to save the day. What do we hope to gain from such a reinterpretation?

Obviously, the reflex is not the unit we should use as the element of behavior: the unit should be the feedback loop itself. If we think of the Test-Operate–Test-Exit unit – for convenience, we shall call it a TOTE unit – as we do of the reflex arc, in purely anatomical terms, it may describe reflexes, but little else. That is to say, the reflex should be recognized as only one of many possible actualizations of a TOTE pattern. The next task is to generalize the TOTE unit so that it will be useful in a majority – hopefully, in all – of the behavioral descriptions we shall need to make.

Consider what the arrows in Figure 1 might represent. What could flow along them from one box to another? We shall discuss three alternatives: energy, information, and control. If we think of *energy* – neural impulses, for example – flowing from one place to another over the arrows, then the arrows must correspond to recognizable physical structures – neurons, in the example chosen. As a diagram of energy flow over discrete pathways, therefore, the TOTE unit described in Figure 1 might represent a simple reflex. Or it might represent a servomechanism.

There is, however, a second level of abstraction that psychologists usually prefer. We can think of *information* as flowing from one place to another over the arrows. According to the method of measuring information that has been developed by Norbert Wiener and by Claude Shannon, information is transmitted over a channel to the extent that the output of the channel is correlated with the input (Miller, 1953; Attneave, 1959; Cherry, 1957). We could therefore think of this second level of abstraction as the transmission of correlation over the arrows. In that case, we are concerned not with the particular structures or kinds of energy that are involved in producing the correlation but only with the fact that events at the two ends of the arrow are correlated. The situation is quite familiar to psychologists, for it is exactly what they mean when they draw an arrow leading from Stimulus to Response in their S–R diagrams or when they define a reflex as a correlation between S and R but refuse to talk about the neurological basis for that correlation.

A third level of abstraction, however, is extremely important for the ideas we shall discuss in the pages that follow. It is the notion that what flows over the arrows in Figure 1 is an intangible something called *control*. Or perhaps we should say that the arrow indicates only succession. This concept appears most frequently in the discussion of computing machines, where the control of the machine's operations passes from one instruction to another, successively, as the machine proceeds to execute the list of instructions that comprise the program it has been given. But the idea is certainly not limited to computers. As a simple example drawn from more familiar activities, imagine that you wanted to look up a particular topic in a certain book in order to see what the author had to say about it. You would open the book to the index and find the topic. Following the entry is a string of numbers. As you look up each page reference in turn, your behavior can be described as under the control of that list of numbers, and control is transferred from one number to the next as you proceed through the list. The transfer of control could be symbolized by drawing arrows from one page number to the next, but the arrows would have a meaning quite different from the two meanings mentioned previously. Here we are not concerned with a flow energy or transmission of information from one page number to the next but merely with the order in which the 'instructions' are executed.

At this abstract level of description we are no longer required to think of the test as a simple threshold that some stimulus energy must exceed. The test phase can be regarded as any process for determining that the operational phase is appropriate. For example, to be clear though crude, we do not try to take the square root of 'ratiocinate'. We may know full well how to extract square roots, but before we can execute that operation we must have digits to work on. The operation of extracting square roots is simply irrelevant when we are dealing with words. In order to ensure that an operation is relevant, a test must be built into it. Unless the test gives the appropriate outcome, control cannot be transferred to the operational phase.

When Figure 1 is used in the discussion of a simple reflex it represents all three levels of description simultaneously. When it is used to describe more complex activities, however, we may want to consider only the transfer of information and control or in many instances only the transfer of control. In all cases, however, the existence of a TOTE should indicate that an organizing, coordinating unit has been established, that a Plan is available.

In the following pages we shall use the TOTE as a general description of the control processes involved. [. . .] In its weakest form, the TOTE asserts simply that the operations an organism performs are constantly guided by the outcomes of various tests.

The present authors feel that the TOTE unit, which incorporates the important notion of feedback, is an explanation of behavior in general, and of reflex action in particular, fundamentally different from the explanation provided by the reflex arc. Consequently, the traditional concepts of stimulus and response must be redefined and reinterpreted to suit their new context. Stimulus and response must be seen as phases of the organized, coordinated act. We might summarize it this way:

> The stimulus is that phase of the forming coordination which represents the conditions which have to be met in bringing it to a successful issue; the response is that phase of one and the same forming coordination which gives the key to meeting these conditions, which serves as instrument in effecting the successful coordination. They are therefore strictly correlative and contemporaneous.[1]

Because stimulus and response are correlative and contemporaneous, the stimulus processes must be thought of not as preceding the response but rather as guiding it to a successful elimination of the incongruity. That is to say, stimulus and response must be considered as aspects of a feedback loop.

The need for some kind of feedback channel in the description of behavior is well recognized by most reflex theorists, but they have introduced it in a peculiar way. For example, it is customary for them to speak of certain consequences of a reflex action as strengthening, or reinforcing, the reflex – such reinforcing consequences of action are a clear example of feedback. Reinforcements are, however, a special kind of feedback that should not be identified with the feedback involved in a TOTE unit. That is to say: (1) a reinforcing feedback must strengthen something, whereas feedback in a TOTE is for the purpose of comparison and testing; (2) a reinforcing feedback is considered to be a stimulus (e.g. pellet of food), whereas feedback in a TOTE may be a

1. This passage is from an article by John Dewey entitled, 'The reflex arc concept in psychology', an article as valuable today for its wisdom and insight as it was in 1896.

stimulus, or information (e.g. knowledge of results), or control (e.g. instructions); and (3) a reinforcing feedback is frequently considered to be valuable, or 'drive reducing', to the organism, whereas feedback in a TOTE has no such value.

When a TOTE has been executed – the operations performed, the test satisfied, and the exit made – the creature may indeed appear to have attained a more desirable state. It may even be true, on the average, that the TOTE units that are completed successfully in a given situation tend to recur with increased probability, although such a relation would not be necessary. Thus it is possible to discuss a TOTE in the language of reinforcements. Nevertheless, the TOTE involves a much more general conception of feedback. The concept of reinforcement represents an important step forward from reflex arcs toward feedback loops, but bolder strides are needed if behavior theory is to advance beyond the description of simple conditioning experiments.

Perhaps variations in the basic TOTE pattern will prove necessary, so for the purposes of the present discussion we shall continue to regard the diagram in Figure 1 as a hypothesis rather than a fact. The importance of this hypothesis to the general thesis of the book, however, should not be overlooked. It is, in capsule, the account we wish to give of the relation between image and action. The TOTE represents the basic pattern in which our plans are cast, the test phase of the TOTE involves the specification of whatever knowledge is necessary for the comparison that is to be made, and the operational phase represents what the organism does about it – and what the organism does may often involve overt, observable actions. Figure 1, therefore, rephrases the problem: How does a plan relate the organism's image of itself and its universe to the actions, the responses, the behavior that the organism is seen to generate?

Let us see what we must do in order to expand this proposal into something useful. One of the first difficulties – a small one – is to say more exactly what we mean by the 'incongruity' that the test phase is looking for. Why not talk simply about the difference, rather than the incongruity, as providing the proximal stimulus? The answer is not profound: We do not want to bother to distinguish between TOTEs in which the operations are performed only when a difference is detected (and where the operations serve to diminish the difference) and TOTEs in which the operations are released only when no difference is detected. When the diagram is used to describe servomechanisms, for example, it

549

is quite important to distinguish 'positive' from 'negative' feedback, but, because we are going to be interested primarily in the feedback of control, such questions are not critical. Rather than treat all these varieties as different units of analysis, it seems simpler to treat them all as examples of a more general type of 'incongruity-sensitive' mechanism. [2]

A second difficulty – this one rather more important – is the question of how we can integrate this TOTE unit into a hierarchical structure of behavior. How can the two concepts – feedback and hierarchy – be reconciled? One method of combining feedback components in a hierarchy has been described by D. M. MacKay (1956), who proposed to make the consequences of the operational phase in one component provide the input to the comparator of a second component; MacKay's suggestion leads to a string of such feedback components, each representing a progressively higher degree of abstraction from the external reality. Although MacKay's scheme is quite ingenious, we are persuaded that a somewhat different method of constructing the hierarchy will better serve a psychologist's descriptive purposes. A central notion of the method followed in these pages is that the operational components of TOTE units may themselves be TOTE units. That is to say, the TOTE pattern describes both strategic and tactical units of behavior. Thus the operational phase of a higher-order TOTE might itself consist of a string of other TOTE units, and each of these, in turn, may contain still other strings of TOTEs, and so on. Since this method of retaining the same pattern of description for the higher, more strategic units as for the lower, more tactical units may be confusing on first acquaintance, we shall consider an example.

R. S. Woodworth has pointed out how frequently behavioral activities are organized in two stages (Woodworth, 1958). Woodworth refers to them as 'two-phase motor units'. The first phase is preparatory or mobilizing; the second, effective or consummatory. To jump, you first flex the hips and knees, then extend them forcefully; the crouch prepares for the jump. To grasp an object, the first phase is to open your hand, the second is to close it around the object. You must open your mouth before you can bite. You must draw back your arm before you can strike, etc. The two phases are quite different movements, yet they are

2. The notion of an 'incongruity-sensitive' mechanism appears to the authors to be related to Festinger's conceptions of 'cognitive dissonance', but we have not attempted to explore or develop that possibility. See Festinger (1957).

obviously executed as a single unit of action. If stimulation is correct for releasing the action, first the preparatory TOTE unit is executed, and when it has been completed the stimulation is adequate for the consummatory TOTE unit and the action is

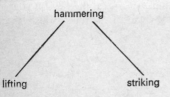

Figure 2. Hammering as a hierarchy

executed. Many of these two-phase plans are repetitive: the completion of the second phase in turn provides stimuli indicating that the execution of the first phase is again possible, so an alternation between the two phases is set up, as in walking, running, chewing, drinking, sweeping, knitting, etc.

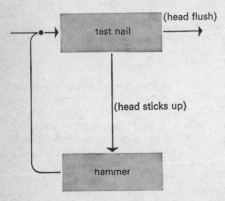

Figure 3. Hammering as a TOTE unit

We should note well the construction of a 'two-phase' TOTE unit out of two simpler TOTE units. Consider hammering a nail as an example. As a plan, of course, hammering has two phases, lifting the hammer and then striking the nail. We could represent it by a tree, or hierarchy, as in Figure 2. If we ask about details, however, the representation of hammering in Figure 2 as a simple list containing two items is certainly too sketchy. It does not tell us, for one thing, how long to go on hammering. What is the 'stop rule'? For this, we must indicate the test phase, as in Figure 3. The diagram in Figure 3 should indicate that when control is transferred to the TOTE unit that we are calling 'hammering' the hammering continues until the head of the nail is flush with

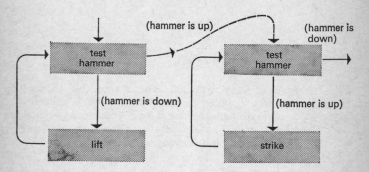

Figure 4. Dashed line indicates how two simple TOTE units are connected to form the operational phase of the more complicated TOTE unit in Figure 3

the surface of the work. When the test indicates that the nail is driven in, control is transferred elsewhere. Now, however, we seem to have lost the hierarchical structure. The hierarchy is recovered when we look at the box labeled 'hammer', for there we find two TOTE units, each with its own test, as indicated in Figure 4. When the pair of TOTE units combined in Figure 4 are put inside the operational phase in Figure 3, the result is the hierarchical plan for hammering nails that is shown in Figure 5.

If this description of hammering is correct, we should expect the sequence of events to run off in this order: Test nail. (Head sticks up.) Test hammer. (Hammer is down.) Lift hammer. Test hammer. (Hammer is up.) Test hammer. (Hammer is up.) Strike nail. Test hammer. (Hammer is down.) Test nail. (Head sticks up.) Test hammer. And so on, until the rest of the nail reveals that its head is flush with the surface of the work, at which point control can be transferred elsewhere. Thus the compound of TOTE units unravels itself simply enough into a coordinated sequence of tests and actions, although the underlying structure that organizes and coordinates the behavior is itself hierarchical, not sequential.

It may seem slightly absurd to analyse the motions involved in hammering a nail in this explicit way, but it is better to amuse a reader than to confuse him. It is merely an illustration of how several simple TOTE units, each with its own test-operate-test loop, can be embedded in the operational phase of a larger unit

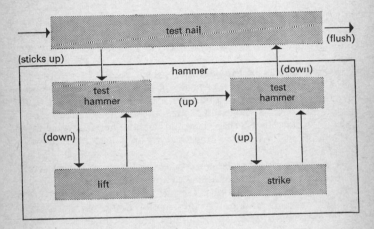

Figure 5. The hierarchical plan for hammering nails

with its particular test-operate-test loop. Without such an explicit illustration it might not have been immediately obvious how these circles within circles could yield hierarchical trees.

More complicated plans – Woodworth refers to them as 'polyphase motor units' – can be similarly described as TOTE units built up of subplans that are themselves TOTE units. A bird will take off, make a few wing strokes, glide, brake with its wings, thrust its feet forward, and land on the limb. The whole action is initiated as a unit, is controlled by a single plan, yet is composed of several phases, each involving its own plan, which may in turn be comprised of subplans, etc.

Note that it is the *operational* phase of the TOTE that is expanded into a list of other TOTE units. If we wish to preserve the TOTE pattern as it is diagrammed in Figure 1, we cannot use it to build up more complicated tests.[3] The tests that are available, therefore, are conceived to be relatively fixed; it is the operational phase that may be quite various and complex. The operational phase may, of course, consist of a list of TOTEs, or it may terminate in efferent activity.[4] If we consider complex plans – TOTE hierarchies in which the operation of one TOTE is itself a list of TOTE units – then some general properties of such systems become apparent:

1. The hierarchical structure underlying behavior is taken into account in a way that can be simply described with the computer language developed by Newell, Shaw, and Simon for processing lists.

2. Planning can be thought of as constructing a list of tests to perform. When we have a clear image of a desired outcome, we can use it to provide the conditions for which we must test, and those tests, when arranged in sequence, provide a crude strategy for a possible plan. (Perhaps it would be more helpful to say that the conditions for which we must test *are* an image of the desired outcome.)

3. The operational phase can contain both tests and operations. Therefore the execution of a plan of any complexity must involve many more tests than actions. This design feature would account for the general degradation of information that occurs whenever a human being is used as a communication channel.

3. The reason that the TOTE of Figure 1 can be expanded only in its operational phase is purely formal and can be appreciated by simple counting: There are four arrows associated with Test; there are two arrows associated with Operate; and there are two arrows associated with TOTE as a unit. Therefore, if the two-arrowed TOTE is used to construct some component of another TOTE, the component it constructs must be the two arrowed Operate, not the four-arrowed Test. However, rigid restrictions such as these are probably unrealistic and justifiable only in terms of pedagogic simplification. Anyone who has studied the hierarchically organized programs written by Newell, Shaw, and Simon to simulate human problem-solving will recognize how primitive and unelaborated these TOTE hierarchies really are.

4. If we take seriously the suggested form of the TOTE, the system may be easily trapped into loops. For example, if the subtests in the expansion of an operational phase all pass, but the basic test fails, a loop will exist. In order to avoid loops we might insist that the basic test imply the disjunction of the subtests. A more realistic solution would accept the occurrence of loops as a signal that the plan was not successful in producing the result for which the basic test was designed; it would then be necessary to provide further machinery for discovering and stopping such loops.

In lower animals it appears that the pattern of their behavior is normally constructed more or less fortuitously by the environment – only man cherishes the illusion of being master of his fate. That is to say, the environment provides stimuli that 'release' the next stage of the animal's activity. It is something of a philosophical question as to whether we wish to believe in plans that exist somewhere outside of nervous systems, so perhaps we should say merely that lower animals appear to have more tactics than strategy.

As we ascend the evolutionary scale we find in mammals an increasing complexity in the kind of tests the animals can perform. In man we have a unique capacity for creating and manipulating symbols, and when that versatility is used to assign names to TOTE units, it becomes possible for him to use language in order to rearrange the symbols and to form new plans. We have every reason to believe that man's verbal abilities are very intimately related to his planning abilities. And, because human plans are so often verbal, they can be communicated, a fact of crucial importance in the evolution of our social adjustments to one another.

References

ATTNEAVE, F. (1959), *Applications of Information Theory to Psychology*, Holt, New York.

BISHOP, G. (1956), 'The natural history of the nerve impulse', *Physiological Reviews*, vol. 36, pp. 376–99.

CHERRY, C. (1957), *On Human Communication*, Technology Press, Cambridge.

CHOMSKY, O. O. (1959), 'Review of B. F. Skinner's "verbal behavior"', *Language*, vol. 35, pp. 26–58.

FESTINGER, L. (1957), *A Theory of Cognitive Dissonance*, Row, Peterson, Evanston.

MACKAY, D. M. (1956), 'The epistemological problem for automata', in C. E. Shannon and J. McCarthy, eds., *Automata Studies*, Princeton University Press, pp. 235–51.

MILLER, G. A. (1953), 'What is information measurement?', *American Psychologist*, vol. 8, pp. 3–11.

SKINNER, B. F. (1938), *The Behavior of Organisms*, Appleton-Century-Croft, New York.

SLUCKIN, W. (1954), *Minds and Machines*, Penguin, Harmondsworth.

WIENER, N. (1948), *Cybernetics*, Wiley, New York.

WISDOM, J. O. (1951), 'The hypothesis of cybernetics', *British Journal for the Philosophy of Science*, vol. 2, pp. 1–24.

WOODWORTH, R. S. (1958), *Dynamics of Behavior*, Holt, New York.

Further Reading

BUCY, P. C., 'Introduction' and 'Effects of extirpation in man' (chapter 14), in P. C. Bucy (ed.), *The Precentral Motor Cortex*, University of Illinois Press, 1949.

KUFFLER, S. W., and HUNT, C. C., 'The Mammalian small-nerve fibers; a system for efferent nervous regulation of muscle spindle discharge', *Res. Publ. Ass. nerv. ment. Dis.*, vol. 30 (1952), pp. 24–47.

RATLIFF, F., *Mach Bands*, Holden Day, San Francisco, 1965.

ROSENBLITH, W. A. (ed.), *Sensory Communication*, Wiley, 1961.

SPERRY, R. W., 'The problem of central nervous reorganization after nerve regeneration and muscle transposition', *Quart. Rev. Biol.*, vol. 20 pp. 311–69.

TEUBER, H.-L., 'Perception', in *Handbook of Physiology*, vol. 3, Waverly Press, Baltimore, 1960.

Acknowledgements

We are grateful to the following for permission to reproduce the material in this selection of Readings.

Reading 1   American Association for the Advancement of Science and Dr D. N. Spinelli
Reading 2   The M.I.T. Press
Reading 3   Charles C. Thomas, Publisher, and Dr F. Morrell
Reading 4   The Williams and Wilkins Company
Reading 5   Academic Press, Inc.
Reading 6   American Association for the Advancement of Science and Professor R. Melzack
Reading 7   The Johns Hopkins Press
Reading 8   American Physiological Society and Dr V. B. Mountcastle
Reading 9   Josiah Macy, Jr., Foundation, and Dr. E. Sokolov
Reading 10   The Jaques Cattell Press
Reading 11   Appleton–Century–Crofts, the North-Holland Publishing Company, *Scientific American* and Dr Denis Williams
Reading 12   The Royal Society
Reading 13   University of Pittsburgh Press
Reading 14   *Behavioral Science*
Reading 15   The Williams and Wilkins Company
Reading 16   The Johns Hopkins Press
Reading 17   *Acta Neurologica Latinoamericana*
Reading 18   Elsevier Publishing Company
Reading 19   Walter de Gruyter and Co.
Reading 20   Butterworths, Professor D. Denny-Brown, *Journal of Neurophysiology*, The Williams and Wilkins Company and Macmillan and Co. Ltd
Reading 21   E. and S. Livingstone Ltd
Reading 22   *Yale Journal of Biology and Medicine*
Reading 23   Cambridge University Press
Reading 24   J. and A. Churchill Ltd
Reading 25   Association for Research in Nervous and Mental Disease
Reading 26   California Institute of Technology
Reading 27   Holt, Rinehart and Winston, Inc.

Every effort has been made to trace all copyright holders concerned. The publishers would be glad to hear from any copyright owners who have been overlooked.

Author Index

Author Index

561

Author Index

564

Subject Index

Subject Index

Epidermis
  as organ of pain, 90–93
  as organ of touch, 90
  see also Skin
Epilepsy, 475–6, 483n
  discharge, 63
  and frontal cortex, 303, 307
  idiopathic, 477
  in monkeys, 257–8
  surgical treatment of, 51–62
  and temporal lobe lesions, 303–20
Evoked potential, 326, 439
Excitation spatial spread of, 240
Experience and discrimination, 293
Extinction and response classes, 295
  see also Conditioning, behavioural
Extrapyramidal, definitions of, 432
  motor areas, 390–4
Extrinsic systems
  bilateral resections of, 299
  geniculostriate, 266–7, 271 ff.
Eye movements, 488–90
  see also Vision

Feedback loops, 545–6, 548–50
Field/vector theories, 241, 243, 250
Figure classification test, 237
Frontal association area, 288
  see also Associative cortex
Frontal cortex epileptogenic lesions of, 303, 307
Frontal intrinsic sector, 288–302
Frontal lobes
  functions of, 365, 429
  lesions in man, 409, 415
Functional equivalence of motor reactions, 247

Galvanic skin response, see Skin galvanic response
Gate control pain theory, 146–56
Generalization
  mechanism(s) of, 242–3, 250, 538
  Pavlov's theory of, 239–41
  perceptual, 236–7
  and similarity, 240
Geniculate body, 39
Geniculate neurons, 20, 22, 27–8, 30, lateral, 81
Geniculate nuclei, lateral, 243
Geniculo-striate systems, 267

see also Extrinsic systems
Gestalt school, 241, 466–8, 496
Gracilis nucleus, 323–6, 330–31
Graded potential changes at synaptodendritic junctions, 253
Graded responses, 543
Gradient fields theory, 242
Grasping automatisms, 412–14
Gustatory discrimination, see Taste, discrimination
Gyrus
  hippocampal, 368
  inferior frontal, 367–8
  precentral, 452–3

Habituation, 252–4
Handwriting, characteristics of, 248
Hemianopsia following temporal lobectomy, 304
Hemiopia, 489
Hemiplegia(s), 431, 472–4, 477–8, 481, 483n, 484, 488–9, 524
Hierarchical systems of behaviour, 550–2, 554
Hierarchy of neuron groups, 492
Hippocampal gyrus, 368
Hippocampal lesions, bilateral, 314–16
Hippocampus
  and seizures, 304–5
  theta rhythm of, 48
Hologram, 254–7
Homeostatic mechanisms, 545
Homologous/myotypic response, 491, 496–500
Huntington's chorea, 414
Hyperpathia, 180
Hypnagogic images, 246
Hypothalamus, 374
  and frontal lobe, 375
Hysteria, 483n

Incongruity-sensitive mechanisms, 550
Individuation
  mechanisms of, 469
  progressive, 257
Induction, 510
Inferotemporal sector, 267, 270
  lesions in, 271, 281, 284
  stimulation of, 340–47
Information measurement of, 546

Subject Index

Microphysiology of cortical
    neurons, 14
Midbrain in submammalian
    species, 235
Modality
  properties of PO neurons, 159–
    66, 178
  specificity
    of lesions of posterior systems,
      297–300, 339
    of PO cells, 178
    of thalamic lesions, 340
  sub-, 505
Modulation, 500, 504, 510
Moiré patterns in interference
    effects, 253–4, 256
Motor cortex, precentral, 439
Motor cortical function, 431, 455
Motor expressions, equivalence of,
    249
Motor function
  of fifth layer cells, 374
  studies of, 107
Movement(s)
  control of, 526–8
  co-ordinated, 454
  discrete, 454
  localization of, 472
  lost form 'destroying lesions',
    472–6
  resulting from discharging
    lesions, 476–90
  skilled, 439–40, 456–7, 519
  systems, 517
  voluntary (*see* Voluntary
    movements/activity *and*
    Willed behaviour)
  see also Chorea, Epilepsy,
    Parkinsonism *and* Spasticity
Multiple object experiment,
    296–9
Myelinated nerve fibres, 90–92,
    102, 112, 143, 146, 152, 177
Myotypic/homologous response,
    491, 496–500, 503, 509

Nerve impulse propagation, 256
Nervous irradiation, 239–40
Neural integration, 467, 515
Neuralgia
  peripheral, 141–2
  post-herpetic, 152
Neuron(s)
  doctrine, 543

excitation of single, 117–38
functional, 468–9
of gracilis nucleus, 323–6
groups, hierarchy of, 492
growth of, and behaviour, 461–71
integrate information, 14–46
and pain receptors, 88–9, 97–8,
    105–6, 110
PO,
  modality properties of, 159–66,
    178
  responses of, 169–73
  topographic properties of, 166–9
post-synaptic, 331–2
process sensory information,
    62–82
receptor, 434–8
tactile, 120–25
thalamic joint, 193–222
Neuronal model(s), 225–34
Neuronography, 375–80
Nocifensor system, 89, 104–8
Nucleus gracilis, 133
Nystagmus, 26
  see also Vision

Occipital lobe, 235, 453
  functions of, 261–5
  interaction with prefrontal areas,
    376
Occipitoparietal sector lesions of,
    267
Oculomotor mechanism, 107
Opercular region, 385–6
Optic cortex, 453
  see also Vision
Optic nerve
  cutting of, 36
  electrical stimulation of, 15, 18–19
  fibres, 15n, 27
Optic reflex, 235
Optic tract, 329, 331
Orienting reflex/reaction, 50, 225–
    34, 252–3, 388

PO (posterior group of nuclei of
    thalamus), *see* Thalamic
    nuclei
Pain
  centre in brain, 139, 151
  fast/slow, 100–102, 146
  first/second, 102, 109
  gate control theory of, 146–56